ATLAS
OF EVOLUTION

ATLAS OF EVOLUTION

by

SIR GAVIN DE BEER

MA DSc (Oxon) Hon. ScD (Cantab) Hon. D de l'Univ. (Bordeaux) Hon. D-ès-L (Lausanne)
Fellow of the Royal Society and of the Society of Antiquaries of London
Correspondant de l'Académie des Sciences de l'Institut de France
Past-President of the Linnean Society of London
President of the XVth International Congress of Zoology
Lately Director of the British Museum (Natural History)

NELSON

1964

THOMAS NELSON AND SONS LTD
LONDON AND EDINBURGH

THOMAS NELSON AND SONS
NEW YORK

THOMAS NELSON AND SONS
(CANADA) LTD
TORONTO

THOMAS NELSON AND SONS LTD
JOHANNESBURG
MELBOURNE

SOCIÉTÉ FRANÇAISE D'ÉDITIONS NELSON
PARIS

COLOPHON
LAYOUT BY JAC. VAN DEN BOS
COLOUR PLATES BY JAAK FL. VAN DER BROECKE (VRI)
DRAWINGS AND MAPS MADE UNDER SUPERVISION OF ELSEVIER'S DRAWING-OFFICE
PRINTED BY VADA NV (LETTERPRESS AND GRAVURE)
AND KOCH & KNUTTEL NV (OFFSET)

FOREWORD

It has sometimes been said that distance lends enchantment and light dispels charm, so that a state of ignorance is conducive to bliss. Whether this be true in any field of human thought is open to question, but in the wonders opened up by the scientific study of the universe it is not. Because Newton discovered the physical laws of nature that account for the movements of heavenly bodies and the fall of earthly things, the revolutions of the planets round the sun have lost none of their marvel; nor have plants and animals since Darwin showed that they have become what they are by evolution, in accordance with the laws of variation and natural selection. The more the secrets of nature are probed, the greater the wonder that they instil. They have yielded enough to enable science to make an intelligible picture of many natural events, and as the pieces of the giant jig-saw puzzle are slowly found and fitted into place, they are seen to conform to order. It is a matter of faith with scientists to believe in such order.

The picture that science constructs is intelligible at a particular level. It can explain how evolution has taken place but has no more pretension to answer the question why than to explain why there is a law of gravitation, a speed of light, or chemical elements with constant properties from end to end of the universe. Science is a system of knowledge based on observation and experiment, verifiable and repeatable, and not on the preferences or opinions of any man. It is not because Darwin concluded that evolution has occurred that scientists believe it, but because he discovered the evidence from which they can see for themselves that it has. Since evolution concerns the history of living beings of which man is one, it is not surprising that the evidence bearing on it based on scientific methods of study may conflict with views held on other grounds. It is instructive to recall the words of Sir John Pringle in answer to George III when the monarch remonstrated with him at the recommendation made by the Royal Society in favour of a type of lightning conductor devised by Benjamin Franklin, then a mutinous subject in open rebellion against his sovereign. 'Sire', said Sir John, 'I cannot reverse the laws and operations of nature', thereby establishing the superiority of scientific truth above any other consideration of reason.

The laws of nature have been found to be of universal application and are held to represent fundamental truths. They are inscrutable and cannot be evaded, suspended, or ignored by a scientist without sacrifice of intellectual integrity, and they inspire wonder. It was neither a philosopher nor a theologian but a scientist, Albert Michelson, who wrote 'what can surpass in beauty the wonderful adaptations of nature's means to her ends and the never-failing rule of law and order which governs even the most apparently irregular and complicated of her manifestations'.

The paths of the heavenly bodies do not excite compassion in the hearts of men, but the manifestations of life do. As a result of his work, Darwin showed that in the evolution of animals nature has been amoral, fiendishly cruel, and opportunistic. 'What a book a devil's chaplain might write on the clumsy, wasteful, blundering, low, and horribly cruel works of nature', he wrote; but this very fact enabled him to claim that there was some human comfort in the conclusion that these frightful events formed no part of the fulfilment of a detailed design. In the light of evolution by natural selection, 'we cease being astonished, however much we may deplore, that a group of animals should have been directly created to lay their eggs in the bowels or flesh of others - that some organisms should delight in cruelty - that animals should be led away by false instincts - that annually there should be an incalculable waste of eggs and pollen. From death, famine, rapine, and the concealed war of nature we can see that the highest good, which we can conceive, the creation of the higher animals has directly come.'

The problem of design never ceased to occupy Darwin's attention. The study of evolution has shown that on the level of plants and animals there has been no design. If there had, it must have been directed to the doom and extinction of the vast majority of species of living things that ever lived, in addition to the suffering that the laws of nature entail. In the state of perplexity induced by these inescapable facts, Darwin wrote, 'My theology is a simple muddle. I cannot look at the universe as the result of blind chance, yet I can see no evidence of beneficent design, or indeed of design of any kind, in the details'. If he is confronted with Darwin's dilemma, the scientist, with the humility always befitting a searcher after truth, can only say that he acknowledges the laws of nature and is not competent to express any opinion on why they are as they are.

For every statement made in this book there is scientific evidence. The subject of evolution is now so vast that in presenting it to the general reader it is necessary to make a selection and include only so much as will enable him to appreciate the evidence, from which he can draw his own conclusions, remembering that science does not claim to 'explain' evolution but shows how it works.

CONTENTS

MAPS

COLOUR PLATES

Chapter I INTRODUCTION

FROM SPECIAL CREATION TO TRANSFORMISM

Little more than a hundred years have gone by since the idea of the evolution of living forms was brought to the attention of the world in a manner that compelled its acceptance. The proof that the different members of the plant and animal kingdoms are as they now are because they have become what they are from something different is one of the most important contributions ever made to knowledge. It means that change is the rule of living things, and the realization of this great truth has been felt in every field of human thought.

It had become clear by the end of the eighteenth century that plants and animals constitute natural kinds, or species. The word 'species' means a category in logical classification, and in applying it to the kinds of plants and animals the English naturalist John Ray (1628–1705) gave it a biological meaning and defined it as a group of individuals that breed among themselves, a definition that is still accepted. It is based on the observed fact that members of a species produce offspring like themselves, and that 'one species does not grow from the seed of another species'. Examples come readily to mind. Primroses are pollinated by primroses and the seedlings develop into primroses. Thrushes breed with thrushes and their offspring develop into thrushes.

Varieties are different forms within the same species and are of course fertile among themselves. But while species are the fundamental natural groups into one or other of which every single plant and animal must fall, some species are very similar to others and these related species are included in larger units of higher rank, known as genera. It is largely to the French botanist Joseph de Tournefort (1656–1708) that science is indebted for the definition of the genus as a biological unit of higher rank than the species. Above the genus even higher and more inclusive groupings can be made out, such as families, orders, classes, and phyla, covering all the plant and animal kingdoms.

Since species were the different kinds of plants and animals then thought to have been brought into existence at the original creation of the world, they were held to be unalterable. However, exceptions to this view began to come to light. In 1680 Robert Morison quoted a case where seeds from a cauliflower had developed into ordinary cabbages. These are two varieties of the same species, *Brassica oleracea*, and the explanation of the case is probably that accidental hybridization occurred through cross pollination of the cauliflower with cabbage pollen, which is liable to occur when the plants grow close together. At the time, however, Richard Baal of Brentford who sold the seed was sued and condemned by the Court at Westminster for fraud, and made to pay compensation in addition to a refund of the purchase money. To John Ray this case was reliable evidence of like not begetting like and an exception to the rule of constancy, which led him to allow the possibility of transmutation between closely similar forms (Pl. 10–18).

Soon afterwards Jean Marchant (*ob* 1738) reported to the French Academy of Sciences that a plant of *Mercurialis* (allied to dog's mercury) in his garden had seeded and given rise to plants that differed from it in the size, shape, and arrangement of their leaves. This was probably due to what is now called a mutation (p. 83), and to Marchant it meant that although genera had been created on fixed models, their species were capable of variation. This conclusion was eventually shared by the great Swedish naturalist Linnaeus (1707–78; Pl. 2), who is usually quoted for his famous dictum published in 1736 that species are as numerous as the Infinite Being created in the beginning. A few years later, however, he was confronted with the fact that some plants of toadflax, *Linaria vulgaris*, differed from the normal in that their flowers were circular instead of bilaterally symmetrical like snapdragons, and that they bred true. This is now known to be the result of a mutation, but to Linnaeus it appeared to be the result of hybridization between toadflax and an unknown father, and it suggested to him the possibility, expressed in 1760, that 'many plants which now appear different species of the same genus, may in the beginning have been one plant, having arisen merely from hybrid generation'. This implied that new species might make their appearance and that the original creative act produced genera.

1. Burns' 'wee tim'rous beastie' looks proverbially harmless, yet if it multiplies too rapidly owing to lack of predators such as the cat or other reasons, it can outgrow its food supply, and bring about its own destruction and reduction in numbers. The balance of nature cannot with impunity be upset by mice or men.

14

2. Carl Linnaeus (1707-1778) introduced a standard system of nomenclature for all plants and animals, consisting of a generic name and a specific name for each species. **3.** Erasmus Darwin (1731-1802) believed that species were not fixed but underwent transmutation into other species. **4.** Jean-Baptiste de Lamarck (1744-1829) held that all plants and animals are descended by transformation from their ancestors. **5.** Georges Cuvier (1769-1832) rejected all possibility of evolution and believed that life on earth had repeatedly been annihilated by catastrophes and replaced by creation of improved types.
6. Charles Darwin (1809-1882) provided the evidence to prove that evolution had happened, and discovered the principle of natural selection of variation to explain how species become transformed. Grandson of Erasmus Darwin.
7. Alfred Russel Wallace (1823-1913) independently concluded that species had undergone transmutation and discovered the principle of natural selection.
8. Gregor Mendel (1822-1884) discovered the mechanism of particulate inheritance.
9. Thomas Henry Huxley (1825-1895) defended evolution and natural selection.

11

The Relationship between Genus and Species

17 18

13

Every living plant or animal belongs to one species or another, for species are the fundamental natural groups into which every plant and animal must fall. Members of species breed among themselves and produce offspring like themselves. As a rule they do not interbreed with other species, although this can occasionally happen with the production of hybrids like mules.
In accordance with the binomial system of nomenclature standardized by Linnaeus, every species is given two names, always printed in italics, a generic name beginning with a capital letter and a specific name beginning with a small letter. The name or initials of the authority who defined and named the species is given immediately after the specific name and printed in roman letters. 'L.' stands for Linnaeus. **10, 11.** The oak, *Quercus robur* L., and the beech, *Fagus sylvatica* L. are two species of plants belonging to different genera of the same family. **12, 13.** The lion, *Felis leo* L., and the tiger, *Felis tigris* L., are two species of mammals which have sufficient points in common for them to be grouped in the same genus *Felis*. Another species of this genus is *Felis catus* L., the domestic cat. Other examples of different species belonging to the same genus are provided by three familiar birds: **14.** The mistle-thrush, *Turdus viscivorus* L. **15.** Song-thrush, *Turdus philomelos* Brehm. **16.** The blackbird *Turdus merula* L. The first two are very similar in appearance and resemble one another more closely than do some varieties of the same species. **17, 18.** This fact is illustrated by the cauliflower and the cabbage, which are different cultivated varieties of the species *Brassica oleracea* L. and show the extent of divergent evolution that they have undergone under conditions of artificial selection by Man. Occasionally cultivated varieties revert, a fact that can be vouched for by all gardeners who grow lupins. Three hundred years ago, when seeds from a cauliflower developed into cabbage plants, the seedsman who sold them was condemned by the Court at Westminster to pay compensation. It is now realised that if cabbage plants and cauliflowers grow near to one another, cross-pollination by insects is liable to produce this result.

15

16

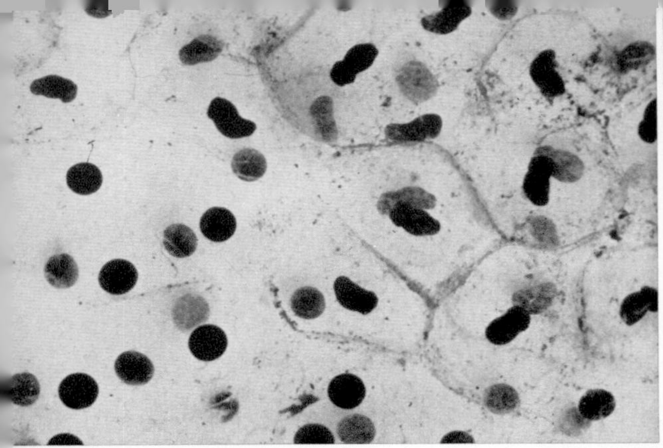

19

20

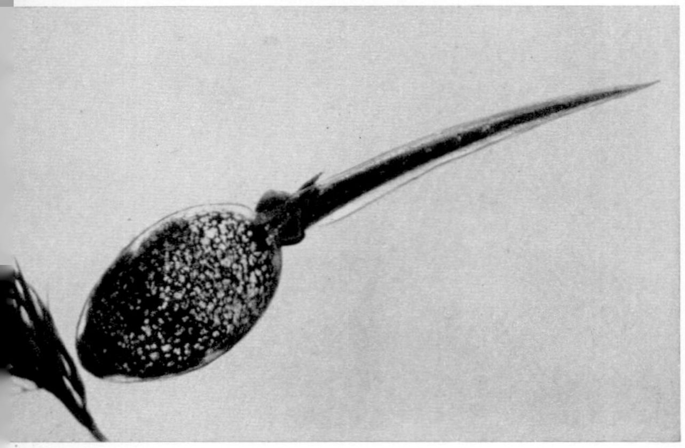

21

22

23

24

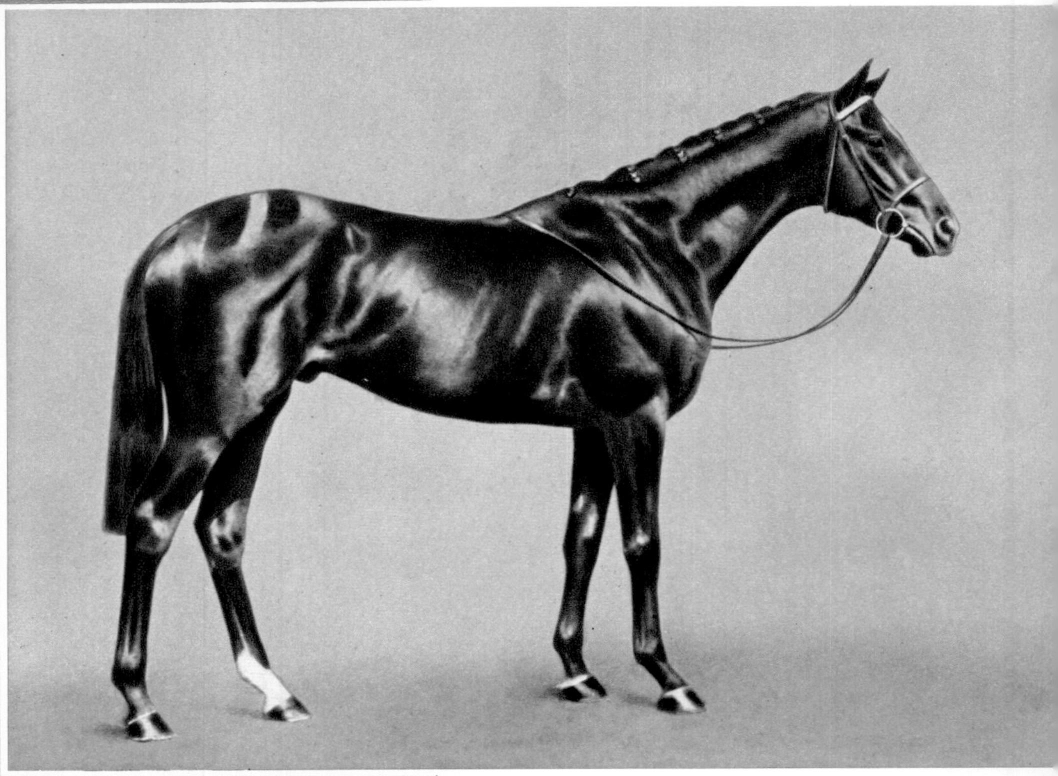

26

Change within a Single Generation

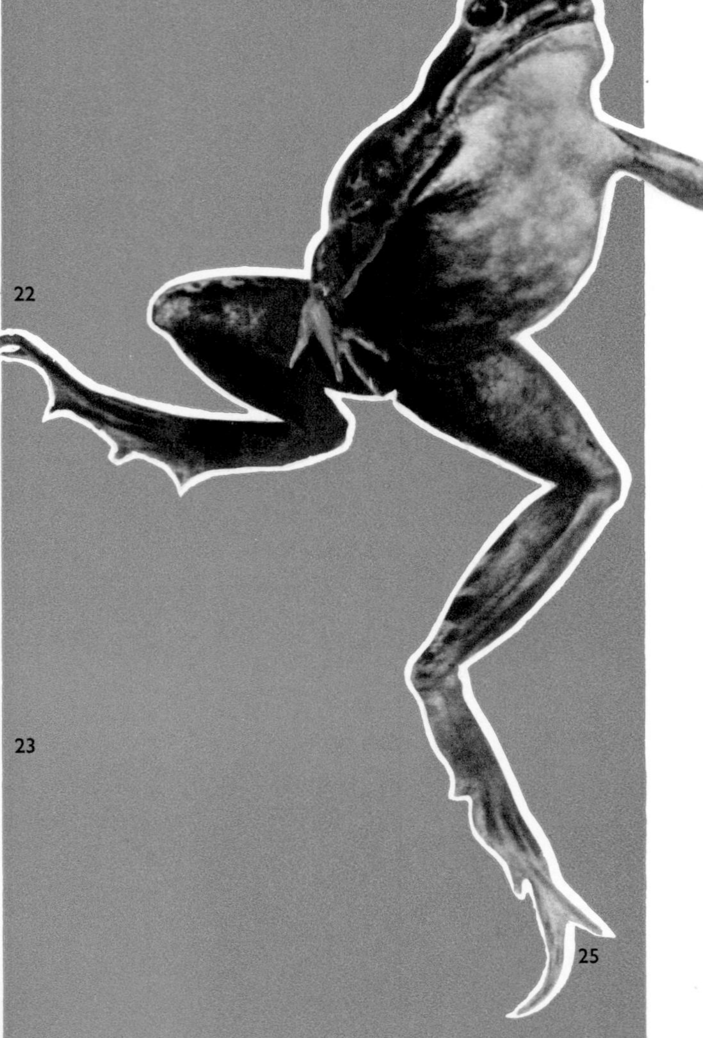

25

One of the reasons why Erasmus Darwin was led to believe that species are not immutable was because such striking changes of shape and habit can be seen to take place during the life-histories of animals which, like butterflies or frogs, undergo a metamorphosis during their development. The frog starts life in water as a spherical fertilized egg, the so-called 'spawn', **19,** which develops into a tadpole, **20.** This is an animal adapted to life in water with a tail used for swimming, gills by means of which it obtains oxygen in solution in the water, and small eyes, **21, 22.** When metamorphosis sets in, the tail is gradually resorbed completely, paired limbs with fingers and toes grow out from the body, **23, 24** lungs are developed enabling it to breathe air, and the eyes enlarge. The frog is then adapted to live on land as well as to swim in water with its webbed feet, **25.** If such changes can occur during a single life, Erasmus Darwin thought that one species might change into another.

It is sometimes difficult to distinguish between species and varieties. Some varieties of the same species may look very different, as do a racehorse **26,** a shire-horse **27** and a Shetland pony **28.** (→**12, 13; 14, 15; 17, 18;** and **44-48.**) On the other hand some species even of different genera may resemble one another deceptively closely. **29.** The Death Cap, *Amanita phalloides*, one of the most deadly poisons to Man. Like the mushroom it peels, blackens silver, and is eaten by rabbits; but it has a basal cup, its gills remain white, and its top is olive-green to yellow. **30.** The mushroom *Agaricus campestris* has no basal cup, its gills become pink and brown, and its top is creamy buff.

27

28

29

30

Species and Varieties

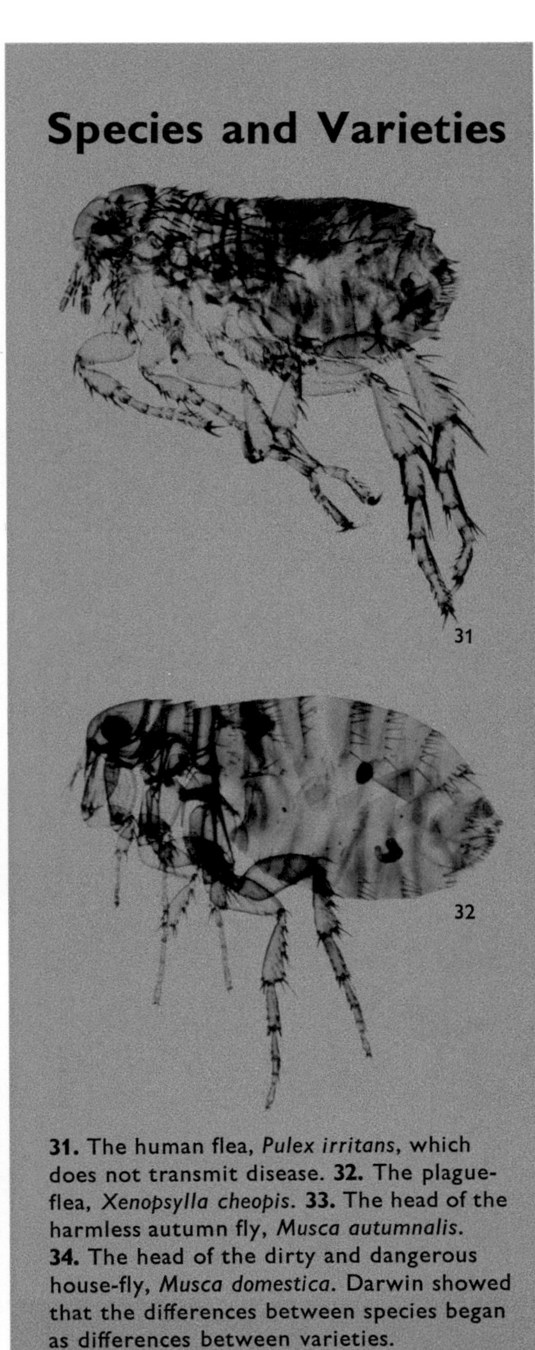

31

32

33

34

31. The human flea, *Pulex irritans*, which does not transmit disease. **32.** The plague-flea, *Xenopsylla cheopis*. **33.** The head of the harmless autumn fly, *Musca autumnalis*. **34.** The head of the dirty and dangerous house-fly, *Musca domestica*. Darwin showed that the differences between species began as differences between varieties.

While the fixity of species was being called in question by some naturalists concerned to explain the facts before their eyes, it was also beginning to be doubted by others, mainly French philosophers, on more general but speculative grounds. Early in the eighteenth century, Montesquieu (1689–1755) thought that reports of the existence in Java of 'monkeys with bats' wings' (i.e. flying lemurs) 'confirmed his feeling that the difference between species of animals can increase every day, and diminish in the same way, and that there were in the beginning very few species, which have multiplied since.' He continued: 'I am persuaded that species change and vary extraordinarily, that some are lost and new ones formed.' It was the principle of gradation applied (wrongly) to the passage from bats to monkeys *via* flying lemurs that led Montesquieu to entertain the view that substantial transformations of species into different species were possible; but it was only a speculation.

Another great Frenchman, Maupertuis (1698–1759), attributed the infinite diversity of animals to transmutation of species, basing himself on the observed facts that races of dogs, pigeons, and canaries had been made to appear which previously had never existed at all, and that fortuitous variations can arise spontaneously, like the accident of men being born with six fingers and capable of transmitting this character to their children. Yet another Frenchman, Diderot (1713–84), speculating on the changes undergone by an individual during its own life-history, and on the significance of monstrous births and imperfections, propounded a theory of transmutation of species based on the supposed principle that organs produce needs and needs produce organs, resulting in change. Other men who speculated on the possibility of transmutation of species but who ended by believing in their immutability included the botanist Adanson (1727–1806) and the zoologist Buffon (1707–88).

In England, Erasmus Darwin (1731–1802; Pl. 3), grandfather of Charles Darwin, published a book, *Zoonomia*, in 1794 in which he accepted the transmutation of species. He was led to this conclusion by the observed changes undergone by organisms during their life-histories such as the metamorphosis of a chrysalis into a butterfly or of a tadpole into a frog, and also by the changes brought about by the cultivation of plants and the domestication of animals. The effects of hybridization and the existence of monstrous births, which, since they represented departures from the original types of the species concerned, further convinced him that species were not immutable.

The later stages of the exploration of the world resulted in a great increase in detailed knowledge of floras and faunas and the discovery of large numbers of new species. The more numerous the species in any genus and the smaller the differences between them, the greater became the problem of distinguishing between species and varieties in the attempt to classify them. This difficulty became so acute that with a boldness and breadth of vision amounting to genius, the French naturalist Lamarck (1744–1829; Pl. 4, 35) who had begun by believing that species were immutable, cut the knot by proclaiming that there was no essential difference between species and varieties, that, like varieties, species could change and had changed into other species, so that 'transformism', not immutability, was the basis of life.

By expounding these views in 1809, Lamarck put forward a full theory of evolution, involving descent of species during long periods of time by modification from

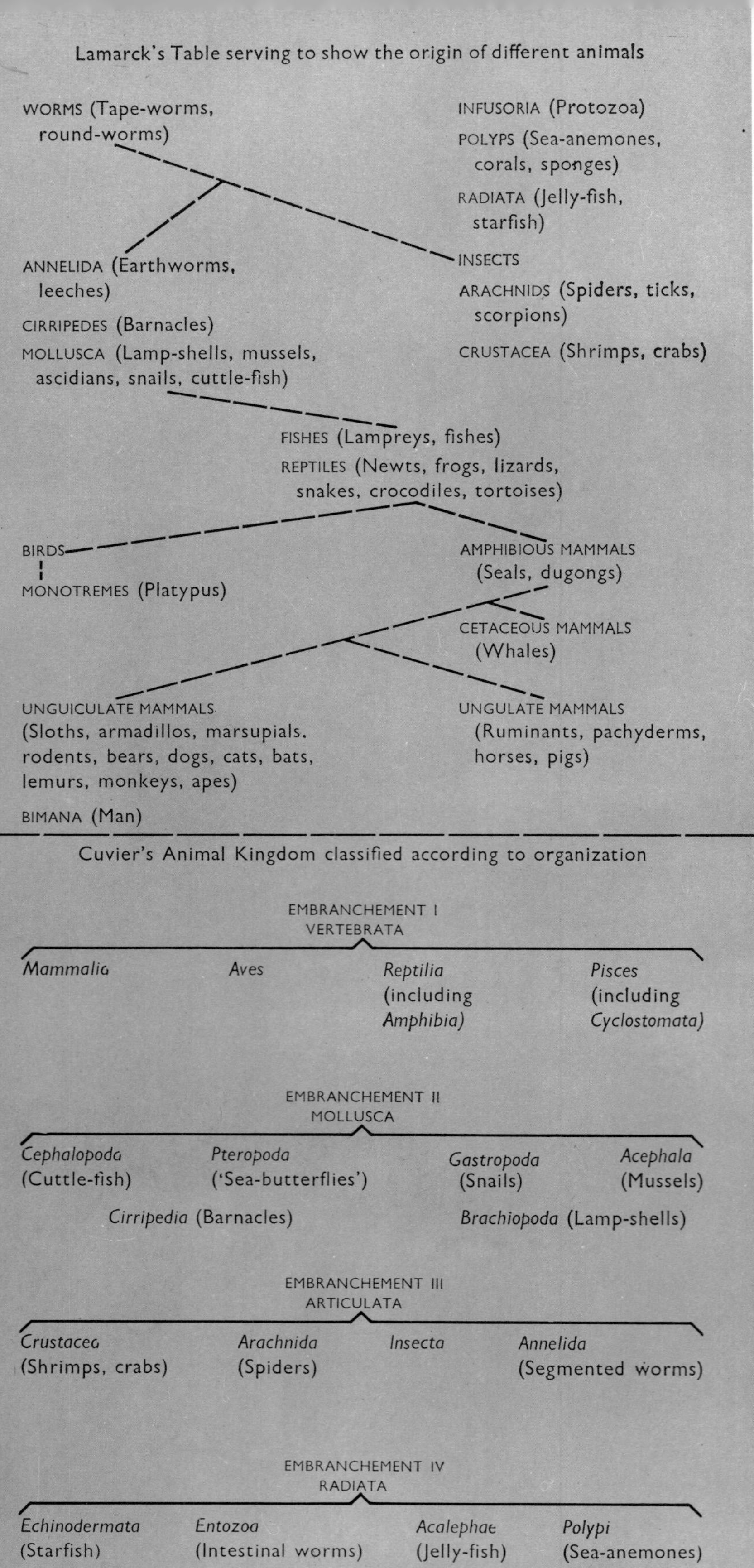

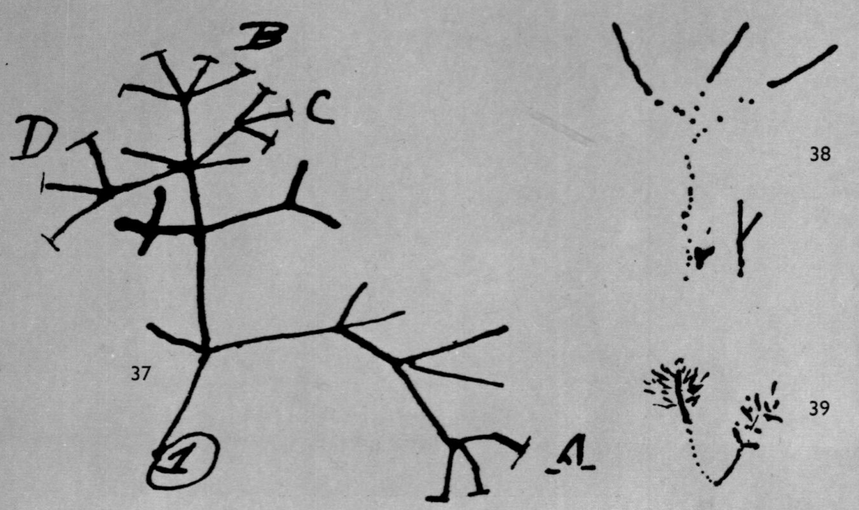

Three Ways of arranging the Animal Kingdom

35. In early times all groups of plants and animals were regarded as strung out along a line like a ladder, the Scale of Beings. Lamarck was the first to convert this into a tree, showing how in his view certain groups of animals had arisen from others. He did not think that species had gone extinct, and he accounted for the disappearance of fossil types by supposing that they had been transformed into other species.
36. Cuvier showed that the Scale of Beings was inadequate to express the different stages of organization found in the Animal Kingdom, and he substituted a system of groups, 'Embranchements', which represented no evolutionary series, for he believed that species were immutable.
37. Darwin's first diagram, drawn in 1837, shows how a number of species could have descended from a common ancestor at the base of the tree (1), and also how the extinction of some species (here shown as twigs ending blindly) results in increasing the gaps between the surviving species (twigs ending in cross-bars). This explains why the differences between species are unequal and how genera are formed from groups of species on one branch; 'Between A and B immense gap of relation, between C and B the finest gradation, between B and D, rather greater distinction'. **38.** illustrates Darwin's statement that 'the tree of life should perhaps be called the coral of life, bases of branches dead so that passages cannot be seen'. **39.** shows that 'fish can be traced right down to simple organization. Birds not'. (First Notebook on Transmutation of Species.)

other species, so that the histories of the plant and animal kingdoms could be represented by branching lines, the last animal line representing man. It must be observed, however, that Lamarck's claim that if enough species are studied they are seen to merge into each other is not correct. If it were, it would have made the classification of plants and animals impossible, which is not the case. However small the differences between closely similar species may be and however difficult to detect, they do not vanish, nor do species merge into each other; the differences between them exist and the species-barrier as a frontier across which interbreeding does not normally take place is a real one, even if its limits are subject to change.

The significance of these objections was not realised when Lamarck wrote, but even at the time there were other reasons why Lamarck's ideas were not accepted. One was that he provided no evidence in favour of evolution; the idea flashed across his mind and he assumed its truth without undertaking any analysis to prove it. Another reason was that he tried to give an explanation of the causes of evolution that raised opposition not only to them but to acceptance of the concept of evolution itself. He accounted for evolution by means of two factors. The first was a tendency to perfection and increased complexity, innate in all organisms, supposedly responsible for the scale of beings from the simplest organisms to man. This concept, which defies causal analysis led Lamarck to suppose that as simple animals exist and have not been perfected, they must have arisen recently by spontaneous generation. The scale of beings, however, is not a perfect gradation but shows anomalies and deviations, and to explain these he invoked a second principle, of the indirect effect of changes in the environment resulting in changes in the animal. Like Diderot and Erasmus Darwin before him, Lamarck supposed that as a result of new needs experienced by the animal, its 'inner feeling' or urge or subconscious activities resulting in bodily movement and habits produced new organs satisfying those needs. Such a system was inapplicable to the evolution of plants, and for them Lamarck was obliged to fall back on supposed direct effects of the environment.

As a cause of change in an animal and of the perpetuation of the change in its offspring, Lamarck elaborated the age-old view held by Maupertuis, Diderot, Buffon, Erasmus Darwin, and many others that effects produced by the environment on the bodies of parents could be transmitted to their offspring by inheritance – the so-called inheritance of acquired characters – and he appealed to this agency to provide a basis for the supposed inheritance of the effects of use and disuse on parts of the body. Belief in the inheritance of acquired characters is deeply ingrained as a folk-belief in many races. It is based on a fallacious combination of two propositions each of which by itself is approximately correct. The first is that under the influence of the environment changes can be induced in the body of an animal, and in many cases these changes have adaptive significance, as when the muscles of the blacksmith become enlarged as a result of wielding the hammer thereby making him better adapted to wield it. The second proposition is that animals produce offspring like themselves, not only in physical features but also in functional characters such as method of speaking or type of gait. Hence the conclusion is drawn that parents which have been modified by the environment can produce offspring showing those same modifications.

The conclusion is invalid because, as modern genetics has proved, offspring are not the direct product of their parents, but of germ-cells formed from the germ-plasm of which the parents are only the life-custodians. If offspring were the direct product of parents there would be no explanation of why brothers are not always identical. The 'old block' produces no 'chip' at all, and the offspring resembles the parent, when and if it does, which is not always, because both parent and offspring are the product of the same ancestral line of germ-plasm, transmitting hereditary factors, some of which are manifest and others not (Pl. 376). In spite of innumerable attempts, some taking the form of experiments undertaken on material of insufficient genetic purity, and others in which the results were deliberately faked, not one case of the inheritance through sexual reproduction of environmentally-produced change in the body of the parent has been substantiated, and there is now positive evidence that even if it did occur it would not contribute to evolutionary change (p. 98).

The tenacity of the belief in the inheritance of acquired characters may be shown by two examples. The first is one of the oldest myths of Greece. When Apollo's son Phaethon drove his father's chariot with the sun across the sky, his inexpert hands were incapable of controlling the horses, with the result that at one stage the sun was carried much too near Abyssinia, where the Ethiopians' skins were scorched black, and their offspring became the Negro race. The other example is the belief in the hereditary transmission of impressions made on the mother before or during pregnancy, and is to be found in the Old Testament. While Jacob was working for Laban, it was agreed between them that if any lambs were born brown or any goats spotted and speckled, Jacob could keep them for himself, whereas white sheep and unspotted goats belonged to Laban. Jacob thereupon selected the strongest animals and subjected them to visual impressions by presenting to their eyes striped patterns of green leaves and white rods just before they conceived, with the result that they 'brought forth cattle ringstraked, speckled, and spotted' which therefore belonged to Jacob, while the weaker, untreated animals produced offspring that remained true to the specification of Laban's property. There was a law in Norway forbidding the exposure of hares for sale in public in case women might give birth to children with hare-lips.

It was not, however, because of his belief in the inheritance of acquired characters that Lamarck failed to gain acceptance for his views; it would never have occurred

Significant Dates in the Study of Evolution

1721.
C. de Montesquieu meditating on gradation between bats and monkeys considered the possibility of transmutation of species.
1745.
P. L. M. de Maupertuis speculated on the origin of new species as a result of fortuitous abnormalities.
1753.
D. Diderot imagined the possibility of a prototype common ancestor from which all species might have been descended.
1760.
C. Linnaeus began to doubt the immutability of species which he thought might have originated from hybridization.
1794.
Erasmus Darwin published *Zoonomia* in which he acccepted transmutation and supported it with reasons.
1809.
J. B. de Lamarck published *Philosophie zoologique* in which he drew up a system of evolution including man and advanced an explanation based on the inheritance of use and disuse and the fulfilment of the needs of organisms.
1838.
Charles Darwin conceived the theory of natural selection as a cause of evolution based on the automatic favouring of more efficient variants producing adaptation enabling them to fill ecological niches.
1858.
A. R. Wallace independently advanced the theory of natural selection. Darwin's and Wallace's papers published together.
1859.
Darwin published *On the Origin of Species.*
1865.
J. G. Mendel discovered the particulate nature of heredity.
1871
Darwin published *The Descent of Man.*
1883.
A. Weismann distinguished between the body which dies and the germ-plasm which produces subsequent generations.
1900.
C. Correns, E. von Tschermak, and H. de Vries independently re-discovered and confirmed Mendel's laws of heredity in plants.
1902.
W. Bateson and L. Cuénot confirmed Mendel's laws in animals.
1919.
T. H. Morgan published *The Physical basis of Heredity* in which he proved that hereditary factors, genes, are carried in chromosomes.
1926.
S. S. Tschetwerikoff extended Mendelian genetics to the study of wild populations in nature.
1928.
H. J. Muller induced mutations by x-rays.
1930.
Sir Ronald Fisher published *The genetical Theory of Natural Selection* in which he showed the paramount importance of selection, integrated Darwinian selection with Mendelian genetics, and laid the foundation of the synthetic theory of evolution.
1938.
T. Dobzhansky and A. H. Sturtevant established the genealogy of species of *Drosophila* from the structure of their chromosomes.
1939.
C. D. Darlington published *The Evolution of Genetic systems.*
1940.
E. B. Ford proved that selection changes the effects of genes.
1942.
Sir Julian Huxley published *Evolution, the modern synthesis.*
1944.
G. G. Simpson published *Tempo and mode in evolution*, integrating palaeontology with the synthetic theory.
1955.
H. B. D. Kettlewell showed natural selection in action in industrial melanism.
1959.
B. Rensch published *Evolution above the species level.*
1963.
Sir Gavin de Beer published *Charles Darwin.*
1963.
E. Mayr published *Animal species and evolution.*
1964.
E. B. Ford published *Ecological Genetics.*

40

40. H.M.S. *Beagle*, a Sloop Brig of 235 tons, was launched at Woolwich in 1820. Under Captain Robert FitzRoy, R.N. with Charles Darwin as naturalist, she sailed in 1831 to survey the coasts of Patagonia, Tierra del Fuego, Chile, and Peru, to visit some Pacific Islands, and to carry a chain of chronometrical measurements round the world. This gave Darwin the opportunity to make the observations which started his work on evolution. This watercolour, preserved in the National Maritime Museum at Greenwich, was painted by Captain Owen Stanley, R. N., in Sydney Harbour in 1841 during a later voyage. *Beagle* was sold for £ 525 in 1870 and bought by the Japanese. She was broken up about 1888.

to any of his contemporaries or successors, including Darwin, to doubt the truth of this, and it was not finally discredited until about 1930 (p. 83). It was the unacceptable assertion that organs arose and were developed by the urges and 'inner feelings' of the animals 'because they are needed' that led scientists, including men like Etienne Geoffroy-Saint-Hilaire (1772-1844) who accepted transmutation, to reject Lamarck's views, while the unpalatable idea of evolution itself, including the descent of man from apes, prejudiced them against it. It is an unhappy irony of fate that has given the name 'Lamarckism' to the inheritance of acquired characters, which was not his invention and does not occur, instead of to evolution, the truth of which he was the first to proclaim fully even if he failed to explain its cause.

It was unfortunate for Lamarck and for science that his work was completely eclipsed by that of his great contemporary and fellow-countryman Georges Cuvier (1769-1832; Pl. 5, 36). He was the first to apply the methods of comparative anatomy to the finds of fossil forms which were then becoming increasingly numerous, and by his principle of correlation he was able to reconstruct entire animals from portions of their skeleton with an accuracy that has frequently been proved by subsequent discoveries of whole skeletons. Deeply convinced of the authenticity of the Biblical Flood, Cuvier was struck by the fact that in the rocks of the Paris Basin, some strata contained fossils of marine animals, others fossils of fresh-water animals, and others again no fossils at all. From the apparently sudden appearance and disappearance of these remains of bygone life, Cuvier drew the conclusion that catastrophes similar to the Deluge had repeatedly destroyed the life on different parts of the earth, and that after each upheaval life had blossomed out afresh through colonization by such forms as had escaped by living elsewhere. There had therefore been widespread extinction of species, which was a new concept.

It was obvious to Cuvier that the living forms that succeeded one another after each catastrophe showed an advance in structure, complexity, and perfection on those that had gone before, and that therefore a principle of progression was involved. But as Cuvier knew of no fossils intermediate between existing types, and he insisted that the extent to which species might vary was strictly limited, he firmly repudiated any possibility of their transmutation and rejected evolution. At the same time, he made a contribution to biology which was to be of great service to the theory of evolution. Lamarck and previous writers had imagined the various members of the animal kingdom as strung out in linear succession, but Cuvier realized that the anatomical diversity shown by different groups of animals could not be accommodated in any single plan of structure or type. He therefore divided the animal kingdom into four great groups or embranchements: Radiata (jelly-fish, sea-urchins), Articulata (worms, lobsters), Mollusca (snails, cuttlefish), and Vertebrates. In this way Cuvier unwittingly provided the basis for the concept of divergent evolution.

Another service which Cuvier rendered to biology was the proof that some species had become extinct. Such a possibility had been excluded on theological grounds by Thomas Jefferson and John Wesley. The fact that extinction has occurred is important because if all species that had ever existed still persisted, there would be no room for new species in the ecological niches of nature.

THE FACT OF EVOLUTION

When Charles Darwin (1809-82; Pl. 6) started on the voyage of the *Beagle* in 1831, he did not doubt the immutability of species (Pl. 40, Map I). The speculations of his grandfather Erasmus counted for nothing with him because they were not supported by evidence, and those of Lamarck on the causes of evolution had the additional demerit of bringing the subject into disrepute with the leading scientists of the day by their fanciful nature. Furthermore, it must be added that the great geologist Charles Lyell (1797-1875) firmly rejected the possibility of evolution having taken place in his *Principles of Geology*, which Darwin had with him on the voyage and to which he owed so great a debt for the principle of uniformitarianism that it advocated in place of catastrophism.

Catastrophism was the name given to the system of causes that had up till then been invoked, as by Cuvier, to account for the ordinary facts of geology by appealing to sudden violent and cataclysmic disturbances such as floods and other catastrophes, on a scale of magnitude for which the phenomena observable on earth provide no evidence or examples. Lyell showed that there is no need to appeal to such disasters to explain the structure of the crust of the earth, and that the uniform effects of forces that can be observed at work, such as pressures in the crustal rocks and erosion by water, ice, and wind, are quite sufficient, given immense periods of time, to account for all the phenomena. This is Lyell's principle of uniformitarianism which has contributed so greatly to scientific progress; and it was another case of the irony of history that by misapplying this principle, Lyell was led to reject the possibility of evolution, because when correctly applied in the field of biology it inevitably leads to the conclusion that evolution by transmutation of species must have occurred.

Three sets of observations started Darwin's revolt against the immutability of species, which began in earnest after his return to England in 1836. The first was occasioned by his studies of the fauna of the Galápagos Islands, where he found that species of finches differed slightly from island to island, while showing general resemblance not only to each other but to the finches on the adjacent mainland of South America (Pl. 41). They presented a perfect gradation in the size of their beaks from one as large as that of a hawfinch to one as small as that of a chaffinch. The former lived on the ground and fed on seeds, the latter lived in trees and fed on insects. If these species had been separately created, why should there have been such a prodigal expenditure of 'creation' just there, why should geographical propinquity have caused these 'creations' to resemble each other so closely; as the Galápagos Islands were raised out of the deep by volcanic action, what was the 'spirit of creation' doing before these islands emerged from the sea; why in spite of the similarity in physical conditions between the islands of the Galápagos Archipelago and the Cape Verde Islands are their faunas totally different, the former resembling that of South America while the fauna of the latter resembles that of Africa?

The second set of observations related to the fact that as he travelled over South America, he saw that the species occupying a particular niche in nature in some regions were replaced in neighbouring regions by other species that were different, yet closely similar. Why are the rabbit-like animals on the savannas of La Plata

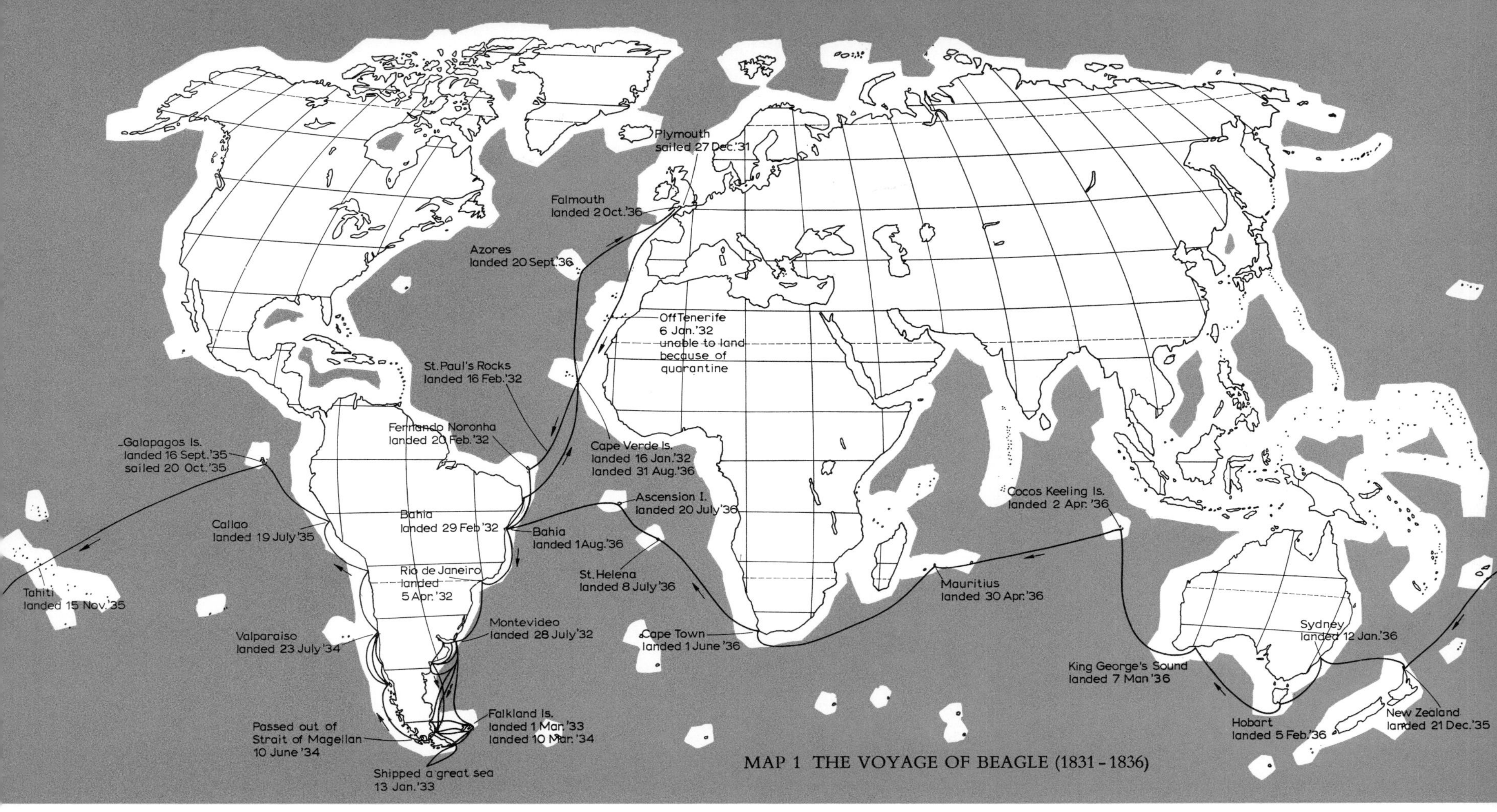

MAP 1 THE VOYAGE OF BEAGLE (1831-1836)

built on the plan of the peculiar South American type of rodent, and not on that of North America or the Old World? Why is the species of rhea in Patagonia replaced on the pampas by another species of South American rhea and not by an Old World ostrich?

The third set of observations was concerned with the fact that in the pampas he found fossil remains of large mammals covered with bony armour like that of the armadillos now living in that same country (Pl. 42, 43). Why were these extinct animals built on the same plan as those now living?

On the view that species were immutable and had not changed since they were severally created, there was no rational answer to any of these questions, which would have to remain as inexplicable mysteries. On the other hand, if species, like varieties, were subject to modification during descent and to divergence into different lines of descent, *all* these questions could be satisfactorily and simply answered. The finches of the Galápagos resemble each other and those of South America because they are descended from a common ancestor; they differ from one another because each is adapted to its own mode of life, and in some instances is restricted to its own particular island. The volcanic nature and physical conditions of the Galápagos Islands resemble those of the Cape Verde Islands, and yet the Galápagos birds all differ from the birds of the Cape Verde Islands. Therefore it is not the physical conditions of the islands that determine their differences. These arose because the Cape Verde Island birds share a common ancestor with the birds of Africa, whereas the Galápagos birds share another common ancestor with those of South America. The hares of South America are built on the South American rodent plan because all South American rodents are descended from a common ancestor. The rheas are also descended from a South American common ancestor. The fossil *Glyptodon* resembles the living armadillo because both share a common ancestor too; and this case is particularly important because, if living species show affinity with extinct species, there is no necessity to believe that extinct types of animals have left no living descendants. They may have representatives alive today, and this means that the whole wealth of the fossil record is available as material for the study of the problem of evolution.

In possession of a working hypothesis that species have undergone evolution and have originated one after the other by descent with modification from ancestral species which are shared with other descendent species, Darwin next proceeded to search the whole field of botanical and zoological knowledge for evidence bearing on his hypothesis; for he realized that no general principle that explained the evolution of animals was acceptable unless it also applied to plants.

In the first place, in cultivated plants and domestic animals, such as the dahlia, the potato, the pigeon, the dog, and the rabbit, large numbers of varieties have been produced from a single original stock. Descent with modification and divergence into several lines is therefore certainly possible within the species (Pl. 44-49).

Comparative anatomy reveals the existence of common plans of structure in large groups of organisms. Vertebrate animals have forelimbs that may be variously used for walking, running, swimming, or flying, but in which the various parts of the skeleton correspond, bone for bone, from the upper arm to the last joints of the fingers, whether the animal is a frog, a lizard, a turtle, a bird, a rabbit, a seal, a bat, or a man. This is what is meant by saying that such structures are homologous, and these correspondences are inexplicable unless the animals are descended from a common ancestor. Fundamental structural resemblance is therefore evidence of genetic affinity (Pl. 96).

The study of comparative behaviour proves that related species inhabiting different parts of the earth under very different conditions retain similar instincts, such as the habit of thrushes in England and in South America of lining nests with mud, or that of male wrens in England and North America of building 'cock-nests'; Why should this be, unless the different species of thrushes and wrens are descended from common ancestors in each case?

Embryology reveals remarkable similarity of structure between young embryos of animals which in the adult stage are as different as fish, lizard, fowl, and man (Pl. 99). This similarity between embryos is explained if the groups to which they belong were descended from a common ancestor.

Embryology also provides evidence of vestiges of structures which once performed important functions in the ancestors but now either perform different functions, or none at all. Examples of such organs are the teeth of whalebone whales, the limbs of snakes, the wings of ostriches and penguins, or the flowers of the feather-hyacinth. Here again, descent with modification from ancestral forms explains all these cases.

Knowledge of the fossil record in Darwin's time was so imperfect that nothing was then available in the way of any graded row of fossils illustrating the course of evolution. Nevertheless, he noticed that in Tertiary strata, the lower the horizon the fewer fossils there were belonging to species alive today. Palaeontology therefore showed that new species had appeared and old species become extinct, not all at the same time but in succession and gradually. Why should this be so unless new species have come into existence from time to time by descent with modification from other species?

Plants and animals are classifed according to their resemblance and they are placed in one or other of a not very large number of groups, such as ferns, conifers, molluscs, or mammals. But within each of these groups, there is subdivision into other smaller groups, mammals being so subdivided into rodents, carnivores, ungulates, and primates, for example. Within these again there is further subdivision, and the important point to notice is that classification always places species in groups that are contained within other larger groups. This is such a commonplace that its significance is often overlooked. Why do organisms have to be classified like this? The reason is that the arrangement of groups as subdivisions of larger groups is a *natural* classification reflecting the course of evolution. It is the result of descent from common ancestors and an indication of affinity; the differences between the groups are due to modification and divergence during such descent.

Darwin also investigated the problem of sterility between species and saw that it was by no means absolute, because numerous examples can be given of different species that produce hybrids, and in some cases these hybrids are themselves fertile. From the point of view of breeding, therefore, such species behave like varieties. Why, then, can species not have originated as varieties, by descent and modification from other species?

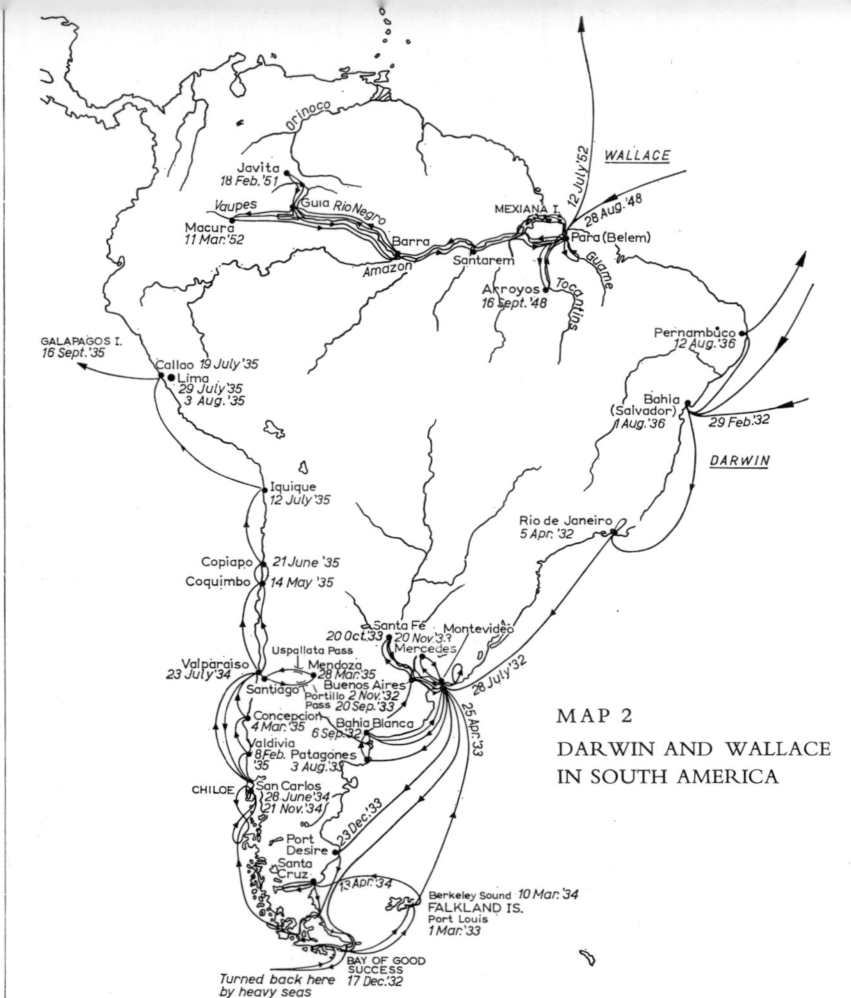

MAP 2
DARWIN AND WALLACE
IN SOUTH AMERICA

Darwin and Wallace in South America

South America was the inspiration and training ground of the naturalists whose researches resulted in the establishment of the fact of evolution, its explanation by natural selection, and its illustration in the phenomenon of mimicry. For Darwin there was the revelation: 'Delight itself, however, is a weak term to express the feelings of a naturalist who, for the first time, has been wandering by himself in a Brazilian forest'. He was particularly struck by three facts: the discovery of fossil animals related to living species, the way in which related species replaced each other in different parts of the Continent, and the South American character of the fauna of the Galapagos Islands. These facts were the start of his work on evolution. Wallace went to the Amazons with H. W. Bates and was similarly struck by 'the wonderful variety and exquisite beauty of the butterflies and birds . . . ever new and beautiful, strange and even mysterious'. On his return to England, Wallace's ship took fire, all the collections that he had with him were lost, and he barely escaped with his life. It was also in South America that his companion H. W. Bates discovered the type of mimicry that bears his name (p. 92), and that Fritz Müller observed his type of mimicry (p. 27).

Wallace in South-east Asia

'There are two islands, named Bali and Lombok, each about as large as Corsica, and separated by a strait only fifteen miles wide at its narrowest part. Yet these islands differ far more from each other in their birds and quadrupeds than do England and Japan.' (Wallace)
'Wallace's Line', so named by Thomas Henry Huxley, marks a belt of deep water separating the continental shelves of the Oriental and Australian geographical regions, Bali belonging to the former, and Lombok lying on a long westward extension of the latter.

41

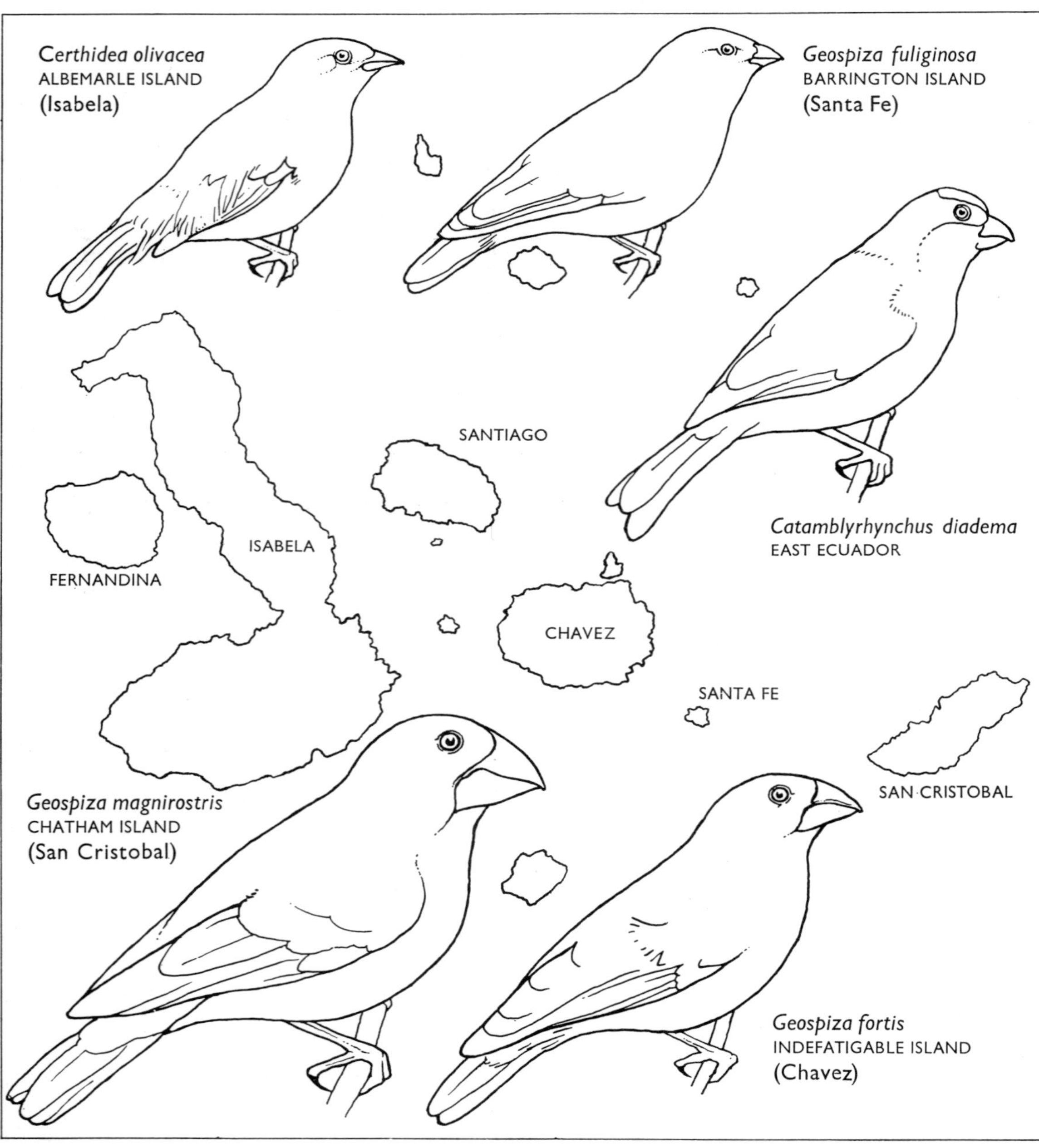

Natural and Artificial Selection

41. The Galapagos Islands as they struck Darwin. 'When I see these Islands in sight of each other and possessed of but a scanty stock of animals, tenanted by these birds but slightly differing in structure and filling the same place in Nature, I must suspect that they are only varieties' (of an original species that have become different species). 'The most curious fact is the perfect gradation in the size of the beaks in the different species of *Geospiza*, from one as large as that of a hawfinch to that of a chaffinch, and even to that of a warbler.' 'One might really fancy that from an original paucity of birds in this archipelago, one species had been taken and modified for different ends'. (Darwin, *Journal of Researches*). These birds have been drawn from specimens in the British Museum (Natural History) collected by Darwin. A recent investigation by D. Lack (p. 115) has revealed the details of their evolution. 'During the voyage of the *Beagle* I had been deeply impressed by discovering in the Pampaean formation great fossil animals covered with armour **(42)** like that on existing armadillos' **43** (Darwin, *Autobiography*). Artificial selection practised by Man since Neolithic times gave Darwin the idea of natural selection. The differences between breeds of domestic animals provided Darwin with evidence of the amount of change that can be produced by Man using artificial selection, 'for who will believe that animals closely resembling the Italian greyhound **47,** the bloodhound **48,** the bulldog **46,** pug-dog **44,** or Blenheim spaniel **45,** etc. - so unlike all wild Canidae (fox, **49**) - ever existed in a state of nature?' (*Origin of Species*). These breeds have reached their present condition as a result of evolution by artificial selection. Almost all domestic animals - sheep, cattle, horses, poultry, pigeons - could provide similar examples.

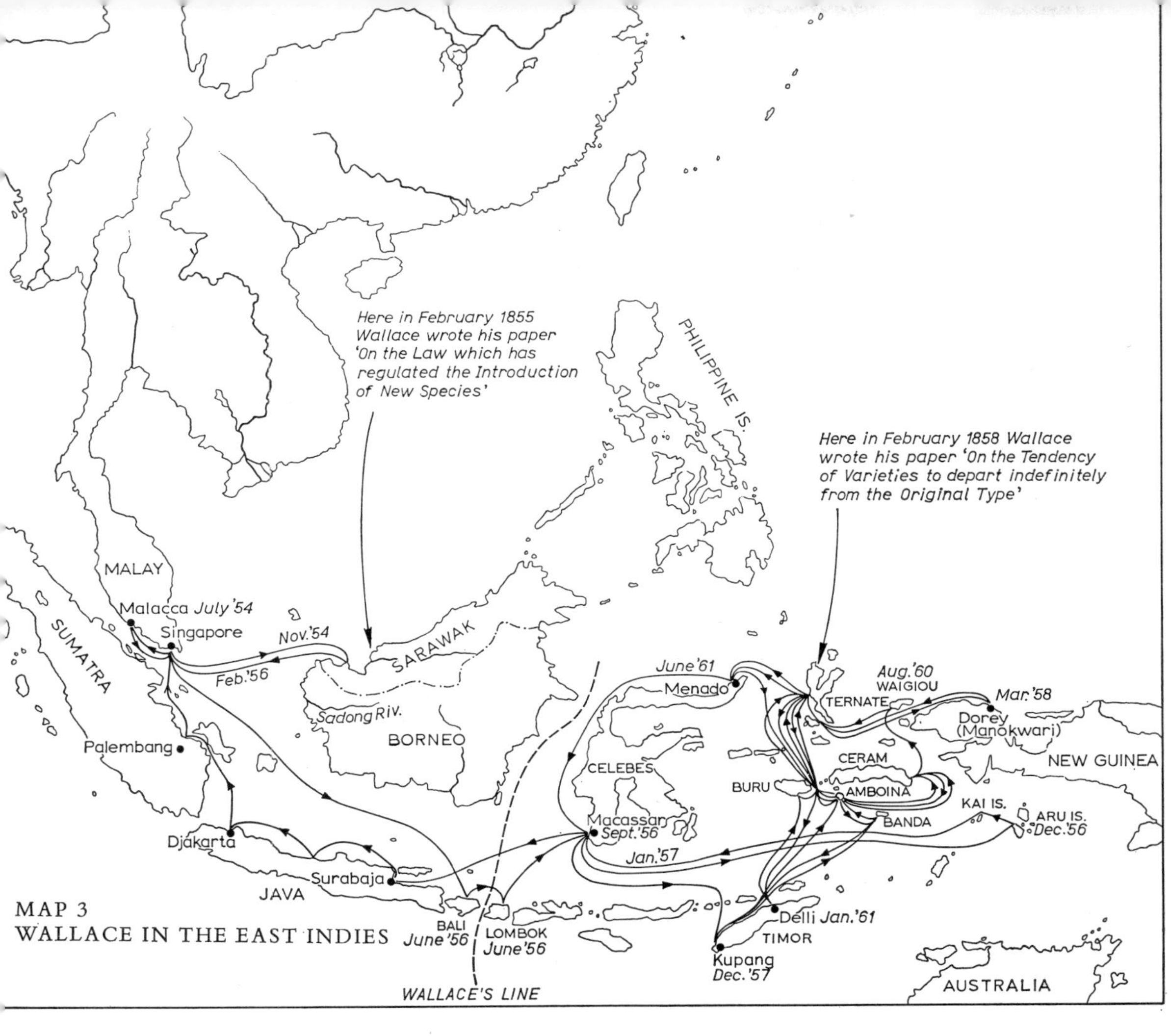

MAP 3
WALLACE IN THE EAST INDIES

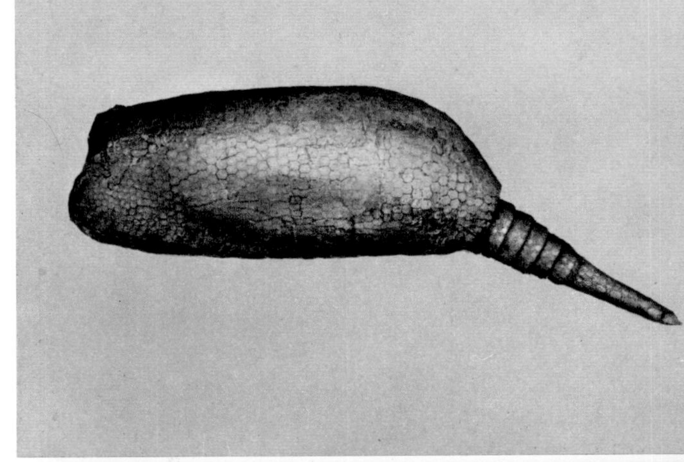

42 43

44  45  46  47

48  49

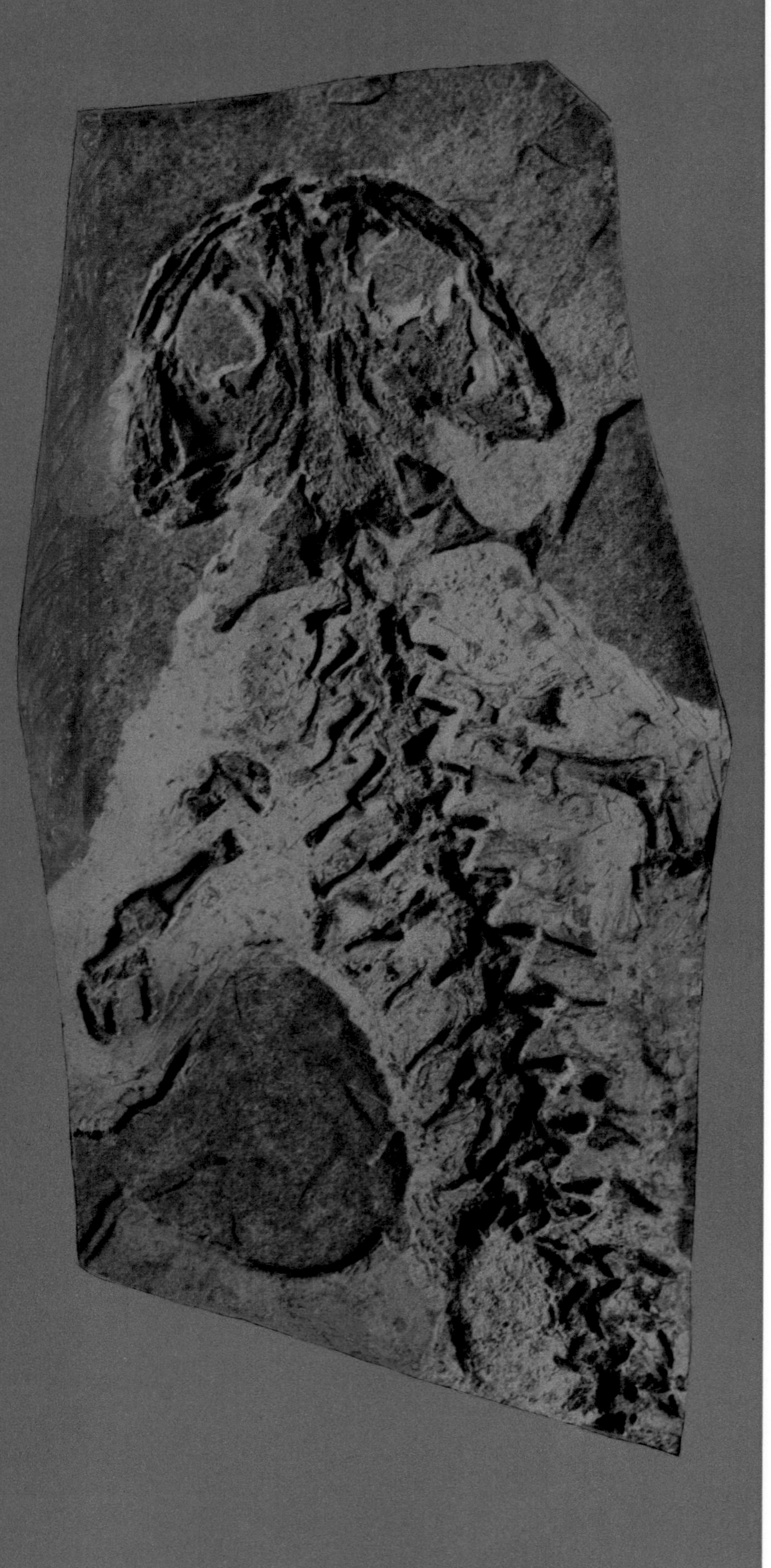

50

A 'Good' Mistake

50. Two hundred and fifty years ago, J. J. Scheuchzer found a fossil skeleton which struck him as so similar to that of a man that he called it *Homo Diluvii Testis*: Man, witness of the Deluge. In fact, as Georges Cuvier was the first to point out, the skeleton is that of a fossil newt about twenty million years old, and related to the living Giant Salamander of Japan. Historically Scheuchzer's fossil is important for two reasons. It was among the earliest to be recognized as the remains of an animal formerly alive instead of being regarded as a stone freak of nature; and the evidence for comparative anatomy which it provides was sufficient to lead Scheuchzer to make what is called a 'good' mistake. It is preserved in the Teyler Museum at Haarlem.

From the evidence provided by all these sources, Darwin built up an irrefutable argument that species have changed and have originated from other species, and that 'animals are descended from at most only four or five progenitors, and plants from an equal or lesser number', figures which are a last reflection of Cuvier's four embranchements (p. 16), and that in fact evolution has occurred.

Evolution means that when a species has split into daughter species, they become a genus. In the same way, the higher categories of family, order, class, and phylum, arose by 'promotion' when their constituent groups had become sufficiently diversified; but the first step in the origin of each category, however high it is now in the scale of classification, was always the origin of a species by descent with modification from another species.

That Darwin should have been able to build up his argument for evolution at all at the time when he worked out his conclusions was a mark of genius, for biological knowledge was then extremely poor and riddled with error. None of the evidence had been discovered that is used now to provide the most striking proofs of the fact, course, and causes of evolution. This evidence includes the discovery of fossils so closely graded that they show complete lineages in the ancestry of groups like the horses and the elephants, and other fossils which show the transition from each class of vertebrates to the others. It includes the discovery of the mechanism of heredity and of the cause of variation; the fact that related hosts tend to be infested with related parasites, meaning that the hosts share a common ancestor which was infested by the common ancestor of their parasites; the demonstration that the hinge of the jaws of reptiles has become included in the chain of ear-ossicles in mammals, and that marsupials have vestiges of the egg-tooth which their ancestors used 100 million years ago to hatch out of egg-shells; the results of research in comparative physiology, biochemistry, serology, and immunology, none of which branches of science were even thought of in Darwin's day. The evidence alluded to in this and the preceding paragraphs will be presented in fuller form in Chapter Two.

The main steps in Darwin's argument for evolution were established in 1837, at which date his Notebooks show that he had convinced himself of their soundness. In 1842 he committed them to paper in the form of a sketch which he expanded into an Essay in 1844, though neither was then published. Darwin knew at the time when he had finished writing his Essay that he had found the key to the most important problem in biology: how adaptations arise and how species originate, but he showed his work to only one other man, the great botanist Joseph Dalton Hooker, and kept his conclusions to himself. The reasons for this were his inveterate caution and the opposition which he knew that his theories would encounter from the leading scientists of the time. Eventually his friends Lyell and Hooker persuaded him to prepare his work for publication in case he was forestalled. He started in 1856. Meanwhile, another naturalist, Alfred Russel Wallace (1823-1913; Pl. 7), was led to explore similar lines of research. Like Darwin, Wallace had had first-hand practical experience of nature in tropical countries. In 1848 he made an expedition with Henry Walter Bates to the Amazons to collect natural history specimens, from which he returned to England in 1852 (Map 2). Two years later he started a visit to the Malay Archipelago that lasted until 1862 (Map 3). From some simple observations on the distribution of organisms, both geographically over the world and geologically in the fossil record, Wallace drew some equally simple conclusions that led to evolution. They show that independently of Darwin and in complete ignorance of his work, Wallace had hit upon the same solution of the problem of the mutability of species.

Wallace's observations were based on the facts, first, that large systematic groups such as classes and orders are usually distributed over the whole of the earth, whereas groups of low systematic value such as families, genera, and species frequently have a very small localized distribution; and secondly, that 'when a group is confined to one district, and is rich in species, it is almost invariably the case that the most closely allied species are found in the same locality or in closely adjoining localities, and that therefore the natural sequence of the species by affinity is also geographical'; and thirdly, the fact that in the fossil record 'no group or species has come into existence twice'.

The conclusion which Wallace drew from these observations was: 'Every species has come into existence coincident both in space and time with a pre-existing closely allied species.' Thought out about 1845, written in Sarawak in 1855, and published in the same year, Wallace's theory already allowed him to say that 'the natural series of affinities will also represent the order in which the several species came into existence, each one having had for its immediate antitype a closely allied species existing at the time of its origin. It is evidently possible that two or three distinct species may have had a common antitype, and that each of these may again have become the antitypes from which other closely allied species were created.'

With the help of this principle, in which it is only necessary to substitute 'ancestor' for 'antitype', for the formulation of evolution to be complete, Wallace showed that it was possible to give a simple explanation of natural classification, of the geographical distribution of plants and animals including those of the Galápagos Islands, of the succession of forms in the fossil record, and of rudimentary organs which would be inexplicable 'if each species had been created independently, and without any necessary relations with pre-existing species'.

So much of the credit for the establishment of the fact of evolution has, rightly, been accorded to Darwin that it is only just that Wallace's contribution to this problem should be recognized and honoured.

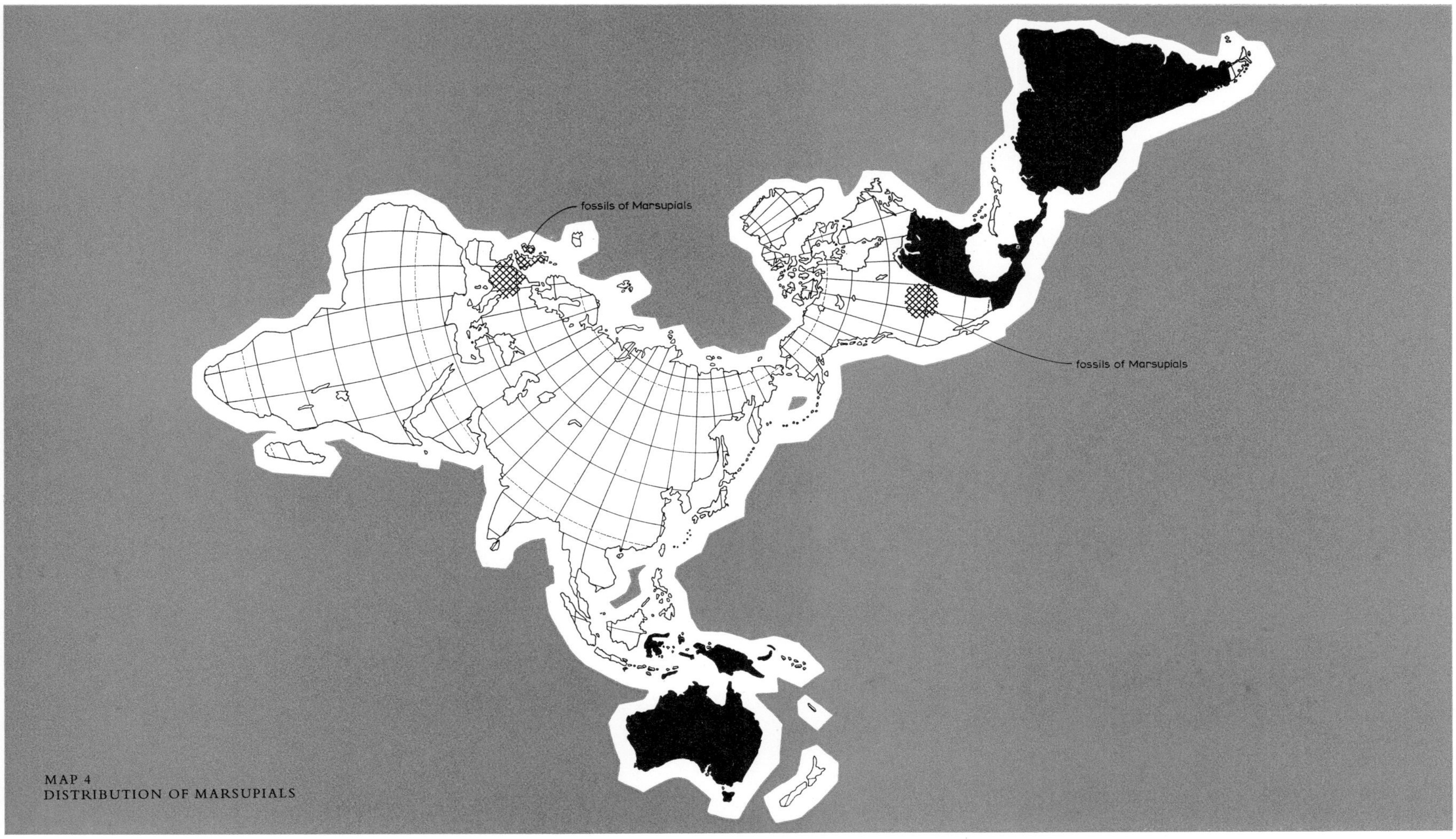

fossils of Marsupials

fossils of Marsupials

MAP 4
DISTRIBUTION OF MARSUPIALS

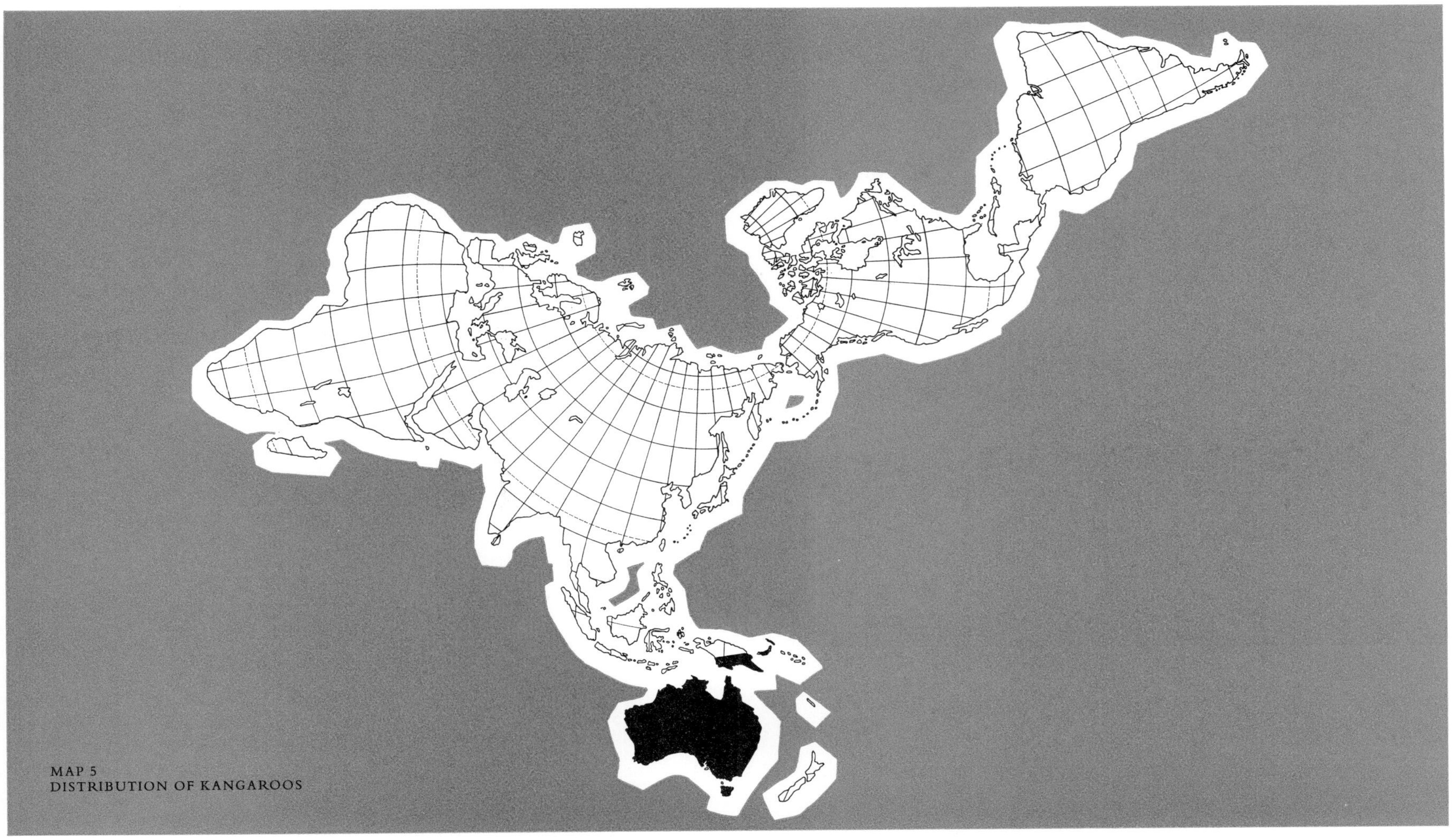

MAP 5
DISTRIBUTION OF KANGAROOS

Independently from Darwin, Alfred Russel Wallace (Pl. 7) came to the conclusion that species were evolved by natural selection. Wallace's approach was largely geographical. He was struck by the fact that large groups such as Orders usually have a wide distribution over the world, e.g. the living Marsupials in Australasia and America and fossils in Europe and North America, while smaller groups such as families and genera have a localized distribution e.g. the kangaroos. Furthermore: 'When a group is confined to one district, and is rich in species, it is almost invariably the case that the most closely allied species are found in the same locality or in closely adjoining localities, and that therefore the natural sequence of the species by affinity is also geographical.' This is well shown by the kangaroos, which are confined to the Australasian region, a natural result of the descent of all species of kangaroos by evolution from a common ancestral species in that region.

51 52

Adaptations for Flight

The Woodpecker

55

51-54. All organisms are adapted to the conditions in which they live, but some have special adaptations to particular environments, such as wings which have enabled animals to invade the air. **51.** Insect wing, an outgrowth of the back. **52.** Pterodactyl, skin stretched between the fourth finger of the hand and the leg. **53.** Bat, skin stretched between all the fingers of the hand and the leg. **54.** Bird, wing formed by feathers on wrist and forearm.
55. Darwin's favourite example of adaptation. The woodpecker has stiff tail-feathers and two of its toes turned backwards with which it secures its hold on a tree-trunk, a stout beak which chisels a hole, and a very long tongue which reaches and takes the grubs on which it feeds. Darwin asserted 'it is preposterous to attribute to mere external conditions' the structure of a woodpecker which could only have arisen by natural selection of variations. **56-58.** Recordings taken by P. Marler of the calls of various animals (to be read like music, kilocycles proportional to pitch). **56.** When calls are sharp, short, repeated and cover a wide range of pitch, they are easy to locate as when birds 'mob' an owl.
57. Continuous calls at the same medium pitch, beginning and ending gently, are difficult to locate (cryptic), as in the alarm-calls of small birds, many species of which use the same call when a bird of prey flies overhead, and benefit from the alarm given by any one of them.
58. The correlation between cryptic calls and vulnerability is seen in the mouse and wren, while the less vulnerable water-shrew and great-tit make locatable calls. The shapes and colours of animals serve as adaptations conferring survival value: by resembling other objects, adopting startling alarm attitudes, and by disruptive camouflage.
59. Leaf-insect. **60.** Stick-insect.
61, 62. Insect pupae like dead leaves.

53 54

Adaptation: Sonic Mimicry

Blackbird Mistle thrush Robin Garden warbler Wren Stonechat Chaffinch

8 6 4 2 0

1 sec.

56

Reed bunting

Blackbird

Great titmouse

Blue titmouse

9 7 5

57

Chaffinch

9 7 5

1 sec.

House mouse Water shrew Wren Great tit

7 9 5 4 3 2 1 0

58

Adaptation: Protective Resemblance

59 60 61 62

69

70

Further Examples of Protective Colouration - and Regeneration

63. Insect pupa like a thorn. **64.** Insect larvae like bird-droppings. **65.** Insect pupa like a snapped-off twig. **66.** Insect larva in alarm attitude. **67.** Frog shaped and coloured like a leaf. **68.** The same frog unconcealed. The phenomenon of Industrial Melanism (p. 93) illustrated by the Peppered Moth *Biston betularia* provides a case of the evolution of an adaptation conferring measurable survival value which has taken place under observation during the past hundred years. It is the most striking case of evolution that has been directly studied and derives its importance from the fact that the animals concerned have become adapted to a changed environment during a measurable period of time. The change in the environment is due to the pollution of the air by soot in the neighbourhood of industrial centres. **69.** Normal *betularia* form, speckled grey in colour, on a lichen-covered tree trunk in a region of England unaffected by industrial soot pollution, together with a melanic *carbonaria* form, black in colour. **70.** The same two forms on a soot-covered tree-trunk devoid of lichen in a soot-polluted area.
(Research by H.B.D. Kettlewell).

MÜLLERIAN MIMICRY

1. *Heliconius pardalinus*

2. *Melinaea madeira*

3. *Melinaea maelus*

4. *Mechanitis egaensis*

5. *Ceratinia anastasia*

6. *Heliconius narcaea*

7. *Melinaea ethra*

8. *Lycorea ceres*

9. *Mechanitis lysimnia*

10. *Ceratinia daeta*

BATESIAN MIMICRY

71. A gecko showing the adaptations of the adhesive lamellae on its toes enabling it to climb flat vertical surfaces, and the parachute flaps at the sides of the body increasing its surface area in gliding flight. **71a.** A Gecko showing protective coloration as a result of colour-change brought about by the expansion and contraction of different coloured pigment cells in the skin. The ability of the chamaeleon to change its colour is proverbial. It has a regenerated tail with less fluted sides, the old tail having become detached at the special 'autotomic' joint when caught by a predator. **72.** The stripes of the zebra are an example of protective coloration combined with disruptive coloration which obscures the outline of the animal. This is also seen in **73** the Banded Krait, and **74** Sir Geoffrey de Havilland's photograph of Thomson's Gazelle. Such animals are not easily detected, even when they are moving, the irregular areas of light and dark make it difficult to discern the exact outline of the animal. This principle is used when ships are camouflaged in war-time.

Mimicry

Colour Plates 1, 2
Müllerian mimicry is close resemblance between different species of butterflies unpalatable to bird predators which learn to shun them. Some butterflies are sacrificed in educating each generation of birds. If two or more species of butterflies resemble one another sufficiently closely to be indistinguishable to birds, each 'lesson' protects all the species which thus share and reduce their losses. The more species share in such a 'mimicry ring' the greater the advantage to all. Two mimicry rings are shown here, each in a vertical column (p. 27).

Batesian mimicry is the resemblance of an unprotected mimic to an unpalatable model. *Papilio dardanus* is widespread in Africa. The males are conspicuous and do not mimic. In Abyssinia and in Madagascar the females resemble the males. Elsewhere the females mimic many unpalatable species of models (shown in the central vertical column). The perfection of the mimicry depends on the distasteful models being more common than the mimics so that predators learn to shun them and the mimics too. At Entebbe the models are twenty times more numerous than the mimics (left vertical column) which resemble them closely. At Nairobi the models are outnumbered four times by the mimics (right vertical column) which resemble them only imperfectly. Batesian mimetic resemblance is built up from variants that confer high survival value where predators learn to shun well-marked unpalatable types and natural selection pressure is exerted in favour of closest resemblance to those types (p. 92; research by E. B. Ford)

71
71a
72
73
74

Although Darwin already knew in 1837 that evolution was the inescapable conclusion following from the evidence, he did not allow himself to say anything about his discovery until he had found an explanation of the fact of adaptation. Any structure or habit that enables its owner to survive more efficiently than its fellows in the conditions under which it lives and to leave the optimum number of offspring is an adaptation. In other words, adaptations have survival-value for the organisms that possess them. In a general way, all plants and animals are adapted to their environment, for otherwise they could not live. A man drowns in the sea because his lungs are adapted to breathe air; a fish dies out of water because its gills are adapted to extract oxygen from solution in water. The shape of the body and the fins of fish and whale enables them, each in its own way, to live and move rapidly in water. Insects, pterodactyls, birds, and bats are or were able to fly through the air by means of their wings, which are constructed on a different pattern in each of these groups (Pl. 51-54). All these animals are closely related to other animals which have no wings and cannot fly. Adaptation to flying through the air has, therefore, been evolved on four separate occasions, and an explanation must be given of the origins of these adaptations.

There are, moreover, some structures and habits in animals and plants which show particularly intricate and delicate relationships between organisms and their conditions of life and which must be in a high state of efficiency if their owners are to survive. That adaptations really mean something can be shown in the parasites of birds. Birds are prone to infestation with head lice, but some species of birds have a comb-like structure on the middle claw of their feet with which they preen their heads, and these species of birds are free from head lice. Some further examples of adaptations will now be given.

The woodpecker

The woodpecker is a classic example of adaptation to which attention was called by Darwin (Pl. 55). It possesses four structures which enable it to carry out its feeding habits with greater efficiency: two of its toes points backwards, enabling it to get a firm foothold on the bark of trees; its tail-feathers are stiff, enabling it to prop itself securely against the tree; its beak is long and strong enabling it to chisel holes in the bark; its tongue is very long, enabling it to reach and catch insect-grubs at the bottom of the holes. This is a simple case of an adaptation serving for the all-important capture of food. Other familiar examples are the poison-fangs of snakes, the beak and talons of eagles, and the claws and tusks of lions, together, in each case, with the instincts that control the method in which these structures are used.

Animal sounds

The sounds made by animals are of two main kinds: those in which the function is to advertise the location of the sound and the caller, and those in which it is advantageous for the location of the sound and the caller to remain undivulged. To the first category belong the recognition sounds made by whales which enable these animals to find one another with the help of an audio-location mechanism in their ears (p. 105). Other examples are the songs of male songbirds, which enable the females to find them and also warn other males off their territory. When a number of small birds together attack an enemy like an owl by mobbing it, their calls are easy to locate and thus serve as a clarion to summon reinforcements and indicate where they are wanted. In these cases, as P. Marler has shown, the sounds cover a wide range of pitch, from nearly 0 to 8 kilocycles per second and take the form of repeated sharp 'clicks' lasting for only very short fractions of a second.

But these same small birds can also make alarm calls of a different nature, taking advantage of the physical principle that it is more difficult for a hearer to locate a sound if it begins and ends gradually and is not interrupted (thereby depriving the hearer of the information that might be provided by time- difference of hearing in his two ears), and if the sound is restricted to a pure note at about 7 kilocycles per second (which deprives the hearer of the directional information that would be supplied by phase-difference and intensity-difference in hearing the sound with two ears).When small birds of any species make an alarm call of this kind, individuals of its own and other species take cover without worrying where the call comes from. There is therefore an advantage in birds of different species learning to make and to react to similar calls, which may be regarded as a kind of sonic mimicry (Pl. 56-58).

Protective resemblance

Many animals show a remarkable resemblance to the objects and backgrounds on which they normally rest, such as leaves, twigs, or bark, from which they derive protection owing to the inability of their predators or prey to see them in their camouflaged condition. The stripes of the zebra and the tiger are examples of the same adaptation serving for defence and offence. In some cases, however, this protective resemblance may be carried to extreme lengths as in leaf-insects, stick-insects, caterpillars resembling sprouting twigs, bugs imitating thorns, and moths looking like the droppings of birds on leaves. In some animals (flat-fish, chameleon), resemblance to the background is obtained by changing the colour and pattern of pigment-cells in the skin (Pl. 59-74).

Regeneration-joints

In some animals with long appendages liable to be caught by predators, such as the limbs of crabs or the tails of lizards, special joints are formed at which the appendages readily break, enabling the animals to escape. This is known as *autotomy*, and the joints are called autotomic joints. After its loss, the missing appendage is then formed anew by regeneration (Pl. 72).

Desert Plants

Plants inhabiting deserts are exposed to the dangers of desiccation and of conspicuousness in environments where plants are few, and they show a reduction in leaves, thickening of the stems, and a smooth surface, all of which tend to minimize the loss of water by evaporation in hot dry climates. This adaptation is often accompanied by the development of prickly spines as in some cacti, which protect the plants from being eaten by animals. This may occur in species of many different

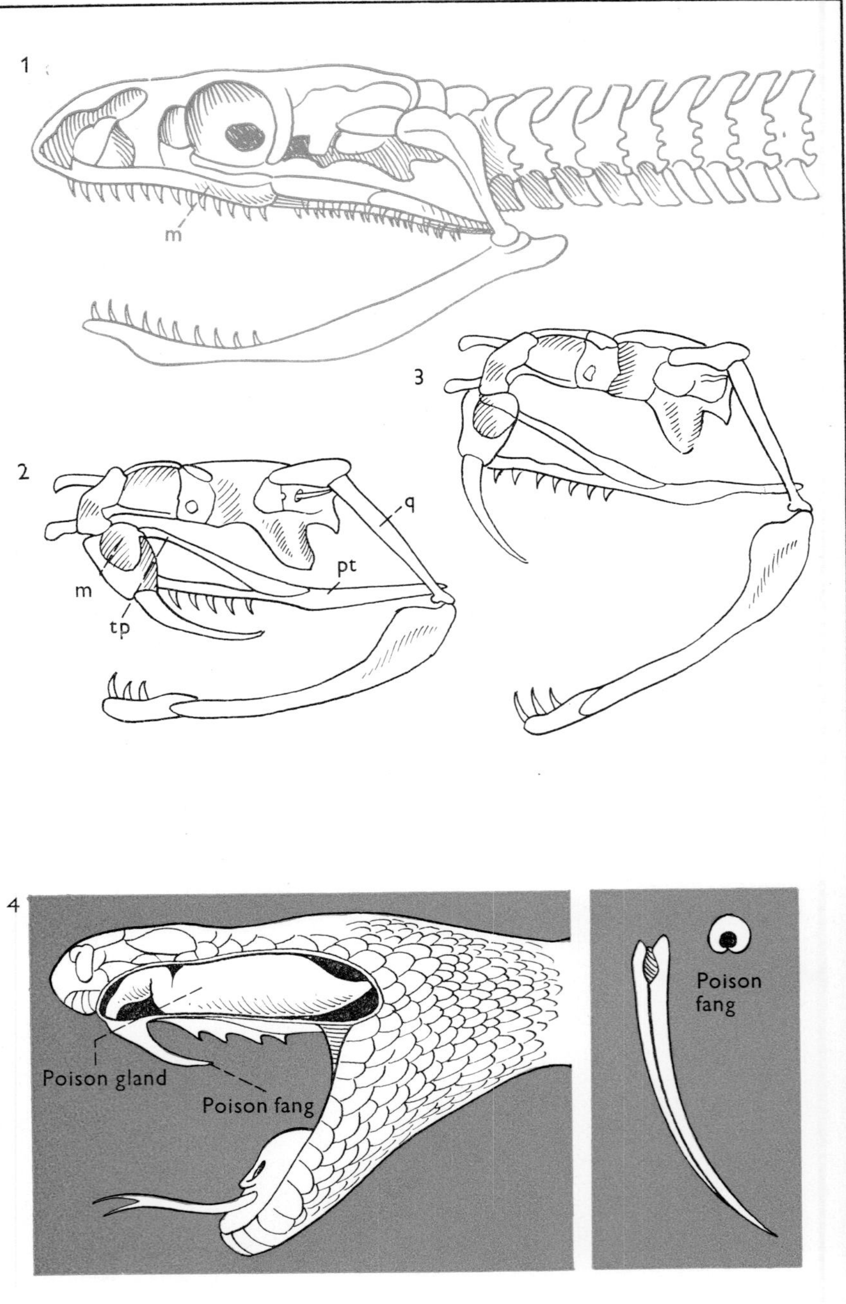

Poison-fangs of snakes

75. (1) left-side view of the skull of an ordinary snake showing the maxilla bordering the upper jaw and bearing numerous teeth. (2) similar view of a specialised snake (rattle-snake) with mouth shut, and (3) open. As the mouth opens and the lower jaw drops, the hinge-bone or quadrate q rotates forward and pushes forward the pterygoid bone pt and the trans-palatine bone tp. The latter articulates with the maxilla which is short, moveable, and bears a large tooth modified into a poison-fang. When the transpalatine presses against it the maxilla rotates and brings the poison-fang down into the striking position. (4) the poison-fang is hollow and contains a canal which connects with the poison-gland, a modified salivary gland that secretes venom. The sharpness of the fang ensures that the snake's victim receives a sub-cutaneous injection of the venom which consists of enzymes, polypeptides, and other substances which cause blood-clotting, and paralysis of respiration. An additional adaptation is that the two halves of the bony lower jaw are separate in front, so that the gape of the mouth can be greatly widened and prey of large size swallowed.

families, which, although resembling each other in these adaptations, are not closely related to each other (Pl. 76).

Seed-dispersal
The dispersal of seeds over wide areas is an important factor in the survival of specie of plants since it enables the populations to increase in number without overcrowding, and use is made of numerous agents to ensure this, including wind, water, birds that eat the fruit and distribute the seeds with their droppings, and mammals that spread the fruits caught up in their fur (Pl. 77–86).

CORRELATED ADAPTATION

Some adaptations involve not only the relations of an individual organism to its environment for its own survival but the collaboration of two or more organisms. These may be members of the same species, as in the male and female huia-bird, or they may be a plant and an animal, as in the flower and the insect. In some cases all the partners derive mutual benefit from the correlated adaptations, in other cases the result is one of parasitism.

Müllerian Mimicry
The term Müllerian mimicry is applied to the resemblance found between different species that are distasteful to their potential predators. Since their distasteful nature has to be learned by these predators as a result of experience, the lesson learned to shun any one species benefits all the others in the same 'mimicry ring' since they share the protection thereby gained. The phenomenon is named after its discoverer, Fritz Müller who drew attention to it among the butterflies of South America.

Müllerian mimicry differs from Batesian mimicry (p. 92) first in that Müllerian mimics are all more or less distasteful whereas Batesian mimics are chemically unprotected and derive their protection from their resemblance to distasteful models. Secondly, while Batesian mimics must not exceed a certain number relatively to the number of their models without forfeiting the protection that is conferred by predators having learned to shun the model, Müllerian mimics cannot be too numerous, since the greater their number the smaller the share of sacrificed individuals falling on each species. This difference leads to a third, which is that in view of the limitation of benefit conferred by Batesian mimicry to a balance between the numbers of mimics and models, there is an inducement for species exhibiting Batesian mimicry to become polymorphic, so that different forms can mimic different models without exceeding the balance exerted by natural selection. Müllerian mimics have no inducement to polymorphism.

The extent to which Müllerian mimicry can alter the characters of a species is shown by those cases in which different species of the same genus belong to different mimicry rings (Col. Pl. 1, 2).

Delayed moult in the male ptarmigan
Adaptation may result from simple alteration of the time-scale. In the ptarmigan, the moult from winter white to summer brown tends to be delayed in the male, with the result that he remains conspicuous and vulnerable to predators, while the female, biologically more valuable when incubating eggs, is inconspicuous. The benefit in this adaptation is to the species as a whole (Pl. 87, 88).

The huia-bird
The huia-bird of New Zealand is an example of adaptation that involves both sexes. The male bird has a short, stout beak with which it chisels holes in trees containing grubs of the particular beetle on which it feeds but the beak is not long enough to reach them. The female has a slender curved beak, twice as long as that of the male and therefore with a longer reach, but not capable of chiselling. Co-operation between the members of a pair of mated huia-birds is therefore indispensable for either to obtain food. It is believed that the huia-bird is now extinct, and it is probable that its extinction was due to this excessively specialized adaptation, preventing it from exploiting other possible food-supplies when the grub on which it fed exclusively became less frequent as the forest area diminished. This example is important in showing that while adaptations may ensure survival in the conditions under which they originated, they may bring about extinction if they are too specialized and the conditions under which the animal lives are changed (Pl. 89).

The pollination of flowers
The function of flowers and of insects in securing cross-pollination of plants is well-known. Attracted to the flowers by their colour or smell and in search of nectar and pollen, the insect inserts its proboscis into the flower where it becomes dusted with pollen that is then conveyed to the stigma of the next flower visited by the insect. As Darwin showed, no plant which is pollinated solely by wind has a brightly-coloured flower. Flowers are therefore adaptations to ensure cross-pollination and the genetic benefits of outbreeding.

In primroses, some plants have flowers with long styles and short stamens (pin-eyed), while others have short styles and long stamens (thrum-eyed). When an insect visits a short-styled flower, it is dusted with pollen on that part of its body which comes into contact with the stigma of long-styled flowers and vice versa. Pollen from a long-styled flower usually fails to pollinate long-styled flowers, and pollen from short-styled flowers does not pollinate short-styled flowers. Darwin showed that this dimorphism known as heterostyly, is an adaptation ensuring cross-fertilization between different individuals, which produces more vigorous and fertile offspring than result from self-fertilization (Pl. 90).

In orchids an additional adaptation has been evolved. The pollen grains in the flowers are arranged in packets attached by elastic threads to a stalk, the whole forming a *pollinium* of which there are two in each flower. When an insect, usually a bumble bee or moth, visits the flower and inserts its proboscis, the pollinia become detached from the flower and attached to the insect by a viscous fluid that rapidly sets hard. As the insect withdraws and flies away it carries the pollinia with it. The stalk of each pollinium bends down in about half a minute, and the pollinia then point forward on the insect and acquire the position in which they come into contact with the stigma of the next flower visited, which, because of the time taken for the pollinia to bend down, will usually be on another plant. Since each pollinium carries several packets of pollen, an insect bearing pollinia can successively pollinate several flowers, each with pollen from another flower and most frequently from a different plant (Pl. 91).

The pollination of the fig
The so-called 'fig' of the fig-tree is an inflorescence that takes the form of a hollow pear-shaped sack, the inner lining of which bears the flowers. A small hole puts the cavity of the fig in communication with the outside world, and through this hole a female fig-wasp, *Blastophaga psenes*, enters and lays its eggs in some of the flowers, where the young wasps hatch and develop parasitically. The young males, which never develop very far, penetrate into other flowers in the same fig where females are developing and fertilize them. The young females, when they have completed their development, emerge through the hole in the fig, but in doing so they become dusted with pollen from the stamens of the male flowers. When the young female wasp enters another fig, this pollen is brushed against the stigma of the female flowers, which thus become pollinated. As the male flowers within each fig become ripe before the female flowers, pollination is effected with pollen from a different fig, brought by the wasp, and self-pollination is avoided. This association between the fig-tree and the wasp has become so intimate that the wasp is dependent on the presence of fig-trees without which it cannot develop, and, as a rule, the fig-tree cannot be pollinated if there are no wasps (Pl. 92).

Mistletoe
Parasitism is an extreme form of adaptation, and while the parasites that are most familiar are animals, parasitic plants also exist. An example, to which attention was called by Darwin, is mistletoe, a parasitic plant which uses sunlight to build up its own sugars in its green leaves from the carbon dioxide of the air, but which is entirely dependent on its host tree for supplies of water and salts from the soil. For its survival, mistletoe is dependent on three factors: an insect, usually a bee or a fly, for the pollination of its flowers; a bird, usually a mistle-thrush, for the dissemination of its seeds by eating the berries and depositing them on branches of trees; and a tree, usually a pine, a spruce, or a broad-leaved tree (according to the race of mistletoe), on which its parasitic relationship can be established (Pl. 134).

THE THEORY OF NATURAL SELECTION

The foregoing examples of adaptation, few as they are, will suffice to show why Darwin kept silent about the fact of evolution until he had solved the problem of how adaptations arise. He observed that in many cases it was possible to make out gradations in adaptations and to see how they might have arisen step by step. Examples are the structure of the vertebrates' eye, the nest-building habit of birds, and the climbing habit of plants. If this was so, adaptations might have arisen gradually, as a result of small variations in structure and habit.

Darwin knew that all members of a species are not identical but show variations in size, strength, health, fertility, longevity, habits, mental attributes, and countless other characters. Such variations are fortuitous and may occur in any direction. He soon perceived that such variations could be, and in fact were turned to good account by man in the course of the artificial selection which he has practised since the Neolithic Age. The various kinds of cereals, dogs, horses, cattle and many other domesticated plants and animals are living proofs of this fact. The key is *selection* or the practice of breeding only from those parents that possess the desired qualities. But how could selection operate on wild plants and animals in nature since the beginning of life on earth, without man or a conscious being to direct it? The solution of this puzzle occurred to Darwin in September 1838 as his mind considered the combined effects of variation, competition, adaptation, and extinction. He had by then already come to his 'view of those forms slightly favoured getting the upper hand and forming species', and realized that under the conditions of competition in which plants and animals live in nature, those variations, however small, provided that they were inherited, would be preserved which increased the organisms' ability to survive and to leave fertile offspring, while those variations which decreased it would be eliminated. Then in October 1838 he read Malthus's *Essay on Population* and saw that competition for food-supply must be heavy, and that mortality must be inevitable and high. Indeed, it is not only for food that organisms, whether plants or animals compete, but for space, light and mates; and they are subject to hazards from predation, disease, and accidents of the physical environment such as floods, drought, cold, heat, and volcanic eruptions, all of which act as selective agents and penalise those organisms that are least effectively

76

77

78

79

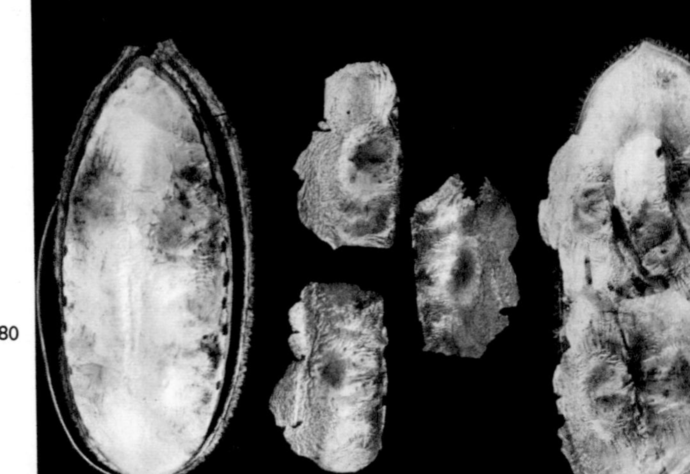

80

Adaptation to Dry Conditions

76. Desert plants ensure minimal loss of water by reduction of surface and a waxy covering, and protection against browsing animals by development of spines as in cactus. The wide dispersal of seeds is an adaptation conferring survival value because it avoids overcrowding and competition for salts and sunshine and promotes colonization of new areas. **77-81.** Most plants make use of the air by developing plumes and wings on the seeds which enable them to be wafted to great distances. **82.** Some seeds are distributed by water. **83, 84.** Other seeds have hooked spines which become entangled in mammal's fur and carried away with them. Others again rely on the colour of their fruit to attract birds to swallow and distribute them with their droppings, as **85** yew with a bright red cup round the seed, and **86** rose where the fruit ('rose-hip') is red. **87.** The male ptarmigan delays the moult in spring and remains white serving as a decoy. **88.** The female is protectively coloured while hatching the eggs.

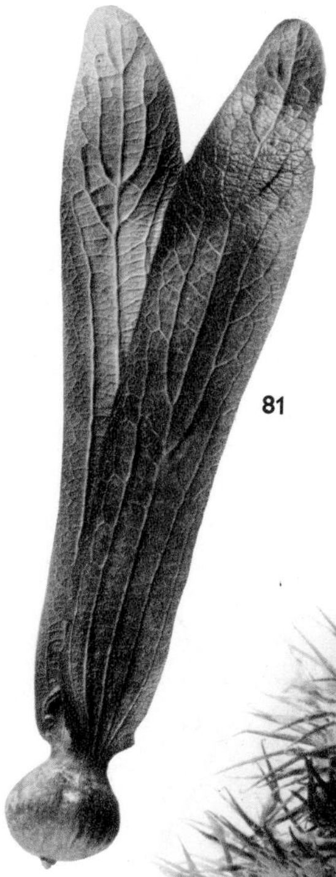

81

82

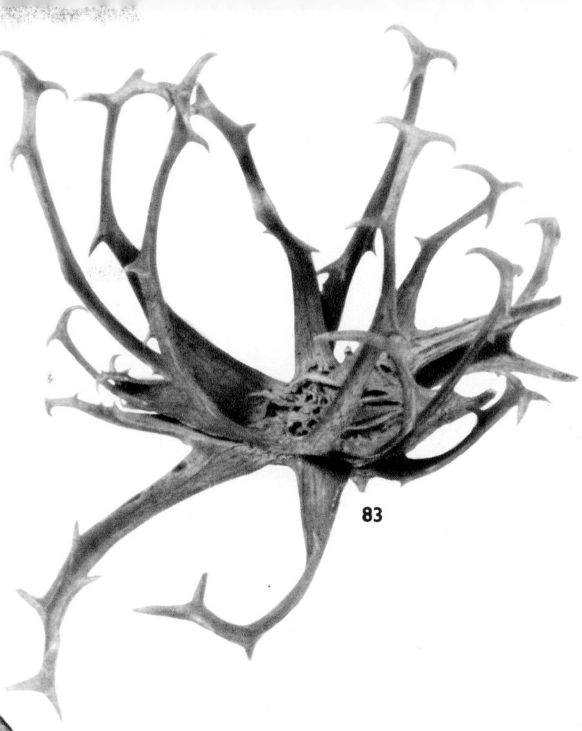

83

84

85

86

Adaptation, Seed Dispersal

Correlated Adaptation

87

88

Correlated Adaptation carried too far, the Huia-bird

89. Huia-birds feed on grubs in trees. The male has a short stout beak that can chisel a hole but is not long enough to reach the grub. The female has a slender beak long enough to reach the grub but not stout enough to chisel a hole. The sexes must therefore collaborate for every meal, but their adaptation is so specialised that since deforestation reduced the supplies of their particular grub, huia-birds are extinct.

89

adapted to escape from their effects. The main point of Darwin's discovery is that in a state of nature, selection works automatically, or 'naturally', which is why he called it *Natural Selection*. Furthermore, it is not only individuals that natural selection eliminates but their potential offspring which, because of the fact of heredity, would have resembled them. Adaptations therefore arise, lineages of organisms evolve, and new species originate from old species as a result of gradual accumulation of fortuitous heritable variations that by chance were favourable.

Darwin was then able to formulate a complete theory providing a rational explanation of the causes as well as of the fact of evolution in plants and animals. It is formally based on four premises which he already knew to be true, and three deductions which are now also known to be true. They may be enumerated as follows:

1. Organisms produce a far greater number of reproductive cells than ever give rise to mature individuals.
2. The numbers of individuals in species remain more or less constant.
3. Therefore there must be a high rate of mortality.
4. The individuals in a species are not all identical, but show fortuitous variation in all characters.
5. Therefore some variants will succeed better and others less well in the competition for survival, and the parents of the next generation will be naturally selected from among those members of the species that show variation in the direction of more effective adaptation to the conditions of their environment (their ecological niches) and the ability to leave most offspring.
6. Heredity ensures resemblance between parent and offspring.
7. Therefore subsequent generations will maintain and improve on the degree of adaptation realized by their parents by gradual change.

This is the formal theory of evolution by natural selection, first grasped by Darwin at the end of 1838 when he was living at 36 Great Marlborough Street in London. Early in 1858, Wallace, at Ternate in the Molluccas, worked out precisely the same theory and sent it to Darwin. Their joint paper was read before the Linnean Society of London on 1 July 1858 and published on 1 August of the same year. Darwin thereupon wrote up all his evidence in book form, and *On the Origin of Species* was published on 24 November 1859.

When Thomas Henry Huxley (1825-95) first read it he exclaimed: 'How extremely stupid not to have thought of that!'. The reception of the book by other scientists and by the general public was at first stormy, and it was some time before

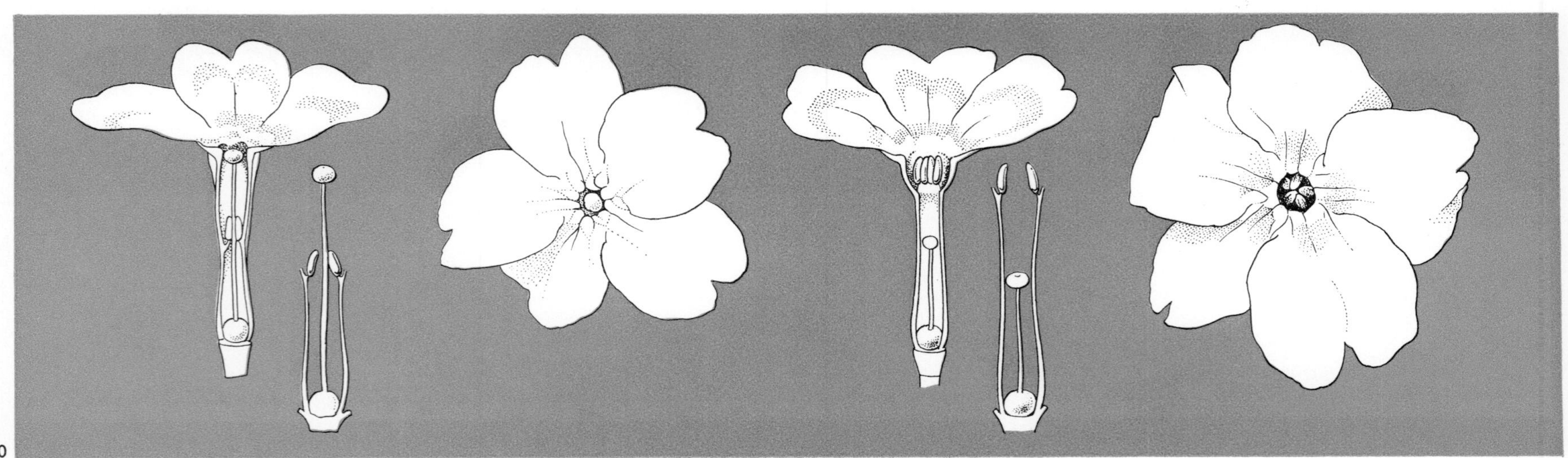

90

Cross Pollination

Although most flowers are hermaphrodite and contain both male and female organs, numerous adaptations ensure that they are normally cross-pollinated from other flowers, thereby securing the benefits of outbreeding, vigour, and variation. The discovery of these adaptations in primroses and in orchids was due to Darwin. **90.** Some primroses have flowers with long styles and short stamens ('pin-eyed'), while others have short styles and long stamens ('thrum-eyed'). When an insect enters a pin-eyed flower it is dusted with pollen on that part of its body which comes into contact with the stigma of a thrum-eyed flower, and vice-versa. The existence of two forms in a species is called dimorphism, and here it results in an adaptation that ensures cross-pollination, secures the genetic benefits of outbreeding and avoids self-pollination and inbreeding. **91.** In orchids the pollen-masses become detached from the flower and attached to an insect as shown in the unique photograph of a moth's head, which then pollinates the next flowers it visits. **92.** The fruit known as a fig is a hollow sack with the flowers inside. The fig-wasp enters a fig and lays its eggs in the flowers, where they develop into young wasps. When these fly out, they become dusted with pollen from the male flowers and on entering another fig this is brushed against the female flowers which are therefore pollinated from another fig. Within each fig the male flowers become ripe before the female, which ensures that the latter are pollinated with pollen from other figs and not from their own. The association between fig tree and fig-wasp is so intimate that the latter cannot develop except in figs, and figs cannot be pollinated except by fig-wasps.

The Struggle for Survival

93. 'The giraffe, by its lofty stature, much elongated neck, fore-legs, head and tongue, has its whole frame beautifully adapted for browsing on the higher branches of trees. It can thus obtain food beyond the reach of other Ungulata or hoofed animals inhabiting the same country; and this must be a great advantage to it during dearths.' (Darwin, *Origin of Species*).

the cogency of Darwin's observations and arguments was realised. In support of it Huxley was soon joined by Hooker and by Lyell, and by a few other scientists in Great Britain, the United States, and Germany. Their number gradually increased all over the world. By others, however he was bitterly attacked for having substituted a natural law in place of what had previously been regarded as evidence for design although, as Darwin pointed out, Isaac Newton had already shown that 'the planets move in their courses and that a stone falls to the ground, not from the direct volition of the Creator', but 'through the intervention of the secondary and appointed law of gravity'. Furthermore, Darwin revealed 'the clumsy, wasteful, blundering, low and horribly cruel works of nature', which doomed creatures to suffering and species to extinction, and he showed that there was some human comfort to be drawn from the view that if the processes of evolution and of the balance of nature were the result of natural laws, 'we cease to be astonished that a group of animals should have been formed to lay their eggs in the bowels and flesh of other sensitive beings; that some animals should live by and even delight in cruelty'.

At the time when Darwin worked and wrote there was complete ignorance of the principles of heredity and of the origin of heritable variation. This lacuna was in fact filled, without Darwin or anyone else at the time realising it, by Mendel's discovery of the particulate nature of heredity, first made known in 1865. It is a remarkable tribute to the soundness of Darwin's general argument that it was not invalidated but helped over its main difficulties when heredity was at last understood. As will be seen below (p. 79) Mendel's 'factors' now known as genes, and the chromosome mechanism (p. 78), supply exactly what Darwin's theory requires to explain evolution by natural selection of heritable variation, itself the result of mutation (p. 83) and recombination (p. 78) of genes. But Mendel's great work remained unknown until it was independently re-discovered and confirmed by C. Correns, E. von Tschermak, and H. de Vries in 1900. Even then, biology was in confusion because geneticists who thought that evolution could be explained simply by means of mutation, and selectionists who thought that mutation was only pathological, failed to see how their researches bore on each other. It remained for Sir Ronald Fisher in 1930 to effect the integration of Darwinian selection with Mendelian genetics and to lay the foundation of the synthetic theory of evolution (p. 97). Today evolution is being studied experimentally, evolutionary change has actually been observed, the origin of species is being witnessed, and the importance of selection in the production of adaptation has not only been confirmed but its pressure has been measured. In conclusion it may therefore be said and may be useful to repeat here that the results of modern research by observation and experiment have confirmed the main lines of Darwin's argument, while refining them in the light of new knowledge, and they have provided definite evidence of the correctness of his three deductions as well as of the four premises on which the theory of evolution by natural selection is based. It is now universally accepted that evolution and the origin of new species take place by this means.

Chapter II EVOLUTION IS A FACT

THE SIGNIFICANCE OF SIMILARITY

If two or more kinds of complex objects such as organisms resemble one another, not merely in superficial appearance but in basic structure, there must be some reason for their similarity, and this presents a problem to be solved. The existence of this problem is not generally realized because the objects concerned are so familiar; but when two species of animals such as mistle-thrushes and song-thrushes are considered together, the question is bound to arise why they are so similar. This question was asked by Aristotle, and he answered it by supposing that underlying the similarities there was a unity of plan. It is the existence of such a plan that makes profitable comparison possible. It may be said to provide the basis for all comparative studies, such as comparative anatomy, which Goethe formalized into a science of shape to which he gave the name of morphology.

Comparative studies were and are extremely useful in enabling classifications to be made, whether of rocks, plants, or animals, for nothing can be classified unless at least two of the objects in question resemble one another sufficiently to be comparable, which means that they must have at least one attribute in common. By themselves, however, comparative studies based only on the supposition of a unity of plan make very little advance in knowledge, because they give no explanation of the question why such unity of plan should exist at all. This was the state of biology when Darwin established the notion of species descended from common ancestors. At one stroke, the similarity between species is explained, if they were evolved along divergent paths from the same ancestors; similarity between different species is a result of their affinity as relatives, and the degree of similarity between them is a measure of the closeness of their relationship as the degree of difference is of their divergence (Pl. 94).

An analogy with biology is provided by the study of languages, or comparative philology. The similarities between the French, Italian, Spanish, Portuguese, Provençal, Romansch, and Romanian languages extend not only to their vocabularies but also to the structure of their words and the ways in which they are used to compose sentences. Nobody could suppose that these languages had been independently invented by the peoples who speak them, and it is known from historical records that they are all derived, or evolved, from Latin. The evolution of languages has long been recognized and accepted, at one time indeed with greater freedom than would now be tolerated, for the sixteenth-century attempts to derive all human languages from Hebrew as the language spoken by Adam contravene the principles of philology. At all events it may be said that the similarities between the languages of the Latin group provide evidence of their derivation from Latin which can be explained in no other way. Similarly, the sciences of comparative anatomy, embryology, biochemistry, serology, and others provide evidence of similarities explicable only if evolution of plants and animals has occurred (Pl. 95).

Morphology

Morphology or comparative anatomy begins with the obvious. Flowering plants have roots, branches, leaves, and flowers consisting of sepals, petals, stamens, and carpels which when pollinated develop into fruits and seeds. There are over a quarter of a million known species of flowering plants, but, however diverse in size, colour, habit, or detail, they are all built on the same plan, and it can be confidently predicted that the countless species still to be discovered will also be found to conform to this plan. This is an example of the principle expressed by Milne Edwards: 'Nature is prodigal in variety, but niggard in innovation.' The reason why flowering plants are all built on the same plan is that they have all inherited it from the same source, a common ancestor, through descent with modification, and their similarity, which is an expression of their genetic affinity, is evidence for evolution.

Examples from the animal kingdom are even more striking, because the basic resemblances in them can be shown to be quite independent of the manner of life that the animals lead. That cats and dogs, horses and cows, all have legs, tails, mouths, eyes, nostrils, and ears in corresponding positions, is due to the fact that

Classification

94

94. Resemblance in fundamental characters between different organisms is due to their descent from a common ancestor, which means that they are related and have mutual affinity; the differences between them are due to their divergence during descent from that ancestor. The history of any group of plants or animals may thus be depicted in the form of a branching system, the point of forking between two branches representing the common ancestor of those branches, as shown graphically in Darwin's classic diagram. Since organisms fall into groups that themselves fall into larger groups, they can be classified; the degree of similarity between them is the measure of their affinity (→ 37, 391).

The Evolution of Languages

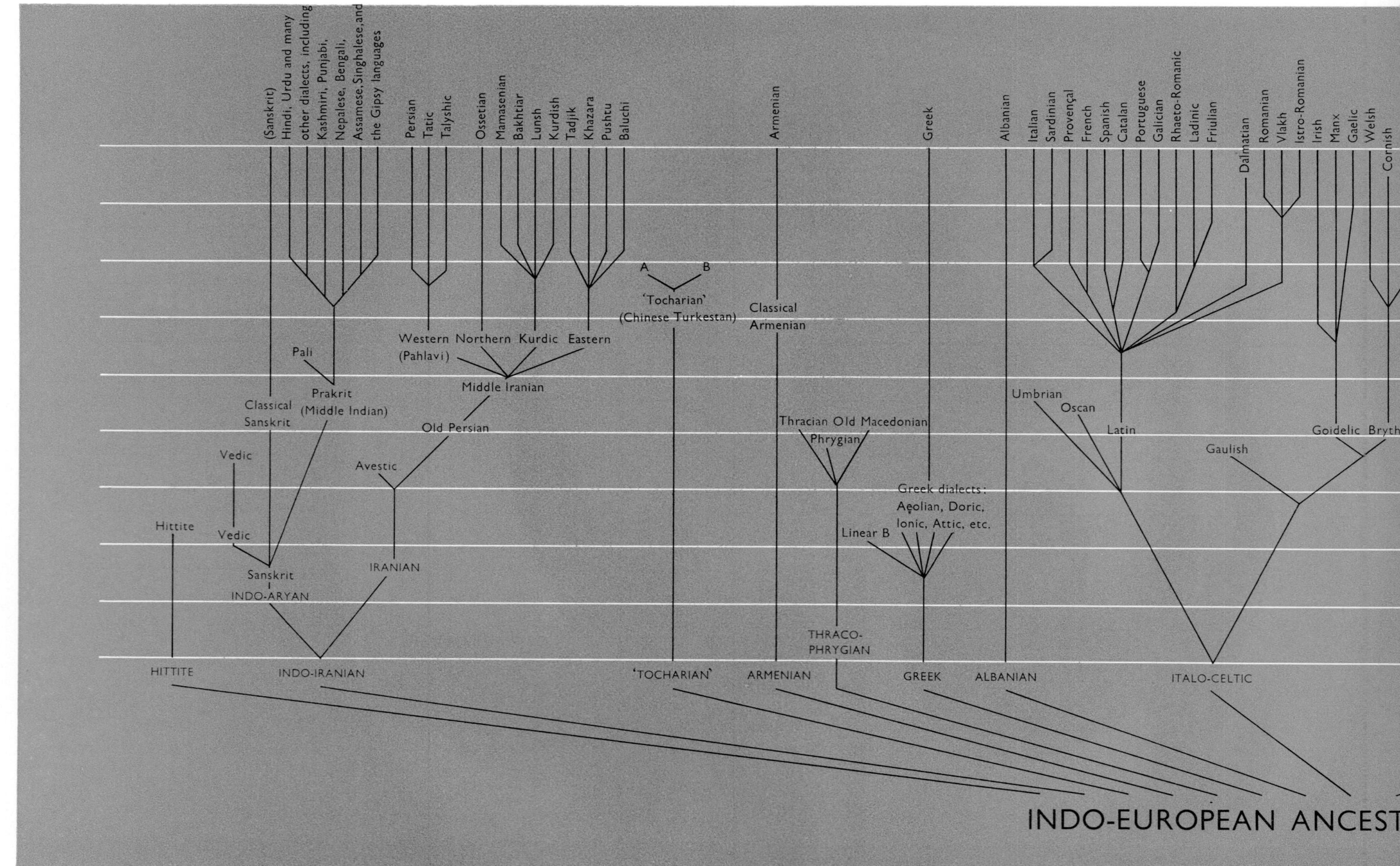

they are all mammals and descended from the common ancestor of mammals. The resemblances go much further than skin-deep, however. In the skeleton, the skull is composed of separate bones which can be identified and traced all the way from fish to man. The vertebral column is made up of separate vertebrae which, likewise, are identical in basic structure from the lowest to the highest vertebrates. The limbs are anchored in the body by means of shoulder- and hip-girdles, and each limb is supported by a skeleton consisting of one bone nearest the body (upper arm-bone or thigh-bone), two bones in the next segment (forearm or shank), a number of small bones in the joint (wrist or ankle), from which a number of slender cylindrical bones radiate in the form of a fan. In the fishes, these radiating bones, or radials, are numerous and support an undivided fin at the extremity of each limb (Pl. 303). In the vertebrates that have adopted a habit of life on land, the radials are typically five in number, the five divided digits, fingers and toes of the hand and foot. As Darwin remarked: 'What can be more curious than that the hand of a man, formed for grasping, that of a mole for digging, the leg of the horse, the paddle of the porpoise, and the wing of the bat, should all be constructed on the same pattern, and should include similar bones, in the same relative positions?'. They have, of course, been evolved in descent from one and the same set of representatives in a common ancestor, and such affinity between the corresponding elements of different animals is expressed by saying that they are homologous structures (Pl. 96). Darwin continued:

'Nothing can be more hopeless than to attempt to explain this similarity of pattern in members of the same class, by utility or by the doctrine of final causes. If we suppose that an early progenitor – the archetype as it may be called – of all mammals, birds, and reptiles, had its limbs constructed on the existing general pattern, for whatever purpose they served, we can at once perceive the plain signification of the homologous construction of the limbs throughout the class.'

Homologous structures in different animals are found to be identically placed in relation to neighbouring structures. Thus if a certain bone in one animal is situated on the inner side of a particular nerve and above a particular artery, that bone will be found to have the same relations to the nerve and the artery in related animals. A striking example of this constancy of morphological relations is provided by the recurrent laryngeal nerve. This nerve which stimulates the muscles of the larynx, runs out of the brain-case, loops round a ligament connected to the pulmonary artery, and then runs forwards to the larynx. In most mammals, the length of this nerve is only a few inches, but in the giraffe, the neck of which is so greatly elongated, the recurrent laryngeal nerve runs several feet down from the brain-case to loop round the pulmonary artery ligament, and several feet up again to the laryngeal muscles; so constant are morphological relations.

The constancy of their spatial relations enables homologous structures to be traced in different groups of animals even when they perform quite different functions. The most striking example of a change in form and function of corresponding structures is provided by the incorporation of the hinge of the reptiles' jaws in the chain of auditory ossicles in mammals. The reptile's lower jaw is made up of several bones of which the dentary carries the teeth, and the articular works against the quadrate bone of the upper jaw forming the hinge. In mammals the lower jaw consists of a single bone, the dentary, which has a joint with the cheek-bone (squamosal) of the skull forming a new hinge. As the new hinge gradually evolved and took over the function of articulation between the jaws, the bones of the old hinge correspondingly lost that function but were just in the right place to acquire a new one, becoming intercalated between the columella of the ear and the tympanic membrane and serving to convey sound vibrations. During this functional transformation, however, down to the minutest detail, the relations of these little bones to their surrounding structures, nerves, arteries, and muscles, preserve a plan that is

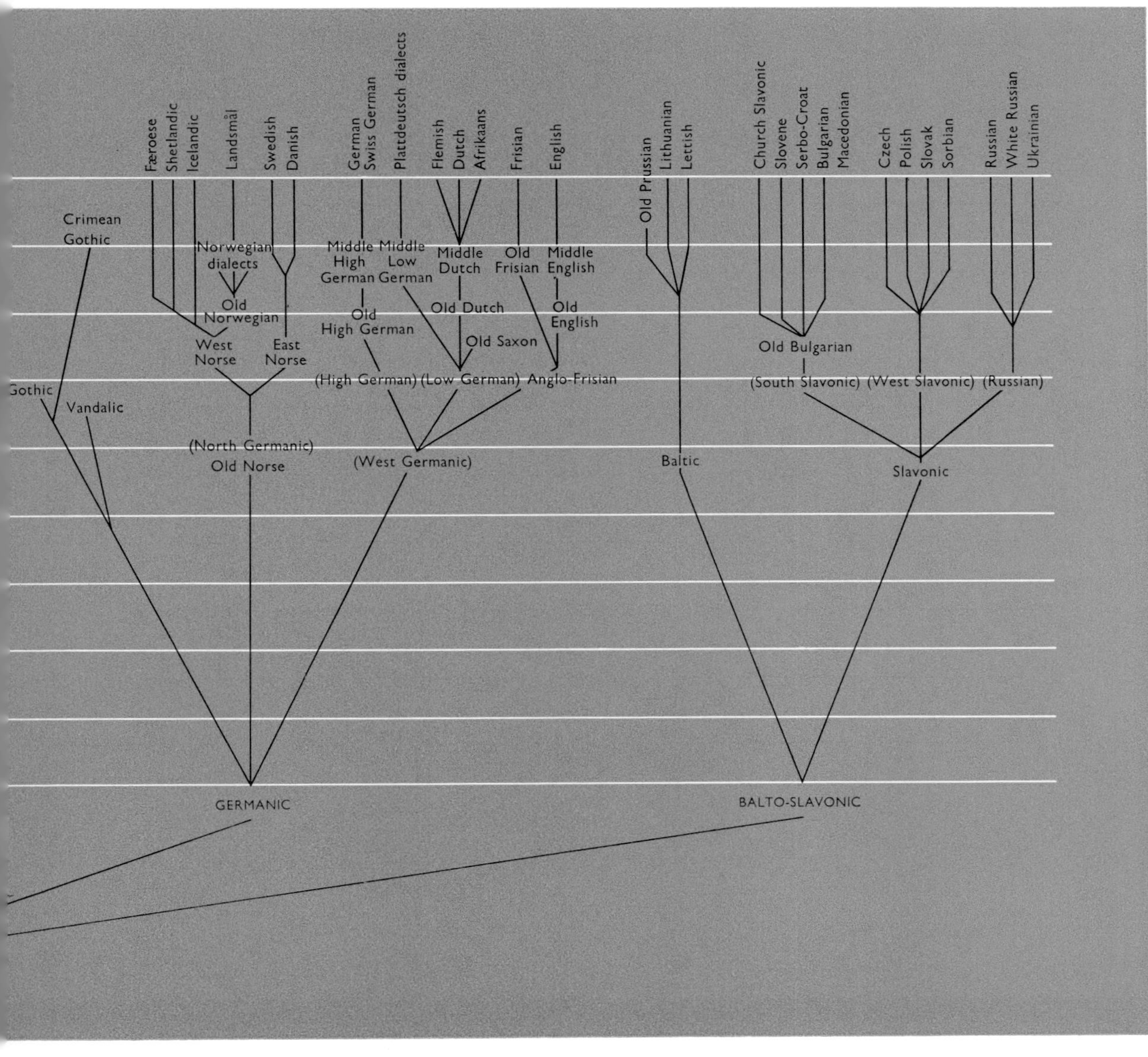

95. A close analogy with the evolution of plants and animals is provided by the history of languages. The different languages of the Indo-European family are arranged to show their descent from common ancestors and relative affinities. The various romance languages owe their similarities to the fact that they all evolved from Latin; their differences are due to divergence. The Germanic languages show similar internal resemblances, and the nature of both the differences and the more remote resemblances between them and the romance languages reveals that the point of contact of the two groups must be placed in the more remote past, but that they do derive from a common ancestor. Like organisms, some languages died out.

identical with that seen in the reptilian jaw, in spite of the difference in function which the structures perform (Pl. 97). This plan is a shared inheritance from a common ancestor, the descendants of which have diverged with modification as is seen in the difference between reptiles and mammals. This descent with modification is nothing other than evolution, and fossils have now been found which show every stage in the transition from the reptile to the mammal, as will be shown (p. 61).

Comparative anatomy presents many other examples of intermediate forms and gradations of structure. In fishes a single stream of blood flows through the heart which has an undivided auricle and an undivided ventricle. In the amphibia blood flows into the heart in two streams, one from the lungs, the other from the rest of the body, and the auricle is correspondingly divided into two, but the ventricle remains single. In most reptiles there is division of the auricle and incomplete division of the ventricle by means of a partition which projects across the cavity but fails to reach the opposite wall. In birds the partition is complete and the two ventricles as well as the auricles are divided and separate the streams of pure and impure blood. In mammals, also, there are two separate ventricles and two auricles. Here is a case of change of structure showing gradation within the unity of plan (Pl. 98).

The facts of comparative anatomy in both vegetable and animal kingdoms are so numerous and cogent that even if there were no other approaches to the problem, they would suffice to prove that only evolution can account for them.

Embryology

The great Russian embryologist K.E. von Baer once wrote: 'In my possession are two little embryos in spirit, whose names I have omitted to attach, and at present I am quite unable to say to what class they belong. They may be lizards or small birds, or very young mammalia, so complete is the similarity in the mode of formation of the head and trunk in these animals'. These words describe an important fact, namely that in the process of development that animals undergo from the fertilized egg to the adult condition, young animals often pass through embryonic stages in which they resemble one another very closely although their adult forms may be strikingly different (Pl. 99). Nobody would mistake adult lizards for birds or mammals, and if their embryos are so very similar there must be a reason for it. The reason, which Darwin was the first to point out, is that all animals whose embryonic stages are similar are related and descended from a common ancestor, from which they have inherited the form of the embryonic stage which they repeat in their own development.

The study of embryology is therefore of value to students of evolution because it provides examples of similarities between different groups of animals, similarities which are not evident when the animals are full grown. The similarity between embryonic stages is evidence that evolution has occurred, and it indicates the affinity between the descendants, just as comparative anatomy reveals basic plans of structure and community of descent.

In many invertebrate animals that live in water, the young after hatching out of the egg-membranes develop into forms specially adapted to floating and drifting about, which results in the wide dispersal of the animals and avoidance of overcrowding. Such forms are called larvae, and a very prevalent larval form is that known as the trochophore. It is shaped like a small whip-top with a tuft of sensory threads (cilia) at the front end, a simple alimentary canal, and a band of beating cilia arranged in a ring round the rim of the top, in front of the mouth. This trochophore larva is found not only in marine worms, but also in snails and mussels, and it means that the two groups to which these animals belong, the Annelida and the Mollusca, are related and have a common ancestor from which each has evolved, inheriting and preserving the same trochophore larval form while the adult forms

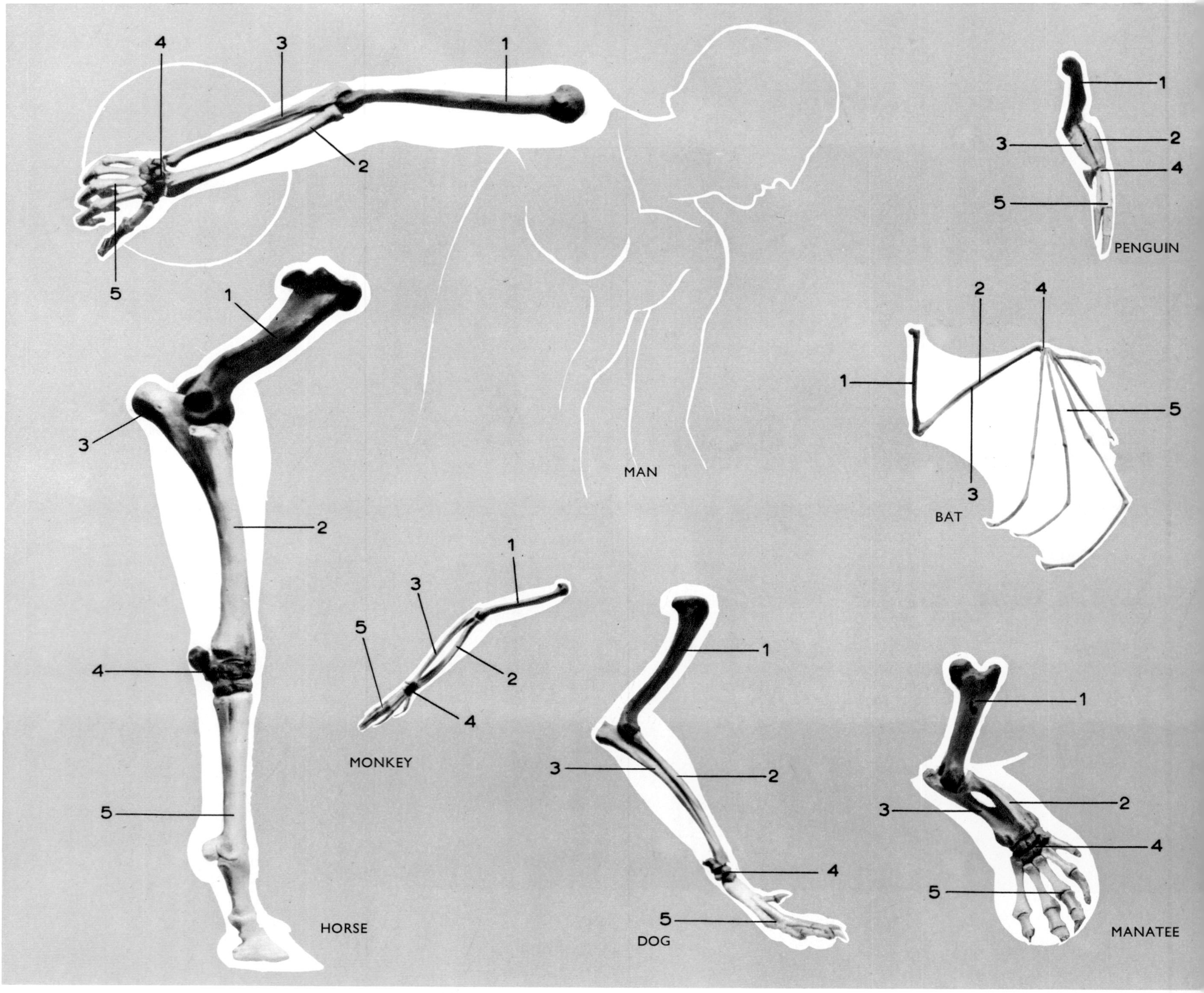

96

97

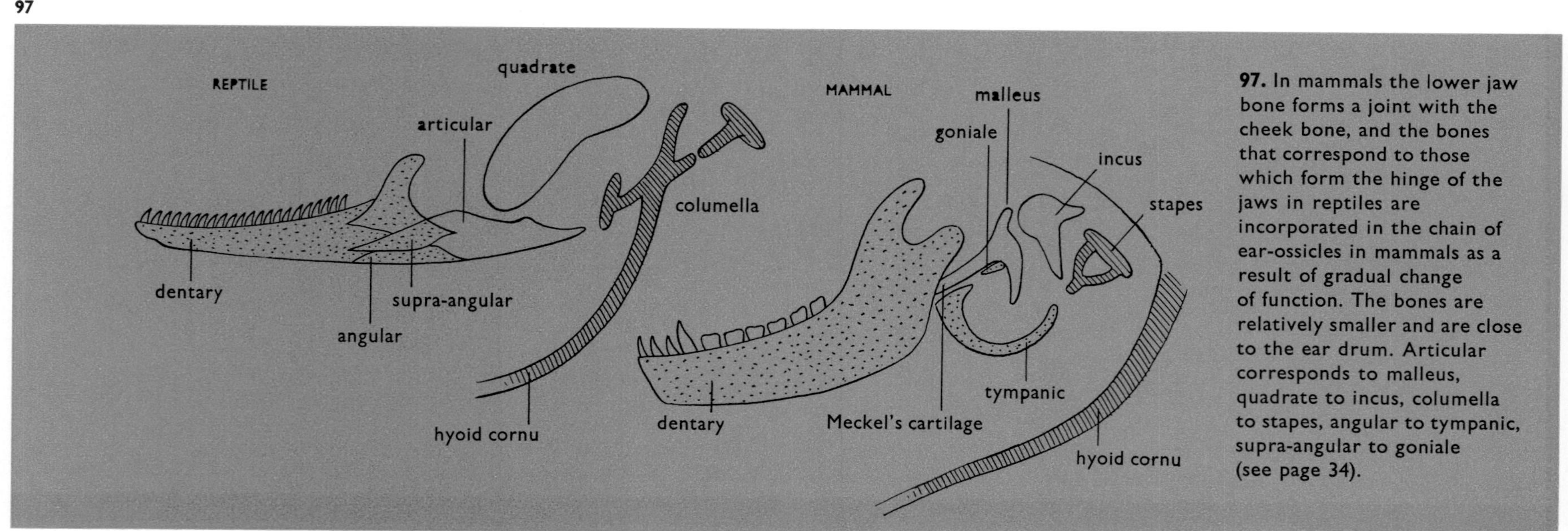

97. In mammals the lower jaw bone forms a joint with the cheek bone, and the bones that correspond to those which form the hinge of the jaws in reptiles are incorporated in the chain of ear-ossicles in mammals as a result of gradual change of function. The bones are relatively smaller and are close to the ear drum. Articular corresponds to malleus, quadrate to incus, columella to stapes, angular to tympanic, supra-angular to goniale (see page 34).

Morphology: Change of function during evolution; Homologous structures; Amphibian, Reptile, and Mammal Hearts

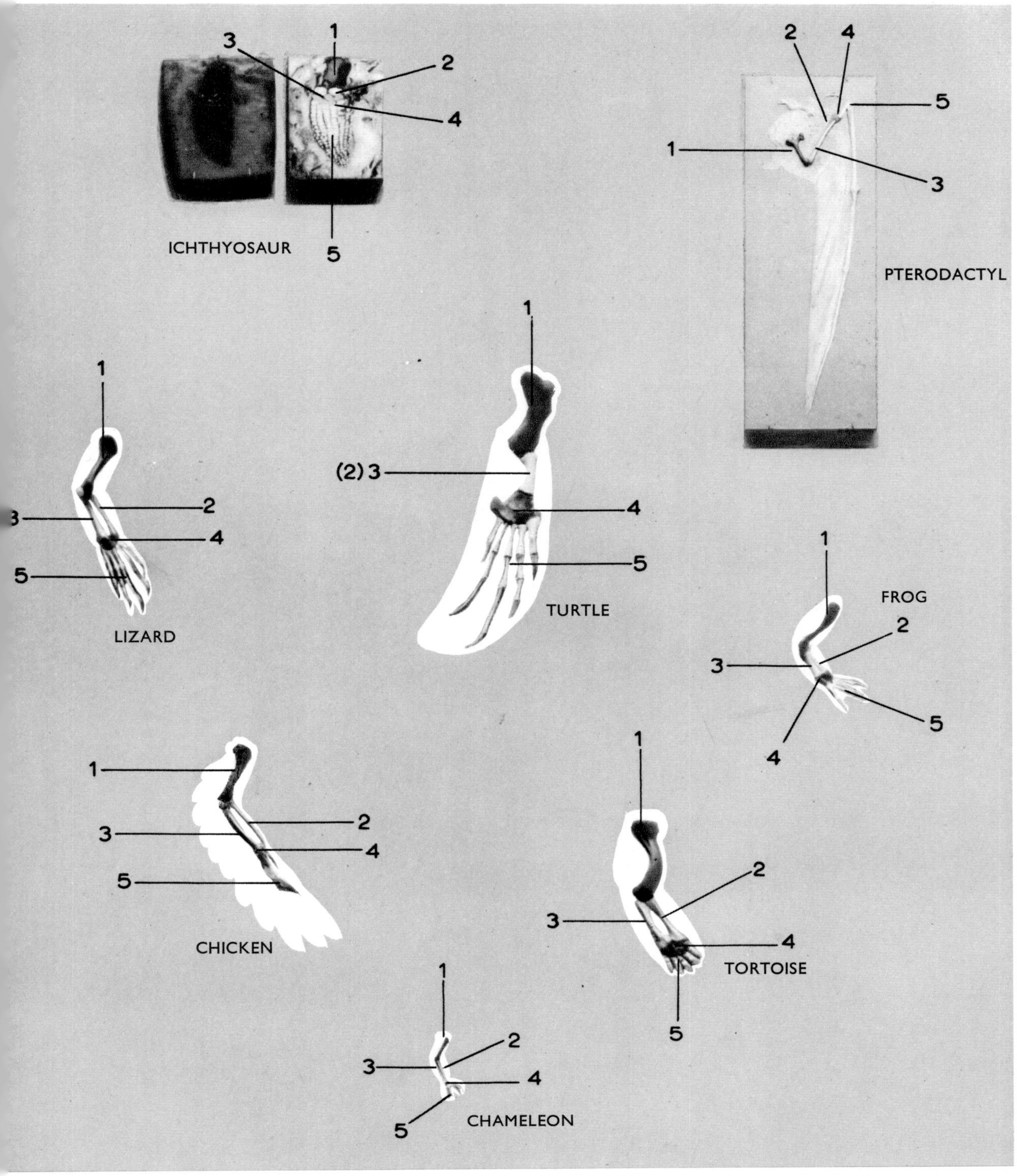

ICHTHYOSAUR

PTERODACTYL

LIZARD

TURTLE

FROG

CHICKEN

TORTOISE

CHAMELEON

96. The bones of the forelimb in different vertebrates show a basic similarity of structure. 'The bones of a limb might be shortened or flattened to any extent, becoming at the same time enveloped in thick membrane so as to serve as a fin; or a webbed hand might have all its bones, or certain bones, lengthened to any extent, with the membrane connecting them increased, so as to serve as a wing; yet all these modifications would not tend to alter the framework of the bones or the relative connexion of the part' (Darwin). (→ 97)
Homologous bones are indicated by the following figures:
1. humerus; 2. radius; 3. ulna;
4. wrist; 5. digit (finger).

98. The ventricle of the heart in amphibia is single and the streams of impure and pure blood are mixed in it. The ventricle in reptiles has an incipient but incomplete partition which, in mammals, is complete and separates the streams of impure and pure blood, the latter going to the brain.

98

1 AMPHIBIAN

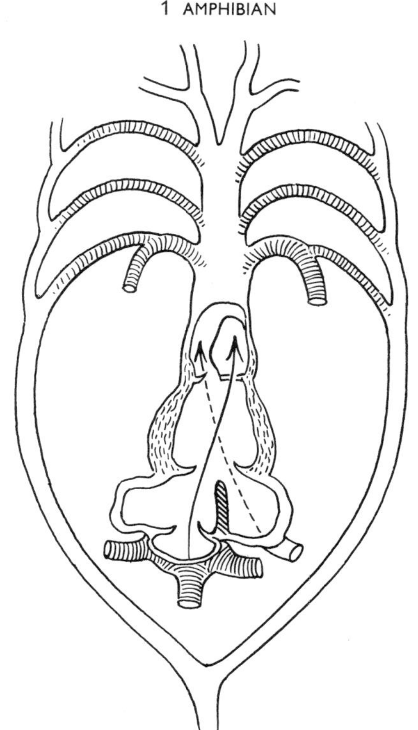

2 REPTILE

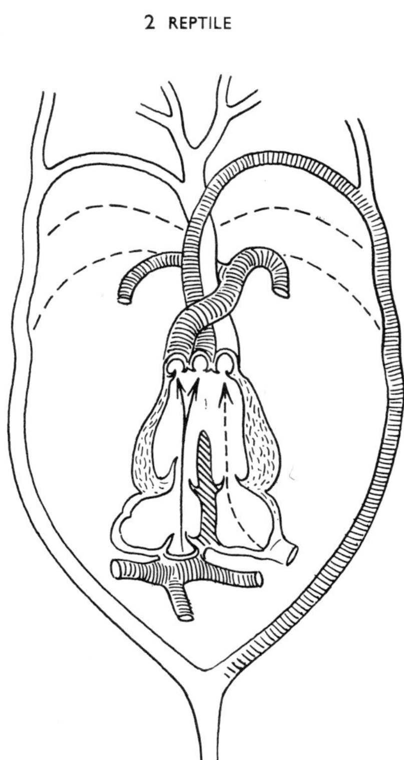

3 MAMMAL

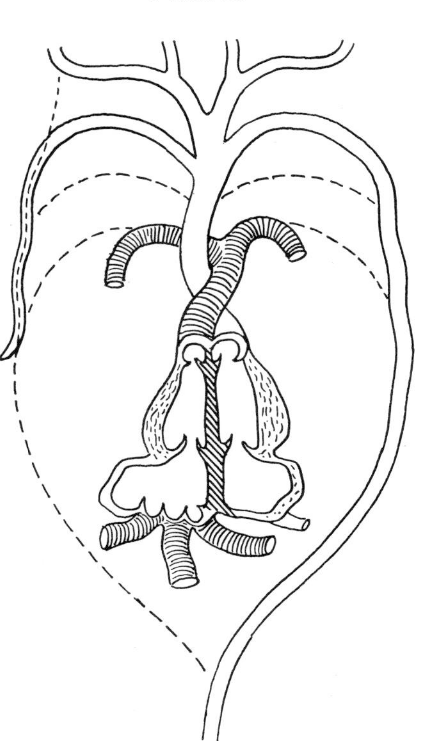

became specialized and as different from one another as are worms and snails. This conclusion is endorsed by many other features of the development and mode of origin of particular structures in these animals, and by the findings of comparative anatomy, which have revealed that in the mollusc *Neopilina* the repetition of parts of the body, so characteristic of the segments of worms, has been preserved though it has been lost in other Mollusca (Pl. 414).

Among other groups of animals living in water, there is a different type of larva, in which the band of beating cilia does not pass round the rim of the top in front of the mouth, but surrounds the mouth itself. This kind of larva, known as the dipleurula, is found both in the echinoderms (starfish and sea-urchins) and in the acorn-worms, the lowest section of the group to which all vertebrates belong (see p. 46). This similarity between their larvae means that the echinoderms and the vertebrates are related and were evolved from a common ancestor that possessed the dipleurula type of larva. This conclusion is also endorsed by a number of other features in the development, the comparative anatomy, and the biochemistry of the echinoderms and the vertebrates (Pl. 102, 389).

An additional service which embryology can perform is to indicate the affinities of highly specialized animals, usually parasites, the adult stages of which are so degraded and featureless that they resemble no other animals. An example is provided by the barnacles, which were included among the Mollusca until 1830 when it was shown that they have a larval form known as the nauplius, which they share with many kinds of Crustacea, water-fleas, and shrimps. The fact that the barnacles share the nauplius larva with other Crustacea means that barnacles are Crustacea, which is not obvious from their adult appearance.

Sacculina is a parasite found in crabs, and in the adult stage it consists of little more than a sack full of germ-cells from which it would be quite impossible to diagnose the group of animals to which it belongs. But *Sacculina* has a larva like that of the barnacles, and therefore belongs to the Crustacea, from the normal forms of which it has diverged very widely during its evolution as a parasite (Pl. 103, 105).

Embryology is thus able to provide evidence of affinity between groups of animals and to show that they have evolved from common ancestors. The enthusiasm of the German zoologist, Ernst Haeckel, however, led to an erroneous and unfortunate exaggeration of the information which embryology could provide. This was known as the 'biogenetic law' and claimed that embryology was a recapitulation of evolution, or that during its embryonic development an animal recaptitulated the evolutionary history of its species. The fact that worms and snails have a trochophore larva means that worms and snails were evolved from an ancestor that had a trochophore larva. But it was then contended that the trochophore larva was itself the adult ancestral form from which worms and snails evolved. By a similar line of reasoning it was claimed that the nauplius represented the adult ancestral crustacean. This can easily be disproved, because the adult ancestors of worms must have had bodies containing a large number of segments, whereas the trochophore larva has none. The same is true of the adult ancestor of crustaceans, whereas the nauplius larva has only three segments. The fact is that the trochophore larva, like the nauplius larva, is a special adaptation for dispersal; it is very old and the common ancestor of worms and snails had a trochophore larva, but the adult of that common ancestor did not look like a trochophore larva, nor can the trochophore larva indicate what that adult ancestor was like. This can be deduced only from studies in the comparative anatomy of adults.

When speaking of vertebrates, it is sometimes said that because the mammalian embryo, including that of man, at an early stage has gill-pouches in its neck, that stage represents the adult ancestor at the fish stage of evolution. This is erroneous, and the gill-pouches in the mammalian embryo are a repetition of the gill-pouches in the ancestral fish embryo, not of the gill-slits of the ancestral fish adult.

The rectification of this error may seem to be a trifling detail, but its importance will emerge in Chapter Four in connection with paedomorphosis. Meanwhile it should be noted that the rejection of the 'theory of recapitulation' in no way detracts from the significance for evolution of the information provided by embryology, which demonstrates affinity between different groups and thereby provides the evidence that these groups have descended with modification from common ancestors.

Vestigial organs

In the *Origin of Species*, Darwin wrote: 'There is no greater anomaly of nature than a bird that cannot fly; yet there are several in this state.' Darwin was referring to the flightless birds, ostrich, emu, cassowary, rhea, etc. He went on: 'We may believe that the progenitor of the ostrich genus had habits like those of the bustard, and that, as the size and weight of its body were increased during successive generations, its legs were used more and its wings less, until they became incapable of flight.' Ostriches are living proofs of their evolution from ancestors that were flying birds.

Although wings of ostriches are small as compared with those of flying birds, they are nevertheless still of considerable size and can serve as sails in the wind. In the fossil moas, however, the wings were reduced almost to nothing (Pl. 106–110).

Teeth and limbs perform adaptive functions for their possessors by enabling them to catch and chew prey or to move over the ground. There are, however, cases of full-grown animals in which teeth are present but are so small that they never erupt through the gums and perform no function at all. Examples are provided by the whalebone whales, and even by the teeth in the lower jaw of the so-called toothed whales. The presence of such useless teeth is inexplicable except on the view that their possessors are descended from ancestors that had normal functional teeth, and that therefore they have achieved their present condition as a result of the reduction of the teeth to vestiges, and this is evolution (Pl. 112).

In the same way, in snakes such as the python, the presence of minute vestiges of the skeleton of the hip-girdle and bones of the hind limbs embedded in the wall of the body and useless for locomotion, means that snakes evolved from animals with normal functional limbs and that in the python they have not yet quite disappeared. In other snakes they have vanished completely. The time during which such vestigial organs may linger on before they finally disappear is considerable. Snakes had diverged from their lizard-like ancestors by the start of the Tertiary era, 70 million years ago (p. 55), and the vestiges of the python's limb must therefore have been retained for at least that length of time (Pl. 113).

The embryos of vertebrates that hatch out of hard-shelled eggs like reptiles, birds, and the egg-laying (monotreme) mammals, feed during their development on the yolk in the egg. Before hatching they develop a small tooth known as the egg-tooth by means of which a hole is made in the eggshell from the inside so that the young animal can get out. Marsupials, on the other hand, are viviparous and develop within the wombs of their mothers where they are fed by a placenta and are born without having to emerge from a shell. Nevertheless, the egg-cell in marsupials contains vestigial masses of yolk and is surrounded by a layer of albumen and a shell-membrane, and eggs are produced in greater number than are developed. Each of these features is inherited from the time when the ancestors of marsupials laid eggs containing yolk in shells, out of which the young had to emerge. It is therefore confirmation of the evolution of marsupials from egg-laying ancestors to find that marsupial embryos possess rudiments of the papilla from which the egg-tooth of lizards and monotremes develops, and of the bone to which the egg-tooth was attached. These traces of a former oviparous condition have been retained by the marsupials for at least 100 million years, since the Cretaceous period, because *Eodelphys* which lived at that time was already a typical marsupial (Pl. 114).

Another example of the retention of a structure which no longer serves a function is the intercostal muscles of tortoises. In these animals, the ribs are firmly cemented together to form the carapace or shell, and no movement of the ribs is possible at all. There is therefore no function for the intercostal muscles to perform, but nevertheless, the embryo of the pond tortoise *Emys* has rudiments of intercostal muscles at an early stage of its development. The earliest known tortoises date from the Triassic period, 200 million years ago, and this is the minimum length of time during which these vestigial structures have continued to be inherited from the ancestors of tortoises which, like all normal reptiles, were able to move their ribs by means of their intercostal muscles (Pl. 114).

Vestigial structures are on the way to disappearance in evolution. That some of them should be 'an unconscionable time a'dying' is a reflection of the fact that the hereditary link is strong and race-history conservative. It also means that these particular vestigial structures are harmless and do not handicap their possessors, for otherwise they would have been rapidly extinguished by selection. Occasionally, however, vestigial structures have turned out to have value by performing functions quite different from those which they originally carried out. Here belong the cases of transformation, as of the hind wings of flies into gyroscopic organs (Pl. 114), or of the feeding organ of primitive vertebrates into the thyroid gland, or of muscles into electric organs serving as transmitters of signals or as lethal weapons. These also are evidence for evolution.

Biochemistry

The production of different chemical substances by different living organisms is in principle no different from the development of different structures; indeed the latter is the result of the former. It is usually easy to tell a plant from an animal by its shape, but even more fundamental is the fact that the cell-wall in plants is mainly composed of a chemical substance called cellulose. In bacteria on the other hand, the cell-wall contains different substances, teichoic acid and certain proteins. Indeed, in respect of particular substances it is possible to construct a chemical classification of living organisms, and when a number of organisms resemble each other and differ from others in the chemical substances which their protoplasm contains, the reason is that they have inherited the ability to form such substances from a common ancestor.

Of the countless examples that might be adduced of this fact, only a small selection of the simpler cases can be included here. The blood of many animals, including vertebrates, contains a red substance an iron compound, haemoglobin, one of the so-called respiratory pigments, which serves to transport oxygen from the gills or lungs to the tissues. In some groups, however, the respiratory pigment is quite different. In many marine worms it is a green compound based on iron and called chlorocruorine, the production and use of which they have inherited from their common ancestor. In molluscs (snails, octopus) and arthropods (crabs, scorpions, king-crabs) it is a blue compound based on copper, haemocyanin. Here again, the distribution of these substances in the animal kingdom is not haphazard but indicates that all the animals that possess one of them are related.

The processes by which life is maintained in an organism involve chemical reactions, and among the most important are those in which energy is restored to a muscle after it has contracted. A key substance in this process in the muscles of vertebrate animals is a compound called creatine phosphate. This substance is also found in the Hemichordates, the most lowly relatives of the vertebrates, and in some of the muscles of sea-urchins and brittle-stars, where it occurs together with another compound called arginine phosphate which is more widely distributed among invertebrate animals, particularly insects. Since sea-urchins and brittle-stars, being

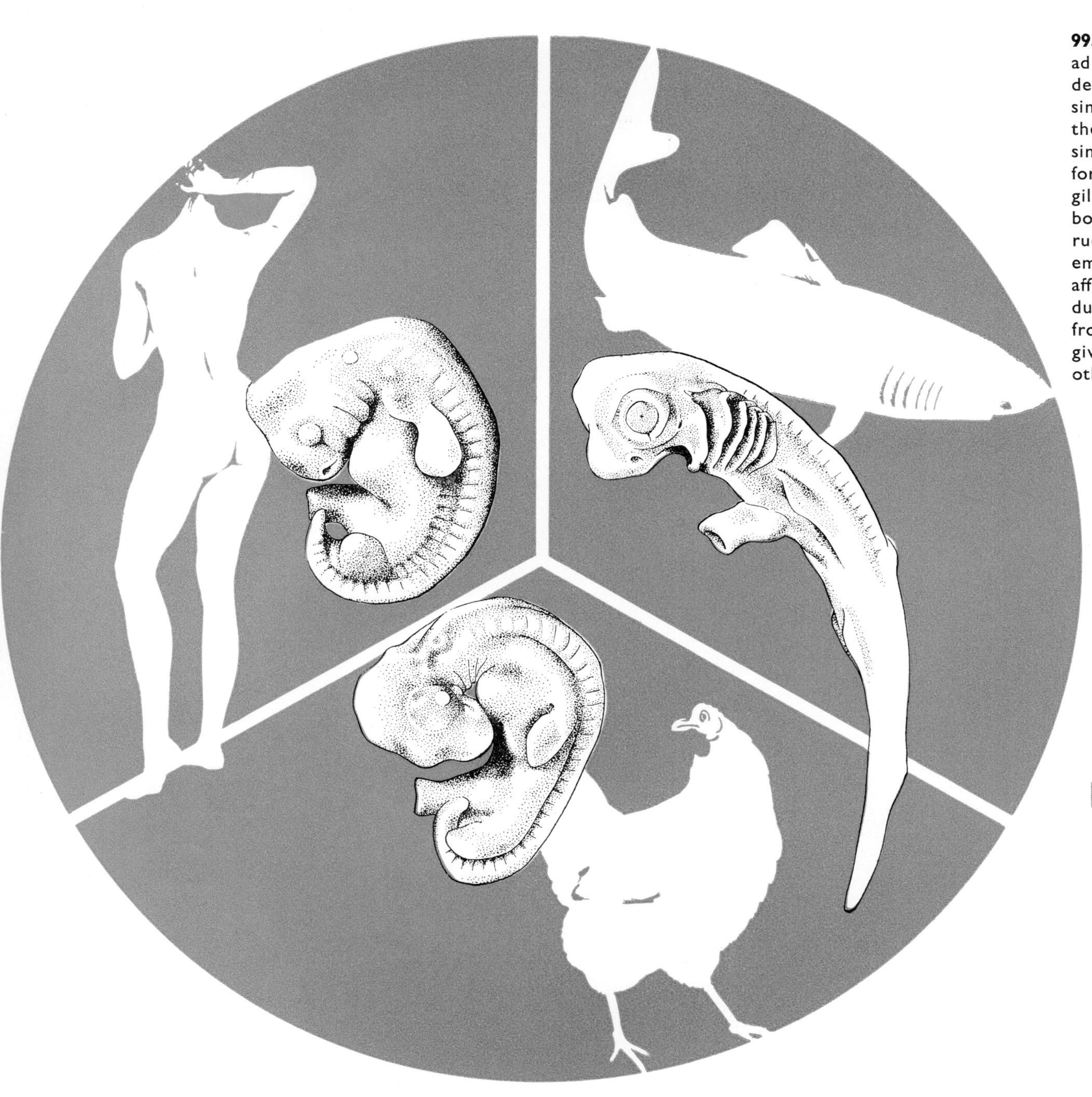

99. Animals that are dissimilar when adult may pass through early stages of development in which they are very similar. The structure of the embryo in the dogfish, the chick, and man is very similar in each case as shown by general form, umbilical cord, head with gill-pouches or slits, eye, nostril, ear, body-muscles, fore- and hind-limb rudiments, heart, and tail. This embryonic resemblance is evidence of affinity and Darwin showed that it was due to descent of the animals concerned from a common ancestor. Embryology gives valuable clues to relationships otherwise difficult to establish.

Embryology

echinoderms, are regarded as related to the vertebrates on evidence supplied by comparative anatomy and embryology, the presence in them and in Hemichordates and vertebrates of creatine phosphate is probably a reflection of their evolution from a common ancestor. Creatine phosphate and other similar substances also occur in worms, but these are not related to vertebrates (Pl. 391).

Another example of the possibility of constructing a chemical classification of the animal kingdom is provided by the colours of the wings of butterflies and moths, which may be due to the presence of a number of different chemical substances. In the Pieridae, the large group of butterflies that includes the cabbage white and the brimstone, the white and yellow colouring substances are chemical compounds related to uric acid, and they are found in no other butterflies. The Pieridae must therefore have inherited this chemical trait from a common ancestor.

In some species of pierid butterflies, other chemical colouring compounds known as anthoxanthins are present, and E. B. Ford found that the species in question are not scattered at random through the Pieridae, but fall into a compact group. Here again, the distribution of this chemical trait shows affinity that is explained by the descent of its possessors from a common ancestor and is evidence for evolution.

The proteins in any species of animal are specific for that species. A method of determining the similarities and differences between the proteins of different species is based on the fact that in an electric field, protein molecules move towards the electrodes at a rate dependent on their electric charges, size, shape, and other qualities. This method of distinguishing between molecules is known as electrophoresis. Applied to the proteins of the egg-white of birds' eggs, it has been shown by C. G. Sibley that this method can be used to estimate the affinities of many orders of birds which are otherwise difficult to assess from their anatomy because the structure of all birds is so similar. It indicates, for instance, that swifts are related to humming-birds, flamingos to storks, owls to nightjars, and ostriches to cassowaries.

Another method, known as paper-chromatography, relies simply on the fact that if mucus from an animal such as a snail is put on filter-paper, and a suitable solvent is allowed to run over the spot, constituents of the mucus will dissolve and spread with the solvent to varying distances and become separated from each other. Patterns are thus obtained that fluoresce under ultraviolet light and enable samples of mucus from different species to be distinguished (Pl. 115-118).

Serology

The most convenient source of proteins is blood, and the comparative study of the bloods of different animals by means of immunity tests has enabled quantitative measurements to be made of the divergence between them.

If blood from one species of animal, say a horse, is injected into the bloodstream of another species of animal, say a rabbit, the rabbit after a time produces a substance which reacts with horse's blood and a precipitate is formed. Horse's blood in the rabbit provokes the production by the rabbit of the appropriate antiserum; this rabbit's blood is said to be immunized against horse's blood and the rabbit goes on forming a serum that will always give a precipitate with horse's blood. This anti-horse serum produces no effect if mixed with blood of, say, a bird, but it will produce a slight precipitation with blood of a pig, and still more with blood of an ass. This means that the proteins of horse's blood are more similar to those of ass's blood than to those of pig's blood or bird's blood. These precipitin blood-tests initiated by

G.H.F. Nuttall therefore provide a means of estimating quantitatively the similarities and differences between the bloods of different species by measuring the relative sensitivities of the blood of different species to various antisera.

The results of serology tests can be expressed in tabular form.

Anti-human serum mixed with blood of		
man	gives	100% precipitation
gorilla	gives	64% precipitation
orang-utan	gives	42% precipitation
baboon	gives	29% precipitation
ox	gives	10% precipitation
sheep	gives	10% precipitation
deer	gives	7% precipitation
horse	gives	2% precipitation
marsupial	gives	0% precipitation

These results show that human blood is closer to that of the great apes than to that of baboons and lower mammals. Extensive tests have been made to establish the similarities and differences between the bloods of many groups of animals.

Anti-ox serum mixed with blood of		
ox	gives	100% precipitation
sheep	gives	48% precipitation
camel	gives	28% precipitation
pig	gives	24% precipitation
peccary	gives	10% precipitation
hippopotamus	gives	8% precipitation

Other tests carried out by A. E. Boyden and his colleagues have shown that the distinction now drawn by anatomists and systematists between rabbits and rats (which used to be classified in the same group) is confirmed by serology; similarly, there is no close affinity between frogs and newts; the whales are more akin to the even-toed ungulates (ox, sheep, giraffe, camel, pig) than to any other orders of mammals; seals are related to dogs; the musk-ox is more closely related to sheep and goats than to cattle, the panda is closer to bears than to racoons (Pl. 125-127).

In providing quantitative evidence of the degrees of divergence between different groups of animals, resulting in a scheme that agrees with the results of comparative anatomy and other branches of biology, the serum precipitin tests are not only a biochemical proof of evolution, but an index of natural classification in accordance with affinity and descent.

A high degree of refinement has been given to studies of bloods of related animals by the discovery of the blood-groups. It is found that human beings can be divided into four groups according to the presence of certain substances on the surface of the red blood-corpuscles. The substances are known as A and B, and human beings can have one or the other or both or neither of these substances, and belong to classes A, B, AB, or O respectively. These substances are known as antigens or agglutinogens and, when introduced into blood of incompatible classes, they provoke the formation of antibodies or agglutinins which bring about agglutination of the red blood-corpuscles. The antibodies to antigens A and B, known as anti-A and anti-B respectively, occur naturally in the blood except when incompatible with the corpuscles' own antigen. Thus, anti-A is present in the blood of group B and group O, anti-B in group A and group O, while group AB has no antibodies. When blood is transfused into another human being, the antigens if present in the donor's blood react with the antibodies (if present) in the blood of the recipient and agglutinate the red blood-corpuscles of the recipient if the blood of the donor is incompatible with that of the recipient. Persons of group O which has no antigens can give blood safely to their own and also to all three other groups, for which reason persons of group O are known as universal donors. But as group O has both anti-A and anti-B antibodies, and the other groups have one or the other or both of antigens A and B, persons of group O cannot safely receive blood from any group other than their own. Persons of group AB which has no antibodies can receive blood safely from their own and all three other groups, but can give it safely only to their own group. Persons of groups A and B can receive blood safely only from their own group and group O, while they can give it safely only to their own group and group AB. It may perhaps be asked why group O blood, that contains anti-A and anti-B antibodies can safely be transfused into persons of groups

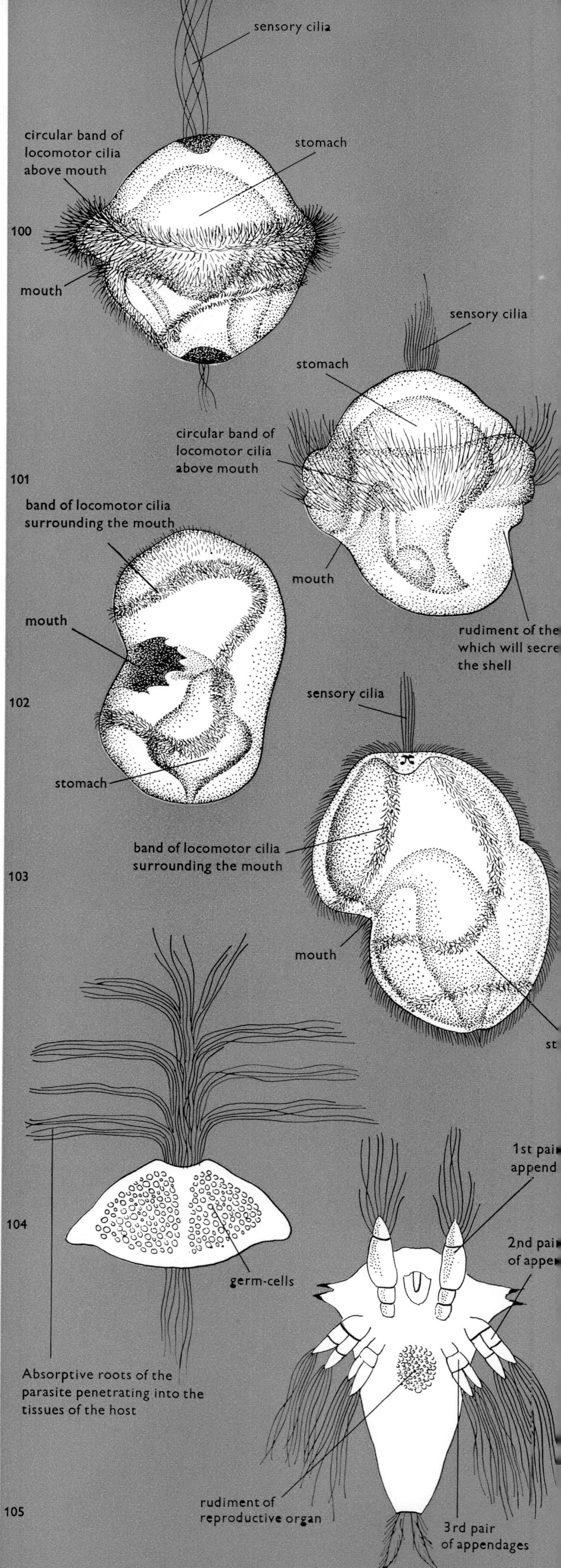

Larval Forms

100. A trochophore larva of Annelid worms is built on a similar plan to **101,** the veliger larva of Molluscs indicating affinity between these groups. **102.** An echinoderm larva is different from both the above but similar to the larva of primitive vertebrates. **103.** A nauplius larva characteristic of Crustacea. **104.** Adult *Sacculina* a parasite so degenerate that it would be impossible to determine its affinities were it not for its larva **105,** which is typical of Crustacea and shows that *Sacculina* belongs to that group.

A, B, and AB whose red bloodcorpuscles contain antigens A or B or both. The reason is that unless very large quantities of blood are transfused, the group O blood is highly diluted in the recipient's circulation and the antibodies are neutralised by antigens situated elsewhere than in the red blood-corpuscles (Pl. 119–124).

The Results of Blood-transfusion in Man involving the ABO Blood-group system.

			Recipient		
	Group	O	A	B	AB
	Serum contains	anti-A anti-B	anti-B	anti-A	no antibodies
	Group	**Cells contain**			
Donor O		no antigen	Trs	Trs	Trs	Trs
A		antigen A	Ag	Trs	Ag	Trs
B		antigen B	Ag	Ag	Trs	Trs
AB		antigen A, antigen B	Ag	Ag	Ag	Trs

Trs = Transfusion possible, no agglutination
Ag = Agglutination

Throughout the animal kingdom and even among plants and bacteria, antigens are found that bear some relation to the human A and B antigens, without necessarily being identical with them. In the apes in particular the resemblance to the human substances is close. All chimpanzees belong to groups A or O, orang-utan and gibbons to groups A, B, or AB. Gorillas, curiously enough, seem to resemble the Old World monkeys in lacking the A and B antigens.

In addition to the ABO blood-group system, there is another known as the MN system, involving antigens on the surface of the red blood-corpuscles known as M and N. The chimpanzee has both M and N antigens. Antigens resembling the M in man have been found on the blood-corpuscles of orang-utans, gibbons, and Old World monkeys, but they are lacking from nearly all New World monkeys and from all mammals below the primates. Here is irrefutable evidence for affinity and evolution.

Finally, there is the Rhesus blood-group system. When rabbits and guinea-pigs were injected with blood of Rhesus monkeys, antibodies were obtained which were then used to detect corresponding antigens in human blood which are therefore known as Rhesus antigens (Pl. 128). (See also Chapter Three, p. 81 and 101, and Chapter Five, p. 190).

Instincts

The instincts of an animal are innate and just as characteristic of its species as the structures which give it its shape. In the *Origin of Species*, Darwin drew attention to 'that common case of closely allied, but distinct, species, when inhabiting different parts of the world and living under considerably different conditions of life, yet often retaining nearly the same instincts. For instance, we can understand, on the principle of inheritance, how it is that the thrush of tropical South America lines its nest with mud in the same peculiar manner as does our British thrush; how it is that the hornbills of Africa and India have the same extraordinary instinct of plastering up and imprisoning the females in a hole in a tree, with only a small hole left in the plaster through which the males feed them and their young when hatched; how it is that the male wrens (*Troglodytes*) of North America build 'cock-nests', to roost in, like the males of our Kitty-wrens – a habit wholly unlike that of any other known bird', (Pl. 130, 131).

The comparative study of instincts is less advanced than that of anatomy or embryology, not only because of the difficulty of isolating 'units' of behaviour, as N. Tinbergen has pointed out, but also because the behaviour is extremely variable. Nevertheless, it is obvious that the possession of social instincts by different species of ants is an indication of affinity between them, and the same is true of the affinity between species of wasps, bees, and termites which have social instincts. The mating behaviour of sticklebacks (→132) shows how some acts evolved from simpler components of behaviour that became 'ritualised'. The biological study of behaviour, or ethology, reveals types of behaviour that are adaptive and, as K. Lorenz showed, significant for the life of their possessors on which they confer added survival value.

An example of great interest, to which Darwin himself drew attention, is that of the cuckoos and their parasitic habit. The habits of the European cuckoo, which makes no nest of its own but lays eggs in the nests of other birds, are well known. The American cuckoo makes its own nest, lays eggs in it, incubates and hatches them, but occasionally also lays eggs in the nests of other birds. An extension of this latter habit would lead directly to that of the European cuckoo, which lays more eggs than it would be able to incubate and hatch if it incubated them itself in its own nest. Finally, the Australian cuckoo can lay eggs of varying sizes, and this shows the origin of one of the most remarkable adaptations of the European cuckoo, which is that its eggs are small, very little larger than those of the small birds, meadow pipits or sky larks, that build the nests that it parasitizes. Further consideration of this case must be reserved for Chapter Three where the gradual progress of adaptation is dealt with. Here, it suffices to point out, as Darwin said, that 'the principle of inheritance' from a common ancestor explains the possession of similar instincts by different species and is evidence for evolution.

PARASITISM

Parasitism is a situation in which an organism – virus, bacterium, plant, or animal – lives on or in and at the expense of another organism on which it is dependent for part or all of its food supply and sources of energy. Examples among viruses and bacteria cover the agents responsible for most of the infectious diseases; among plants are mistletoe, dodder, and *Rafflesia* (which has the biggest flower in the world); among fungi are the moulds responsible for ring-worm and athlete's foot; among animals are the lice on the skin, feathers, and hair of mammals and birds; the malarial parasite, the trypanosomes that cause sleeping sickness, and round-worms responsible for elephantiasis in the blood of vertebrates; and the amoebae of dysentery, liver-flukes, and tape-worms in the alimentary canal of vertebrates (Pl. 134-142). Parasitism is no recent invention on this earth, for fossil parasitic snails have been found on sea-lilies dating from the Carboniferous period, 300 million years ago (Pl. 190).

In every case, the parasite shows degeneration of form in respect of those vital functions which it does not carry out for itself and for which it relies on its host. Mistletoe dispenses with roots, dodder dispenses with roots and leaves, tape-worms, which live bathed in the food of their hosts, dispense with head, sense-organs, organs of locomotion, and an alimentary canal of their own. The only function that parasites preserve at all costs is that of reproduction, and in some extreme cases the parasite is nothing but a sack containing germ-cells, which are produced in numbers commensurate with the improbability that they will succeed in attaining the adult state.

Internal parasites usually have very complicated life-histories. An example is the liver-fluke that infests the bile-duct of sheep, on which it inflicts the disease known as liver-rot. The fluke is hermaphrodite and produces both eggs and sperm. The fertilized egg passes out of the bile-duct through the alimentary canal of the sheep and out with its droppings onto the ground. If this ground is damp, the young stage of the fluke swims in the film of moisture, but perishes unless it meets with a pond-snail into which it bores its way. Inside the snail it multiplies repeatedly by a process of reproduction without fertilization known as parthenogenesis. The products of this multiplication leave the body of the snail and settle on blades of grass, each surrounded by a protective coat. There they perish unless the grass is eaten by a sheep, in which case the protective coat is dissolved in the sheep's stomach and the fluke makes its way up the bile-duct where the cycle starts all over again (Pl. 139).

The tape-worm has a comparable life-history in which the fertilized eggs pass out of the alimentary canal of the definitive host, man or dog, and in the course of feeding into that of the alternative host, pig or rabbit, where they develop into bladder-worms. If the alternative host is then eaten raw by the definitive host, the bladder-worm turns into the tape-worm and the cycle starts all over again (Pl. 140).

Among the most remarkable cases of parasitism are those in which the males of a species are parasitic on the females. This condition is found among invertebrates in the barnacles and among vertebrates in the deep-sea angler-fishes. In the barnacles the males are dwarfs, more or less degenerate in structure, attached inside the mantle-cavities of the females or hermaphrodites. In the angler-fishes the males are also dwarfs, organically attached to the females in such a way that the blood-vessels of the females are continuous with those of the males. The jaws are toothless, the fins are reduced, the eyes are vestigial, and the alimentary canal ends blindly. All these marks of degeneration are typical of the loss of the free-living condition so that the parasite no longer requires to see, move, and eat, but is dependent on its host for food supply conveyed in this case through the blood (Pl. 141). The reasons for this remarkable adaptation are probably to be found in the conditions of life of angler-fishes; they live at great depths where sunlight does not penetrate and are numerically rare and sluggish. The difficulties which individuals of opposite sex must experience in finding one another under such circumstances point to the reason why it must be advantageous for the young males to become attached to females at an early stage and provide them with permanent portable mates.

As is the case with any organisms showing marked adaptation, the parasitic mode of life cannot (except perhaps in the case of viruses) have been the original condition of the parasites, which must be descended from organisms that led a normal free-living existence. The structural features of parasites must therefore have been produced during descent with modification from normal ancestors. The very existence of parasites is evidence that they have become what they are from a previous condition in which they were free-living, and parasites are therefore living proofs of their own evolution.

The study of parasitism, however, provides even more evidence on evolution. Some parasites are widely tolerant of variable conditions and can become adapted to new hosts as a result of these living in the same habitat, pond, or burrow as the old host, or eating the same food containing the parasite. Other parasites are very intolerant of any sudden change in their conditions of life, such as would be caused by their introduction into a new host, and fail to survive it. Host-specificity of this kind means that the hosts have had their parasites handed down to them from their ancestors, and this fact acquires great significance for evolution because related species of parasites are often found to be restricted to related species of hosts. Fleas of the family Macropsyllidae are found only on rodents of the sub-family Murinae. Lice of the genus *Pediculus* are found only on man and chimpanzee. The species of tape-worms found in chicken are never found in ducks, and vice-versa. The virus of herpes simplex infests man and the monkey.

Vestigial Organs

The ostrich **106,** rhea **107,** emu **108,** cassowary **109,** and kiwi **110** are all flightless birds but structures in their brains, wings, and tails are adaptations to flight and show that they had the power of flight and lost it, which implies evolution.

111. Like all mammals, whales have hair but as its function of retaining heat has been taken over by blubber the hairs are reduced to follicles on the nose. Some vestigial organs are so reduced that they can only be seen inside the body of animals, such as teeth in whales that do not erupt **112,** and the hindlimb skeleton in the python **113. 114.** Other vestigial organs can be found only in early stages of development, such as (*top right*) the rudimentary papilla for an egg-tooth in marsupials, which have not hatched from eggs for 100 million years, and (*top left*) the rib-muscles in turtles, unused for 200 million years. Vestigial organs may be used for new functions as in flies (*bottom left*) in which the hindwings, reduced to knobs, are converted into gyroscopic organs that give information to the fly of its movements in flight. (*Bottom right*) magnified model of a hindwing or 'haltere'.

107

108

109

110

106

111

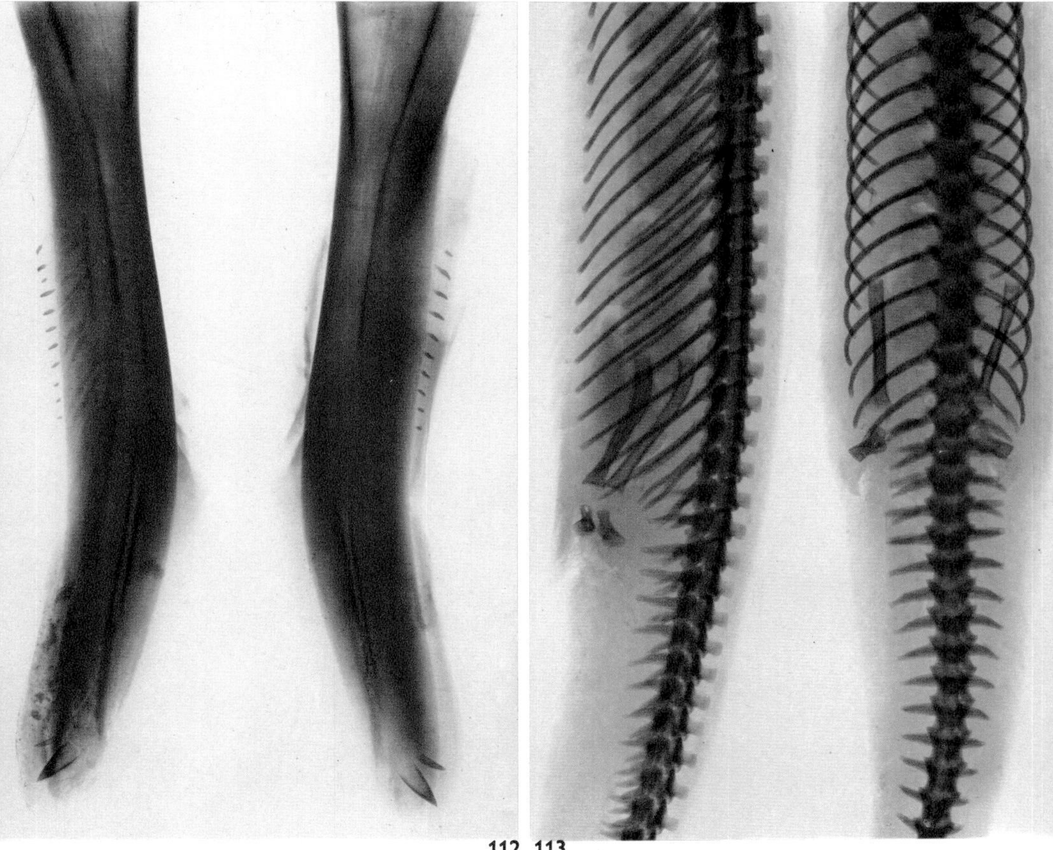

112 113

These facts mean that related hosts harbouring related parasites are descended by evolution from a common ancestor, which harboured the common ancestor of the parasites. Furthermore, as the conditions under which the parasites live are more stable than those under which the hosts live, it is normally found that the evolution of the parasites has been slower and the degree of their divergence from one another less extensive than in the case of the hosts. The parasites may then retain traces of affinity which the hosts may have lost, and the affinities and evolutionary histories of the hosts can be indicated by those of the parasites.

The species of lice of the genus *Pediculus* found on man and chimpanzee are so different from those found on other mammals that these parasites must have had a common ancestor some 40 million years ago living on the common ancestor of the hosts, and this is independent evidence of the related descent of these particular hosts (Pl. 142). The similarity between the lice found on seals, camels, and peccaries indicates that these animals must have had a common ancestor in the remote past.

The genus of bird-lice *Struthiolipeurus* is found only on the South American rhea and the African ostrich, and the two species of bird-lice are very similar. This indicates that the rhea and the ostrich are closely related in spite of their widely discontinuous geographical distribution (Map 15).

The classification of flying birds is extremely difficult because of their general similarity and lack of clean-cut divergent features. It is therefore important that, from the identity of the bird-lice which it carries, it is almost always possible to determine the order to which a bird belongs. From the tape-worms which they harbour, parrots are seen to be related to pigeons. Again from the similarity between their tape-worms, monitor lizards and pythons have probably shared a common ancestor, and this conclusion is endorsed by studies in palaeontology.

Conversely, the classification of tape-worms is closely parallel to that of the vertebrate hosts which they infest. For example, the Tetraphyllid tape-worms are found exclusively in the Selachian fishes (sharks and skates), the Ichthyotaeniidea in freshwater fishes, amphibia, and reptiles, and the Cyclophyllidea in terrestrial reptiles, birds, and mammals. This is explicable only if hosts and parasites are descended in each case from common ancestors whose descendants underwent parallel lines of divergent evolution.

The study of parasites, now carried to a very high degree by Theresa Clay on bird-lice and by Jean Baer on tape-worms, is therefore of great value not only in providing evidence of the fact that evolution has occurred, but also in revealing corresponding affinities between different groups of hosts.

CLASSIFICATION

'It is a truly wonderful fact,' Darwin wrote in the *Origin of Species*, 'the wonder of which we are apt to overlook from familiarity – that all animals and all plants throughout all time and space should be related to each other in groups, subordinate to groups, in the manner which we everywhere behold – namely, varieties of the same species most closely related, species of the same genus less closely and unequally related, forming sections and sub-genera, species of distinct genera much less closely

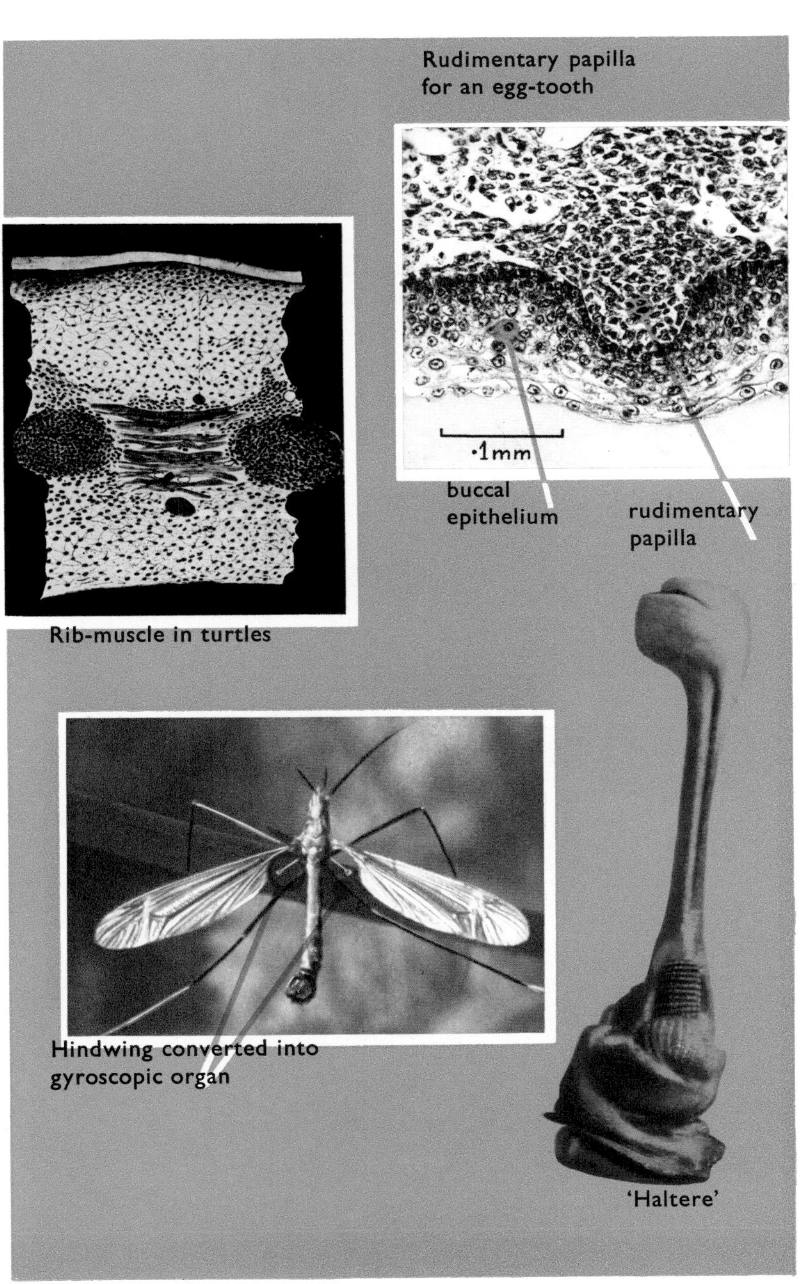

114

115

116

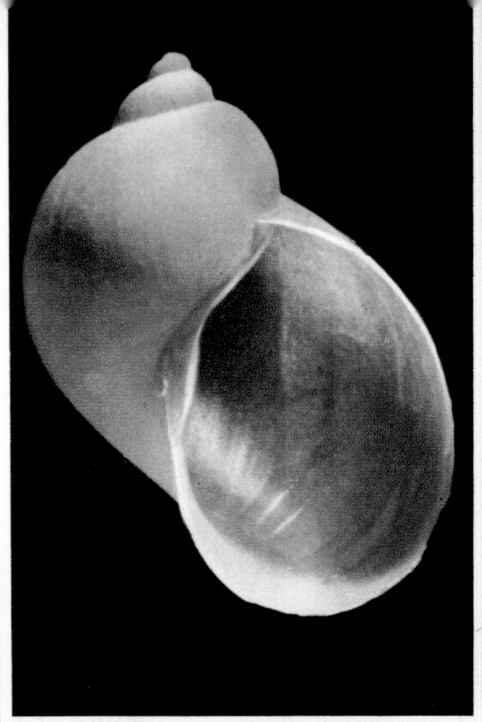

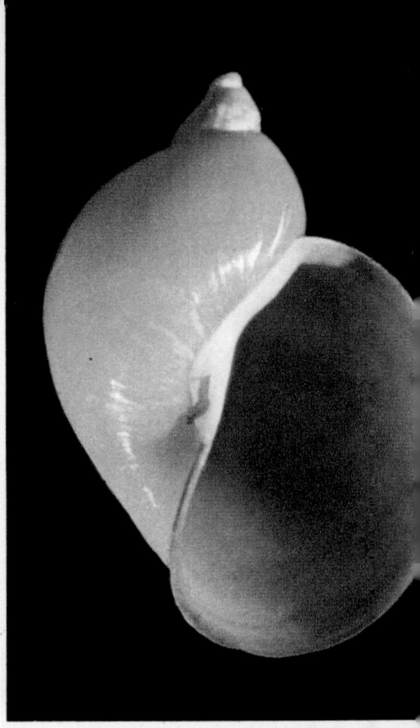

117

118

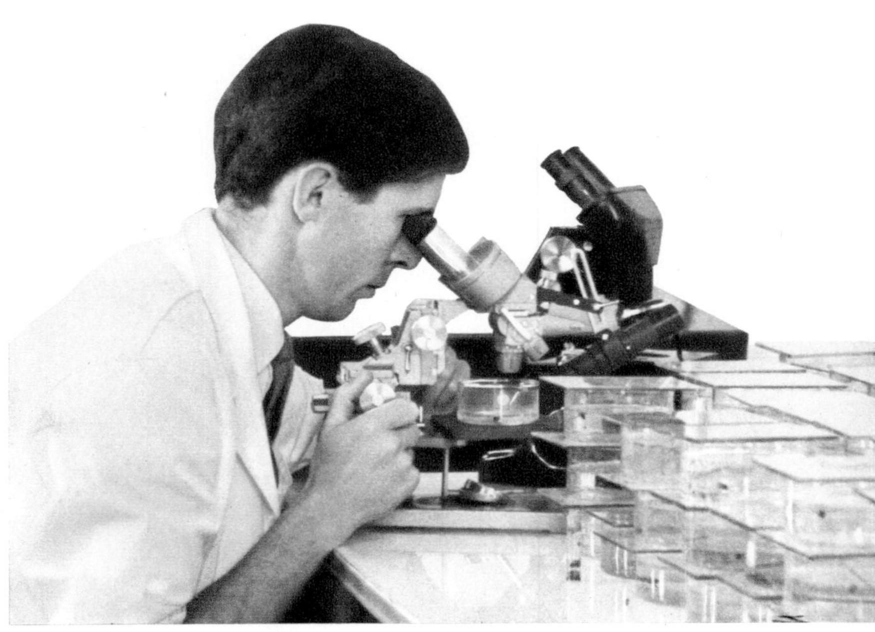

119

Snails of the species *Limnaea peregra* **115,** and *L. auricularia* **116,** are hard to distinguish by eye but easy by the method of paper-chromatography. Mucus from the snails is put on filter-paper and a solvent (e.g. butyl alcohol, acetic acid, and water) run over the paper. Components of the mucus are dissolved and spread with the solvent for distances depending on their chemical constitution. Resulting patterns of *L. peregra* **117,** and *L. auricularia* **118,** under ultra-violet light. **119, 120.** Typing blood-groups. Blood-cells to be tested are added to blood-serum of previously tested groups to see if agglutination occurs. Group O serum, containing anti-A and anti-B agglutinins, agglutinates cells of groups A, B, and AB; A serum, containing anti-B, agglutinates cells of groups B and AB; B serum, containing anti-A, agglutinates cells of groups A and AB; AB serum agglutinates none. These reactions must not be confused with those of transfusion into a person, because the quantity of blood in a recipient is much greater than that transfused (p. 41). **121,** all blood-cells are separate; **122-124,** increasing degrees of agglutination. **125.** Musk-ox, shown serologically to be more closely related to goat **126,** than to ox **127. 128.** Rhesus monkey, has given its name to a human blood-group system (p. 81). **129.** One of the laboratories at Rutgers, New Brunswick, where work on blood groups has been carried out.

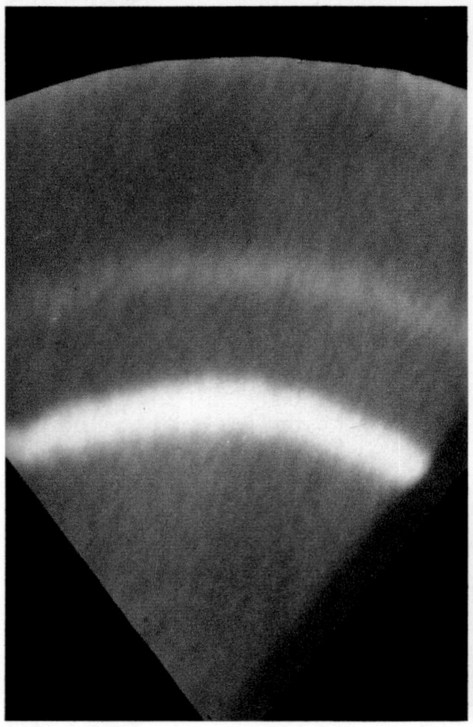

120

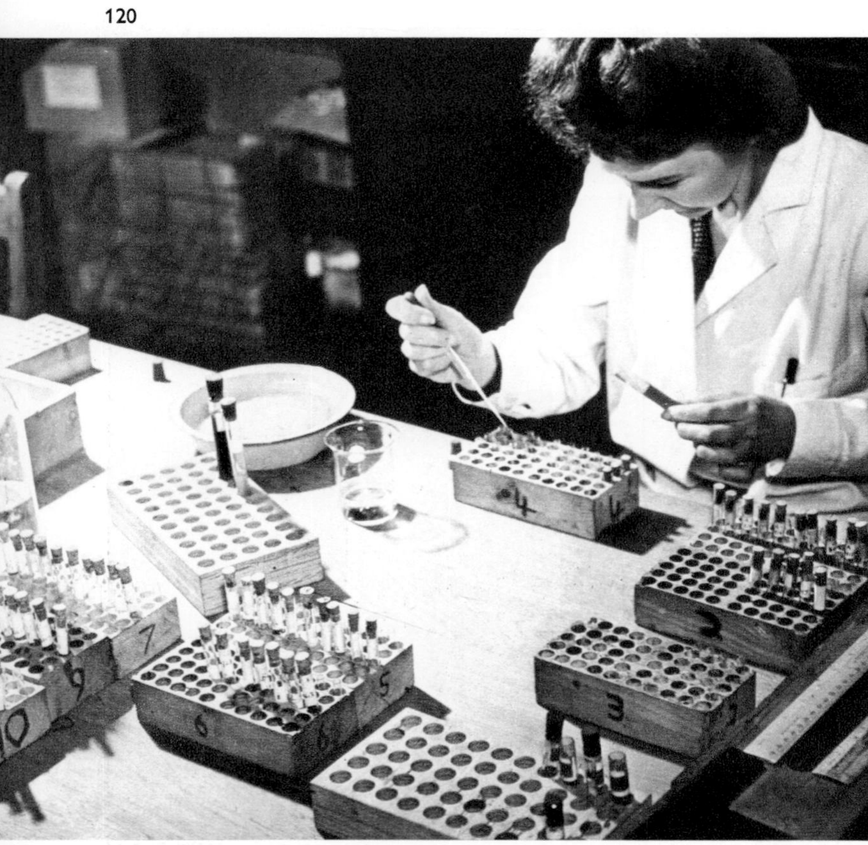

121

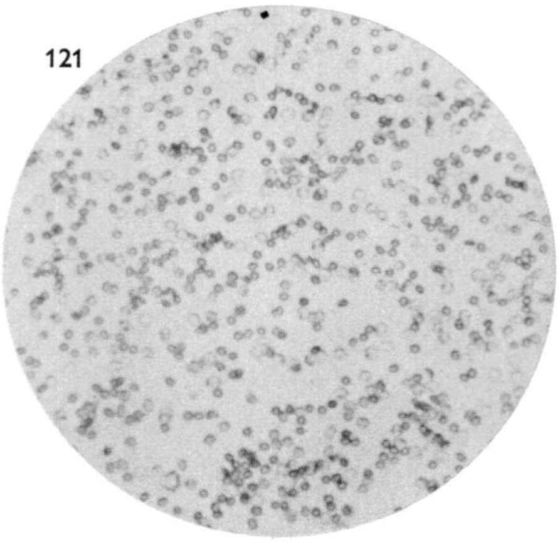

122

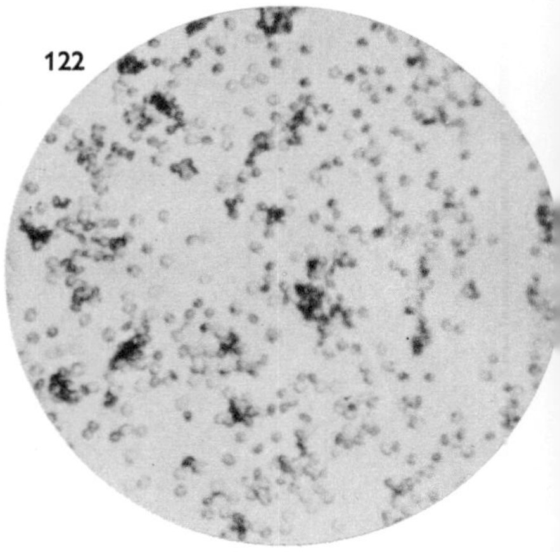

123

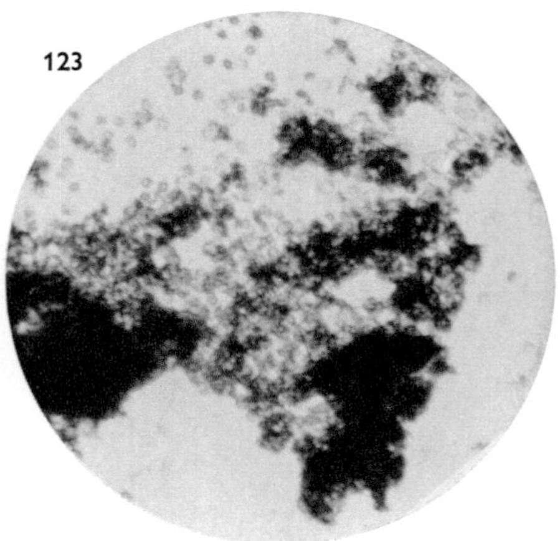

124

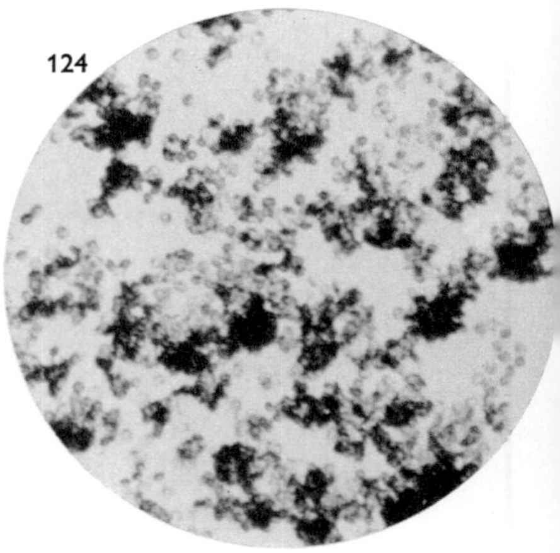

125 126 127

Blood Groups and Affinities

129 128

130

Behaviour Patterns

related, and genera related in different degrees, forming sub-families, families, orders, sub-classes and classes. The several subordinate groups in any class cannot be ranked in a single file, but seem clustered round points, and these round other points, and so on in almost endless cycles. If species had been independently created, no explanation would have been possible of this kind of classification; but it is explained through inheritance and the complex action of natural selection, entailing extinction and divergence of character.'

In these words, Darwin expressed the fact that plants and animals are classified in groups that are contained within larger groups. This classification is not fortuitous like that of pebbles on a beach, nor arbitrary like the grouping of stars in fanciful constellations. The members of each group of plants and animals are placed together because they have characters in common and resemble each other, and the groups in turn are characterized by other resemblances. The resemblance between organisms, or between groups of organisms, is due to their relationship or genetic affinity; the difference between them is due to descent with divergence and modification from ancestors shared in common. The degree of resemblance between groups is expressed by the rank in the systematic hierarchy held by the group in which they are included, as Darwin explained. A natural classification such as this provides a family tree of relationship and reflects the course of evolution. The principles of classification can be applied to the entire realm of living things and they can be illustrated by means of one large group of animals, called a phylum, for example the Chordata, the group of animals that includes the vertebrates (Pl. 143).

The Chordata

The Chordata are grouped together because they (and no other animals) all have the following three structures:

I. an internal skeletal rod called the notochord, which is the forerunner of the backbone;
II. a tubular nervous system running down the back, namely the brain and spinal cord;
III. a series of gill-pouches on each side of the throat which produce gill-slits in fishes, and in man the Eustachian tube, tonsils, and other structures.

The Chordata may be divided into those animals without skulls, which are called the Acrania, and those with skulls, which are called the Craniata. The former include the Cephalochordata (the lancelet *Branchiostoma*), Hemichordata (the acorn-worm *Balanoglossus*), and Urochordata (Tunicates and sea-squirts). The Chordata with skulls can be divided into those without jaws, the Agnatha, and those with jaws, the Gnathostomata. The former include the Cyclostomata (lampreys) and some extinct groups such as the Ostracodermi. The Gnathostomata can be divided into those with fins, the fishes or Pisces, and those with limbs ending in hands and feet with five fingers and toes, the Tetrapoda.

The Pisces include several orders: the Placodermi, a diverse assemblage of extinct fishes representing a number of early and unsuccessful experiments in fish-structure; the Chondrichthyes, fishes with a skeleton of cartilage (gristle) among which are the Selachii (sharks and skates); the Osteichthyes, fishes with a skeleton largely composed of bone, including the Crossopterygii which gave rise to the land-vertebrates or Tetrapoda, the Coelacanthini, the Dipnoi or lung-fishes, and the Actinopterygii, which include nearly all the living bony fishes. The Tetrapoda or land-vertebrates are divisible into those which develop without special embryonic membranes, the Anamnia, and the Amniota, which possess the chorion, amnion, and allantois, embryonic membranes.

The Anamnia are represented by the Amphibia, a dominant group at the time of the fossil Labyrinthodontia, which ultimately gave rise to the reptiles, but today reduced to the tailless Anura or frogs, the tailed Urodela or newts, and the limbless Gymnophiona, an obscure group of primitive forms.

The Amniota include the reptiles, and the birds and the mammals to which they gave rise. The reptiles were the dominant class of animals throughout the Secondary era and radiated into a very large number of groups or orders, among which may be mentioned the Rhynchocephalia of which the Tuatara persists, the Chelonia of

131

130. A male wren in its 'cock's nest' - a habit common to wrens in both America and Britain. **131.** Hornbill males in both Africa and India plaster up the female in the nesting-hole. Darwin drew attention to these instances of similarity of instinct indicating affinity in animals widely separated geographically. It can be shown in some cases how instincts envolve. The three-spined stickleback has a complicated courtship behaviour involving a rigorous sequence of activities that follow one another as stimulus and response. **132.** The male stakes out a claim to his territory and digs a nest. Then follow ten steps alternately by female and male: (1) the female enters territory, (2) then the male does zigzag dance, (3) the female approaches the male, (4) the male leads the female to the nest, (5) the female follows the male, (6) the male points at entrance to the nest, (7) the female enters the nest, (8) the male quivers at female's tail, (9) the female spawns, (10) the male fertilizes eggs, and courtship ends. (Research by N. Tinbergen.) Comparison with a related species, the ten-spined stickleback **133,** shows similarities and also reveals the evolutionary origin of some of these acts from simpler components of behaviour that have become 'ritualized' under influence of the sex and aggressive instincts, as Huxley, Lorenz & Tinbergen showed.

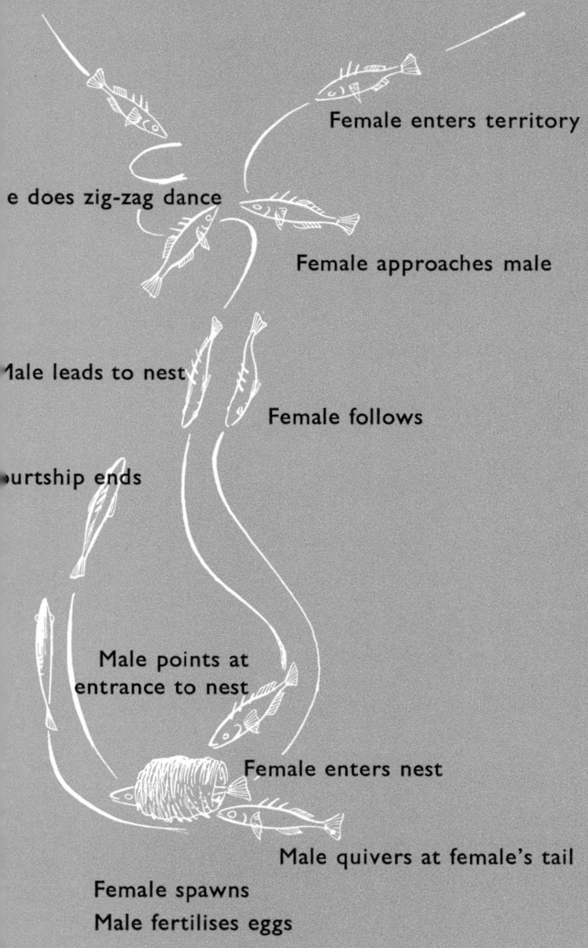

Female enters territory

e does zig-zag dance

Female approaches male

ale leads to nest

Female follows

urtship ends

Male points at
entrance to nest

Female enters nest

Male quivers at female's tail

Female spawns
Male fertilises eggs

which the tortoises and turtles persist, the Ichthyosauria, Plesiosauria, Dinosauria, and Pterosauria, all of which are extinct, the Lacertilia or lizards, Ophidia or snakes, Crocodilia, and the ancestors of the birds (Pseudosuchia) and of the mammals (Therapsida).

The class Birds, which are nothing but warm-blooded reptiles with feathers, are divisible into the Archaeornithes represented by the fossil *Archaeopteryx*, which was only able to glide through the air, and the Neornithes which include all living birds, some of which, such as the ostrich, have lost the power of flight.

The class Mammalia, which are only warm-blooded reptiles with mammary glands and hair, and in which, as explained on page 34, the lower jaw articulates with the skull by means of the dentary and squamosal bones, are divided into the Monotremata which have a single opening for the genital and alimentary canals, and the Ditremata in which these canals have two separate openings. The former include the duck-billed platypus and the spiny ant-eater, both of which lay eggs. The Ditremata are divided into the Marsupials in which the young are born prematurely and complete their development in the marsupium or belly-pouch of the mother (as in kangaroo, wombat, bandicoot, opossum, koala, thylacine), and the Placentals.

The Placental mammals all have an elaborate placenta, an organ for the provision of oxygen and food materials to the embryo during its development in the mother's womb and for the removal of its waste products. They include many orders of animals: the Perissodactyla, with the tapir, rhinoceros, and horse; the Proboscidea, with the elephant; the Artiodactyla, with the pig, camel, giraffe, deer, sheep, goat, and cattle; the Cetacea, with the whale and porpoise; the Hyracoidea, with the coney; the Carnivora, with the dog, cat, bear, civet, badger, seal; the Sirenia, with the dugong and manatee; the Edentata, with the sloth and armadillo; the Pholidota, with the pangolin; the Tubulidentata, with the aard-vark; the Lagomorpha, with the rabbits and hares; the Rodentia, with rats, squirrels, beavers, porcupines; the Insectivora, with shrews, moles, hedgehogs; the Cheiroptera with bats; and the Primates.

The Primates are characterized by large brains, grasping hands and fingers ending in nails rather than claws. The order is divided into two sub-orders: the Prosimii, including the lemurs and tarsiers, and the Anthropoidea, which are divided into three superfamilies: the Ceboidea or New World monkeys, the Cercopithecoidea or Old World monkeys, and the Anthropoidea. The Anthropoidea are divided into two families: the Pongidae include the fossils *Proconsul* and *Dryopithecus*, the living apes, and the fossil australopithecines, and the Hominidae include the fossil *Pithecanthropus*, *Homo* of the fossil species *neanderthalensis*, and the living *Homo sapiens*.

GEOGRAPHICAL DISTRIBUTION

The geographical distribution of plants and animals over the globe is of great importance in the study of evolution. It was certain curious little facts in the geographical distribution of fossil and living animals that first drew Darwin's attention to the possibility of species arising by change from other species. (See Chapter One, pp. 9, 20). He also realized that as evolution means that every species arose from its ancestral species in one area only and once only, discontinuous geographical distribution of related forms requires that they migrated to where they now are and became extinct in intervening regions. The discovery of fossil forms in different parts of the world has provided direct evidence in support of this. A simple example is provided by marsupials (see Maps 4 and 5, p. 166).

The only alternative is special creation of each species, whatever that might mean, and on that view it costs little to the imagination if a species was created in two or more separated places rather than in one. Darwin's notebooks bring out very clearly the impossibility of explaining the similarities between species geographically separated if they were created where they now are.

The island of Tristan da Cunha in the southern Atlantic Ocean between Africa and South America provided Darwin with an additional argument, because its flora contains plants characteristic of both these continents. There would be no difficulty in explaining the mixed nature of the flora of Tristan da Cunha if the ancestors of these plants had evolved on their respective continents and had reached the island through natural dispersal, carried by winds, birds, and currents (Map 6, p. 124). On the other hand, Darwin continued, the alternative view that American and African forms of plant were created in Tristan da Cunha, could be likened to the old belief that fossils were created in the rocks as freaks of nature 'to deceive man'.

'Shall we then allow,' he wrote, 'that the distinct species of rhinoceros which separately inhabit Java and Sumatra and the neighbouring mainland of Malacca were created, male and female, out of the inorganic materials of these countries? Without any adequate cause, as far as our reason serves, shall we say that they were merely, from living near each other, created very like each other . . .? Shall we say that without any apparent cause they were created on the same generic type with the ancient woolly rhinoceros of Siberia and of the other species which formerly inhabited the same main division of the world; that they were created less and less closely related, but still with interbranching affinities, with all the other living and extinct Mammalia; that without any apparent adequate cause their short necks should contain the same number of vertebrae with the giraffe; that their thick legs should be built on the same plan with those of the antelope, of the mouse, of the monkey, of the wing of the bat, and of the fin of the porpoise; . . . that in the jaws of each when dissected young there should exist small teeth which never come to the surface? That in possessing these useless abortive teeth, and in other characters, these three rhinoceroses in their embryonic state should much more closely resemble other mammalia than they do when mature. And lastly, that in a still earlier period of life, their arteries should run and branch as in a fish, to carry blood to gills, which do not exist . . . I repeat, shall we then say that a pair, or a gravid female, of each of these three species of rhinoceros, were separately created with deceptive appearances of true relationship, with the stamp of inutility on some parts, and of conversion in other parts, out of the inorganic elements of Java, Sumatra and Malacca? Or have they descended, like our domestic races, from the same parent stock? For my own part I could no more admit the former proposition than I could admit that the planets move in their courses, and that a stone falls to the ground, not through the intervention of the secondary and appointed law of gravity, but from the direct volition of the Creator'. (Pl. 144–148).

PALAEONTOLOGY

Palaeontology is the study of the fossilized remains of plants and animals found in the strata of the crust of the earth. The preservation of any fossil is the result of an accident. First the plant or animal must have contained in its body some hard and chemically stable substance such as wood or bone, without which the body would have decomposed and except in very rare cases nothing would have been preserved of its shape. Next, the plant or animal must have died in a position and in circumstances where its remains were covered by preservative material, water-borne mud or sediment in rivers or seas, or wind-borne sand on land, which would consolidate it, and then it must have lain relatively undisturbed. It is therefore not surprising that the record of fossils is incomplete; the astonishing thing is rather that so many fossils of different kinds have been preserved, over a period known to exceed 1,700 million years, which is the age of the oldest fossil plants, algae, and fungi, that are known. Equally astonishing is the degree to which fine and delicate detail is sometimes preserved, such as the sepia of a cuttlefish eaten by a fish and still visible as a black stain inside the fish, the surface of the skin of dinosaurs, the footprints of dinosaurs, the black pigment in the cells of the skin of ichthyosaurs, the skeleton of an embryo inside an ichthyosaur showing that these animals were viviparous, the cast of the brain of *Archaeopteryx* and the brown pigment of its feathers, and the eyeballs of anaspid fishes, all after hundreds of millions of years (Pl. 152–161).

The study of palaeontology and comparison between the fossilized organisms that have been preserved provide three lines of evidence bearing on evolution. First there is the broad fact of persistent change: the floras and faunas which have covered the earth in the past have constantly altered. New types of plants and animals appeared, flourished, became extinct, and were succeeded in turn by other types which went through the same cycles. This *geological succession of forms* in the fossil record is evidence of change, of the former existence of plants and animals different from those that succeeded them. It is evidence that new species have come into existence and have gone out of existence, and unless, like Cuvier, one is prepared to believe in successive acts of creation and successive catastrophes resulting in their obliteration, there is already a strong presumptive indication that evolution has occurred.

This conclusion is reinforced by the second line of palaeontological evidence, which reveals the existence of *precursors and transitional forms* between types. In the vertebrates, for example, there are five distinct main classes: fish, amphibia, reptiles, birds, and mammals; but fossils have been found that are in each case roughly intermediate between the class below and the class above and thus show how the evolutionary transition was effected.

The third line is a refinement of the second and provides detailed evidence of *lines of evolution*, of lineages such as those of the ammonites or of the horses, in which the temporal succession of strata unfolds the transformation of one species into another, all the way along the line from the ancestor to the descendant. This reveals the actual course of evolution.

Palaeontology: Evolution of the Horses

Colour Plate 3

Five stages in the evolution of the horse. 1, *Eohippus* (Eocene) 4-toed browser. 2, *Mesohippus* (Oligocene) 3-toed browser. 3, *Merychippus* (Miocene) 3-toed grazer. 4, *Pliohippus* (Pliocene) 1-toed grazer. 5, *Equus* (Pleistocene to present) improved 1-toed grazer. Three different trends contributed in zig-zag manner to the evolution of the horse. From *Eohippus* to *Mesohippus* selection favoured 3-toed browsers with short grinding teeth; from *Mesohippus* to *Merychippus*, 3-toed grazers with long grinding teeth; from *Merychippus* to *Equus* 1-toed grazers with still longer teeth. Inset A, corresponding stages in the evolution of molar teeth seen from the grinding surface, from short low crowns with cones subjected to little wear adapted for browsing on soft leaves, to high crowns with file-like ridges hard-worn adapted to grazing on flinty grass. Inset B, corresponding stages in the evolution of the feet from 4 toes to 1, seen in front view of left fore-foot. This process of evolution occupied 60 million years during which the stock passed through stages equivalent to 30 species.

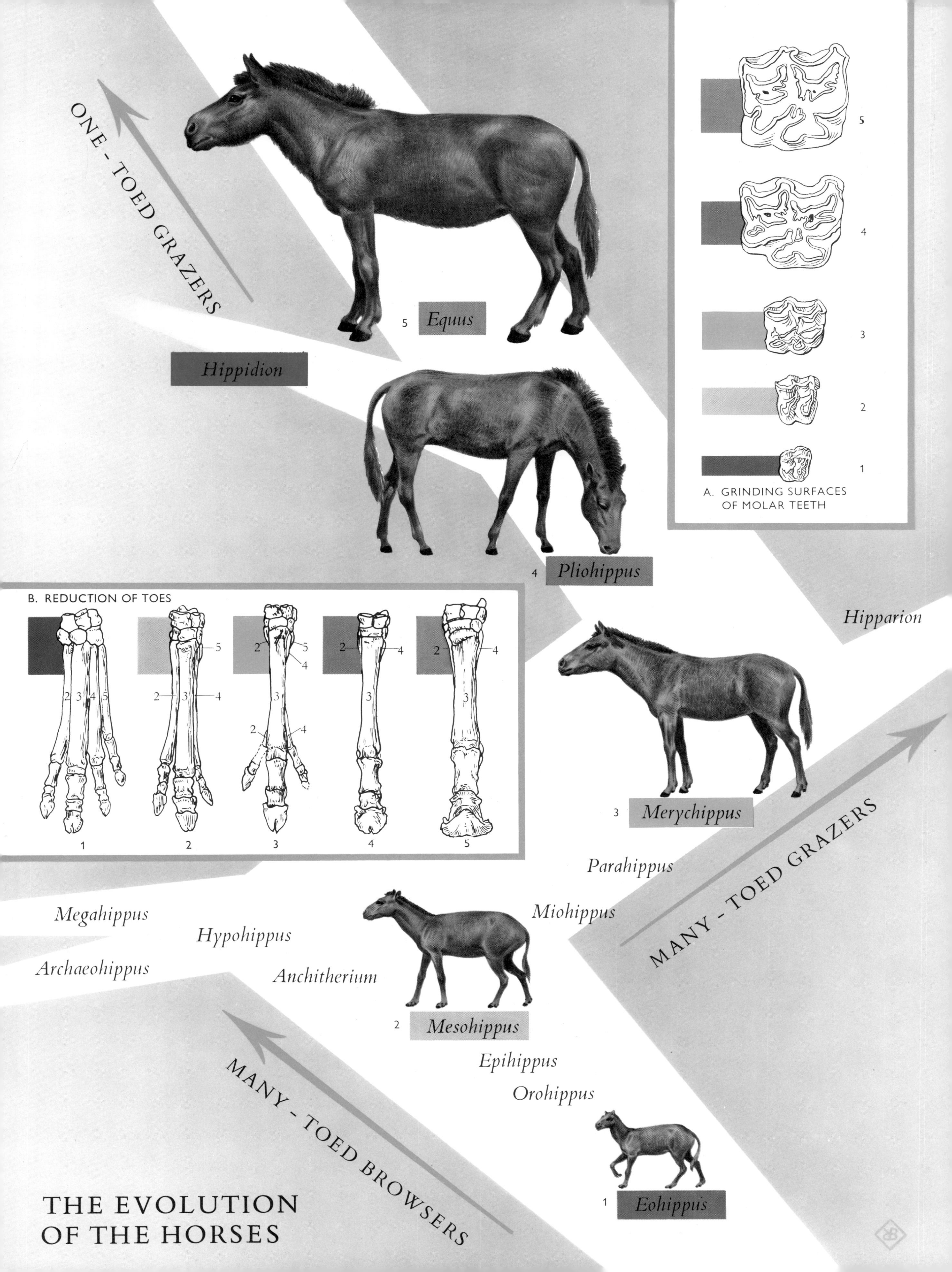

THE EVOLUTION OF THE HORSES

ONE - TOED GRAZERS

5 *Equus*

Hippidion

4 *Pliohippus*

A. GRINDING SURFACES OF MOLAR TEETH

5

4

3

2

1

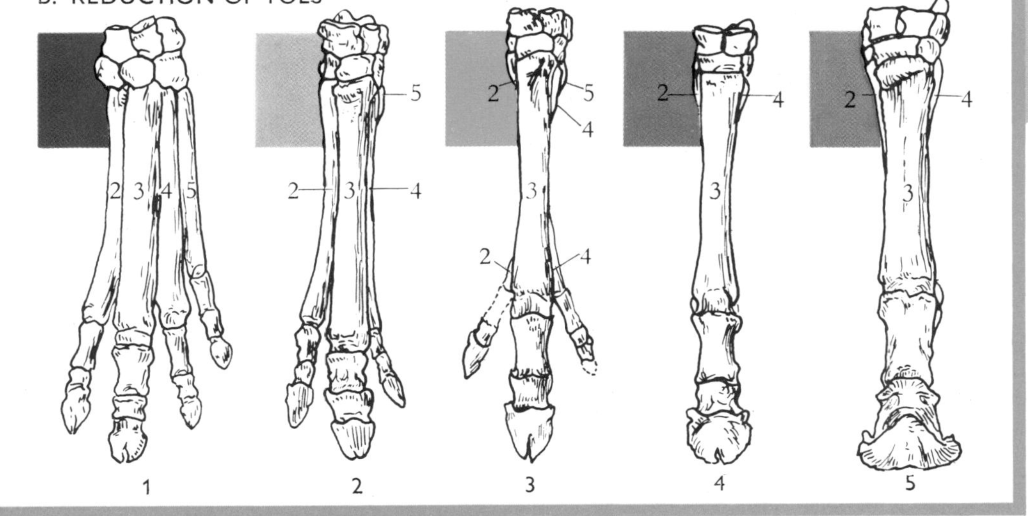

B. REDUCTION OF TOES

Hipparion

3 *Merychippus*

MANY - TOED GRAZERS

Parahippus

Miohippus

Megahippus

Hypohippus

Archaeohippus

Anchitherium

2 *Mesohippus*

MANY - TOED BROWSERS

Epihippus

Orohippus

1 *Eohippus*

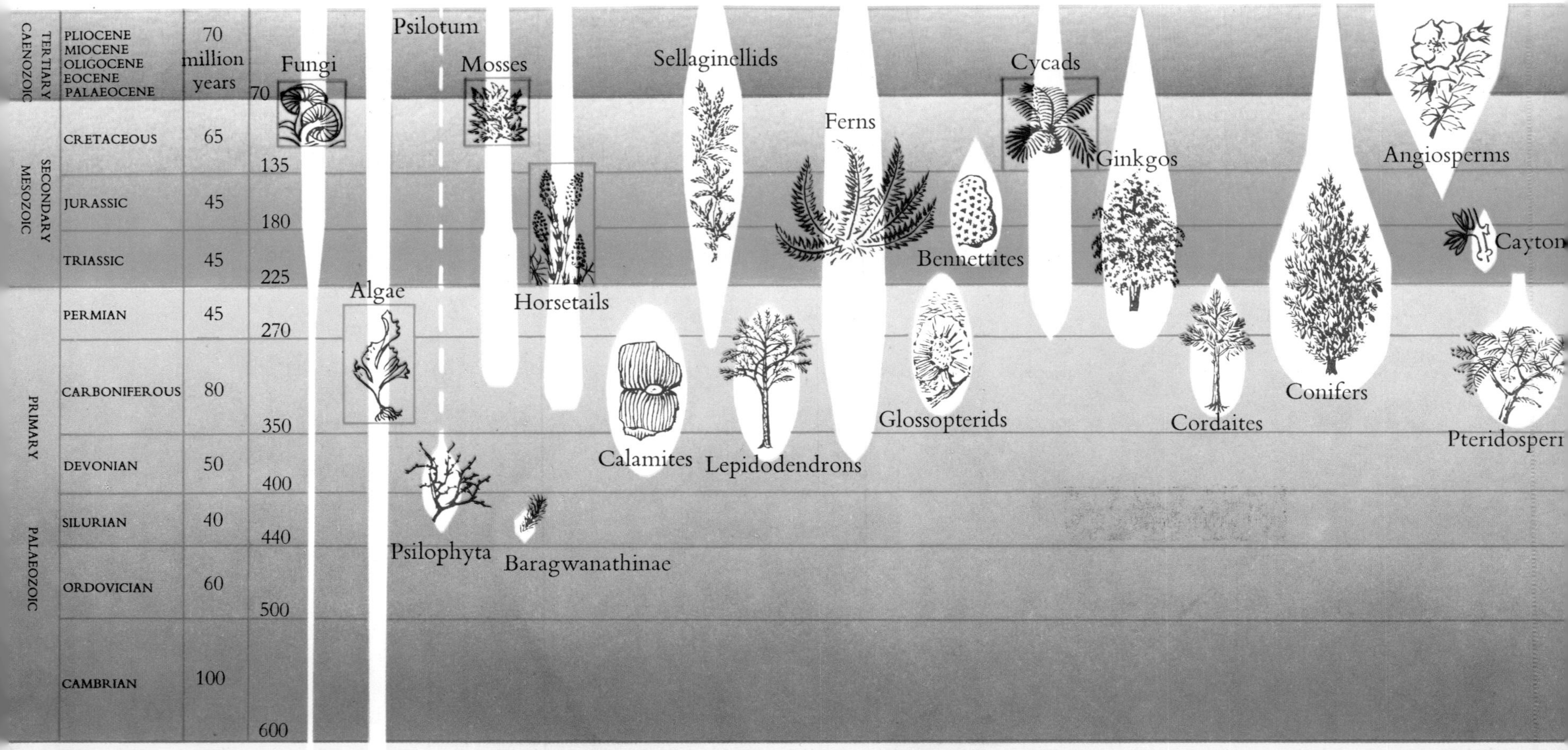

Era	Period	Duration	Age
TERTIARY CAENOZOIC	PLIOCENE MIOCENE OLIGOCENE EOCENE PALAEOCENE	70 million years	70
SECONDARY MESOZOIC	CRETACEOUS	65	135
	JURASSIC	45	180
	TRIASSIC	45	225
PRIMARY PALAEOZOIC	PERMIAN	45	270
	CARBONIFEROUS	80	350
	DEVONIAN	50	400
	SILURIAN	40	440
	ORDOVICIAN	60	500
	CAMBRIAN	100	600
	PRECAMBRIAN		

TIME-SPANS AND IMPORTANCE OF THE PRINCIPAL GROUPS OF PLANTS AND ANIMALS KNOWN AS FOSSILS

The succession of life revealed by the flora and fauna of different strata in the geological record shows that the types of plants and animals that have inhabited the earth have undergone continuous change. Types have come into existence, persisted for a certain time and become extinct. The fact of this widespread extinction is itself important. In many cases it is possible to prove that some types have become converted into others and this is what evolution is. The diagrams on these pages do not show the relationships between different groups for which see Pl. 391, but they show the times of appearance and disappearance of a few of the main groups of plants and animals, their time-spans, and the change in emphasis and in dominant groups of the floras and faunas at different periods. The thicknesses of the strata are shown to scale and include the earliest known preserved fossils, algae and fungi, 1,700 million years old, groups that have persisted up to the present. At the same scale the diagram would need to be

Gun-flint Huronian of Ontario
1,700 million years

Undated interval extending back to the Continental Crust, about 4,500 million years ago, on this scale represented by a total depth of 90 cm. (1 cm = 50 million years).

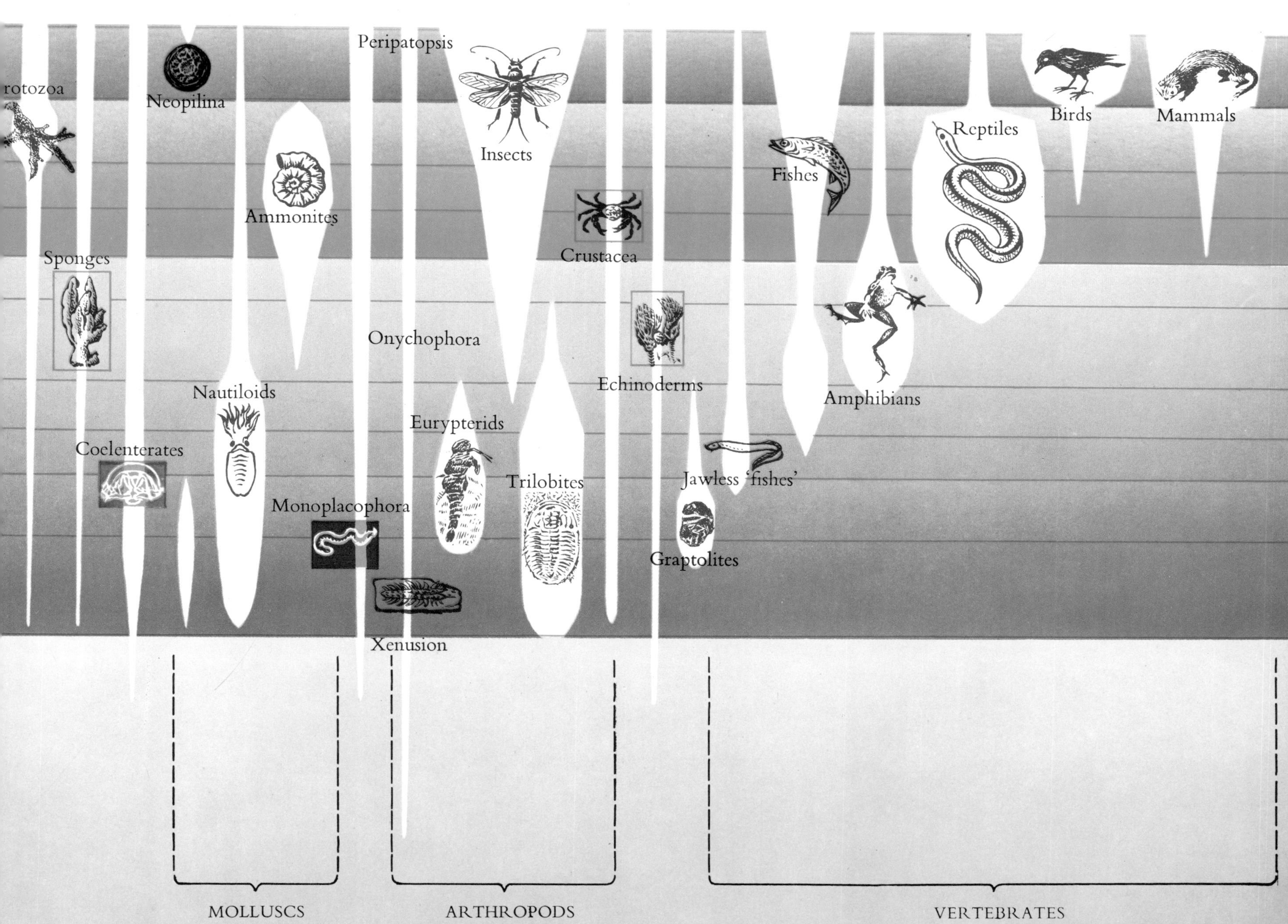

On this scale the Hominidae, half a million years old, would occupy 0.1 mm.

prolonged about 20 cm below the bottom of the page to include nodules of algal origin (*Collenia*) 2,700 million years old. In general it can be seen that the Primary Era was the 'Age of Cryptogams' with its calamites, lepidodendrons, and spore-ferns, and the 'Age of Invertebrates' with trilobites, nautiloids, and eurypterids. The Secondary Era was the 'Age of Gymnosperms' with Bennettites, cycads, conifers, and ginkgos, and the 'Age of Reptiles' with many orders. The Tertiary Era was the 'Age of Angiosperms' with many existing families of flowering plants, and the 'Age of Mammals'. The Quaternary Era was the 'Age of Man'. It may be seen that true vertebrates appeared in the Ordovician, colonisation of land by plants and animals was well under way in the Devonian, with wingless insects and amphibia; high trees, winged insects and reptiles appeared in the Carboniferous, mammals in the Triassic, birds in the Jurassic; Angiosperms in the Cretaceous era. In view of the part that insects play in pollination it is probable that flowers with their colours and scents evolved as adaptations attracting them.

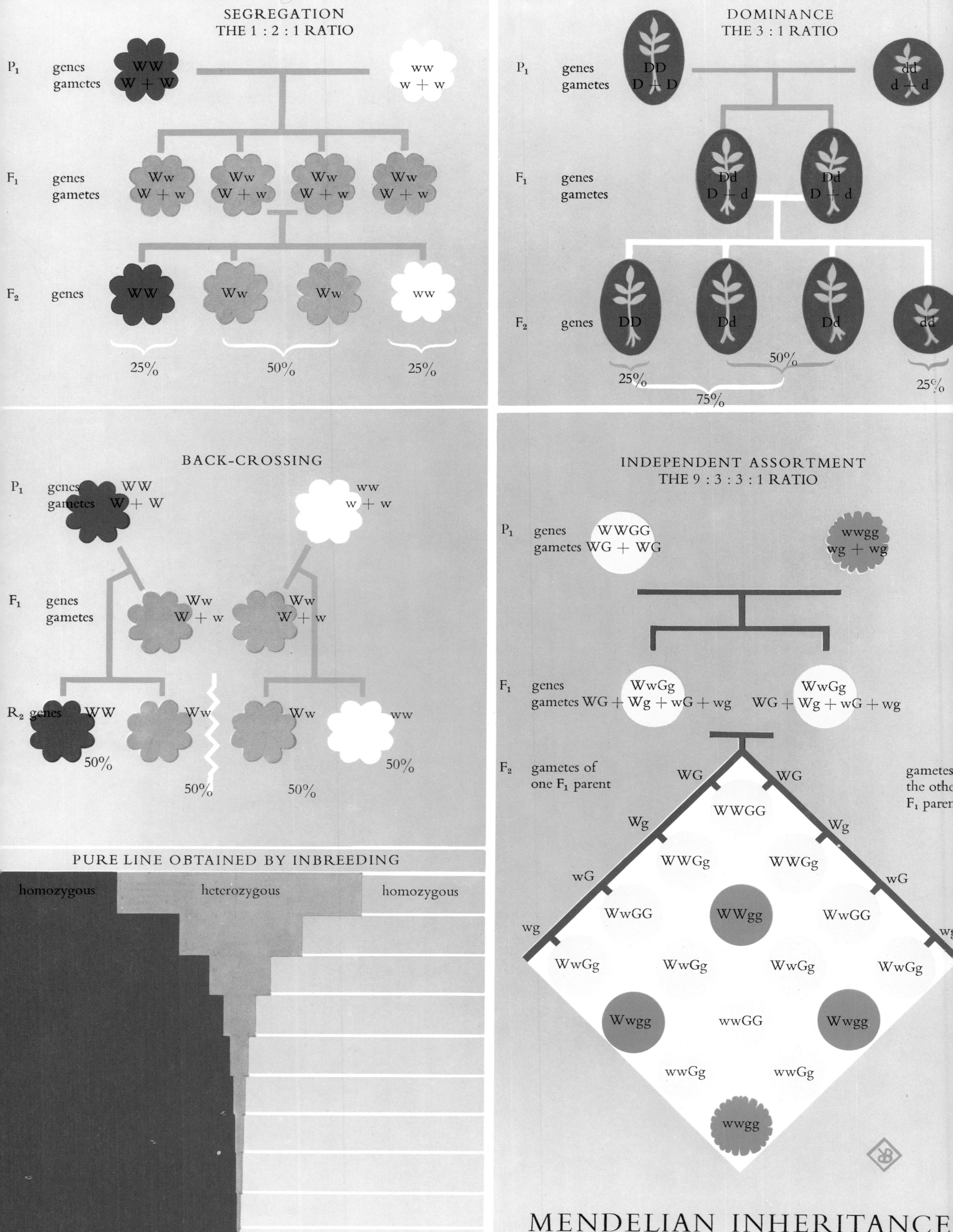
SEGREGATION
THE 1 : 2 : 1 RATIO
P1 genes WW gametes W + W
ww w + w
F1 genes gametes
Ww W + w
F2 genes WW Ww Ww ww
25% 50% 25%
DOMINANCE
THE 3 : 1 RATIO
P1 genes gametes DD D + D
dd d + d
F1 genes gametes Dd D + d
F2 genes DD Dd Dd dd
25% 50% 75% 25%
BACK-CROSSING
P1 genes gametes WW W + W
ww w + w
F1 genes gametes Ww W + w
R2 genes WW Ww Ww ww
50% 50% 50% 50%
PURE LINE OBTAINED BY INBREEDING
homozygous heterozygous homozygous
INDEPENDENT ASSORTMENT
THE 9 : 3 : 3 : 1 RATIO
P1 genes WWGG gametes WG + WG
wwgg wg + wg
F1 genes WwGg gametes WG + Wg + wG + wg
WwGg WG + Wg + wG + wg
F2 gametes of one F1 parent
gametes of the other F1 parent
WG Wg wG wg
WWGG WWGg WWGg WwGG WWgg WwGG WwGg WwGg WwGg WwGg Wwgg wwGG Wwgg wwGg wwGg wwgg
MENDELIAN INHERITANCE

In addition, geological studies provide yet another line of evidence, based on the fact that modern research on radioactivity makes it possible to estimate the actual ages of the various strata in calendar years. This not only enables the time of appearance of the various types of plants and animals to be dated, but also the speed of evolution in the different lineages to be measured. This evidence and the three lines mentioned above will be described in the remainder of this chapter, but first one further aspect of geological evidence has to be considered.

While the remains of plants and animals preserved as fossils in the earth's strata represent the actors in the pageant of evolution, the background and stage scenery, that is the physical and climatic conditions under which the organisms lived, must not be neglected, for they were the dominant factors in the environment and, as Darwin was the first to realize, the fact that the environment changes is of supreme importance for the fate of the organisms that live in it. Geology gives irrefutable information on whether a given region of the earth at any time was dry land or submerged beneath the surface of freshwater lakes or seas, and the nature of the deposits shows whether the sea was shallow with a sandy bottom or deep with a muddy bottom. If the region was submerged, the proximity or distance of dry land can also be deduced from the deposits. Lava flows betray volcanic action, while striated rocks, moraines, moraine deposits, and erratic blocks bear witness to the former existence and extent of glaciers. The wind-blown, dusty deposits known as loess which cover large tracts in central Europe indicate dry cold conditions. On the other hand the deposit known as laterite, consisting of weathered aluminium minerals, found in many parts of Africa, indicates a tropical region of seasonal rainfall which leached rocks, evaporated, and left concentrated insoluble deposits.

Measured differences in the proportions of the isotopes oxygen-16 and oxygen-18 in the lime of which the shells of marine animals are composed enable calculations to be made of the temperature of the water in which the animals lived. A belemnite from the Jurassic period that lived for four years showed from its growth-rings that during its short life 150 million years ago the temperature had oscillated between of four summers at 18° C (64° F) and three winters at 12° C (53° F).

Corals can live only at temperatures between 20° C (68° F) and 35° C (95° F) and at depths of less than 50 fathoms. The distribution of fossil reefs over the globe therefore gives much information on the physical conditions that prevailed when the corals were alive, and in many cases it indicates that the latitude of the land has changed through continental drift. Diatoms flourish in cold seas, radiolarians in warm tropical waters. There are arctic and tropical kinds of foraminifera which indicate the temperature at the surface of the ocean at the time they were alive. Information of this kind on past climates is very material to an understanding of the reasons why some organisms survived and others became extinct.

Geological time-clocks

The age of the earth is a subject which has fascinated men from time immemorial. The crust of the earth is largely composed of sedimentary strata deposited under water and superimposed on each other in succession, the oldest stratum being the lowest, except in cases where inversion has occurred as a result of crustal movement. Early attempts to measure the time since any particular strata were deposited relied on the assumed speeds of natural processes, such as the time required for the deposition of given thicknesses of sedimentary deposits, the time required for the erosion of rocks to given depths, or the time required for the sea to have reached its present degree of salinity on the assumption that its salts have all been derived from the earth's crust. None of these methods could claim any degree of accuracy, and it is only since the discovery of radioactivity and of isotopes of elements that a reliable and accurate method, first suggested by Lord Rutherford, has become available for measuring the age of the various parts of the earth's crust.

Radioactive elements undergo spontaneous disintegration, giving off the nuclei of atoms of helium and electrons, and thereby become converted into other elements. The rates at which radioactive elements undergo disintegration are constant for each element and known, and are expressed as the number of years required for half the amount of the element originally present to disintegrate. This number is known as the half-life of the element, and it varies in different elements from tens of thousands of millions of years to fractions of a second. One gram of radium, for example, is reduced to half a gram in 1,600 years.

The end-products of disintegration of radioactive elements are known, and by measuring the amount of these end-products that have been formed, the length of time required for the transformation can be determined. The success of the method depends on none of the end-products having been present together with the parent radioactive element when the latter was originally deposited. Since the minerals present in volcanic rocks often contain radioactive elements, it is possible to measure the time since these minerals crystallized, and by determining the position of such volcanic rocks relatively to the underlying and overlying sedimentary strata, the ages of the latter can be ascertained (Pl. 150, 151).

An atom of the isotope uranium-238 successively loses eight helium nuclei becoming lead-206 (Pl. 149). An atom of another isotope, uranium-235, loses 7 helium nuclei and becomes 'transmuted' into an atom of lead-207.

In addition to measuring the amount of lead produced, it is possible to measure the amount of helium given off in such radioactive disintegrations. If the mineral contains mica, the helium may be estimated by measuring the halo that is formed in the mica by bombardment with helium nuclei from the radioactive source.

A different 'family' of radioactive elements starts from the element rubidium-87. An atom of this element loses one electron from its nucleus, which transforms it into an atom of strontium-87. This disintegration takes place very slowly, the half-life of rubidium-87 being 50,000 million years, which enables this process to be used for measuring the oldest rocks in the earth's crust.

The isotope potassium-40 is unstable and undergoes radioactive change in one of two possible ways. Some atoms loose an electron from their nucleus and become converted into calcium-40, but this calcium is indistinguishable from the abundant calcium already existing in rocks. However a known proportion of the atoms of potassium-40 are stabilised by capturing an electron from outside the nucleus when they are converted into argon-40. The amount of argon can be measured. The fact that these different radioactive series give results that are consistent with one another within the limits of experimental error is part of the reason why their rates of disintegration are believed to be constant.

Even without going into details of the various processes or operations involved, it is now clear that the measurement of geological time rests on a solid scientific basis, the results of which will become increasingly accurate as the technique of estimation develops and more material becomes available. The age of the oldest minerals of the earth's crust so far measured is about 3,000 million years. The methods used on the earth have also been found to be applicable to material of extra-terrestrial origin in the form of meteorites and give an age of the same order of magnitude. Calculations by various methods based on radioactivity and isotopes give an estimate of 4,500 million years for the age of the earth.

Mendelian Inheritance

Colour Plate 6.

SEGREGATION illustrated diagrammatically by crossing Four o'Clock plants with red and white flowers, P 1. The first filial generation, F 1, are all pink. When these are crossed the offspring in F 2 are 25% red, 25% white, and 50% pink. The reds bred with reds breed true to red; the whites bred with whites breed true to white; the pinks bred with pinks give the same split into 25% red, 25% white, and 50% pink. This 1 : 2 : 1 ratio of distribution of parental characters among offspring is mendelian and due to the control of characters by discrete particles, the genes, that exist in allelic pairs the members of which segregate at the formation of germ-cells and recombine at random when the eggs are fertilised to form zygotes. The reds and the whites are homozygous because both members of each pair of allelic genes are identical in each individual. The pinks are heterozygous because the members of each pair of allelic genes are different.

BACK-CROSSING. When a heterozygote is *back-crossed* to a homozygote, equal numbers of homozygote and heterozygote offspring are produced.

DOMINANCE. In many cases the heterozygotes are not intermediate in character between the two parental heterozygotes, but are visibly indistinguishable from one of the parental types. This is illustrated diagrammatically by the cross between tall and dwarf peas. The F 1 offspring are all tall like their homozygous tall parent. The character tall is therefore called dominant and the character dwarf recessive. When F 1 heterozygous tall peas are bred together, the F 2 consists of 75% tall and 25% dwarf or 3 : 1, but of the talls, one third are homozygous and breed true to tallness while two thirds are heterozygous like the F 1 talls and segregate like them when bred. The F 2 therefore consists really of 25% homozygous talls, 50% heterozygous talls, and 25% homozygous dwarfs. Dominant characters appear even when inherited from only one parent, while recessive characters appear only when inherited from both parents. An individual showing recessive characters must therefore be homozygous, which is useful because the only way of testing an unknown tall is to back-cross it with a dwarf; if heterozygous it will give equal numbers of talls and dwarfs, if homozygous, all offspring will be tall.

INDEPENDENT ASSORTMENT. Living organisms contain more than one pair of allelic genes, and when individuals differing in more than one pair are crossed, each pair of genes segregates independently. This *independent assortment* is illustrated diagrammatically by a cross between peas in which seeds are round and yellow and peas in which the seeds are wrinkled and green. The characters 'round' and 'yellow' are dominant and the F 1 offspring are all 'round-yellow'. In F 2, each pair of alleles segregates independently so that 12 are 'round' and 4 'wrinkled', which is 3 : 1. Similarly 12 are 'yellow' and 4 'green', again 3 : 1. But although the parents were of only two classes, 'round-yellow' and 'wrinkled-green', four classes emerge in F 2 which contains the two parental classes and also 'round-green' and 'wrinkled-yellow', and they occur in the ratio 9 'round-yellow': 3 'round-green': 3 'wrinkled-yellow': 1 'wrinkled-green', a ratio which is only two 3 : 1 ratios superimposed. This emergence of different types through independent assortment shows the importance of recombination of genes in sexual reproduction in that it gives wider ranges of variation.

PURE LINE OBTAINED BY INBREEDING. Starting from parents differing in 1 pair of genes, the F 2 consists of 25% red, 50% pink, and 25% white. As the reds breed true to red and the whites breed true to white, but the pinks, being heterozygous, produce 25% red, 50% pink, and 25% white, the total number of heterozygotes decreases in each generation by one half, while the numbers of homozygotes increase. After 10 generations of inbreeding the population will contain only 1 heterozygote in 1024 individuals. After 8 generations the proportion of heterozygotes is too small to be shown. At the same time it can be seen how inbreeding promotes homozygosity.

134

135 136 137

Parasites in Plants and Animals

134, 135. Mistletoe, a plant with flowers, leaves, chlorophyll, and stems with which it is able to perform photosynthesis and build up its living matter from inorganic substances; but as it is not planted in the soil and has no roots it is parasitic on its host-plant for water and salts. **136.** Dodder has lost leaves and chlorophyll as well as roots and depends on its host-plant for all its nourishment. **137.** *Rafflesia* is an enormous flower and nothing else, for it springs directly from the roots of the plant that it parasitises. **138.** Trypanosomes in man's blood cause sleeping sickness, transmitted by tse-tse flies. **139.** The liver-fluke is adult in the liver of sheep and has a complicated life-history involving larval stages in an alternative host, the pond-snail. **140.** The tape-worm in man's intestine has the rabbit or pig as alternative hosts. **141.** Males parasitic on females in angler-fishes have lost teeth, eyes, fins and intestine. Affinity between parasites may indicate the affinity of their hosts. **142.** The human louse (*left*) and chimpanzee louse (*right*) are very similar but so different from other lice that they must have evolved from a common ancestor that parasitized the common ancestor of chimpanzee and man, 40 million years ago. Parasitism is a form of adaptation and all parasites have *become* parasitic by evolution from a previous free-living condition. It is sometimes possible to observe intermediate stage in this process.

138

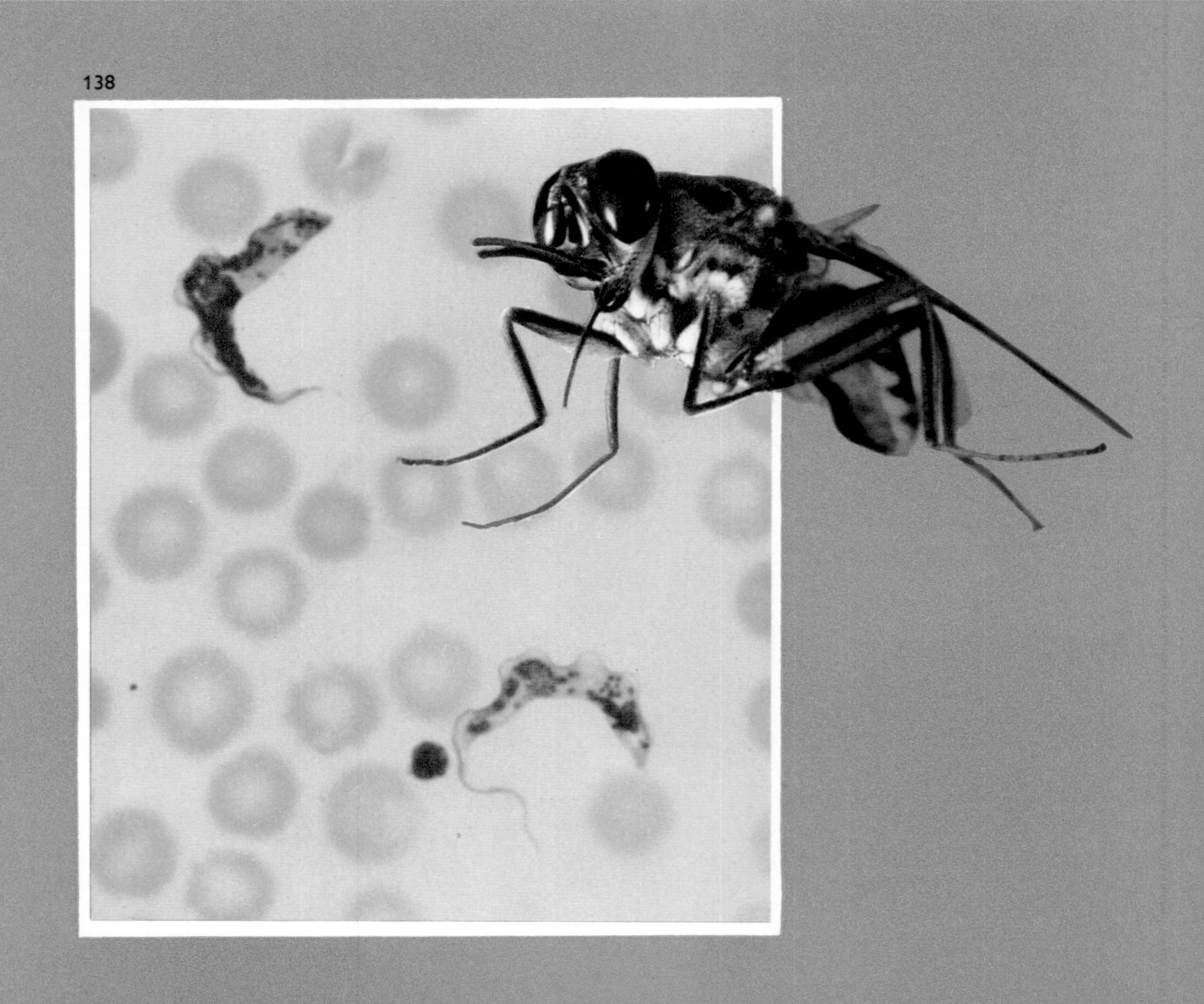

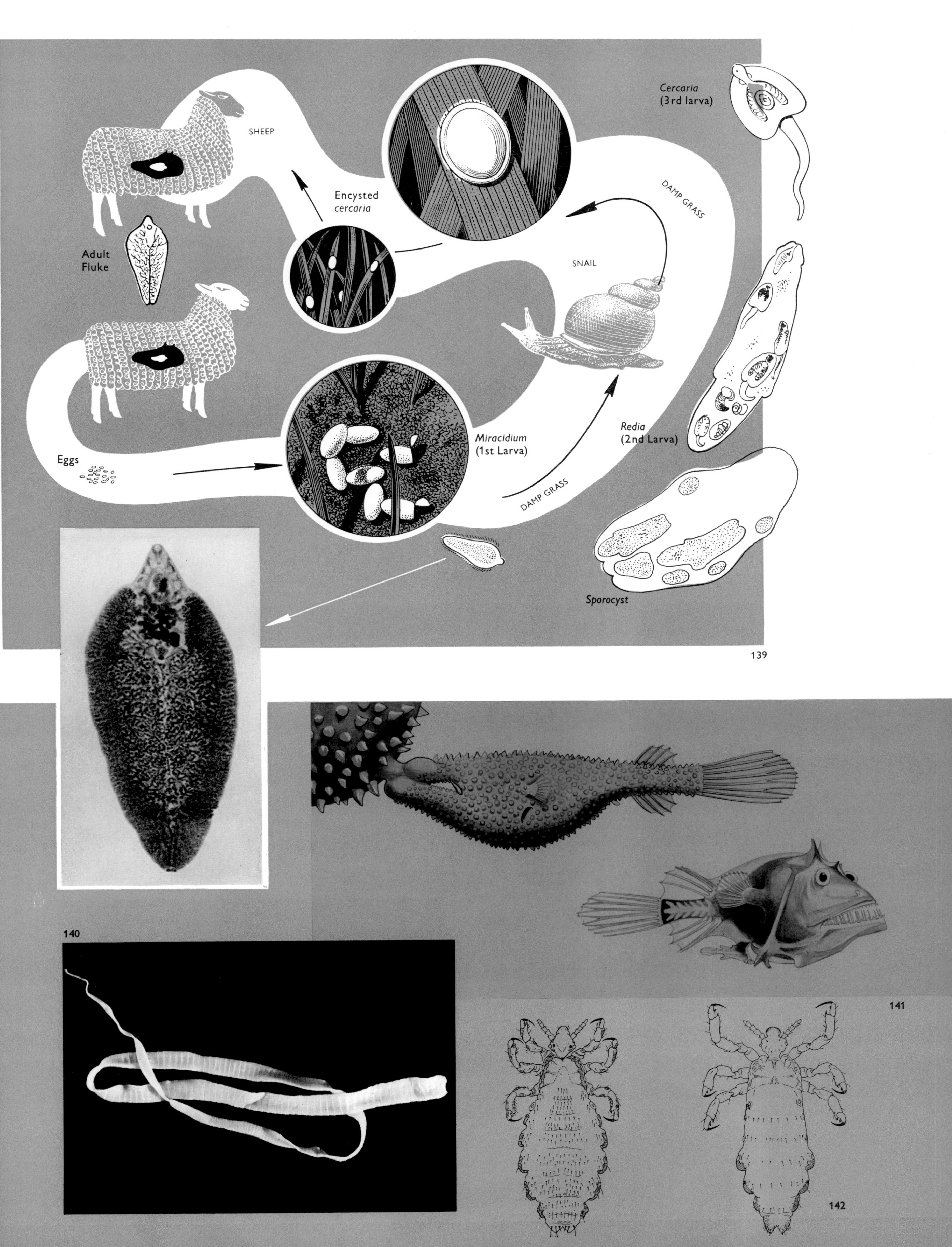
SHEEP
Encysted
cercaria
Cercaria
(3rd larva)
DAMP GRASS
Adult
Fluke
SNAIL
Miracidium
(1st Larva)
Redia
(2nd Larva)
Eggs
DAMP GRASS
Sporocyst
139
140
141
142

143. The aim of classification is to place together the groups that have characters in common and separate them from others. Monocotyledons and Dicotyledons are put in Angiospermae because their seeds are enclosed, and separated from Gymnospermae whose seeds are exposed. Both these groups having seeds are put in Phanerogamia and separated from Cryptogamia, which have no seeds; and so on. In practice it is very difficult to draw up a classification for general use because knowledge is incomplete, two-dimensional representation insufficient, and accepted names of groups confuse *grades* of organisation and *clades* (p. 166) of divergence. There can be no doubt that Angiospermae evolved from some Gymnosperm, and Phanerogamia from some Cryptogam, just as birds and mammals evolved from reptiles. These names express grades of organization arrived at during a continuous evolutionary process and the limits between them must be arbitrary. Bryophyta and Pteridophyta are clades of divergence, as are plants and animals. A classification must be workable, and lines of descent are left to phylogenetic trees (→ 391).

All Chordata and only they have: an internal skeletal rod down the back, a tubular nervous system along the back, and a number of gill-slits or pouches on each side of the throat. Chordata are divided into those without and with skull (Acrania and Craniata), the latter into those without and with jaws (Agnatha and Gnathostomata), the latter into those with fins (Pisces) and those with 5-fingered limbs (Tetrapoda), the latter into those without and with amniotic embryonic membranes (Anamnia and Amniota), the latter into cold-blooded reptiles and warm-blooded birds with feathers and mammals with hair, the latter into oviparous Monotremata and viviparous Ditremata, the latter into those with placenta imperfectly developed (Marsupialia) and well developed (Placentalia), the latter into some dozen orders the last of which is Primates divided into Prosimii and large-brained Anthropoidea, the latter into Ceboidea with prehensile tails, Cercopithecoidea, and Hominoidea without tails, the latter into apes and men.

This is a very simple guide to the principles of classification as applied to one group, Chordata leading right through to man.

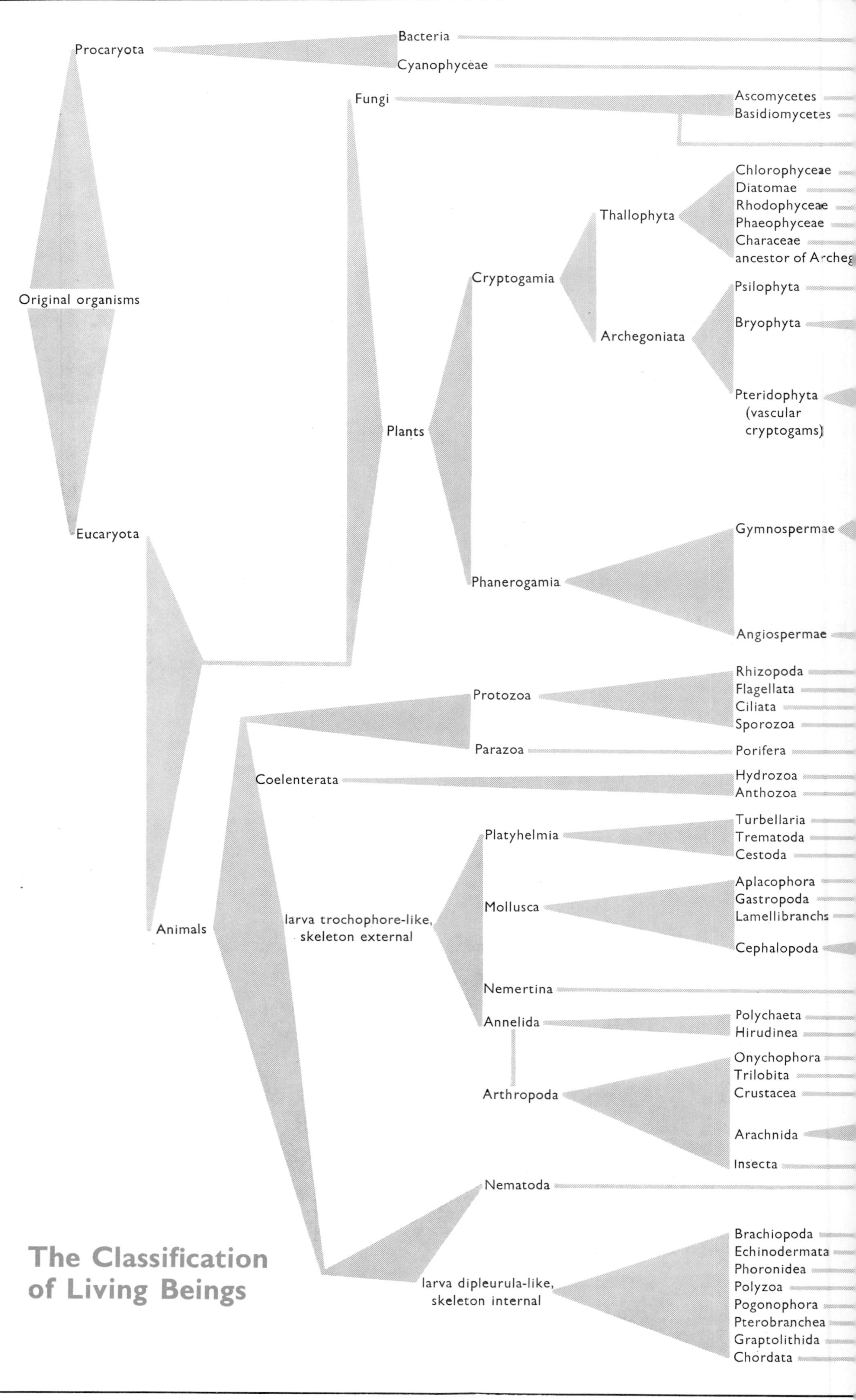

bacteria
blue-green algae
moulds
mushrooms
lichens
green algae
diatoms
red algae
brown algae
stoneworts
Psilotum
mosses
liverworts
selaginellids
sphenophylls
horsetails
ferns
ancestors of Phanerogamia
pteridosperms
Cordaites
cycads
maiden-hair trees
Glossopteris
Bennettites
conifers
Gnetum
ancestors of Angiospermae
Monocotyledons
Dicotyledons
amoebae
trypanosomes
ciliates
malarial parasite
sponges
jelly-fish
corals
turbellarians
liver-flukes
tape-worms
Neopilina
snails
oysters
ammonites
nautiloids
cuttle-fish
nemertines
worms
leeches
Peripatus
trilobites
lobsters
eurypterids
scorpions
spiders
insects
thread-worms
many minor groups
lamp-shells
starfish
Phoronis
sea-mats
pogonophores
Cephalodiscus
graptolites
chordates — Chordata

Chordata
Craniata
Gnathostomata
Tetrapoda
Amniota
Mammalia
Ditremata
Placentalia
Primates
Anthropoidea
Hominoidea — man, apes
Cercopithecoidea — Old world monkeys
Ceboidea — New world monkeys
Prosimii
Tarsioidea — tarsiers
Lemuroidea — lemurs
Tupaioidea — tree-shrews
Insectivora — moles
Cheiroptera — bats
Rodentia — rats
Lagomorpha — rabbits
Proboscidea — elephants
Hyracoidea — coney
Cetacea — whales
Artiodactyla
Ruminantia — camels, cattle
Suina — pigs
Perissodactyla
Hippoidea — horses
Tapiroidea — tapirs
Rhinoceroidea — rhinoceroses
Sirenia — dugong, manatee
Carnivora
Pinnipedia — seals
Fissipedia — dogs
Tubulidentata — aard-vark
Edentata — sloths
Pholidota — pangolin
Marsupialia — kangaroos
Monotremata — platypus
Aves
Neornithes
Ratites — flightless birds
Carinata — flying birds
Archaeornithes — *Archaeopteryx*
Reptilia
Theriodontia — Ictidosauria — ancestors of Mammalia
Thecodontia
Crocodilia — crocodiles
Pseudosuchia — ancestors of Aves
Squamata
Ophidia — snakes
Lacertilia — lizards
Rhynchocephalia — *Sphenodon*
Chelonia — turtles
Pterosauria — pterodactyls
Dinosauria — dinosaurs
Plesiosauria — plesiosaurs
Ichthyosauria — ichthyosaurs
Prosauria — *Seymouria*
Anamnia — Amphibia
Anura — frogs
Urodela — newts
Gymnophiona — coecilians
Stegocephalia — *Ichthyostega*, ancestors of Reptilia
Pisces
Chondrichthyes — sharks
Placodermi — acanthodians
Osteichthyes
Dipnoi — lung fishes
Actinopterygii — common bony fishes
Crossopterygii — ancestors of Tetrapoda, coelacanths
Agnatha — ancestors of Gnathostomata
Cyclostomata — lampreys
Ostracodermi — *Jamoytius*
Acrania
Cephalochordata — lancelets
Urochordata — ascidians & salps
Hemichordata — acorn-worms

The geological succession of forms

The Pre-Cambrian era is as old as the crust of the earth, at least 3,000 million years. As it ended 600 million years ago it covered four-fifths of geological time. It is a puzzling fact that fossils found in its strata are few in number, but this does not mean that there is no trace of living organisms in Pre-Cambrian rocks (Pl. 162–174). Even in the absence of actual bodily remains in the form of fossil plants or animals, there are other ways in which evidence of their former existence can be obtained.

For example, in the Bulowayan Limestones of the Pre-Cambrian of Rhodesia and in other places, nodules are found consisting of thin concentric layers of limestone deposited in a manner similar to that in which lime-secreting algae deposit them today. The name *Collenia* has been given to these Pre-Cambrian algae, which have been dated from associated radioactive minerals at 2,700 million years old.

Small, flat, coal-like masses found in the Pre-Cambrian rocks of Finland, introduce another method of detecting the traces of former organisms. The isotopes carbon-12 and carbon-13 are found in different proportions in plants and in inorganic limestones. The coal-like masses in question give an isotope ratio that shows that they were the product of algae, to which the name *Corycium enigmaticum* has been given, and their date has been estimated at 2,500 million years ago.

In the Huronian Pre-Cambrian deposits of Ontario, the earliest known visible fossil organisms have been found preserved in flint nodules. They are easily recognizable as algae and fungi, with filaments and spores, and microchemical analysis has enabled E. S. Barghoorn to identify seven amino acids preserved in them. They are 1,700 million years old (Pl. 163, 164).

The earliest animal fossil known is *Xenusion auerswaldae* found in a block of Algonkian Pre-Cambrian Dala Sandstone from Sweden. Its body shows 14 segments with paired limbs and it must have been intermediate between the worms and arthropods. Its age is about 800 million years (Pl. 165).

The Pre-Cambrian strata of the Ediacara Hills, South Australia, have provided fossils of sea-pens, jellyfish, worms, echinoderms, and animals of uncertain nature (M. F. Glaessner). Some of these are similar to fossils found at Charnwood Forest in England and in Namaqualand in southern Africa (Pl. 166–174). Apart from these, the Pre-Cambrian has revealed inprints of jellyfish, traces of shells, corals, spicules of sponges, and tracks of worms.

The richness in fossils of the Cambrian and all later geological periods raises the question why the Pre-Cambrian deposits should be relatively poor, when it is certain from those fossils that have been found that plants and animals were in existence and undergoing the considerable amounts of evolution that must have been

144

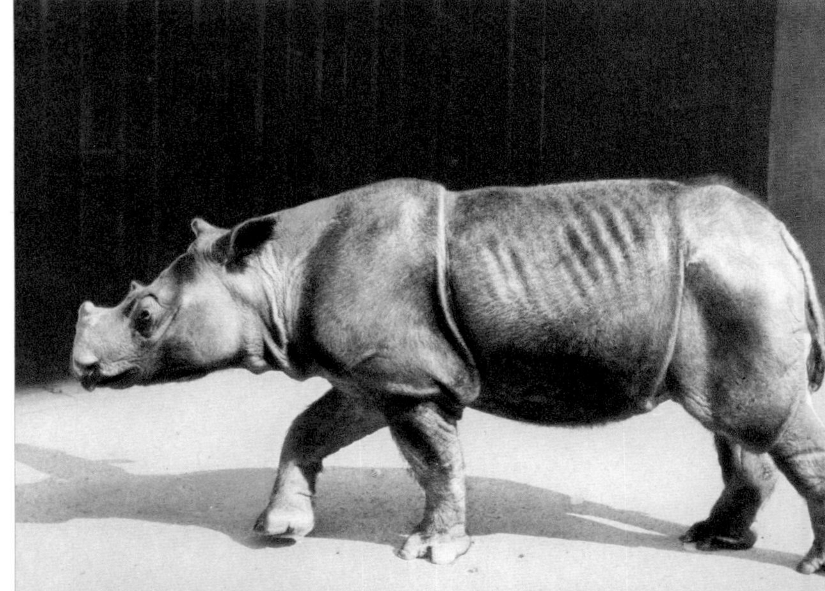

145

147

146

Geographical Distribution, Related Species

When Darwin considered the living and fossil species of rhinoceros; the one-horned from India **144,** Sumatra (two-horned) **145,** and Java (one-horned) **146,** the ancient woolly rhinoceros of Siberia **147,** of which whole specimens are known, preserved by the very low temperatures that have persisted in parts of Siberia, and the two-horned black rhinoceros of East Africa **148,** he was convinced that they came from the same parent stock. The species that live closer geographically show greater affinity with each other than with those that are more remote.

148

necessary to produce the flora and fauna of the Cambrian rocks. To this question there are three answers. First, the Pre-Cambrian rocks, being the oldest, have in most cases undergone alteration by heat and pressure, which destroys fossil remains.

GEOLOGICAL TIME-SCALE

Era	*Period*	*Millions of years since beginning of period*	*Duration of period in millions of years*
Quaternary	Holocene		
	Pleistocene	2	2
Tertiary or Caenozoic	Pliocene	12	10
	Miocene	25	13
	Oligocene	40	15
	Eocene	60	20
	Palaeocene	70	10
Secondary or Mesozoic	Cretaceous	135	65
	Jurassic	180	45
	Triassic	225	45
Primary or Palaeozoic	Permian	270	45
	Carboniferous	350	80
	Devonian	400	50
	Silurian	440	40
	Ordovician	500	60
	Cambrian	600	100
	Pre-Cambrian:		
	Algonkian (Dala)	800	
	Huronian (Gunflint)	1,700	
	Finland (shales)	2,500	
	Rhodesian (pegmatites)	2,700	
	Oldest known rocks	3,000	
	Origin of the Earth	4,500	

Next, for the same reason that the Pre-Cambrian rocks are the oldest, they underlie all the other rocks in the geological series, and can be studied for fossils only in the areas where they are exposed by the overlying rocks having been eroded away. Finally, the plants and animals alive during the Pre-Cambrian era mostly had soft bodies without hard parts capable of preservation as fossils. The paucity of fossils from Pre-Cambrian rocks must therefore be regarded as natural.

The Cambrian (600-500 million years ago) is the earliest geological period from which well-preserved fossils are obtained, and they occur in large quantities. The richness of these fossil records and the numbers of groups of plants and particularly of animals which they represent is evidence that evolution had already made considerable progress during the previous Pre-Cambrian eras. Indeed, most of the groups of invertebrate animals are already present. The Cambrian rocks contain algae or seaweeds, protozoa, sponges, impressions of jellyfish, corals, worms, shells of gastropod and lamellibranch molluscs, polyzoa, echinoderms, lamp-shells, trilobites, and graptolites. The notable absentees are land-plants and land-animals, and vertebrates.

Fish-like vertebrates first appeared in the Ordovician (500-400 million years ago); eurypterids or sea-scorpions, true fishes, and the first land-plants in the Silurian (440-400 million years ago); ferns, horsetails, seed-ferns, spiders, mites, wingless insects, coelacanths, and amphibians in the Devonian (400-350 million years ago); mosses, selaginellids, conifers, winged insects, and reptiles in the Carboniferous (350-270 million years ago); tortoises in the Permian (270-225 million years ago); lobsters, cycads, ammonites, belemnites, dinosaurs, ichthyosaurs, and mammals in the Triassic (225-180 million years ago); maidenhair-trees, monkey-puzzles, crabs, king-crabs, flies, beetles, bugs, hymenoptera and lepidoptera, frogs, pterodactyls, and birds in the Jurassic (180-135 million years ago); deciduous trees, flowering plants, newts, lizards, and snakes in the Cretaceous (135-70 million years ago); honey-bees and ants in the Oligocene (40-25 million years ago); and man in the Middle Pleistocene period (500 thousand years ago).

The strata of earlier geological periods lack many types of plants and animals of the later periods, and conversely the strata of later geological periods do not contain many types of plants and animals found in earlier periods. New forms were continually appearing and old forms becoming extinct. Graptolites became extinct in the Carboniferous, trilobites and eurypterids in the Permian, seed-ferns in the Trias, ammonites, ichthyosaurs, dinosaurs, and pterodactyls in the Cretaceous, belemnites in the Eocene period. The remaining groups have survived until the present day (Col. Pl. 4, 5).

Different groups of plants and animals have therefore had very different life-spans. A further point of importance is that within the life-span of each group, the numbers and predominance of the groups varied very greatly. For instance, among plants, seed-ferns were extremely numerous and dominant in the Carboniferous but dwindled in the Permian before petering out in the Triassic period. The cycads were dominant in the Jurassic and Cretaceous periods, but have survived until today only in very reduced numbers. On the other hand, flowering plants, which began

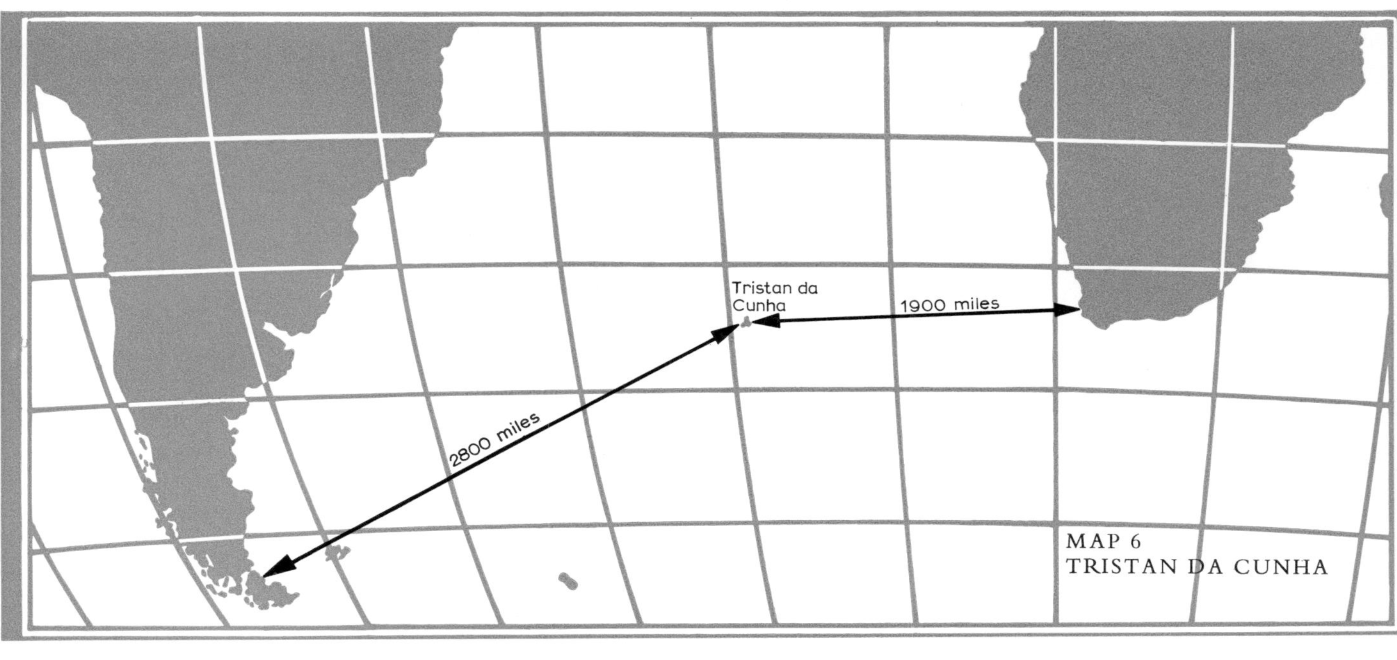

The problem of geographical distribution is presented very clearly by the flora and fauna of oceanic islands. **Map 6.** Tristan da Cunha in the South Atlantic Ocean has a flora with affinities both in South America and Africa. It is impossible to believe that they were created there in South American and African form, merely because of the intermediate geographical position of Tristan da Cunha.

The Significance of Oceanic Islands

The peculiarities of the flora on the island of Tristan da Cunha played an important part in the shaping of Darwin's ideas towards the concept of evolution. After he had read a scientific article by Captain Dugald Carmichael published in 1818 in which a list of the island's flora is given, Darwin realised in 1837 that some undoubtedly African and some equally undoubtedly American plants were represented in the island. He wrote: 'Now when we hear that the whole island is volcanic, surmounted by a crater and studded with others, we see a beginning to the island'.

This meant that the island was volcanic in origin, had emerged from the waters of the ocean and had never had a land-connection with any continent. He went on, 'Would the creator, when this volcanic point appeared in the great ocean, have made plants of American and African form, merely because of its intermediate (geographical) position?'. Joseph Hooker, director of the Royal Botanic Gardens at Kew, found that of 28 species of flowering plants on the island 19 were of universal distribution, 7 confined to Tristan da Cunha and South America, and 2 to Tristan da Cunha and South Africa. The Norwegian Scientific Expedition to the island found that the corresponding number of species of ferns are 5 and 2 respectively, of liverworts 30 and 5. Comparable pairs of figures were found for certain groups of animals. Darwin's information was therefore correct, and he concluded that no species had been created on Tristan da Cunha, but that the species represented in its flora had evolved, some in South America, some in South Africa, and others elsewhere, and had been introduced into the island by one or other of the various means of passive dispersal (→ Map 11).

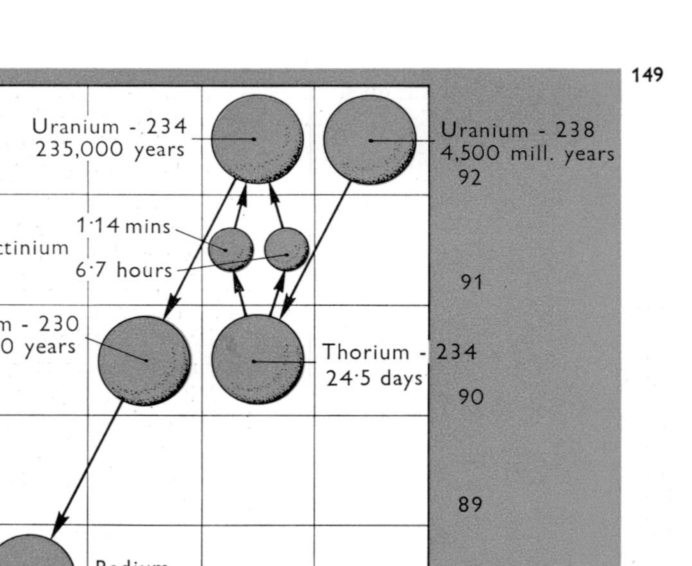

149

Geological Time Clocks

149. The fact that radioactive elements undergo decay at rates constant for each element makes it possible to measure the age of rocks containing them with an accuracy that is increasing with refinement of technique. Such elements are found in the minerals of igneous or volcanic rocks. (Isotopes are forms of a chemical element with identical chemical properties because they carry the same electric charge on their nuclei, but different atomic weights because their nuclei may contain additional neutrons. Isotopes are distinguished by adding the atomic weight to the name of the element.) An atom of uranium-238 successively loses 8 atoms of helium and passing through intermediate stages, eventually becomes lead-206. The speed at which this conversion occurs is known: one million grams of uranium-238 give rise to 1/7600 gram of lead-206 in one year. By measuring the residual amount of uranium in a mineral and the amount of lead produced and of helium given off, the age of this mineral can be calculated.

very modestly in the Cretaceous period, have become the dominant plants at the present time (Pl. 175-187).

In the animal kingdom the picture is similar. Trilobites had their hey-day in the Cambrian and Ordovician and eurypterids in the Silurian periods, but both groups declined until their extinction in the Permian (Pl. 189, 191). Reptiles of various orders were supreme in the Jurassic and Cretaceous periods but nearly all of them became extinct at the end of the Cretaceous when their place was taken by the mammals (Pl. 203-205, 429-436).

An additional point of great importance is that even during the continued existence of a group of animals, there was constant replacement of its constituents. For example, during the Triassic period there were twelve families of ammonites, and during the following Jurassic period there were twenty-three families; but of these, twenty-two arose from one of the twelve Triassic families, the other eleven having become extinct (Pl. 215). Similar examples of massive extinction and recruitment of survivors from a small portion only of the previous populations can be found in many other groups, and they indicate the pattern along which the geological succession of forms has occurred.

A comparative study of the floras and faunas of the past therefore shows a constantly changing distribution of emphasis, in which it is possible to discern a competitive succession of dominant groups in particular walks of life. The decline of the seed-ferns coincided with the rise of the cycads, and the decline of these coincided with the rise of the flowering plants. The decline of the amphibians coincided with the rise of the reptiles, and the decline of these coincided with the rise of the mammals. Big as is the world, and numerous as are its niches, there is a limit to the number of groups of organisms that can occupy them, and the result of the competition to occupy these niches is reflected in the geological succession of forms which is the direct result of evolution.

Precursors and transitional forms

The groups in which plants and animals are found today are clear-cut. Not even a layman would mistake a sea-weed for a fern, or a fish for a newt, and the reason for this is that there are certain types of structure that have enabled plants and animals to become successfully adapted to new conditions of life, which may be compared to floors in a building. On each floor a remarkable amount of variation is possible, which may be illustrated by the difference between a shark and a minnow, a lumbering labyrinthodont and a frog, a dinosaur and a snake, an ostrich and a sparrow, or a mole and a man. In each of these cases the variation has not transcended the level of the floor; yet in the past, if evolution has occurred, there must have been some break-through from each floor to the one above. Evidence of these break-throughs is provided by fossils representing intermediate stages between the ancestral group below and the evolved group above.

In the history of the vegetable kingdom, the most important event was emergence from aquatic life in the sea and the colonization of dry land, as will be described in Chapter IV. In the sea, plants such as sea-weeds have very simple bodies known as thalluses in which there is no differentiation into specialized parts. In peat-beds of the Devonian period, well-preserved remains have been found of the simplest land-plants so far known. One of these psilotums, as they are called, *Rhynia major*, consisted of a stem continuous with an underground stem or rhizome which was not differentiated into a root but bore absorbent root-hairs. Above, the stem branched and at the end of some of the branches there were sacks full of spores in groups of four, as in ferns. The surface of the stem was perforated here and there by small holes or stomata that admitted air, just as in all land-plants. A related plant, *Asteroxylon mackiei* also had rudimentary leaves. It is clear that these Devonian land-plants were derived from marine algae, and although it cannot be claimed that they are directly ancestral to any known group of land-plants, they nevertheless serve to show what plants were like when they first came out of the sea on to dry land and became adapted to live in air (Pl. 206, 207).

Starfishes (asteroids) and brittle-stars (ophiuroids) can be traced to common ancestors in the group of somasteroids that became extinct in the Ordovician period. Somasteroids were flattened and star-shaped, and their skeleton was intermediate in character between the mosaic pattern of the starfishes and the frond-like pattern seen in the arms of sea-lilies (crinoids). It is therefore probable, as Barraclough Fell has shown, that somasteroids, and therefore asteroids and ophiuroids, were evolved from crinoids, and that the free-living habit of the asteroids and ophiuroids was derived from the sessile habit of the stalked crinoids. The interest of this case is heightened by the fact that the somasteroids are represented by the living *Platasterias*.

The origin of the vertebrates has always been a favourite subject for research, and in the Silurian fossil *Jamoytius* palaeontology has presented the most primitive form yet discovered. It was fish-shaped with large paired eyes, but it had no jaws to its mouth, which must have admitted food by creating a current of inflowing water, as in the modern lancelet, by beating cilia. There was a notochord not replaced by vertebrae, the alimentary canal was straight and simple, the muscle-plates of its sixty-odd segments were shaped like simple chevrons, the convex angle pointing forwards as in the lancelet. The most interesting feature is that in addition to the dorsal fin which ran down the back, there was on each side a continuous lateral fin of exactly the type and shape previously postulated from studies of anatomy and embryology to explain the origin of the paired pectoral and pelvic fins of fishes and their successors, the limbs of land-vertebrates. The pectoral and pelvic fins of fishes and limbs of land vertebrates are interrupted portions of the continuos lateral fin of *Jamoytius* (Pl. 208).

It cannot be claimed that *Jamoytius* itself was the ancestor of the fishes because being of Silurian age, it was too late to be that ancestor. It does nevertheless show that animals were then still in existence of the type from which the fishes must have been derived, and for that reason *Jamoytius* represents a transitional form between the Proto-Chordates and the true vertebrates represented by the fishes.

The next group above the fishes is the amphibia, characterized by passing the earliest stages of their development in water before coming out on to land as adults. (Pl. 19, 209 and Chapter IV p. 160). Structurally, the chief differences between amphibia and fishes is that the former have five-fingered limbs instead of paired fins, that the median fin (which survives only in the young in water) has lost its skeletal support of rods, and that the system of sensory canals which serve for audio-location are lodged in grooves in the skin of the head instead of in tubes in the bones of the skull as in fishes. The Devonian fossil *Ichthyostega* had sensory canals in tubes in the bones of the skull, and skeletal supports to the median fin, but its limbs ended in five-fingered hands and feet. If it were not for this last character, *Ichthyostega* would inevitably have to be classified with the fishes, but this feature alone is sufficient to show that it belonged to the group of former fishes that had succeeded in breaking through to the new level of life on land (Pl. 209). Here again, *Ichthyostega* itself cannot be claimed as the direct ancestor of amphibia and all land-vertebrates because it is not old enough, and because it possesses some characters which show that it had already gone off on an evolutionary line different from that of the later land vertebrates. Nevertheless, it provides an example of what the transitional forms between fishes and amphibia were like.

The transition from the amphibian to the reptilian level of vertebrates was largely concerned with dropping out the aquatic early stages of development. Fertilization was internal and the egg was laid on dry land, protected by embryonic membranes and a shell (p. 162). None of these features would lend itself to detection in fossil specimens. At the same time, the reptiles raised the efficiency of many of the bodily processes, such as walking with the belly off the ground, breathing by means of movements of the ribs, and biting and chewing. The Permian fossil *Seymouria* is such a perfect mixture of amphibian and reptilian characters that it is difficult to decide to which group it belongs (Pl. 210). Signs of sensory canals indicate that it was still an amphibian and therefore that it had just failed to reach the reptilian level, but it is none the less invaluable as an example of the transitional stage between amphibians and reptiles.

The transition from reptiles to birds is shown in a manner better than could have ever been hoped for by the Jurassic fossil *Archaeopteryx*. This animal resembled the reptiles in having a long tail of twenty vertebrae, simple articulations between the vertebrae of the vertebral column, a simple brain like that of a lizard, and abdominal ribs. But it was already a bird because it had feathers, and they were arranged on the wing just as in modern birds. Its collar-bones were joined to form a furcula (wish-bone), and the first toe on each foot pointed backwards, showing that it was adapted to grasp branches and to perch on trees (Pl. 212–214). Nothing has so far

150

151

The word 'fossil' means something dug up from the ground. The body of a plant or animal may be preserved under layers of sediment, deposited in shallow seas, lakes, or rivers. Typical sedimentary rocks are limestone, sandstone and clay, and cliffs and quarries often show the successive layers of sedimentary rock clearly. 150. The relative ages of fossils can be arrived at from the relationships of the strata in which they are found, the oldest strata normally being the lowest, though this sequence can be disturbed by folding and faulting. The age of sedimentary rocks can be deduced from the age of minerals in neighbouring igneous rocks. 151. Some typical fossils in situ.

152

153

154

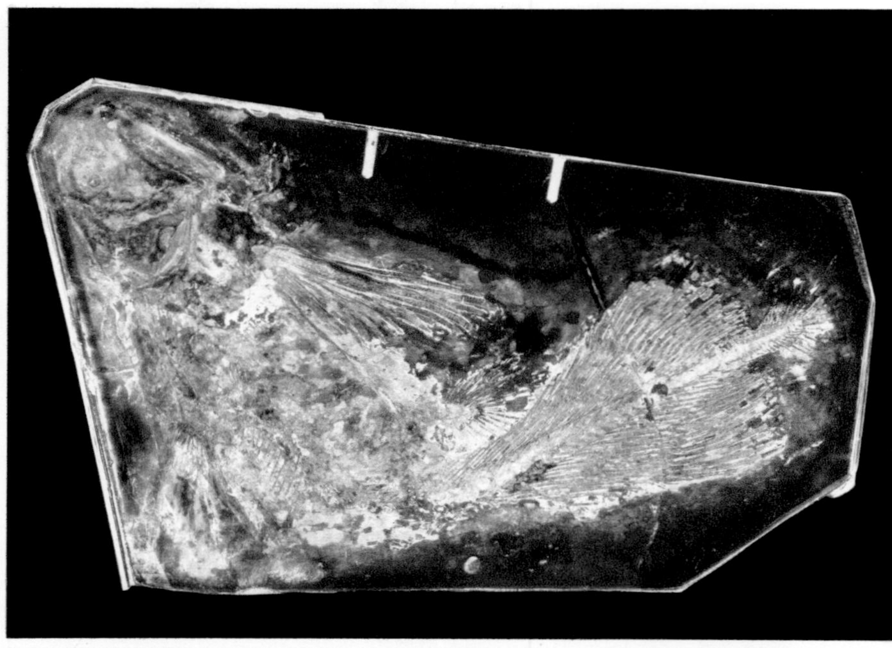
155

156

157

Fossils, Detail and Methods of Investigation

158

159

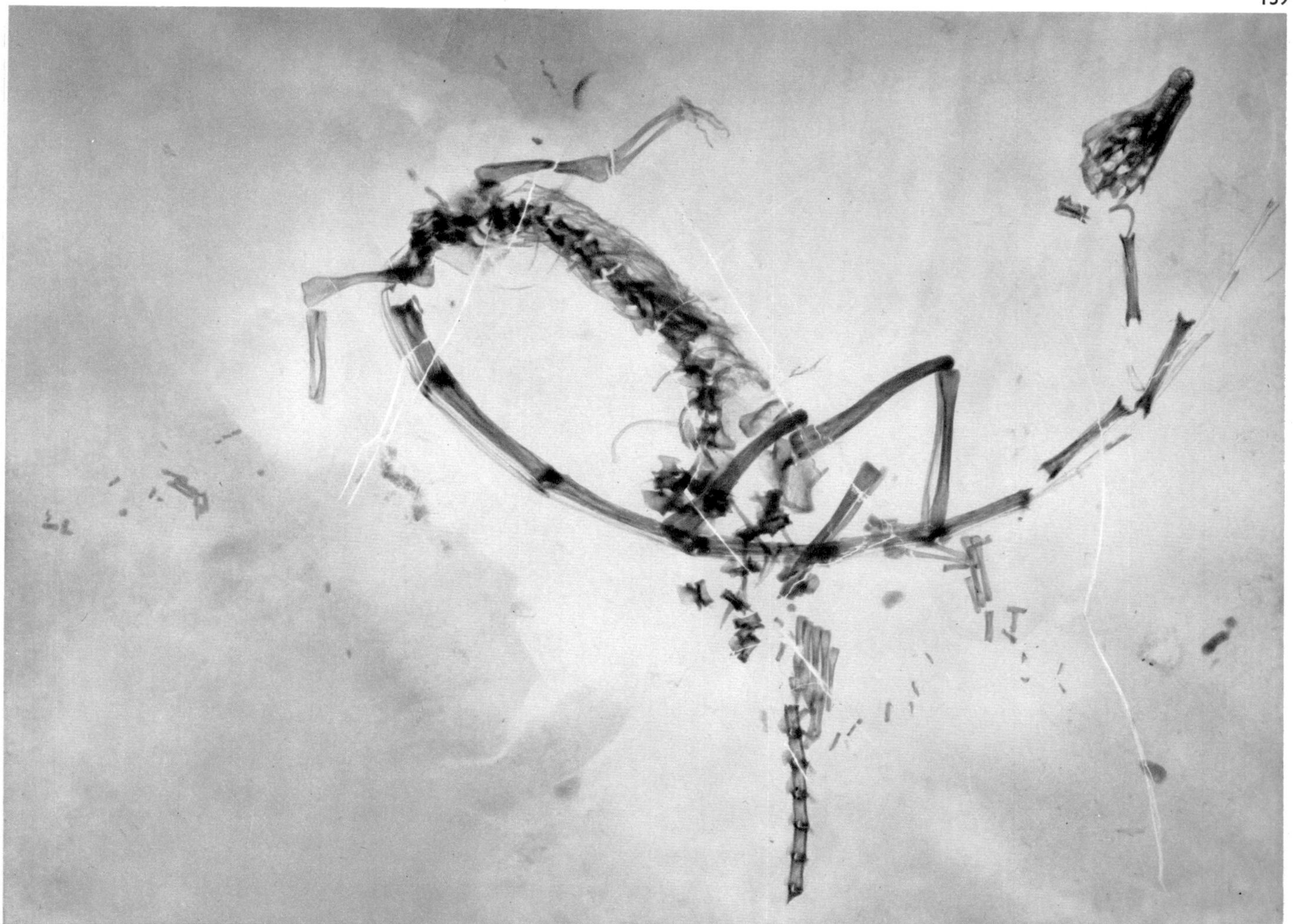

160

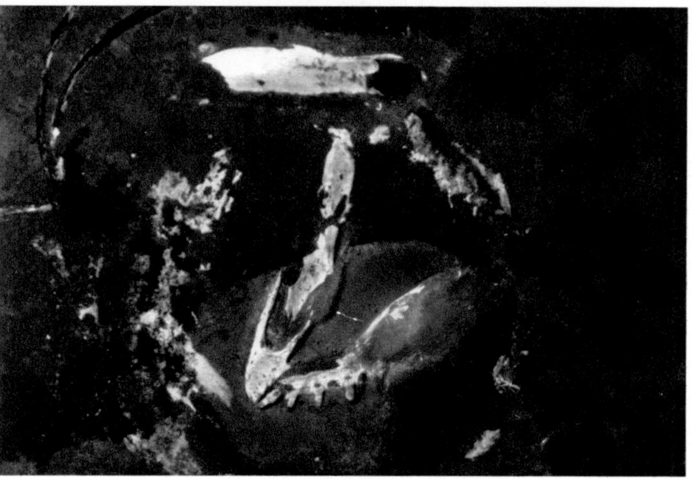

161

Fossils may be well preserved so that in some cases their structure is as well known as that of living organisms. **152.** Wing of a dragonfly (*Liassophlebia jacksoni*, Jurassic). **153.** Leaf of a flowering plant (Miocene). Special treatment is often required to reveal the structure. A method developed by the British Museum (Natural History) uses dilute acid to dissolve the surrounding matrix. **154.** Part of a fish-scale (*Pteraspis*, Devonian), thus treated, showing its minute structure and the sensory canals. **155.** A coelacanth (*Coccoderma suevicum*, Cretaceous) before, and **156,** after acid treatment from the back. Footprints of animals may be preserved **157.** A Triassic surface with prints of reptiles provisionally called *Chirotherium storetonense* (the larger ones) and *C. beasleyi*. X-ray photography of fossils in their matrix has been perfected in Zurich **158.** A lizard (*Askeptosaurus italicus*, Triassic), and **159,** the problematical reptile (*Tanystropheus longobardicus*, Triassic), with neck vertebrae so long that they were first taken for limbs. Ultra-violet light reveals bone by fluorescence **160,** jaws and teeth of a bird (*Archaeopteryx*, Jurassic), by ordinary light, and **161,** by ultra-violet light. The fossils illustrated on these pages have been particularly well preserved in spite of their age; some of them are 600 million years old. They serve not only to give information on the structure of the organisms to which they belonged, but also to identify the strata that were deposited at the time when they were fossilised. This information assists in the exploitation of mineral wealth, for deposits of coal, oil, and ores occur in particular geological formations that fossils enable prospectors to identify.

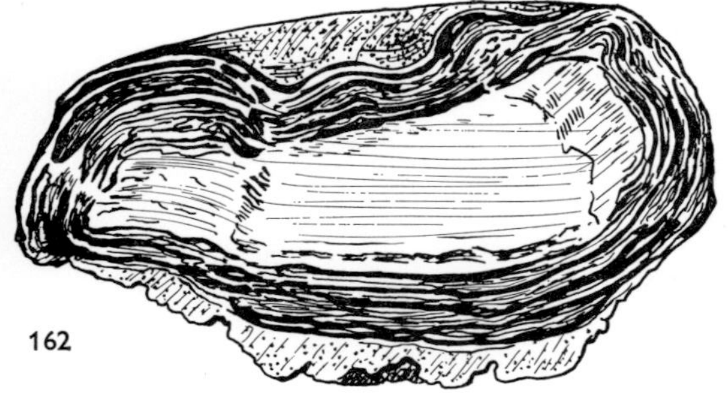

162

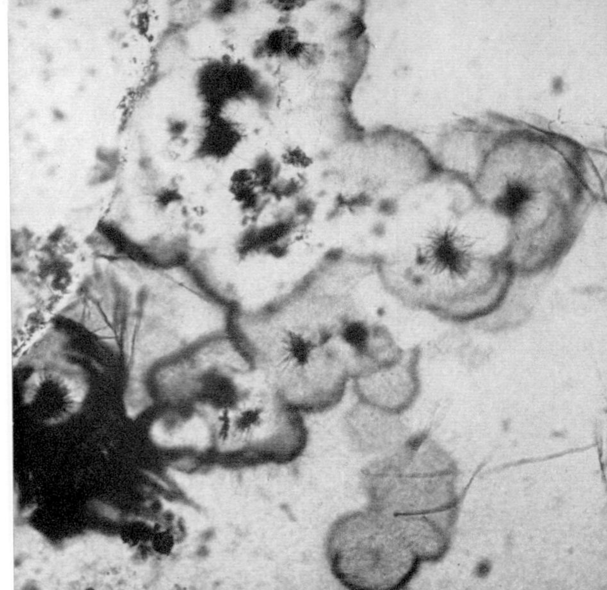

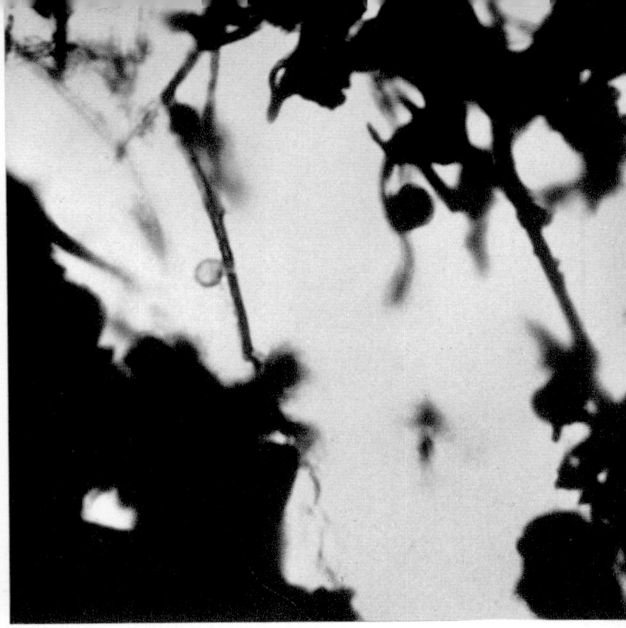

163

Pre-Cambrian Fossils

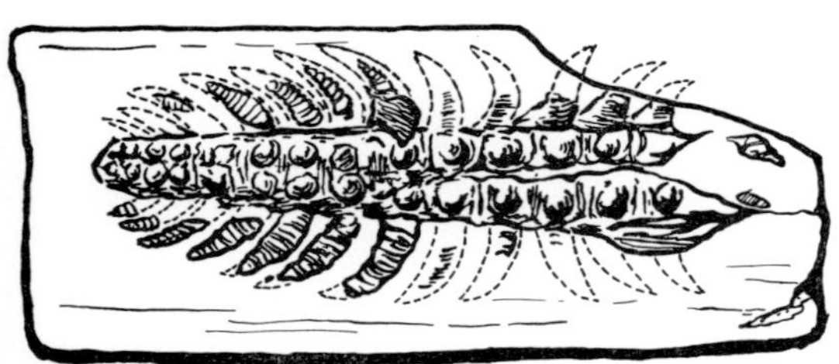

165

166

168

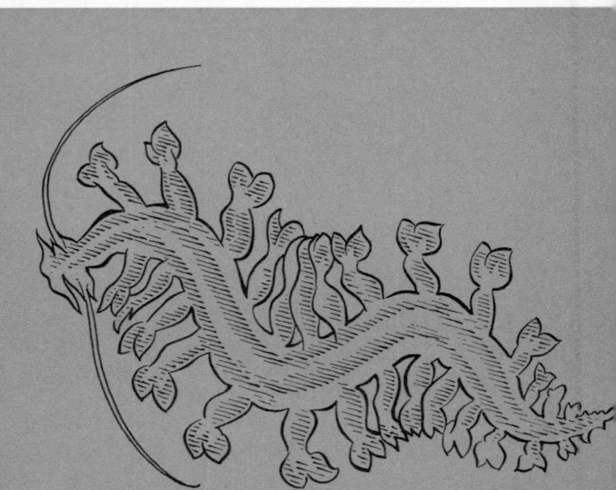

Contrary to general belief, Pre-Cambrian rocks are not entirely devoid of fossils, but they are rare, poorly preserved, and difficult to interpret. **162.** *Collenia*, a nodule of concentric layers of limestone, believed to have been secreted by a blue-green alga, Montana, U.S.A., 2,700 million years (m.y.) old. **163.** Filaments and colonial aggregates of an alga, Ontario, 1,700 m.y. **164.** Filaments and spores of fungi, Ontario, 1,700 m.y. **165.** *Xenusion*, a segmented animal related to annelids and arthropods, Sweden, 800 m.y. **166.** *Charnia*, a coelenterate resembling the sea-pens, Charnwood Forest, U.K., *c.* 650 m.y. and also found at Ediacara Hills, Australia, together with the following: **167.** *Ediacara*, a coelenterate jelly-fish; **168.** *Spriggina*, an annelid resembling **169,** *Tomopteris;* **170.** *Dickinsonia*, an annelid resembling **171,** *Aphrodite;* **172.** *Tribrachidium*, probably an echinoderm resembling the Cambrian fossil **173,** *Lepidodiscus*. **174.** *Parvancorina*, an organism of unknown type. In addition to these formed structures, Pre-Cambrian rocks supply evidence of former life where schists and graphites contain carbon isotopes in certain ratios.

170

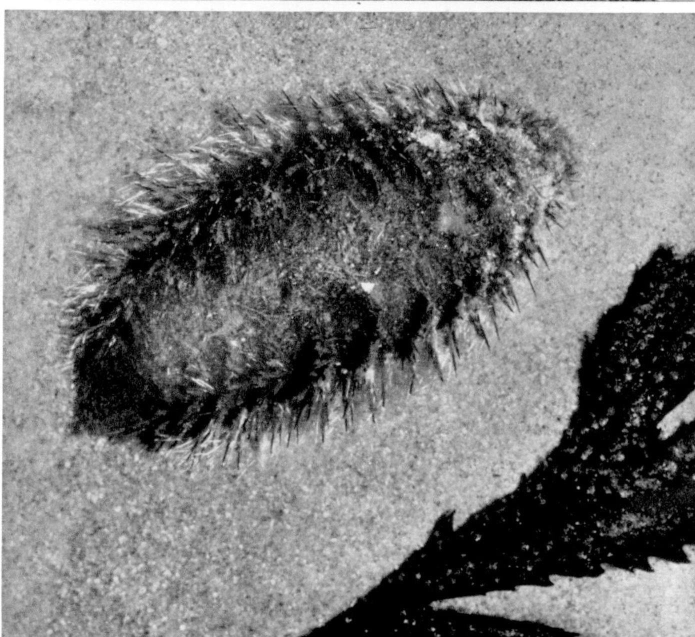

171

173

174

been discovered to disqualify *Archaeopteryx* from being regarded as on the direct line of descent from the reptilian crocodile-like ancestors to all modern birds. It is the most perfect case of a transitional form so far known.

From reptiles of another kind, mammals were evolved by progressive improvement and co-ordination of all the organ-systems in the body. The definition of a mammal as an animal which possesses hair, mammary glands, and three ear-ossicles including the incus and malleus representing the quadrate and articular hinge-bones of the jaws of reptiles, is arbitrary because the evolution of these structures was gradual. Nevertheless, in the Triassic Ictidosauria, fossils have been found which bridge the gap between the reptilian and mammalian conditions (Pl. 211).

Archaeopteryx is a good illustration of an important principle found in transitional forms. It was completely reptilian in those structures that reflected its reptilian ancestry, and completely bird-like in those structures in which it anticipated its descendants. The fact that individual features of this kind are not intermediate between the two classes concerned but clearly conform to the characteristics of one or the other is expressed by the term 'mosaic evolution'. Mosaic evolution can be recognized in the ancestry of man (p. 174) and also in the vegetable kingdom. In the seed-ferns or Pteridosperms the structure of the young stem and frond were like those of a true spore-bearing fern, that of the old stem resembled a cycad. The stamens were like the spore-bearing fronds of true ferns, but the seeds resembled those of cycads. A comparable mosaic of characters is found in the Bennettites where the compound stamens with a dense covering of flat scaly hairs resemble the spore-bearing fronds of a true fern (Pl. 187).

Lines of evolution

Research in palaeontology has revealed several sequences of fossils in continuous series without gaps, from which it is possible to follow the actual lines along which different groups of animals have evolved. The series are constructed by paying strict attention to stratigraphical sequence and finely graduated changes of structure. The speeds of evolution or rates at which forms have succeeded one another can be estimated from the ages of the rocks in which they are found as determined by measurement of radioactivity and other methods. Examples ofevolutionary lineages well worked out are to be found in trilobites, oysters, snails, ammonites, sea-urchins, horses, elephants, and camels. Here, one example will be given from invertebrates (ammonites) and one from vertebrates (horses).

The evolution of ammonites

Ammonites are an extinct group of shellfish, related to the modern squid, octopus, and nautilus, characterized by a spirally-coiled external shell wound into whorls. The inner whorls represent the body of the animal in its young stages of development, the outer whorls being added as it grew older. The evolution of ammonites can be illustrated by a line representing successively two families, the Liparoceratidae and Amaltheidae, which lived in the Liassic seas of the Lower Jurassic period about 175 million years ago. The time-span of the two families is roughly five million years. The succession of forms corresponds with the order of their appearance in the Liassic rocks. The sequence demonstrates not only evolutionary change but divergence into different evolutionary lines characterized by changes in the degree of overlapping of the whorls, size, and the development of ornament in the form of ribs and chevrons (Pl. 215).

The lineage of ammonites described lived at a time when the rate of evolution in ammonites was at its highest, passing through five genera in perhaps five million years, giving an average duration for a genus of one million years. In the preceding Triassic period ammonites had evolved very slowly.

It may be noticed that the changes which the ammonites underwent during their evolution were diverse and incoherent. They affected the thickness or thinness of the whorls, fine or coarse ribbing, chevron-pattern, and ornament among other characters, in a haphazard manner, without any programme. Although it is not possible to evaluate the significance of or to give the reasons for the changes the ammonites underwent, owing to lack of knowledge of the conditions of life under which they lived, it is nevertheless clear that the species changed into one another, and this is what evolution means.

The evolution of horses

The evolutionary history of the horses can be traced step by step through continuous series of fossils, showing their descent from a small four-toed browsing animal no bigger than a fox-terrier, into a large one-toed grazing animal, with corresponding changes in feet and teeth. The centre where this evolution took place was North America. In addition to the line which gave rise to modern horses, there were also some side lines at various periods which failed to survive (Col. Pl. 3). The following is based on G. G. Simpson.

The earliest identified ancestors of the horses lived in the Early Eocene period about 60 million years ago. *Hyracotherium* or *Eohippus* was about 11 inches high at the shoulder and had pads on its feet like a dog, with four toes on the front and three on the hind foot. The wrist and ankle joints were very flexible. Such limbs show that the animal was adapted for living and running on soft marshy ground. Its back was arched and flexible, its tail was long, and its hindquarters high. The grinding teeth were small, low-crowned, and suitable only for a diet of soft herbage on which the animal browsed. The four upper premolar teeth were triangular with three cusps, and the molars square with four cusps. The eye socket was situated about half-way back from the front of the skull.

175

Fossil plants

In the Carboniferous period, 350 m.y. ago plant life on land was luxuriant, as W. E. Spradbery's restoration **(175)** shows with true (spore-bearing) ferns, horsetails, Selaginellids, seed-ferns and primitive conifers of large tree size. **176.** Remains of a Carboniferous forest with stumps of *Lepidodendron* (Selaginellid). **184.** Reconstruction of a *Lepidodendron* tree. **185.** Piece of trunk of *Lepidodendron*. **178.** Part of stem of *Calamites* (horsetail), showing branch-scar. **179.** Leaf of *Neuropteris*, a seed-fern. **177.** Reconstruction of *Dorycordaites*, a gymnosperm related to conifers and ginkgos. The foregoing Carboniferous plants comprised the flora that gave rise to the most important coal deposits, by accumulation in swamps, conversion into peat, compression, and concentration of carbon through loss of water and gases. **180.** Leaf, and **181,** fructification of *Glossopteris* (Permian). **182.** Leaf of *Ginkgo* (Jurassic), the maiden-hair tree that remains unchanged today **(183)**. **186.** Part of the stem or trunk of *Araucarites* (Lower Cretaceous), gymnosperm 'monkey-puzzle'. **187.** Stem of *Bennettites* (Lower Cretaceous), gymnosperm related to cycads showing leaf-bases.

176

178
179 180
177
181
182 183
184
185
186
187

Fossil Invertebrates

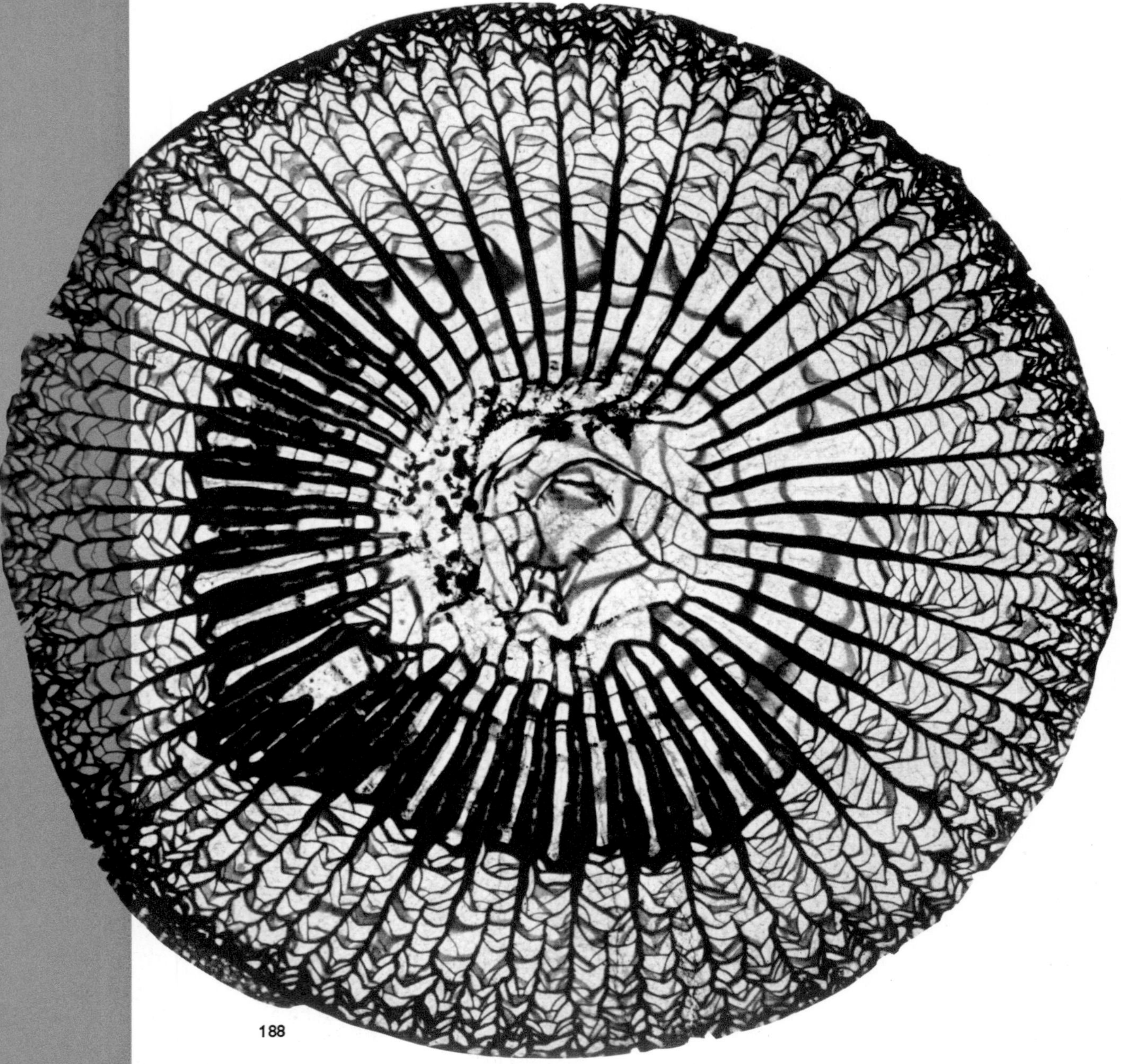

Invertebrate fossils. **188.** *Caninia ovibos* (Permian, Melville Is., Arctic), coral; corals supply information on their climate because they require clear shallow seas and temperature not below 21° C. **189.** *Xystridura saint-smithi* (Cambrian, Queensland). Trilobites are the dominant fossils of early Palaeozoic strata. **190.** *Gissocrinus goniodactylus* (Silurian, Wales), crinoid or 'sea-lily', stalked echinoderm; between the two specimens a curled-up trilobite is lodged. **191.** *Eurypteris fischeri* (Silurian, Scotland), 'sea-scorpion', dominant predators of the time reaching 100 cm in length. **192.** *Medusina boulengeri* (Carboniferous, Belgium), 'jelly-fish', rarely preserved because of its soft tissues. **193.** *Limulus ornatus* (Jurassic, Germany), 'king-crab', a genus that persists to the present. **194.** *Euhoplites truncatus* (Cretaceous, England), ammonite with complex suture-lines and ribs. **195.** *Hoploparia stokesii* (Cretaceous, Antarctica), lobster, contemporary specimens of which are found in England. **196.** *Rusinga* (Miocene, Africa), millipede.
They are already highly evolved invertebrate animals, and their sudden wholesale appearance in Cambrian strata, the oldest fully fossiliferous formation, presented Darwin with a difficulty, for if they really were the earliest-formed strata, evolution would have to be abandoned. Actually, Pre-Cambrian fossils, hundreds of millions of years older than Cambrian, are now well known (162-174).

188

189

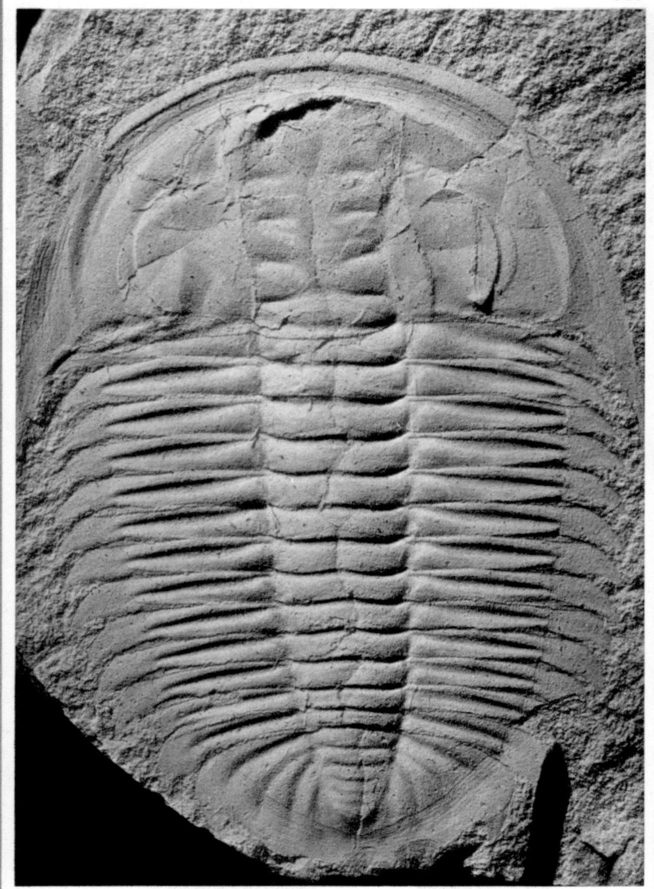

190

191 194 192 195

193 196

By the Middle Eocene period about 50 million years ago, a small change had taken place in the grinding teeth and the upper fourth premolar had become square with four cusps like the molars. This change shows that the line *Eohippus* had now passed into the condition of a new genus, and this stage is called *Orohippus*. The same process was carried a stage further in the Late Eocene period about 45 million years ago when the third premolar had become square and molar-like. This stage is known as *Epihippus*.

In the Lower Oligocene period, 40 million years ago, the animals had increased in size and were about 24 inches high at the shoulder. The front part of the head was beginning to elongate and the eye socket was situated about three-fifths of the way back from the front of the skull. Meanwhile, other changes had taken place. In the teeth, the second premolar had four cusps, which means that all six upper grinding teeth were alike, and the grinding surface of the teeth showed a few crests linking the cusps. In the legs, the ankle and wrist joints were firmer and allowed movement only in the plane of advance; the weight of the body was still carried by pads as well as toes, but there were only three toes on the fore foot, and three on the hind. This stage is called *Mesohippus*.

In the Upper Oligocene period, 30 million years ago, the size of the animal had increased further and *Miohippus* was 30 inches high at the shoulder.

In the Miocene period, beginning 25 million years ago, the change in the form of the feet already foreshadowed in earlier stages was continued. Fossil grass seeds in Miocene rocks show that grass had become plentiful, and this means that there was hard dry ground. The pads were lost in the feet and the weight was carried by the three toes, of which the middle toe was the largest, with a spring mechanism that bounced the animal forwards. The skull shows that the front of the head was developing into the muzzle used for cropping grass. Meanwhile, a new set of changes was beginning to take place in the teeth. Premolars and molars were similar, the crown of these teeth were twice as high as before, and their grinding surfaces were developed into deep furrows in which was deposited an additional growth of bone, called 'cement'. The result was that the surface of the teeth wore down to ridges according to the different hardness of the enamel, dentine, and cement of which they were composed, and formed efficient millstones adapted to grind the new food on which horses were now feeding, namely grass. Grass contains a very hard substance, silica, which would (and no doubt did) wear down the teeth of the primitive browsing horses until they were unserviceable and the animals were unable to feed. The growth in height of the grinding teeth of the new grazing horses protected them from this calamity. In the Early Miocene *Parahippus*, which arose from the preceding *Miohippus*, traces of the browsing type still remained, but in the

Late Miocene *Merychippus* into which *Parahippus* had turned, the grinding tooth-pattern of grazing horses was fully established. *Merychippus* was 40 inches high.

In the Pliocene period, 10 million years ago, *Merychippus* had turned into *Pliohippus* in which the lateral toes were finally lost. The weight of the animal was then carried entirely on one enlarged toe on each leg, the last joint of which was expanded into a hoof. To all extents and purposes, the condition of the modern *Equus* had then been reached. This arose from *Pliohippus* in the Pleistocene period in North America, one million years ago, and dispersed into the Old World where it gave rise to the true horses, asses, zebras, and quagga. In North America, however, *Equus* went extinct and horses were re-introduced into the American continent by the Spaniards.

The transition from *Eohippus* to the modern horse thus took 60 million years during which the evolving stock passed through the stages of eight genera and some thirty species. The series therefore enables the duration of genera and species in these mammals to be estimated at seven-and-a-half million years and two million years respectively.

This would, however, be a gravely incomplete and misleading account of the evolution of horses if it were restricted to a description of the one devious line of descent from *Eohippus* that has survived to the present day and produced the modern horse. During the 60 million years that have passed since *Eohippus* lived, there were a dozen other divergent lines of descent from it which branched off at different periods and persisted for shorter or longer times, but all went extinct sooner or later. It is just as important to study these failures as the one success, because the record of evolution is mostly one of extinction.

From *Mesohippus* there arose in addition to *Parahippus* a line of horses represented by the Miocene *Anchitherium* and its descendant *Hypohippus*. These animals continued the programme of evolution that had characterized the transition from *Eohippus* to *Miohippus* and remained three-toed, browsing animals. From them one line became the large *Megahippus*, another became the dwarf *Archaeohippus*, which shows that variation was widespread. All of these, however, died out early in the Pliocene period and the reason for this is the same as that which resulted in the success of *Merychippus*; flinty grass to eat meant that horses with high-crowned grinding teeth survived and those without died. This is evidence not only for evolution but for natural selection.

The same principle is seen in offshoots from *Merychippus* such as *Hipparion* which carried to its extreme the lengthening of the molar teeth and complication of the grinding surface, but it remained three-toed and died out in the Pliocene period. The same fate overtook a dwarf variant, *Nannipus*. This means that at this stage horses with single toes were better able to run on hard ground.

Finally, from *Pliohippus* in addition to *Equus* there arose *Hippidion*, a one-toed horse with high-crowned grinding teeth, which invaded South America in the Pliocene period. In the Pleistocene period, however, *Equus* itself invaded South America and *Hippidion*, which was short-legged, gave way before it and died out.

A comparison between the failures and the successes in the evolution of the horses shows that the retention of characters which were once useful is penalized if they are kept beyond the time when new environmental conditions require a change. The line which led from *Eohippus* to *Equus* did not continue the same old trends in regard to teeth and then to toes, but zig-zagged, first in the direction of many-toed browsers with low-crowned teeth, next in that of many-toed grazers with high crowned teeth, and finally of one-toed grazers. There was increase in size, but it was not regular or constant. It was not the fulfilment of any single anatomical programme of improvement that led to survival, but opportune variations in directions that enabled the animals to cope with changed conditions of existence and to compete successfully with less well adapted rivals.

It is only by means of evolution that extinction may be, but is not always, successfully side-stepped or postponed in the incessant series of crises to which organisms are exposed. The zig-zag course of evolution that can be shown to have occurred in ammonites, horses, and in many other groups illustrates a principle of great importance. When evolutionary lineages were first traced, some palaeontologists, drawing premature conclusions from incomplete evidence, thought that they could discern trends of evolution in constant directions, such as increase in size, lengthening of teeth, or reduction of toes, to explain which they imagined that there was a force which secured evolution according to a programme, in straight lines, and they called it 'orthogenesis'. Critical study of fossil lineage on adequate material shows beyond question that 'orthogenesis' is nothing but a product of the imagination and that evolution fulfils no predetermined programme at all. It is controlled and directed at every stage by the selective factors of the environment which allow some types to survive and others not, as will be shown in Chapter Three.

In this chapter, ten different branches of science have been consulted on the question whether evolution of plants and animals has occurred, and it has. Studies in palaeontology have shown how floras and faunas have changed and succeeded each other, and in many cases the actual path of evolution from ancestor to descendant has been demonstrated, step by step, species by species, so that the rates of evolution in different lineages can be measured. In addition, as will be shown (p. 121), experiments in genetics have proved that man has been able to copy nature.

With the cumulative evidence now available, however, with the reality of evolution established by the production of new species in the laboratory, and the course of evolution shown in the record of the rocks, it would be as reasonable to deny the fact of evolution as to believe that the earth was flat and the sun went round it.

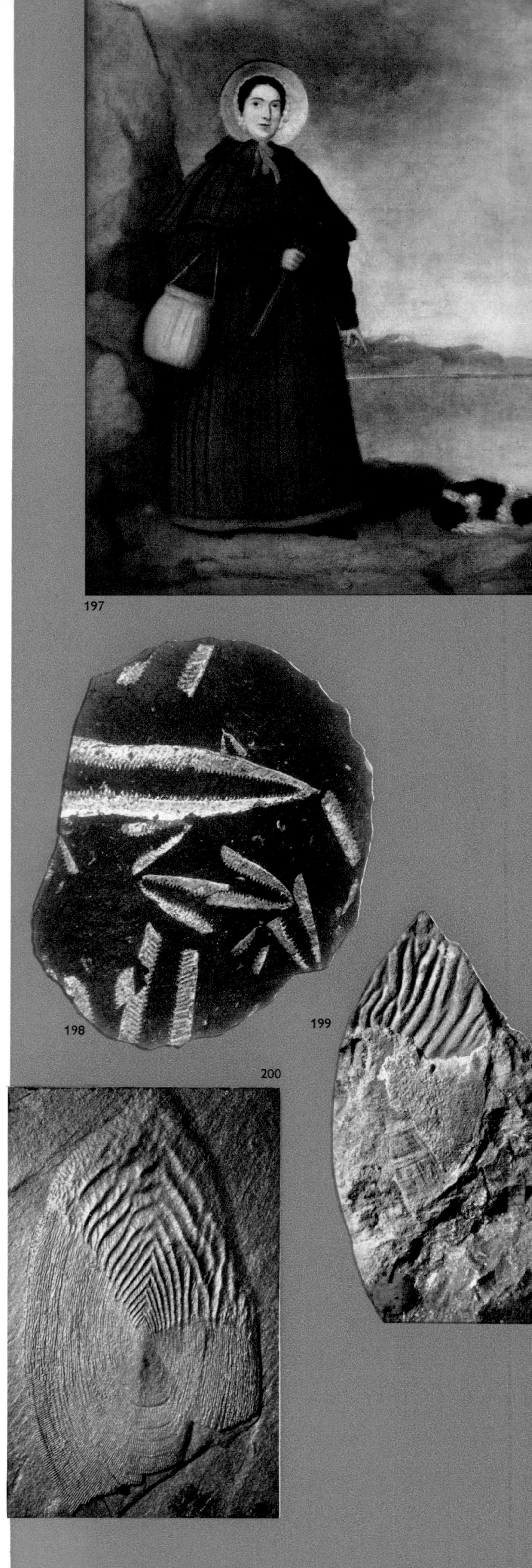

197

198

199

200

Fossil Vertebrates

201

202

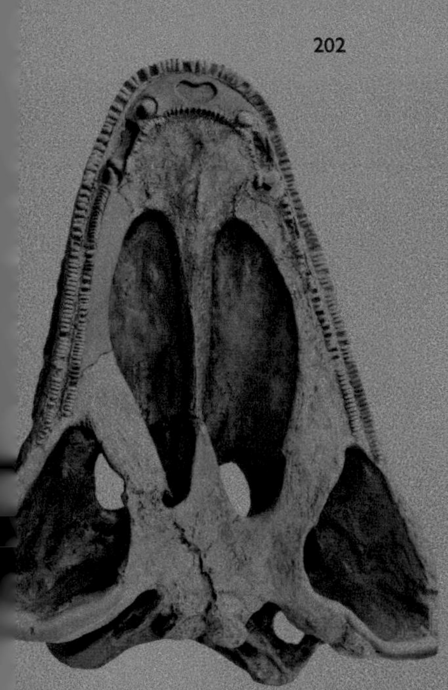

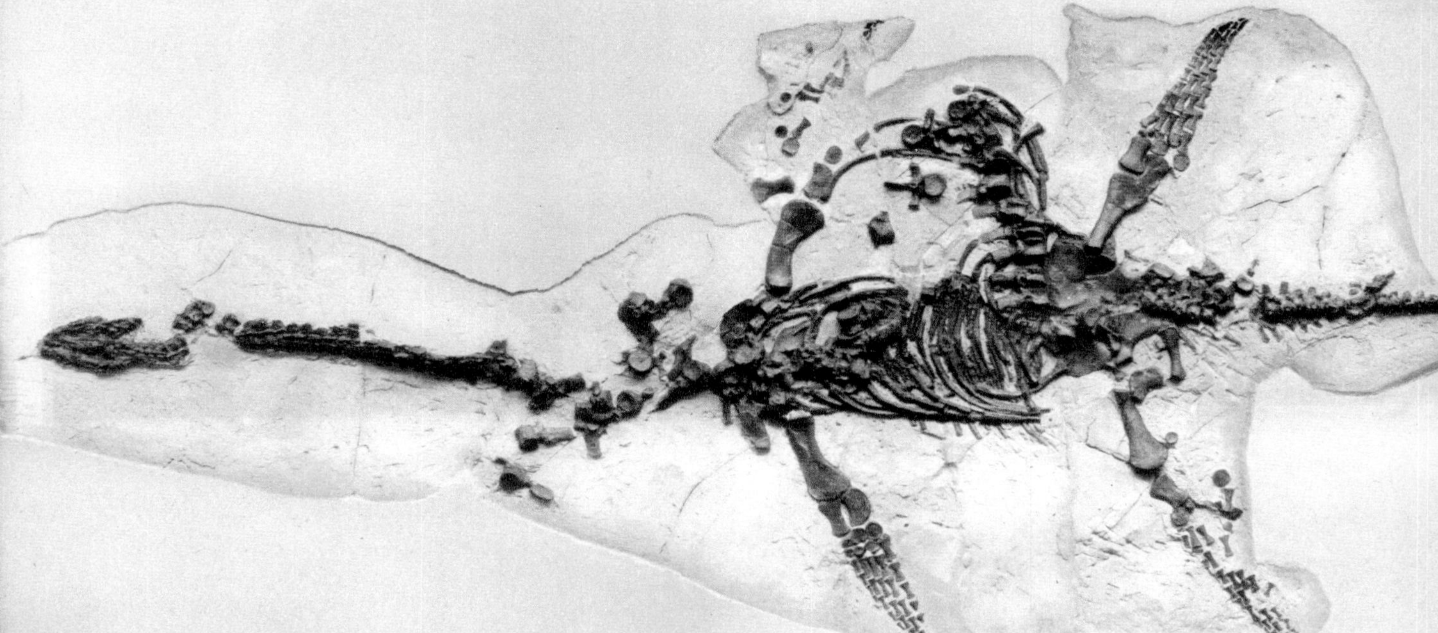

203

204

205

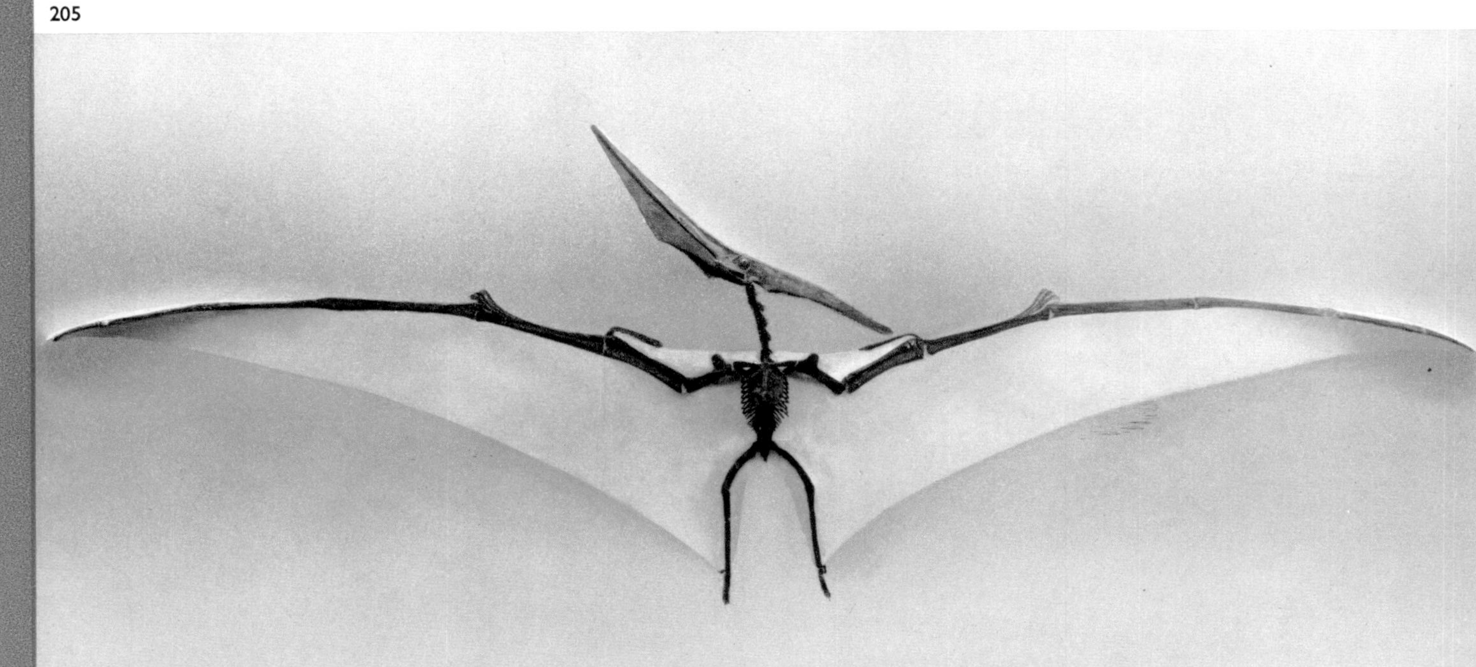

197. Mary Anning (1799-1847) of Lyme Regis, Dorset, England, who at the age of 11 found the first known associated skeleton of *Ichthyosaurus* and later did the same for *Plesiosaurus* and the first discovered Pterosaur in Great Britain. At that time Lyme Regis was on one of the coach routes to the West of England, and the fossils that Mary Anning sold to travellers helped to disseminate knowledge and public interest in them. **198.** *Didymograptus murchisoni* (Ordovician, Wales), graptolite, related to Chordates. **199.** *Holoptychius flemingi* (Devonian, England), Crossopterygian fish. A scale brought up from a bore-hole at Southall proved that there is no coal under London as the coal-bearing strata had been passed. **200.** Scale of *Rhizodopsis sauroides* (Carboniferous, England), indicator of coal. **201.** *Latimeria chalumnae*, 'living fossil' coelacanth. **202.** Palatal view of skull of *Paracyclotosaurus davidi* (Triassic, Australia), enormous amphibian, reconstructed in the British Museum (Natural History) by pouring plaster into the natural mould in the rock matrix. **203.** *Plesiosaurus dolichodeirus* (Lower Jurassic, England). **204.** *Ichthyosaurus acutirostris* (Lower Jurassic, England). **205.** *Pteranodon longiceps* (Upper Cretaceous, Kansas), pterosaur with a wing-span of 25 feet.

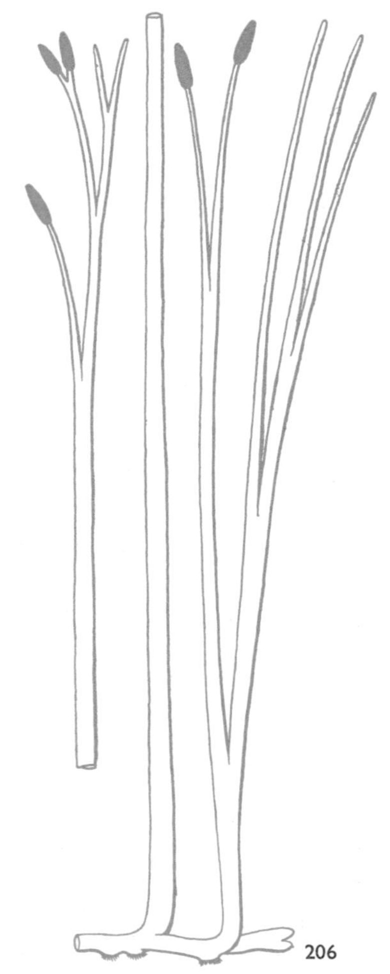
206

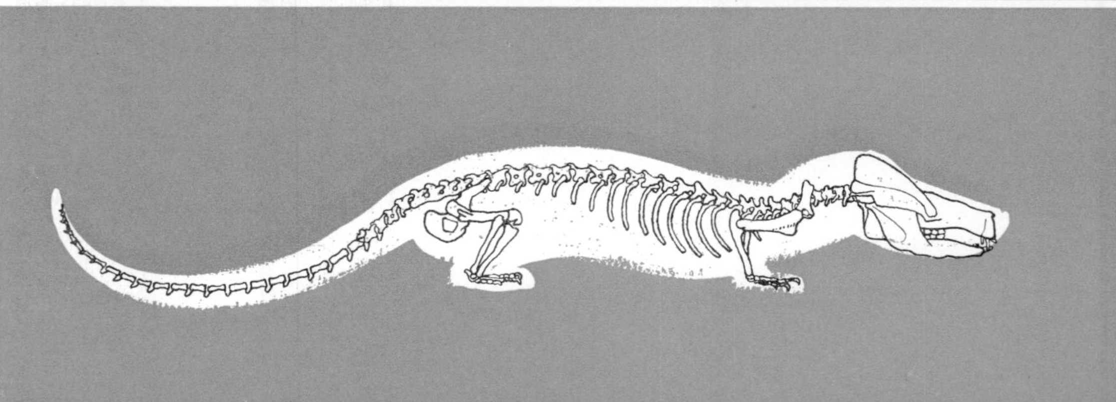

207

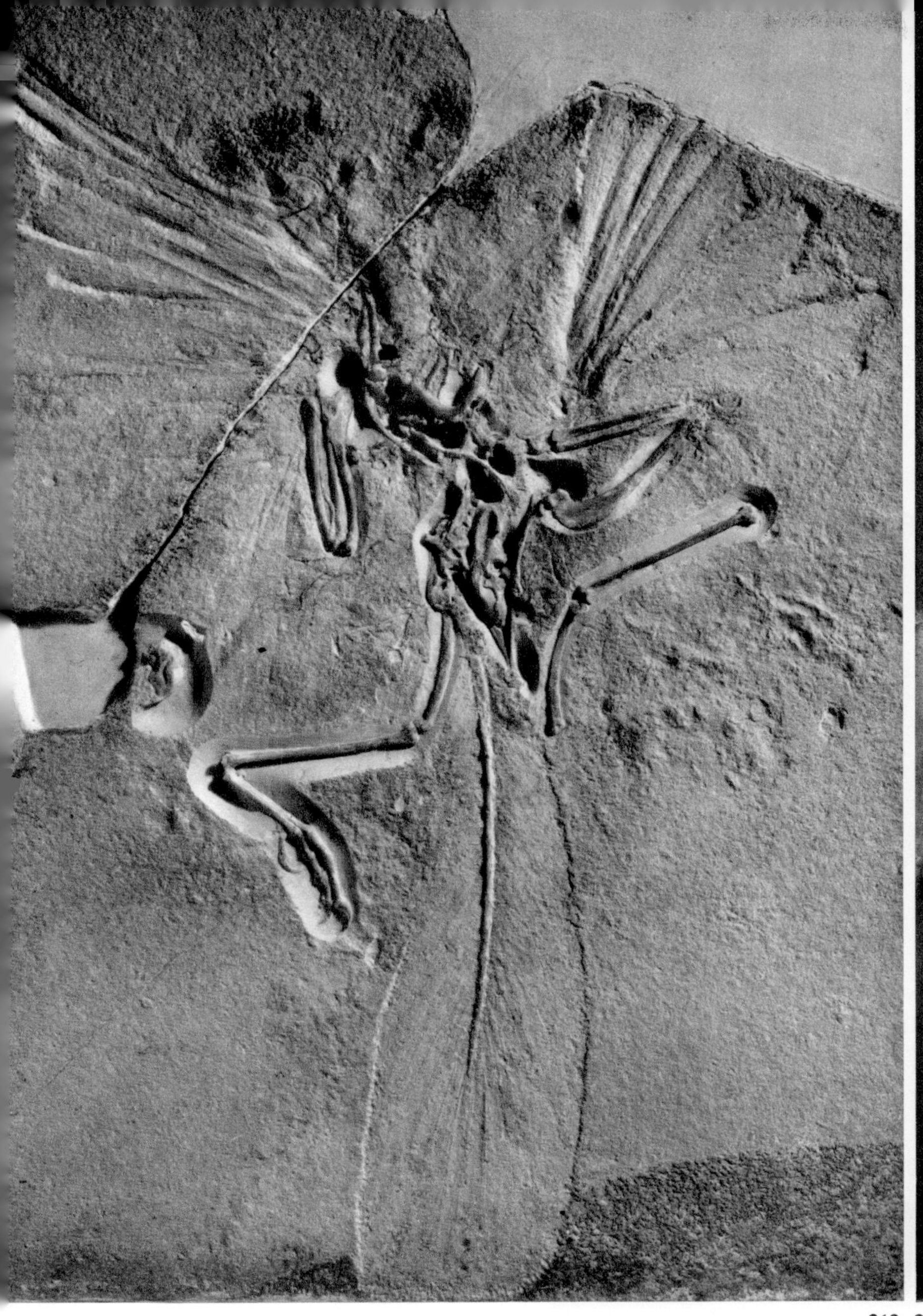

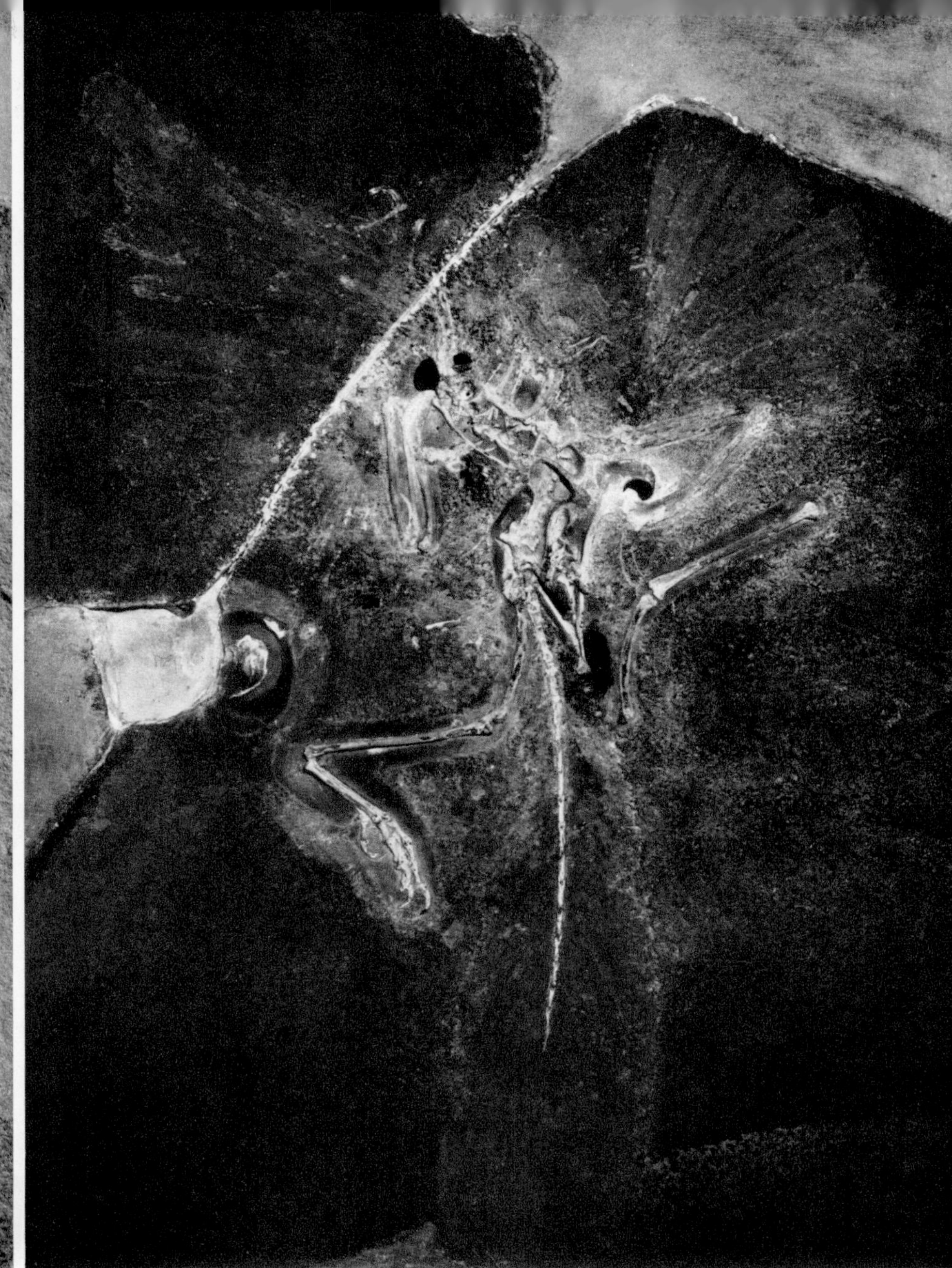

212 213

Precursors and Transitional Forms

The earliest known land plants. **206.** *Rhynia* (Devonian) showing stems and branches ending in groups of spores and an interconnecting underground rhizome but no roots. **207.** *Asteroxylon* (Devonian) with rudimentary leaves.

Precursor and transitional forms leading to the five classes of vertebrates. **208.** *Jamoytius* (Silurian) with continuous lateral fin-fold from which paired fins of fishes evolved. **209.** *Ichthyostega* (Devonian) showing 5-toed limbs on an otherwise fish-like anatomy. **210.** *Seymouria* (Permian) a mosaic of amphibian and reptilian characters. **211.** *Oligokyphus* (Ictidosaur, Triassic) in which the hinges of the jaws and ear-ossicles are intermediate between the reptilian and mammalian conditions (97). **212.** *Archaeopteryx* (Jurassic) a perfect mosaic of reptilian (long tail, claws on forelimbs, simple brain and vertebrae), and avine characters (feathers, wing, furcula, grasping feet). **213.** The same under ultra-violet light. **214.** A reconstruction. These transitional forms illustrate mosaic evolution: some parts retain completely ancestral characters, other parts are equally completely descendental, showing that the transformation of different parts of the body took place more or less independently in the evolution from one type of organism to another.

214

Lines of Evolution: Ammonites

Pleuroceras hawkserense

Pleuroceras yeovilense

Pleuroceras spinatum

Pleuroceras solare

Pleuroceras transiens

Amaltheus gibbosus

Amaltheus subnodosus

Amauroceras lenticulare

Pseudoamalthe
engelhardti

Amauroceras ferrugineum

Amauroceras wertheri

Amaltheus stokesii

Amaltheus bifurcus

Amaltheus margaritatus

215. Lines of evolution in ammonites in successive strata of Lias (Jurassic). *Liparoceras cheltiense* from the Lower Lias starts the series with large thick whorls, the inner overlapped by the outer. *Androgynoceras maculatum* with whorls more slender, not overlapping, and ribs more strongly marked. *Oistoceras figulinum* with ribs reflected forward on the back of the whorls forming chevrons when seen end-on. *Amaltheus stokesii*, with whorls laterally compressed and chevrons duplicated. From *stokesii* three evolutionary lines diverge. First *Amaltheus margaritatus* leading to *Pseudoamaltheus engelhardti* in which the original ribs and chevrons have been lost and a new spiral ribbing evolved. Second, *Amauroceras lenticulare*, a degenerate line in which all ornament is lost and the shell is smooth. Third, *Pleuroceras solare* with whorls quadrangular in cross section, leading to *Pleuroceras spinatum* with massive whorls and ribs. All lines became extinct in the Upper Lias; time-span *c.* 5 m.y.

Oistoceras figulinum

Androgyroceras maculatum

Liparoceras naptonense

Androgyroceras subhybrida

Liparoceras nautiliforme

Liparoceras gallicum

Liparoceras contractum

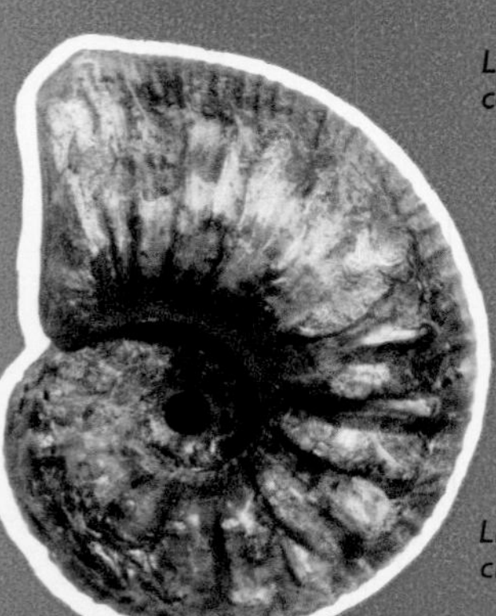

Liparoceras cheltiense

Chapter III HOW EVOLUTION WORKS

As a result of a century of research, it is now possible to give a succinct definition of evolution and of its causes. The evolution of plants and animals is brought about by the occurrence of heritable *variation*, due to *mutation* and *recombination* of Mendelian *genes*, such variation being acted upon by *natural selection* and resulting in changes in portions of *populations isolated* by geographical or other factors, leading to gradual improvement in the *adaptation* of individuals to their environment and to progressive divergence between different portions of populations until the differences between them prevent them from interbreeding, in which condition they have undergone *speciation*, or, in other words, have become different species.

This statement is deliberately terse, but it will be found useful as a guiding thread through a series of descriptions of results of scientific observations and experiments which may be unfamiliar. The remainder of this chapter will be devoted to an expansion of this statement by providing illustrations of and evidence for each of the principles concerned.

VARIATION

Plants and animals occur in populations of interbreeding individuals constituting groups known as species. They do not exist in any other condition. While each species has definable characteristics of form, habit, and life-history, the populations constituting species are not composed of identical individuals. Parents and offspring, brothers and sisters are never quite alike, and the differences between them are referred to as variation. Adequate knowledge of a species demands not only a definition of its mean or average structure and normal life-history, but also an estimate of the amount by which members of the species can differ from the average, which will provide a measure of the variation which the species shows in its normal environment.

Some species show little variation; others are very variable. No two plants of the same species in the same flower-bed are exactly alike. Starfish normally have five arms, but in the species *Oreaster reticulatus* the number of arms may be four, five, six or seven (Pl. 218). In the common snail *Cepaea nemoralis* some shells show dark-coloured bands while others are clear. The bands vary in number between one and five. The bands may be all separate and distinct, or they may fuse and become confluent. In clear-coloured shells, the colour may be dark or pale pink, or dark or pale yellow, or brown.

The species in which variation is most apparent is that which is best known: the human species (Pl. 220, 254). No two men have the same fingerprints. The rate at which the heart beats in different adult people may vary by a factor of 2:3, nearly two-and-a-half times. The number of blood-platelets in the blood may vary by a factor of 4:6. Some people have 1:9 times more phosphate concentrated in their blood than others. The minimum concentration of alcohol in the blood producing a state of intoxication may be eight times greater in one person than in another. The activity of the thyroid gland in different people may vary by a factor of 6:2. The so-called normal man is a rare specimen, as G. Hardin has stressed.

Variation is no recent phenomenon of degeneration; it is not confined to living plants and animals, for it is found in fossils. For instance, in the lamp-shell *Epithyris oxonica* of the Jurassic period, 150 million years ago, the line of closure between the two valves of the shell may be straight, or slightly, or markedly undulated. In the sea-urchin, *Micraster coranguinum* of the Cretaceous period, 100 million years ago, variation between different individuals may be seen affecting the shape and structure of any part of the body.

Causes of variation

Variation may be caused by changes in the environment in which the plant or animal lives or by changes in the hereditary constitution, or, most commonly, by a combination of both these causes. So much misapprehension exists regarding the relative importance of heredity and environment, or of nature and nurture, in controlling the production of a living individual, that it is necessary to go into this question in some detail before proceeding further.

Every living plant or animal is the result of the reaction of a particular genetic make-up inherited from its parents to the environment in which it lives and develops. Every living plant and animal is thus the joint product of heredity and environment. Neither hereditary factors nor environmental factors, by themselves, are capable of producing a living organism at all. The simplest proof of this statement is provided by experiments on the development of paired eyes in fishes. That vertebrate animals have possessed paired eyes, one on each side of the head, for a very long period of time is known from the fossils of fish-like vertebrates found in rocks of the Silurian period, 500 million years ago, which possessed paired eyes. It might be thought that after such a very long period of time, the possession of paired eyes was 'fixed' in the inheritance of vertebrates. But when fish-embryos are made to develop in water containing added magnesium chloride, they develop into fish with one median eye like a Cyclops instead of fish with a normal pair of eyes. The same experiment also shows that although fishes have lived in the same environment for 500 million years, this length of time has not enabled the environmental factors to 'fix' the character of paired eyes (Pl. 219).

A comparable experiment was performed when a sparrow fledgling, less than one day old, was rescued, nursed, and reared in her home by Clare Kipps. In sharp distinction to sparrows in their normal environment, 'Clarence' developed, in place of the simple chirrups and calls of his normal brethren, two real bird songs as a result of her playing the piano, walked with alternate steps, as no other sparrow has been known to do, instead of hopping, lay with pleasure on his back, played, scolded, bullied, 'acted', developed a fetishism for her hairpins, and showed devoted affection to his human foster-mother. None of these characters would have developed if he had been reared in his mother's nest (Pl. 217).

The meaning of these fundamental experiments is that all characters are the result of interaction between the innate and inherited factors of heredity and the external factors of the environment. No character owes its existence to either heredity or environment alone. The factors of inheritance can control the development of normal characters only if the environmental factors in which the development takes place are also normal. If either set of factors is abnormal, the characters of the developed organism must be abnormal.

Strictly speaking, characters are not 'inherited' at all; nor are they 'acquired'. What is inherited is the capacity of a given genetic make-up to react or respond in certain determined ways to normal and abnormal environmental conditions. The limits to possible variation caused by changed environmental factors are set by the genetic make-up, and the final product of any genetic make-up is conditioned by the environmental factors to which it is exposed. The genetic make-up of an organism is known as its *genotype*, which is determined by the hereditary factors or *genes* that it has inherited from its parents in the germ-cells which have produced it. What the organism actually looks like is known as its *phenotype*, which is the result of the reaction between its genotype and the factors of the environment. A given genotype can therefore give rise to a number of different phenotypes, which also change with age. The stages through which an organism passes during its life-history from embryo to adult are different phenotypes of the same genotype. In the example of the paired eyes of fish already described, the genotype produces a phenotype with normal paired eyes in a normal environment, but it produces a phenotype with a median single eye when the environment is rendered abnormal by the addition of magnesium chloride.

The use of the terms genotype and phenotype aids clarity in considering the cause of variation. Whether any given variation exhibited by a phenotype is due to a change in the genotype inherited from the parents, or to a change in the environmental factors without any change in the genotype, can be determined only by experiment. If a variation appears only when the conditions of the environment are changed (as when a plant is moved from one climate to another), and disappears when the conditions of the environment are made to revert to what they were before (as when the plant is brought back to its original climate), the variation is non-heritable, and as it is not built into the genotype, it provides no permanent step on which evolutionary change can be based. Variation of this kind is known as *phenotypic*, and examples of it are called *modifications*.

If a variation appears without any change in the conditions of the environment, and if this variation continues to appear in the offspring as a result of breeding experiments, the variation is heritable and liable to provide a permanent step on which evolutionary change may be built. Variation of this kind is known as *genotypic* and examples of it are called *mutations*.

The causes of variation may therefore be classified as phenotypic and genotypic, due respectively to environmental change and to genetic change; but it must not be forgotten that the genotype plays a part in phenotypic variation by prescribing the limits between which it can occur, and that the environment plays a part in genotypic variation by providing the factors against which the genotype reacts.

Variation, Selection, Evolution

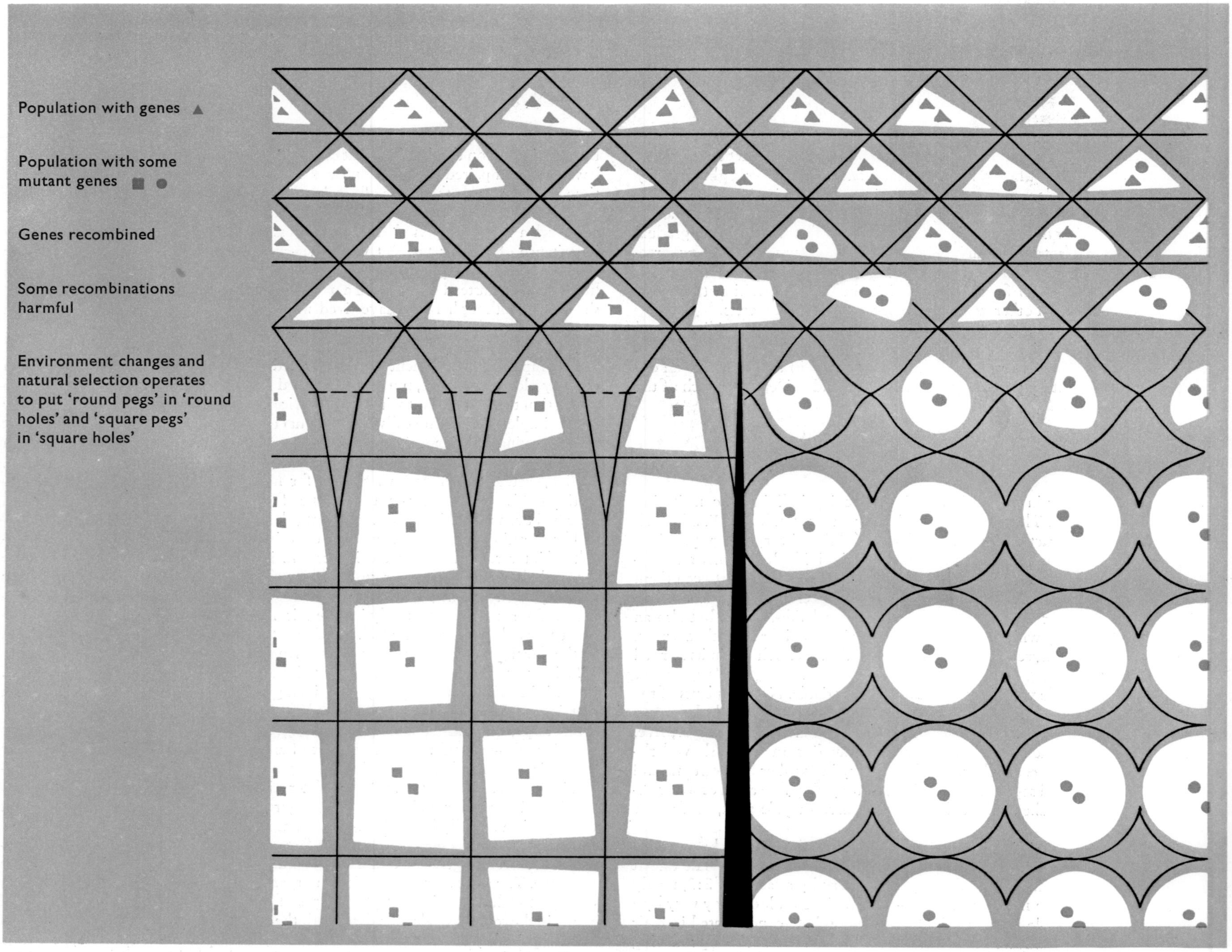

Population with genes ▲

Population with some mutant genes ■ ●

Genes recombined

Some recombinations harmful

Environment changes and natural selection operates to put 'round pegs' in 'round holes' and 'square pegs' in 'square holes'

216

217

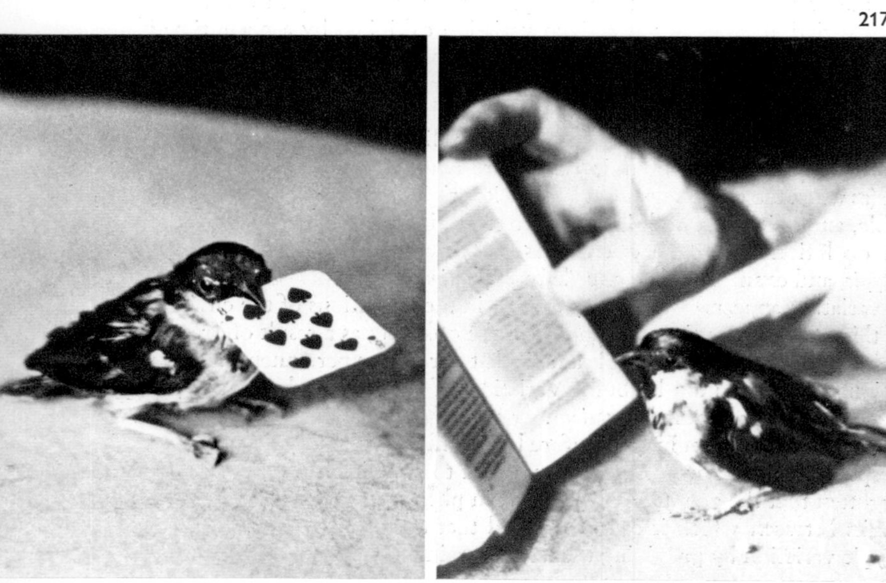

216. Diagrammatic representation of evolution as a result of variation due to mutation (shown as change from triangular to square and round 'genes'), followed by recombination (triangular with triangular, triangular with square, triangular with round, square with square, square with round, round with round), resulting in different genotypes, some disadvantageous and others advantageous when subjected to changed environmental conditions (shown by disappearance of triangular 'ecological niches' and appearance of square and round 'ecological niches'). Under the action of natural selection the different genotypes are forced into the 'ecological niches' to which they are best adapted, the population becomes divided into two isolated portions which diverge, and each will eventually give rise to a different species. **217.** The effect of changed environment on a fledgling sparrow brought up in a human household, showing phenotypic variations from normal sparrows in gait, song, and general behaviour that would never have occurred in nature. **218.** Genotypic variation in the starfish *Oreaster reticulatus* that may have four, five, six, or seven arms. Since this variation does not prove disadvantageous for any one form the pressure of the environment has not eliminated any, and all forms occur.

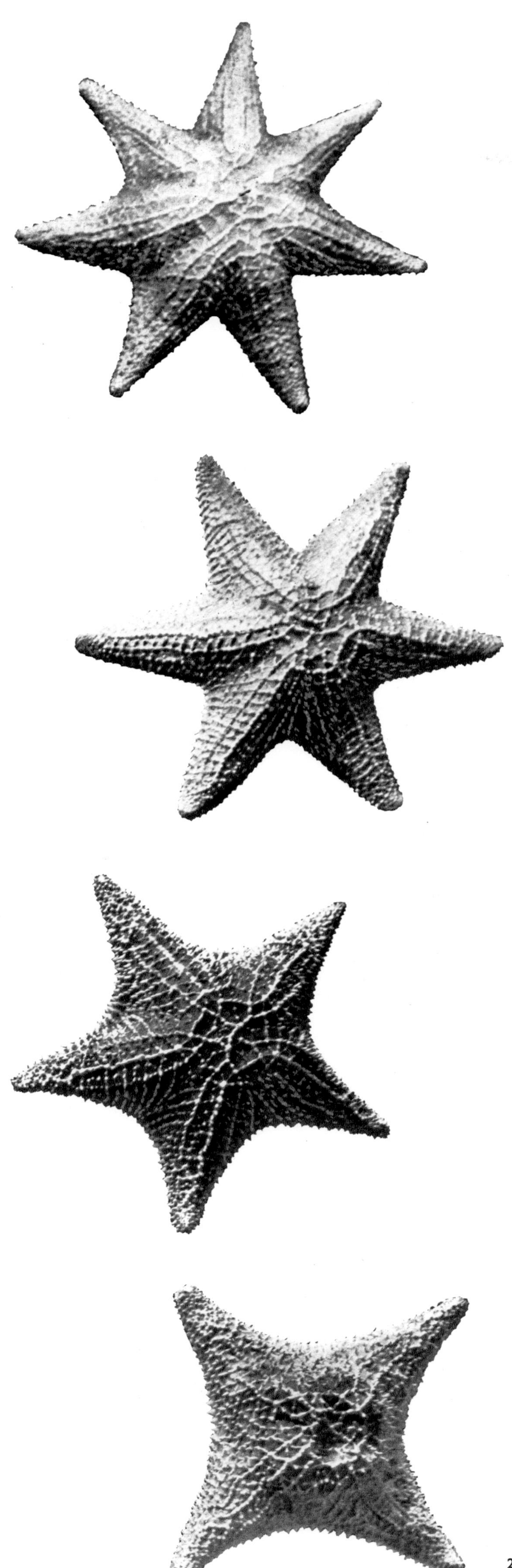

218

What this means is that where a population shows no variation between its individuals, this fact by itself is no evidence that the population is genotypically uniform, and similarly, that where a population does show variation between its individuals, this fact by itself is no evidence that the population is genotypically variable. Only experiments by breeding and transplantation can distinguish between the different possibilities of variation (Pl. 221).

PHENOTYPIC VARIATION

The factors of the environment in which plants and animals live are so numerous that it is impossible to include them all under a simple classification. From the point of view of resultant phenotypic variation, however, the most important are climatic and soil factors, food-supply, and mechanical factors.

Variation due to climatic and soil factors

The effects of these factors can be shown simply and conclusively by transplanting plants to different places. In order to make certain that the plants so transplanted are genetically similar, that is, that the genotype is constant, a special technique for providing the plants is adopted. By dividing a single plant into several pieces, each of which can produce a new plant, it is possible to obtain a number of plants of identically the same age and the same genetical constitution. Plants obtained in this manner are called a *clone*. If members of the same clone are transplanted to different places, or grown under different conditions in the same place, any differences that arise between them cannot be due to genotypic variation but must be the result of phenotypic variation caused by environmental factors.

Experiments on transplanting clones of plants to different altitudes were performed by J. Clausen, D. D. Keck, and W. M. Hiesey, who transplanted clones of plants in California to stations at Stanford (100 feet above sea-level), Mather (4,600 feet), and Timberline (10,000 feet). Different species showed remarkable differences in the way they reacted to different conditions. *Penstemon pachyphyllus*, which grows wild at 7,560 feet, became markedly dwarfed when transplanted to nearly sea-level, and when transplanted to high altitudes it was prevented by the short growing-season from ripening seeds. On the other hand, *Horkelia californica*, which grows wild at 700 feet, throve luxuriously when transplanted down to sea-level but became dwarfed at higher altitudes and usually died in winter. The phenotypic variations produced by these experiments show that the conditions that are favourable for some species are unfavourable for others, and they show, further, that different ranges of tolerance with different optimum points are determined by the genotypes of the species (Pl. 222-224).

Experiments on growing plants on different soils were performed by E. M. Marsden-Jones and W. B. Turrill at the Potterne Biological Station in Wiltshire. Plants of the plantain, *Plantago major*, all of the same age and of the same genotype were planted on the same day on different soils. On sand the plants showed a flat meagre growth with small and few leaves, in marked contrast with the luxuriant growth of plants on clay soils with more numerous and much larger ascending leaves. The phenotypic nature of the variations so produced is further shown by the fact that when plants are transferred from one kind of soil to another they quickly change their habit of growth (Pl. 225).

Genotypic uniformity can also be obtained in a stock of organisms by close in-breeding and by self-pollination. The reason for this will become apparent in the next section. A strain of plants resulting from self-pollination over many generations is genotypically uniform and known as a *pure line*. Pure lines of beans were used by W. Johannsen in a classic experiment. When the seeds of a pure-line bean are sown, the seedlings are affected differentially by a number of environmental conditions such as the richness of the soil, light, shade, and moisture, and when the young bean plants come to set their own seed, the weight and size of each seed is affected not only by these factors but also by such contingencies as the number of seeds and their position in each pod. The sizes of the seeds vary about a mean value; but it makes no difference whether a small seed, a medium-sized seed, or a large seed is selected for breeding the next generation. Whatever their size, all seeds from a pure line bean plant produce a population of offspring that varies exactly like that produced by the parent plants, with the mean value exactly in the same place. This means that the favourable environmental conditions that have led to the production of large seeds do not make the offspring of such large seeds larger. Conversely, the unfavourable environmental conditions that have led to the production of smaller seeds do not make the offspring of such small seeds smaller. The variations which the populations of offspring from pure lines show are phenotypic and not inherited.

Variation due to food-supply

Among the most important environmental factors capable of producing phenotypic variation in animals are the quality and quantity of foodsupply. Feeding experiments carried out on pigs by J. Hammond and C. P. McMeekan have shown that differences not only of size but also of shape can be caused by changing the food. In a pure strain of pigs, where genotypic variation can be discounted, if some animals are given restricted amounts and others unrestricted amounts of the same food for equal periods of time, differences are found in the development of the bones, leading to differences of shape in the animals. In animals of the same age, at sixteen weeks those that have eaten an unrestricted diet have bones which are absolutely larger and relatively more massive. When they are full grown, however, pigs that have been fed on a restricted diet have longer and narrower skulls, a longer lumbar region

Cyclopia

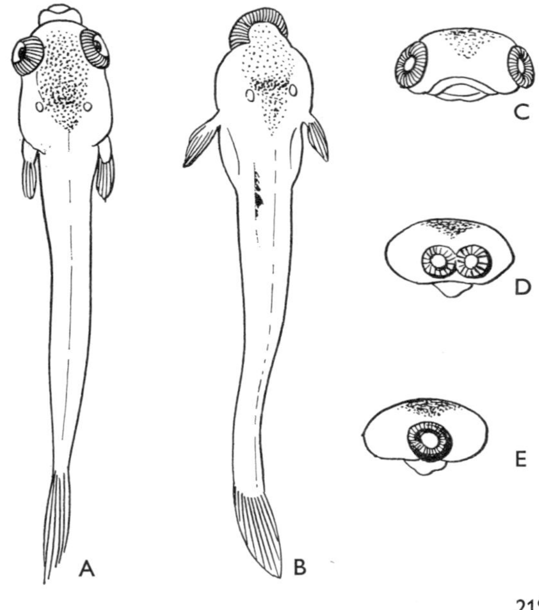

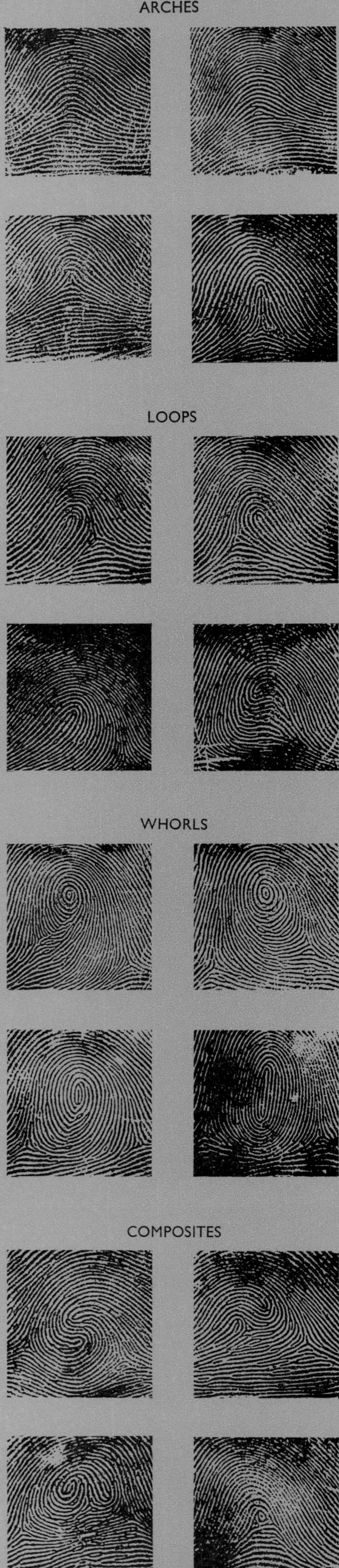

219. Cyclopia induced in the larvae of embryo fish by adding magnesium chloride to the water, notwithstanding the fact that fish have had paired eyes in normal water for 500 million years. **220.** Differences in the finger-prints of men showing the effects of genotypic variation, no two prints being identical.

of the vertebral column (the 'loin'), and larger hip-girdles than pigs fed on an unrestricted diet, although they take a longer time than the latter to reach a comparable stage of development. These facts are of importance to breeders.

Variation due to mechanical factors
In man, artifical deformation of the shape of the head in certain African natives or of the feet in Chinese women is known to result from binding, producing physical pressure and abnormal development. The same phenomenon occurs in nature where organisms have insufficient room for development. The common oyster of the Queensland coast, *Ostrea glomerata*, often shows great irregularity in the shape of the shells according to the substratum on which the spat settled and the space available for growth. Such differences are so marked that the variants were originally considered to be different species before it was realized that they were due to phenotypic variation in a single species. (Pl. 226-228).

GENOTYPIC VARIATION

Heritable, or genotypic variation, is due to changes in the particles which are the units of heredity, called genes. The Mendelian theory of the gene, as worked out by T. H. Morgan and his colleagues using enormous numbers of experiments from the breeding pen and from microscopical studies of cells and their chromosomes, has established the fact that hereditary resemblances between parents and offspring are controlled by discrete, 'granular' particles, the genes. It is the genes that carry the inherited 'information' from parents to offspring in the form of a message coded in chemical molecules situated in the chromosomes of the cells and these genes are usually copied exactly at every cell-division. The genes remain unchanged for an indefinite period until they suddenly undergo a change called *mutation*, after which they are known as *mutant genes* and are copied exactly in their new changed condition, indefinitely, until they undergo mutation again. Mutation is the basis of genotypic variation and will be considered in greater detail later in this chapter (p. 83). Whether they have mutated or not, genes are transmitted to offspring in accordance with the mechanism of the formation of germ-cells, and conform to a pattern of distribution known as Mendelian inheritance. Mendelian inheritance can best be described by means of examples selected to illustrate the two principles of *segregation* and *independent assortment*.

Segregation
The 'Four o'Clock' plant, *Mirabilis jalapa*, is a species in which some plants have red flowers and some white. If red plants are crossed with other red plants, they breed true and produce nothing but red plants. Similarly white plants crossed with other white plants breed true and produce nothing but white plants. If a red plant is crossed with a white (together constituting the parental or P_1 generation), the

Phenotypic and Genotypic Variation

221

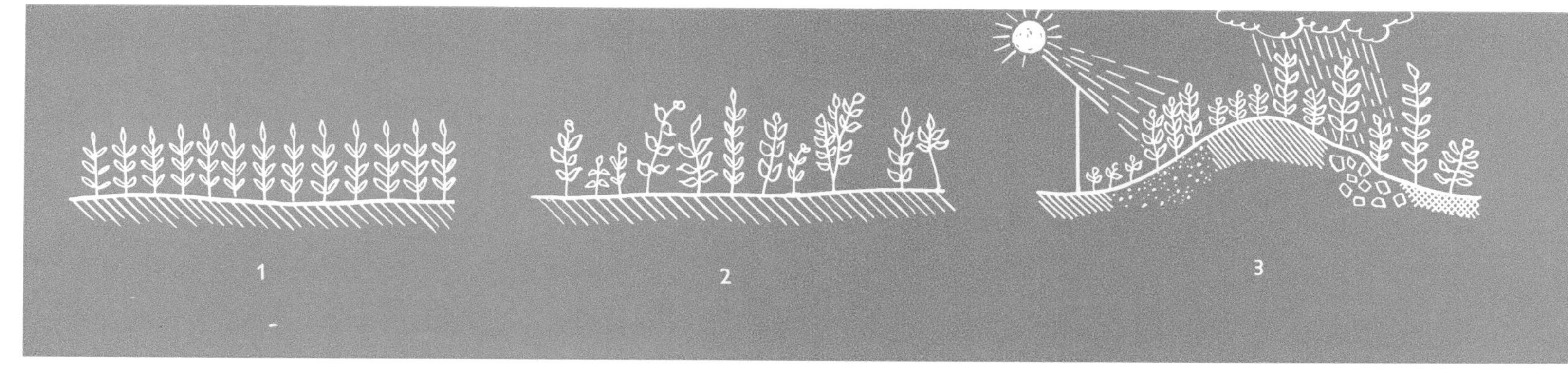

221. (1) The same genotypes produce similar phenotypes in the same environment, whereas (2) different genotypes produce different phenotypes. (3) When the same genotypes are grown under different conditions, different phenotypes are produced with results that may look like (2).

offspring of the first filial generation (known as the F_1) are pink. If such a pink plant is crossed with another pink plant, the offspring of the second filial generation (known as the F_2) are 25% red like the P_1 red grandparent, 50% pink like the F_1 and 25% white like the P_1 white grandparent. A distribution of this kind is called a 1:2:1 ratio. The F_2 reds when crossed with reds breed true to red; the F_2 whites when crossed with whites breed true to white; the F_2 pinks when crossed with pinks breed exactly like the F_1 pinks and produce an F_3 consisting of 25% red, 50% pink, and 25% white. The fact of fundamental importance shown by these experiments is that pure reds and pure whites can be extracted from pinks (Col. Pl. 6).

Mendel showed that results like this can be explained by making a few simple assumptions. These are:

1. that the colours are controlled by factors now called genes which are never contaminated, mixed, or diluted, and that in all individuals these genes exist in pairs, one member of each pair having been derived from each parent;
2. that when the plant produces reproductive cells (or *gametes*), only one member of each pair of genes goes into any one gamete owing to a process known as *segregation*, which results in the splitting and separation of the two members of each pair of genes;
3. that the number of gametes containing one member of a pair of genes is equal to that of the gametes containing the other member of the same pair of genes;
4. that at fertilization a gamete containing any one gene has equal chances of meeting and fusing with a gamete containing either gene of a pair.

In diagrammatic form (Col. Pl. 6) the factor for red colour is denoted *W* and that for white *w*, in accordance with rules of nomenclature which lay down that members of one pair of genes must always be designated by the same letter of the alphabet.

The fact that pure reds and pure whites can be extracted from pinks shows that while the factors *W* and *w* collaborate in producing a pink, *they do not contaminate each other*. As will be shown later in this chapter, this is of fundamental importance in evolution. Factors that function as *W* and *w* in this scheme are known as *genes*. Members of a pair that are different, like *W* and *w*, are known as *alleles* because they can take each other's places. The fact that there *are* contrasting characters, such as red and white coloured flowers, that are distributed among offspring according to the pattern of Mendelian inheritance, means that one of these characters arose as a result of the mutation of a gene, which then differed from its allele. An individual containing similar genes of a pair, such as *WW* or *w w*, is called *homozygous*. An individual containing dissimilar genes of a pair of alleles, such as *W w*, is called *heterozygous*. Homozygotes crossed with similar homozygotes breed true; heterozygotes crossed with similar heterozygotes never breed true, as shown above; nor do they breed true when crossed with homozygotes. This can be shown by 'back-crossing' F_1 individuals with either of the original P_1 forms.

Back-crosses

In the case of the Four o'Clock, the heterozygotes can be visibly distinguished from the homozygotes by their colour, because in the heterozygote the pair of alleles collaborate in such a way that neither dominates over the other. There are other cases, however, in which one allele of a pair does dominate over the other as with the genes controlling tall and dwarf size in the common pea, *Pisum sativum*. If a pure tall pea is crossed with a dwarf, all the F_1 are tall. If two such F_1 tall peas are crossed, the resulting F_2 consists of 75% tall and 25% dwarf. A distribution of this kind is known as a 3:1 ratio. This result is really similar to that obtained with red and white colour in *Mirabilis jalapa*, except that as tall is *dominant* and dwarf is *recessive*, the heterozygotes are indistinguishable from the dominant homozygotes, so that the 75% tall in F_2 are made up of 25% homozygous tall and 50% heterozygous tall. This means that the 3:1 ratio is the same as the 1:2:1 ratio but with the first 1 and the 2 lumped together. The 25% dwarf recessives are homozygous, as indeed, they must always be, because if they contained one tall allele, it would dominate over the dwarf allele and the recessive character would not be apparent.

Strictly speaking, dominance and recessiveness apply to characters, not to genes, but in practice it is usual to refer to dominant and recessive genes remembering that some genes are neither, and that others control several characters of which some may be dominant and others recessive (Pl. 268, 269 and p. 79). The dominant gene is always designated by a capital and its allelic recessive by a small similar letter of the alphabet, in italics, the letter representing the character of the mutant gene, in this case *d* for dwarf (Col. Pl. 6).

Simply stated, a dominant gene can show its effect when inherited 'in single dose', from one parent only. A recessive gene cannot show its effect unless inherited 'in double dose', from both parents.

The phenomenon of dominance and recessiveness in allelic genes is one of great importance, both because of its prevalence and the explanation of how it arose, which will be described later in the chapter. For the present, it is to be observed that it introduces the fact that the phenotype 'tall' conceals under its external appearance two genotypes: the homozygous tall which breeds true, and the heterozygous tall, which is tall because tall is dominant over dwarf, and which does not breed true.

Since it is impossible to tell by simple inspection whether a given tall is homozygous or heterozygous, in order to distinguish between these two phenotypes, it is necessary to make breeding experiments and, in particular, back-crosses. But since the tall gene is dominant, it is useless to back-cross a plant with the dominant homozygous parent, because all the offspring would be tall. The recessive dwarf, which must be homozygous or it would not be dwarf, can be relied upon to produce gametes all of which contain the recessive gene *d*. If a tall plant that is being tested by crossing with a dwarf gives nothing but tall offspring, then the tall plant was homozygous and produced gametes all of which contained the dominant gene *D*. If the offspring are 50% tall and 50% dwarf, the tall plant was heterozygous and produced gametes of which 50% contained the dominant gene *D* and 50% the recessive gene *d*.

The Mendelian pattern of segregation of alleles has been found to apply in all groups of living organisms and is one of the most firmly established principles of biology.

The facts that genes persist uncontaminated, that they can be carried concealed as recessives through any number of generations, and that they segregate, explain why it is possible for offspring to differ from one another and from their parents, and to resemble grandparents or earlier ancestors and avuncular relations, or to resemble no previous member of the family at all. This would be inexplicable if offspring were literally the products of their parents. They are the products of germ-cells which may or may not carry the genes manifested in the phenotypes of the parents (Pl. 376).

The Mendelian pattern of distribution of genes by segregation between parents and offspring explains why it is possible to obtain genotypically pure strains, or *pure lines* (p. 73), by prolonged inbreeding and self-pollination. As was seen in the case of the Four o'Clock, the F_2 of a cross between red and white gives 25% homozygous red, 50% heterozygous pink, and 25% homozygous white. The homozygotes, whether red or white, breed true, but the heterozygote pinks when interbred (or self-pollinated in plants where this is possible) segregate again into 25% homozygous reds, 50% heterozygous pinks, and 25% homozygous whites. The number of heterozygotes is thus halved in every generation produced by heterozygotes and decreases so rapidly that after ten generations of such breeding the number of heterozygotes is negligible. When that stage has been reached, the strain may be called a pure line, which can also be defined as a strain in which every individual is homozygous for all its genes and the genotypes of all individuals are

222

223

Mechanical Action Producing Phenotypic Variation

226. The effect of wind on trees in exposed situations is to cause asymmetry and stunted growth because of excessive water-loss and death of shoots exposed to windward. Mechanical deformation of the body in man can result from binding the head or the feet when young, or stretching the neck with rings as in **227**, the 'giraffe women' of the hinterland of Burma or **228**, the lip of plate-lipped Indians.

225

Phenotypic Variation due to Changes in Climate and Soil

Variation is phenotypic when it is the result of environmental factors acting on individuals of identical genetical constitution. **222.** Material for demonstrating phenotypic variation is obtained by dividing a single plant into portions forming *clones*. **223.** The effect of climate at different altitudes shown by *Penstemon pachyphyllus* that grows wild at 1400 m., is dwarfed when transplanted to sea-level, and is prevented from ripening seed at 3050 m. **224.** *Horkelia californica* grows wild at sea-level, but is progressively dwarfed at higher altitudes, 1400 m. and 3050 m. **225.** The effects of different soils on clones of *Plantago major* growing on clay (top), on chalky clay (middle), and on sand (bottom).

224

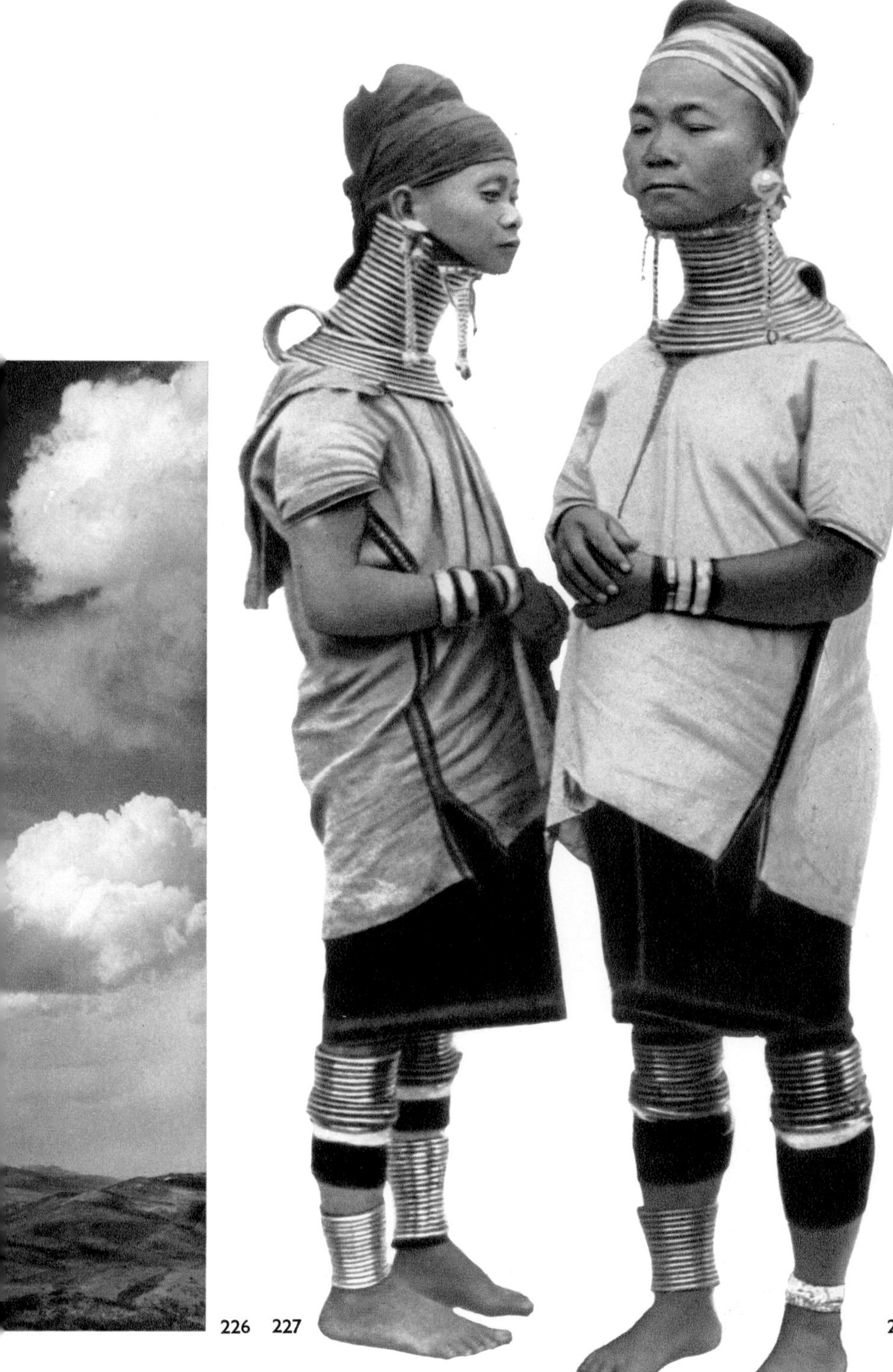

226 227

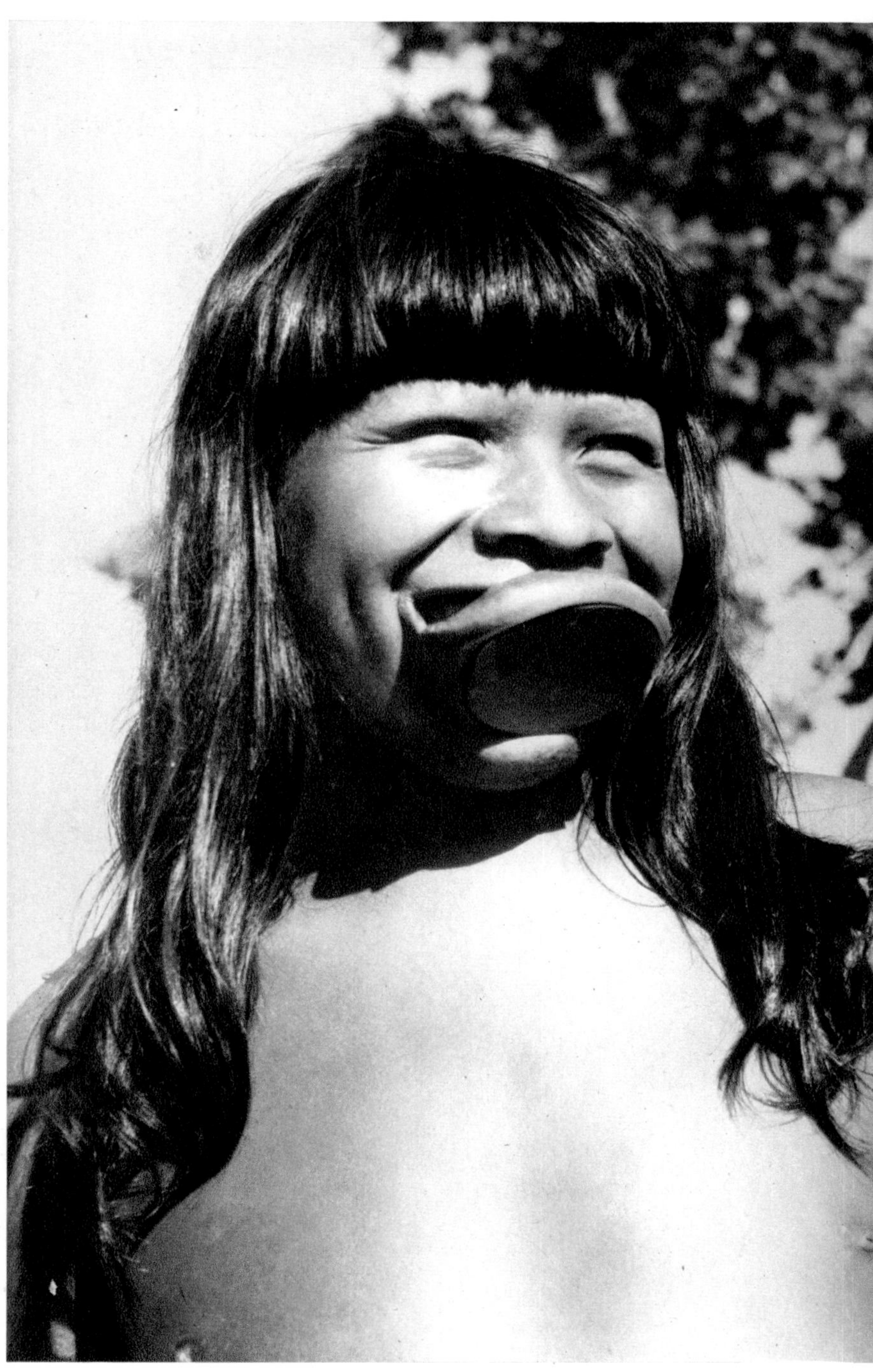

228

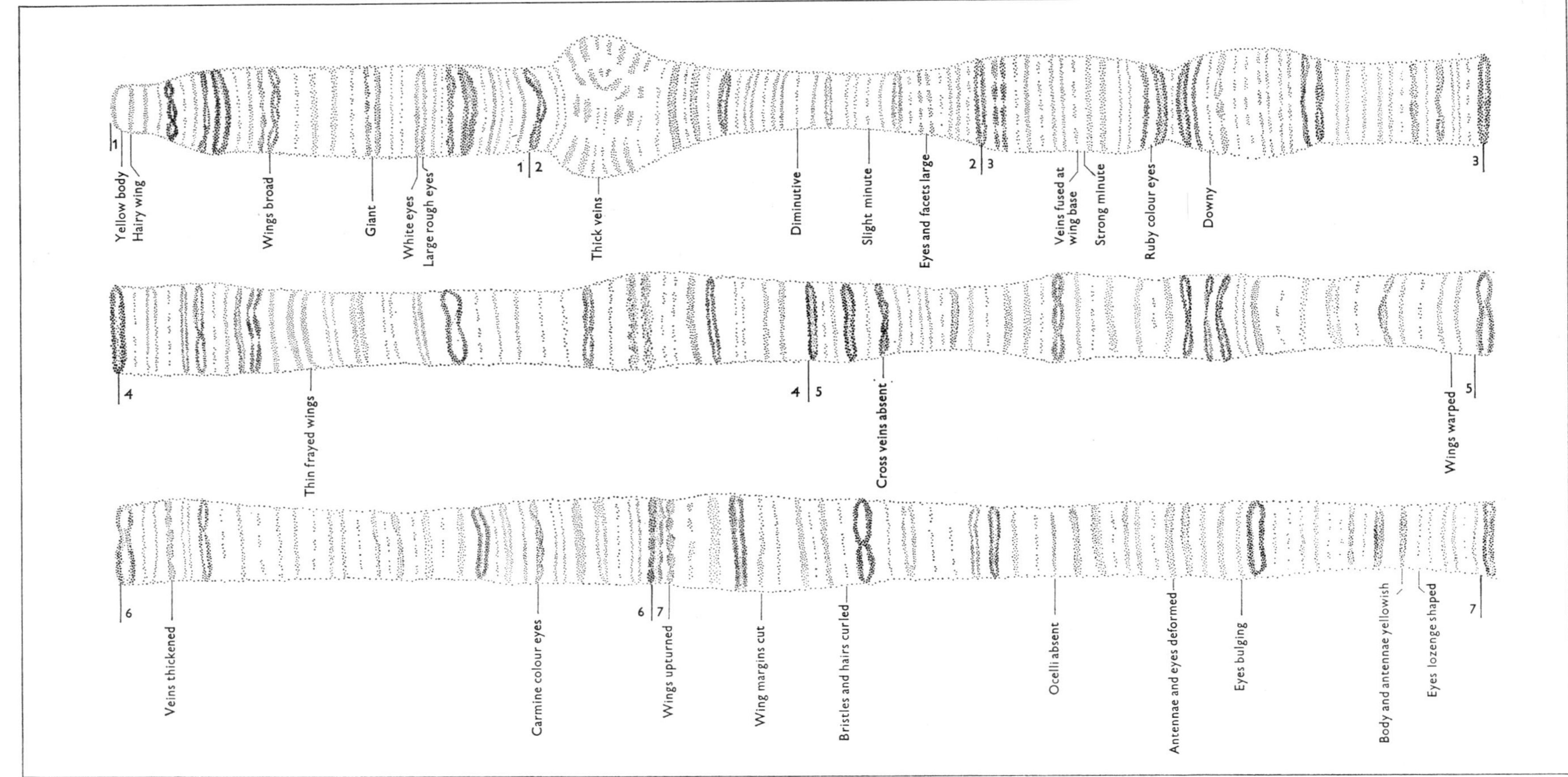

Chromosomes are the vehicles of the factors of heredity, the genes, which are arranged in linear order along their length. 229. Genetic and cytological experiments have made it possible to map out the loci of the different genes along the length of the chromosomes.

identical. The importance of this fact will emerge when the effects of selection on wild populations are considered later in this chapter.

Independent assortment

Living organisms contain more than one pair of contrasting characters, and Mendel's second contribution was the demonstration that the pairs of genes controlling such characters segregate independently. Again taking our example from peas, we find that seeds may be round or wrinkled in shape, and yellow or green in colour. If a plant possessing round yellow seeds is crossed with a plant possessing wrinkled green seeds, the F_1 hybrids all have round and yellow seeds, which shows that in the pair of allelic genes controlling shape the gene producing round is dominant and that producing wrinkled is recessive, and that in the other pair of allelic genes controlling colour, the gene producing yellow is dominant and that producing green is recessive.

If the F_1 hybrids are crossed, the resulting F_2 consists of plants in the proportion of 9 round-yellow, 3 round-green, 3 wrinkled-yellow, and 1 wrinkled-green. This result is the simple consequence of the independent segregation of the two pairs of allelic genes *W* and *w*, *G* and *g*, as may be seen in the diagram in Col. Pl. 6.

From this table of all the possible combinations of the four kinds of gametes produced by each F_1 parent, it can be seen that among 16 F_2 offspring, 9 will contain at least one *W* and one *G* and be round-yellow, 3 will contain at least one *W* but no *G* and be round-green, 3 will contain no *W* but at least one *G* and be wrinkled-yellow, and 1 will contain no *W* and no *G* and be wrinkled-green.

It is to be noticed that the rounds number 12 and the wrinkleds 4, which is the same as the 3 to 1 ratio found in the case of simple crosses with a single pair of alleles; similarly, the yellows number 12 and the greens 4, which also is the same as the 3 to 1 ratio.

The most important fact to emerge from this demonstration is that although only *two* types, round-yellow and wrinkled-green were put into the original cross, *four* types have been produced in the F_2: round-yellow, round-green, wrinkled-yellow and wrinkled-green. This phenomenon which is known as *recombination*, is the result of segregation and independent assortment of pairs of genes in organisms which practise the sexual method of reproduction.

It may be noted that this capacity for recombination of genes also explains the phenomenon of 'reversion to type' which occurs when different varieties of a species are crossed. Any variety may bring in the normal dominant allele while the other brings in the corresponding mutant recessive allele, with the result that the old genotype from which the varieties arose can be 'reconstituted'. As a classic example of reversion, when fancy varieties of pigeons are crossed, Darwin found that they revert to the wild blue rock-pigeon (Pl. 278).

The importance of recombination of genes can be shown from the following consideration. Supposing that in a species of organism without sexual reproduction ten new types appear by mutation, then after any number of generations, there will still be only ten types (unless further mutations occur), because there is no possibility of mixture of genes from different parent individuals, no segregation of genes in the production of gametes, and no recombination of genes in the process of random fertilization. On the other hand, in species where sexual reproduction occurs, if ten new types appear by mutation, the number of possible types resulting from segregation, independent assortment, and recombination in all possible permutations of ten pairs of allelic genes, is not 10 but 2^{10}, which is 1,024.

The significance of this fact will be referred to again in connection with the evolution of sex. Here, its importance lies in the fact that the mechanism of Mendelian heredity, involving segregation, independent assortment, and recombination of genes, is the most powerful method by which genotypic variation is produced. In evolutionary language it is an adaptation, conferring survival value on those forms that provide the maximum number of variations for their own subsequent evolution.

THE CHROMOSOME MECHANISM

Remembering that, when Mendel discovered his principles of segregation and independent assortment, his explanation of the mechanism of the distribution of the genes was based on assumptions, we may now state that the validity of these assumptions has been completely confirmed by the discovery that the structure and distribution of the chromosomes provide a physical basis for the distribution of the genes which is concordant with the observed facts of genetical inheritance down to the most minute details.

Chromosomes are present in the nucleus of every cell of the body of all plants and all animals. They are rod-shaped bodies formed out of the materials present in the nucleus of the cell each time that it undergoes division or *mitosis*. The nucleus at the resting stage is surrounded by a nuclear membrane. At the onset of mitosis (prophase) this is seen to take the form of coiled threads or chromosomes that are double; replication has taken place and each chromosome has produced a twin chromosome, rigorously identical. The nuclear membrane dissolves and the mitosis enters the next phase (metaphase) with the chromosomes lying in a plane in the middle of the cell, on and attached by a structure called a centromere to a system of fibres called the mitotic spindle. Next (anaphase) the daughter centromeres spring apart from each other and pull their respective chromosomes towards opposite ends of the spindle. Finally (telophase) each of the two groups of daughter chromosomes at each end of the spindle becomes compacted into a nucleus, and the cell divides into two, each containing a nucleus that is quantitatively and qualitatively identical with that of the parent cell. This elaborate machinery ensures that all the cells of the body of an organism contain replications of the same genes (Pl. 237-245). The chromosomes are present in pairs, one member of each pair coming from each parent. The number of chromosomes in the body cells of any species is (except for possible differences between sexes) constant for that species, and detailed study by modern methods and techniques has enabled the structures and features of the individual chromosome-pairs to be recognized, in the same way as the structure and features of the external form of a plant or an animal can be recognized. In the broadbean the chromosomes in each of the cells of the plant-body number 6 pairs, or 12 in all. In the fruit-fly, *Drosophila melanogaster*, the chromosomes in each of the cells of the body number 4 pairs, or 8. In man, they number 23 pairs, or 46 (Pl. 229-235).

At each division of the cell, the chromosomes divide by splitting lengthwise, one daughter-chromosome going into each daughter-cell, with the result that the number of chromosomes in each cell of the body remains constant, and the daughter chromosomes are exact replicas of each chromosome in the cell that has divided. As there are about 50 cell-generations in the course of development of a man from the single fertilized egg-cell, the chromosomes divide 2^{50} times during that period in the thousand million million cells of every man in every generation.

Germ-cells or gametes are, of course, cells and two of them, one male (the sperm) and the other female (the egg) fuse to form a *zygote* (fertilized egg), which is the start of a new generation (Chapter Four, p. 151). An important feature of germ-cells, whether ovules or pollen grains, eggs, or sperm, is the fact that they contain only half the number of chromosomes characteristic of the cells of the body of their species. In general, the number of chromosomes in the germ-cells is known as the *haploid* number and designated by the term *n*. In the cells of the body the number of chromosomes is known as the *diploid* number and designated by 2*n*. In beans the haploid number is 6, and the diploid number 12; in *Drosophila* the haploid number is 4, and the diploid number 8; in man the haploid number is 23, and the diploid number 46. The haploid number is of course the number of chromosomes received by the individual from each of its parents.

It is easy to see that if it were not for this reduction of the number of chromosomes in the germ-cells to half the number in the ordinary cells of the body, the number of chromosomes in the cells of the body would become doubled at each generation. This is avoided by means of the *reduction-division* or *meiosis* that the parent-cells of the germ-cells undergo. The chromosomes appear in pairs, attached to one another, and although they split longitudinally once into daughter-chromosomes, the cell itself divides twice in such a way as to ensure that the daughters of each pair of chromosomes are separated from one another, no two going into the same germ-cell. In other words, the chromosomes segregate at the formation of the germ-cells, exactly as the genes were assumed to do, and the behaviour of the genes is completely explained by the fact that the genes are actually carried in the chromosomes (Pl. 236).

The members of the different pairs of chromosomes segregate independently during the process of meiosis, and this provides the physical and visible basis for the independent assortment of two or more pairs of alleles, exactly as assumed by Mendel. An exception is occasionally found to the law of independent assortment of genes. In some cases, the members of two pairs of alleles do not segregate independently of one another, but are distributed together, a phenomenon known as *linkage*.

For example, in the fruit-fly, *Drosophila melanogaster*, there is a gene producing black body-colour, *b*, which is recessive to the gene producing the normal wild grey body-colour, *B*, and a gene producing curved wings, *c*, which is recessive to that for normal wings, *C*. A female fly that is heterozygous for both these pairs of alleles, *BbCc*, having been produced from a grey-normal (homozygous dominant *BBCC*) and a black-curved (homozygous recessive *bbcc*), produces gametes *BC*, *Bc*, *bC*, and *bc*, but not in equal numbers as would have been expected in accordance with the principle of independent assortment. Instead, *B* and *C* stay linked together in about 75 per cent of the gametes, and so do *b* and *c*, while *B* separates from *C* and *b* from *c* in about 25 per cent of the gametes. The explanation for this apparently anomalous behaviour is that the genes *B* and *C* are carried in one and the same chromosome, and the genes *b* and *c* in one and the same chromosome. *B* and *C* are therefore liable to be distributed together, and so are *b* and *c*; but in about 25 per cent of cases, the daughter-chromosomes at meiosis break and the portion containing *B* becomes joined up with the portion containing *c*, while the portion of the other daughter-chromosome containing *b* becomes joined up with the portion containing *C*. This process of interchange of portions of chromosomes is known as *crossing-over*, and may actually be seen under the microscope, which shows the chromosomes attached to one another at the point where crossing-over occurs. This apparent exception to the rule of independent assortment therefore provides an additional proof that genes are carried in the chromosomes (Pl. 246, 247).

Each chromosome contains many genes, and the frequency with which they are separated by crossing-over may be calculated from the results of breeding experiments. It has been found that if the crossover value between gene *X* and gene *Y* is 20 per cent, and the cross-over value between gene *Y* and gene *Z* is 10 per cent, the cross-over value between gene *X* and gene *Z* may be either 30 per cent or 10 per cent. Since the frequency with which genes become separated by crossing-over would be expected to depend on their distance apart on the chromosomes, these results can be interpreted if the genes are arranged in linear order along the chromosomes and each gene has its own place or *locus*. On this hypothesis, maps of genes have been constructed for a number of species, showing the place of each known gene on each chromosome, and the validity of the hypothesis has been established by the fact that in some cases mistakes take place at cell-division by which portions of chromosomes may be dropped out of the cells, or interchanged, or attached to the 'wrong' other chromosomes. In such cases the results of the abnormal gene-distribution, as revealed by the characters visibly shown by the fly, conform exactly to the position of genes on the chromosome-maps (Pl. 229); the flies show abnormalities in the characters controlled by genes located in the missing or misplaced pieces of chromosomes (Pl. 253). The detail and precision with which the proofs have been provided of the linear order of genes in chromosomes and confirmed by breeding experiments and examination of chromosomes under the microscope represent one of the most striking achievements in biology, for which T. H. Morgan and his colleagues and C. D. Darlington are largely responsible.

There is a further point to notice regarding crossing-over, for the amount of crossing-over that takes place is controlled by genes. From the point of view of genotypic variation crossing-over acts as a regulator, for when the cross-over values between loci of genes are high there is segregation and independent assortment of the allelic genes resulting in variation; when the cross-over values are low, tending towards complete linkage between loci of genes, these genes do not undergo independent assortment and variation is correspondingly reduced (p. 97).

GENES

A gene may be defined as a discrete particle that plays a definite causal part in heredity, remains unchanged indefinitely until it suddenly changes by mutation and then continues indefinitely in its changed condition until it mutates again.

When contrasting characters are distributed among the offspring of a cross in a 1:2:1, or a 3:1, or a 9:3:3:1 ratio, the factors controlling them are recognizable as genes by their segregative action, and they are found in all groups of the plant and animal kingdoms. In *Drosophila* over 800 mutant genes have been recognized. Of the hundreds of genes discovered in man, a small selection may be given to show the variety of range of characters which they control.

The following genes in man are dominant and the effects appear in the offspring if they have inherited the gene in question from even one parent:

- Blood-groups A and B
- Atrophy of the auditory nerve causing deafness
- Coloboma of the iris of the eye
- Habsburg jaw
- Night-blindness
- Premature baldness in men
- Supernumerary teeth
- White forelock in men
- Woolly hair in Europeans

The following genes in man are recessive and the effects appear in the offspring only if the genes in question have been inherited from both parents:

- Blood-group O
- Albinism (one form)
- Blue or grey eye-colour
- Deaf-mutism (one form)
- Ear-lobes adherent to the side of the head
- Hare-lip and cleft palate
- Amaurotic idiocy
- Polydactyly or supernumerary fingers and toes
- Inability to taste phenylthiourea

Studies on the breeding of several species of plants and animals have made it possible to observe the origin of new genes from old genes by mutation, a process which will call for closer attention later in this chapter (p. 83). Here, attention may be drawn to some of the characters which genes have been found to control. In *Drosophila* they can affect the colour of the body, the colour of the eyes, the colour of the kidney-tubes, the length, stoutness, and shape of the bristles on the surface of the body, the size of the eyes, of the antennae, and of the legs, the processes of early development; they can turn the 'balancers' which represent the hinder pair of wings in flies into recognizable wings, or wings into balancers (Pl. 253); they can turn antennae into legs, and they can produce a pair of wings on the first segment of the thorax, which normally does not bear wings at all.

In many cases, and perhaps in all, genes control more than one character. For instance, in *Drosophila* the gene that converts the colour of the eye from red to white also alters the structure of the reproductive organs and affects the length of life and general viability of the fly. The gene that results in the reduction of the size of the wing to a condition known as 'vestigial' also modifies the structure of the balancers, the bristles, the muscles of the wings, the shape of the reproductive organs, the speed of development, the production of eggs, and the length of life. In the American sulphur butterfly, *Colias philodice*, there is a gene that changes the yellow colour of the female insect to white and at the same time modifies its behaviour by reducing the optimum temperature at which it is active, with the result that it flies earlier in the morning and later at night than insects containing the allelic gene. In the coffee plant one gene controls the habit of growth of the plant, branching, size and shape of the leaves, and the structure of the flower, fruit, and seeds.

In some carefully analysed cases it has been possible to see how these multiple effects of genes are brought about. In the rat, Hans Grüneberg discovered a gene that produces a marked overgrowth of the cartilage of the ribs, sternum, and tracheal rings, which makes the thoracic cage a rigid structure and prevents the ribs from

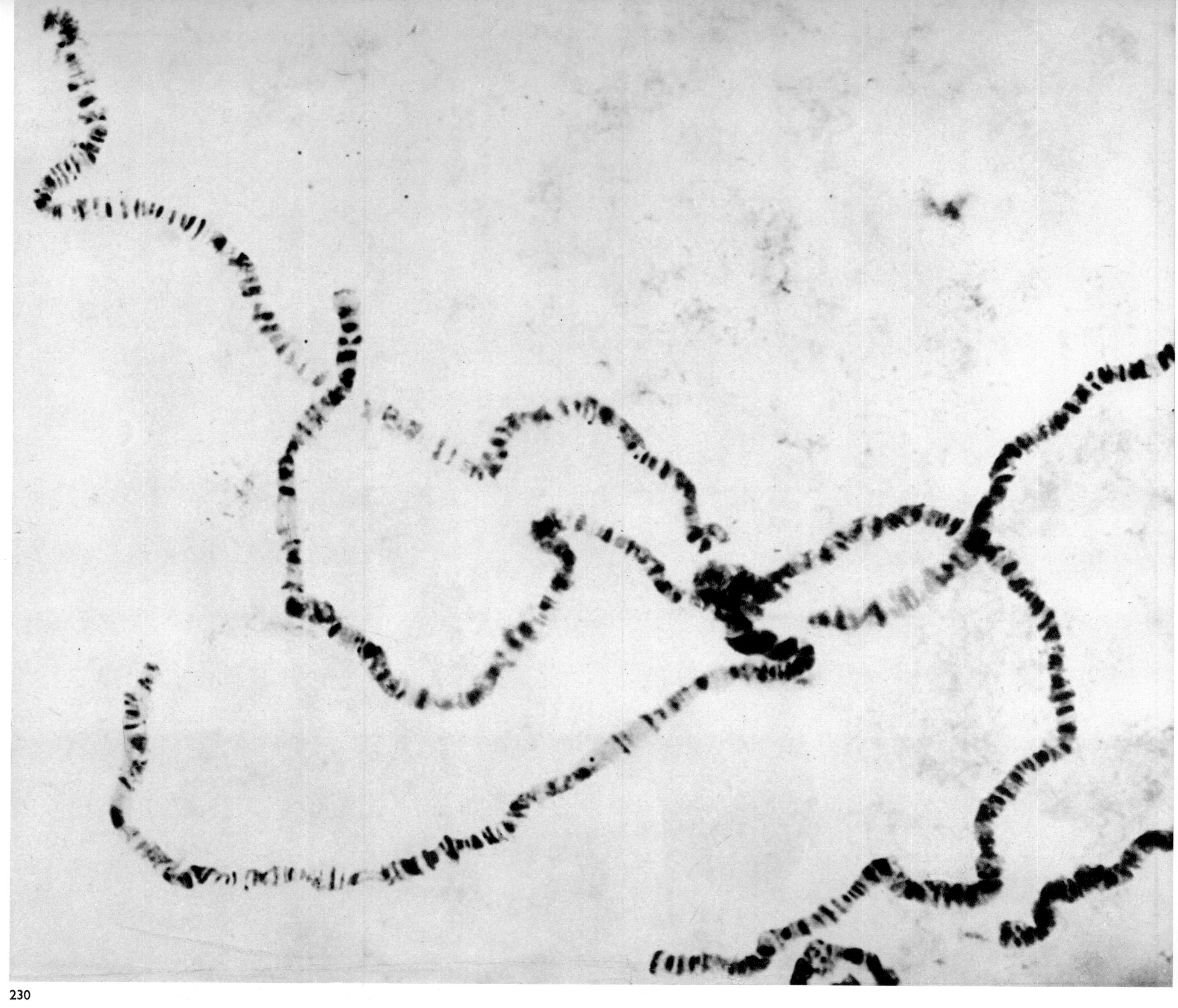
230

231

232

rising and falling as they do during normal breathing. This leads to an arrest of development of the lungs and insufficient respiration, in compensation for which there is an increase in red blood-corpuscles. As the bloodvessels in the lungs have a reduced cross-section, the blood-pressure is increased and the right ventricle of the heart hypertrophied in consequence, and for one reason or another the animals possessing this gene die young.

Up to now, attention has been restricted to cases in which the corresponding locus in a pair of chromosomes is occupied by a pair of identical or allelic genes. There are many cases, however, where the gene at a given locus has mutated more than once and given rise to more than one allele. The result is systems of *multiple alleles*, any one of which can take the place of any other, but only two of which can be present together in any organism because, as the chromosomes are in pairs, there are only two loci. In the common snail, *Cepaea nemoralis*, brown, pink, and yellow shell-colours are controlled by three genes each of which can be allelic to the others, but only two can be present in any one snail. The yellow gene is recessive to both the others.

Here belong the genes responsible for blood-groups of the ABO system in man (Chapter V, p. 190). Gene G^A produces an antigen A on the surface of the red blood-corpuscles; gene G^B produces an antigen B; gene G produces no antigen, and is recessive to both G^A and G^B. This system allows six genotypes and four phenotypes:

GG, group O
G^AG^A, and G^AG, group A
G^BG^B, and G^BG, group B
G^AG^B, group AB

The Rhesus blood-group system is controlled by genes at three loci designated C, D, and E, situated very close to one another in the chromosome and segregating together. All these loci accommodate multiple alleles, each of these genes determines the presence of a corresponding antigen in the red blood-corpuscles, and each antigen provokes the formation of an antibody. Persons with at least one dominant gene *D* are Rhesus-positive and have antigen D in the red blood-corpuscles. Homozygous recessives *dd* are known as Rhesus-negative, regardless of which genes they possess at the C and E loci. The Rhesus blood-groups are important for two reasons: they may give rise to serious pathological conditions when a mother and her unborn child belong to incompatible groups (p. 101), and they serve to distinguish between different races of man because of the different percentages of the population in which the genes occur (p. 190), as A. E. Mourant has shown.

The genes so far considered are recognizable from the visibly contrasting characters into which they segregate in definite proportions. This fact has enabled an important principle to be discovered governing the proportions in which the genes of a single pair of alleles will be found in a natural population, mating freely at random. If the number of homozygous individuals carrying the dominant gene is p, and the number of homozygous individuals carrying the recessive gene is q, the proportion of heterozygotes in that population can be calculated by G. H. Hardy's and W. Weinberg's law:

$$p^2 \quad : \quad 2pq \quad : \quad q^2$$

dominant homozygotes : heterozygotes : recessive homozygotes

which represents the condition of equilibrium reached in the first generation after random mating and is maintained in all subsequent generations unless environmental or genetic conditions change.

An example given by E. B. Ford illustrates the working of this relation as follows. If a white-flowered variety of a plant is recessive to that with coloured flowers, and therefore homozygous, and if in a given field the white-flowered plants form 5 per cent of the population, then the homozygous dominant variety will form 60.3 per

230. In the salivary gland of the fruit-fly, *Drosophila melanogaster* the chromosomes are enlarged and their structure more easily visible.

Human Chromosomes

231. The chromosomes in a normal human male during a phase in the reduction divisions when the members of each pair of chromosomes are associated together; twenty-three pairs of chromosomes are present, the X-chromosome and Y-chromosome are attached to one another end to end forming an S-shaped pair. **232.** The same chromosomes sorted out. **233.** The chromosomes of a normal human female in a division of ordinary body cells, showing forty six chromosomes in process of division. **235.** The chromosomes of a human mongoloid subject **234,** showing forty seven dividing chromosomes instead of the normal forty six, because one, at the lower right-hand corner, is present in triplicate instead of the normal duplicate. In the rare instances where mongoloids have produced offspring, it is found that the condition is inherited, as one would expect now that a direct connection with abnormal chromosome structure has been established. These photographs are obtained by staining the chromosomes with Feulgen reagent and observing in a powerful optical microscope.

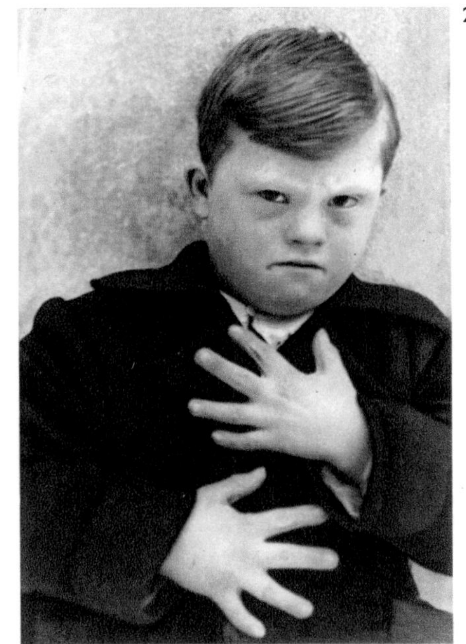
234

233

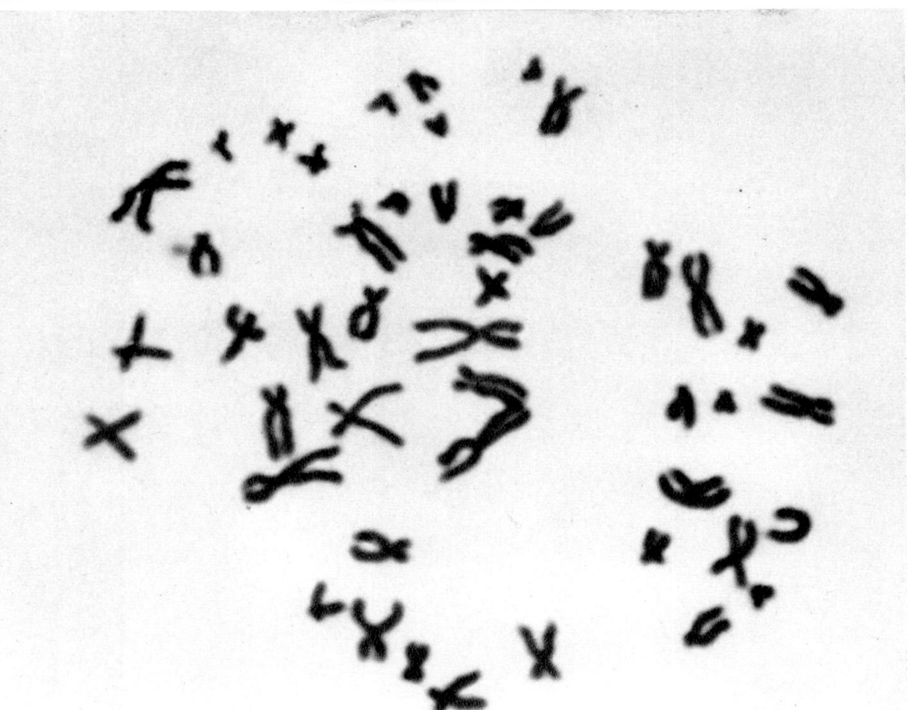
235

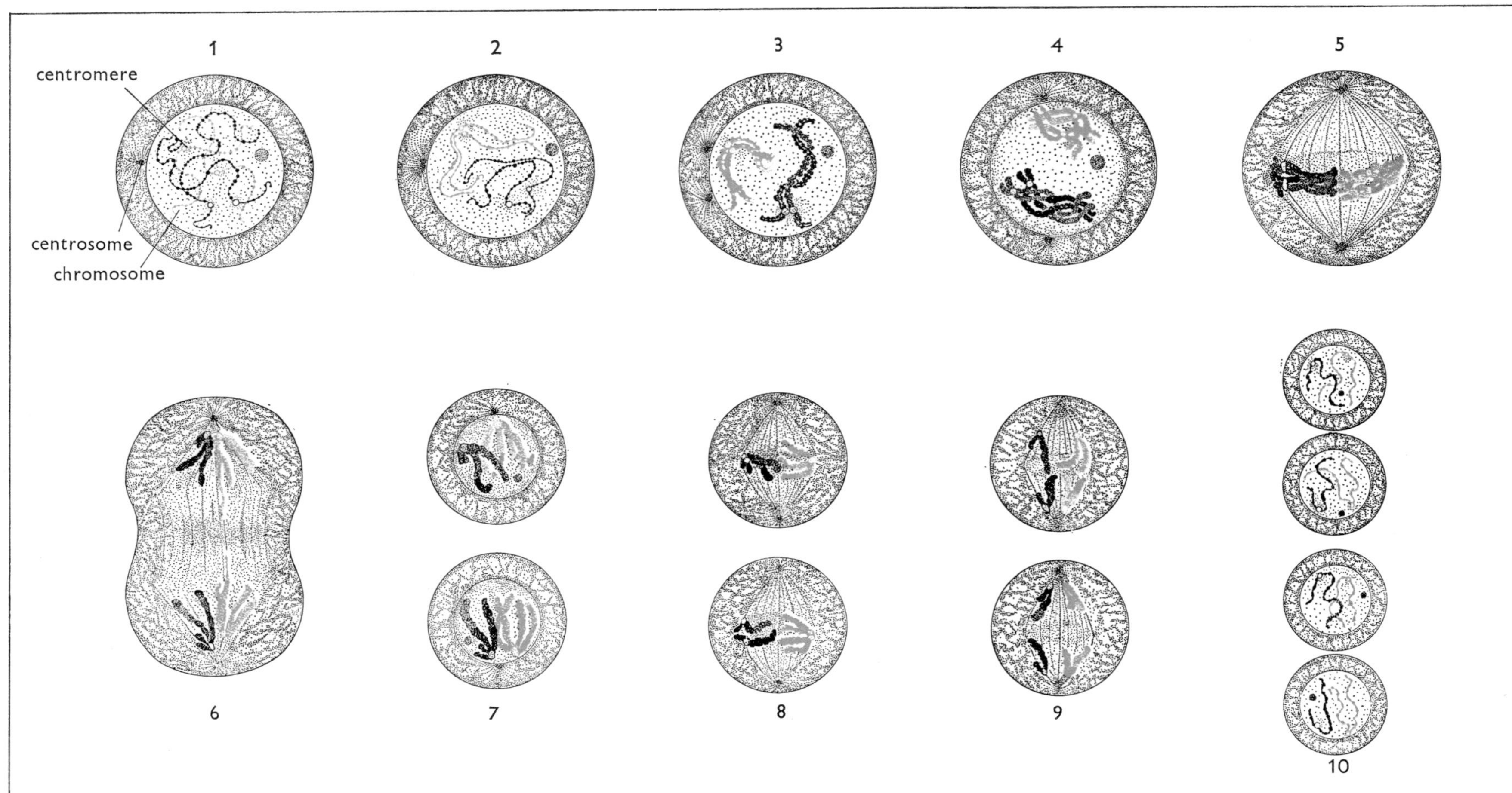

The Chromosomes, Carriers of Units of Inheritance

236. **In the formation of germ-cells, eggs and sperms, the number of chromosomes in the body (the diploid number) is reduced to half (the haploid number) because the chromosomes divide once but the cells divide twice. (1) leptotene stage with four chromosomes as single threads; (2) zygotene stage with chromosomes arranged in two pairs alongside each other; (3) diplotene stage, each chromosome is split lengthwise so that there are two bundles of four threads, the centromere of each chromosome remains single; (4) crossing-over may take place between chromosome-threads (→ 246), as the bundles wind spirally round each other; (5) first metaphase, chromosome-pairs arranged on the spindle; (6) first anaphase, chromosome-pairs pulled apart, leading to first telophase in which the cell divides into two (7) each containing two chromosome-pairs; (8) second metaphase, chromosome-pairs on the spindle; (9) second anaphase, members of each chromosome-pair are pulled apart; (10) second telophase leading to division into cells each containing two single chromosome threads. This is half the number of chromosomes in the original cell before meiosis began.**

cent of the population and the heterozygotes 34.7 per cent. This relation is of importance not only because of the information which it can give of the distribution of the genotypes in a population, but also because of the stability of the equilibrium it reveals throughout many generations and the bearing of this fact on the question of the loss or conservation of variation capable of supplying 'raw material' for evolution.

Not all genes, however, have the clear-cut effects that result from controlling contrasting characters enabling them to be recognized by the 1:2:1, or 3:1, or other comparable ratios obtained in the offspring from breeding experiments. Some genes have additive effects, and even similar effects to other genes, with the result that the segregative results of their distribution among offspring are masked. For example, in wheat, there are three dominant genes that change the colour of the plant from white to red, and their effect is to increase the intensity of the red colour cumulatively. If a red wheat is crossed with a white wheat the F_1 are pink, and if these F_1 are then interbred the F_2 contains plants ranging from red to white without it being possible to make out clear-cut classes or to discover the ratios in which the classes appear. Nevertheless the genes concerned are behaving strictly according to the Mendelian scheme. If the genes producing red are *R*, *S* and *T*, their alleles *r*, *s*, and *t* producing white, the homozygous red parent will be of the genotype*RRSSTT* and can be called a grade-6 red. When crossed with the homozygous recessive *rrsstt*, the F_1 will be *RrSsTt*, grade-3 reds or pinks. In F_2 there will be 1 grade-6, 6 grade-5, 15 grade-4, 20 grade-3, 15 grade-2, 6 grade-1, and 1 grade-0. The classes grade into one another.

Genes of this kind, known as multiple genes or polygenes, are of great importance because such characters as height, weight, growth-rate, longevity, temperament, and mental capacity in man as well as in animals are under the control of polygenes. Unfortunately the study of their distributions in populations is extremely difficult and requires the discovery and perfection of new statistical techniques. It is therefore not yet possible to predict the results of inheritance involving polygenes as it is in the case of genes that control clear-cut characters in which segregative action can be detected.

Probably of the same nature as the polygenes are the so-called modifying genes whose effects are minimal but can modify the expression of ordinary genes. These effects, which are of fundamental importance for an understanding of how genes have contributed to evolution, will be considered later in connection with the gene-complex and the origin of dominance and recessiveness. (p. 88).

GENES DETERMINE SEX

In all but the most lowly organisms, the determination of sex results from a special case of the segregation of genes and chromosomes at the moment of formation of germ-cells. It will be remembered that chromosomes exist in the cells of the body in pairs, one member of each pair having been contributed to the organism from each of its parents. The members of each pair of chromosomes are similar (except that, of course, they may carry alleles at corresponding loci) in all the pairs except one, the pair of so-called *sex-chromosomes*, all the other chromosomes being referred to as *autosomes*. In organisms such as flies or mammals, the cells of females contain a pair of similar sex-chromosomes, called the X-chromosomes. In the cells of males the members of the pair of sex-chromosomes are dissimilar, one of them being like the X-chromosomes in the female, and the other different and called the Y-chromosome. The females therefore have a sex-chromosome pair designated XX while the males are XY.

At the meiotic division in the formation of the germ-cells, the members of the pair of sex-chromosomes separate from one another, with the result that the gametes contain only one sex chromosome and a single set of autosomes. As both the sex-chromosomes in the females are X, all the eggs contain one X. In the males the sperms contain *either* X *or* Y, and the numbers of X-bearing and of Y-bearing sperms are equal. An egg therefore has equal chances of being fertilized by an

X-sperm or a Y-sperm. In the former case, the fertilized egg or zygote will contain 2X and be a female; in the latter case the zygote will contain 1X and 1Y and be a male (Pl. 258). The mechanism is therefore self-perpetuating and ensures that the number of individuals of each sex in every generation are approximately equal.

As is so often the case, it was by means of exceptions to the normal procedure that the function of the chromosomes in determining sex was proved. In *Drosophila*, the diploid number of chromosomes is 8, so that there are 6 autosomes (3 pairs) and 2 sex-chromosomes. Occasionally, as a result of imperfections in the processes of meiosis, germ-cells are produced containing too many chromosomes of one kind or another. If the members of the pair of X-chromosomes fail to separate from one another (a condition known as 'non-disjunction'), both may pass into the same germ-cell which will therefore be an exception and contain 2X. If this then fertilizes a normal egg which also contains 1X, the zygote will contain 3 X-chromosomes. Similarly, the number of autosomes may exceptionally be increased in a zygote from the normal 6 to 9 if by non-disjunction a germ-cell contained 6 of them. A whole series of exceptional individuals can thus be obtained in which the ratio of the number of autosomes to the number of X-chromosomes varies, and can be expressed in tabular form as C. B. Bridges showed.

Number of X-chromosomes	*Number of Autosomes*	*Ratio of X to autosomes*	*Sex phenotype*
3	6	2	Super-female
3	9	3	Female
2	6	3	Female (normal)
1	3	3	Female
2	9	4.5	Intersex
1	6	6	Male (normal)
1	9	9	Super-male

From this table it will be seen that the determination of sex is due to a balance between the number of X-chromosomes and the number of autosomes. It follows that the X-chromosomes carry preponderatingly female-producing genes and the autosomes male-producing genes. The Y-chromosomes are largely 'dummies', mute dancing-partners for the X-chromosomes in the males and may play little or no part in producing the sexual characters. In some species the Y-chromosome is absent altogether. In other species such as man the details may by different.

There are two features in this mechanism of sex-determination that deserve particular attention. One is the fact that one sex, called the hetero-gametic sex because it produces two kinds of gametes, in the case described the male, is the instrument by means of which the determination is made, although it is not the 'determiner' since this depends on the chance meeting of a X-bearing or a Y-bearing sperm with an egg.

The second fact is that the male, with 1X can receive that X only from his mother, because all X-bearing sperms will produce XX zygotes and be females. The male can thus transmit his X-chromosomes only to his daughters. This 'criss-cross' type of inheritance is responsible for the distribution of so-called sex-linked characters because the genes controlling them are carried in the X-chromosome. The condition known as haemophilia, in which the blood fails to clot after a wound, is such a *sex-linked* character in man. It is recessive and therefore usually found only in women who are heterozygous for this gene, because the homozygous condition is lethal. A woman heterozygous for haemophilia produces eggs carrying the haemophilia gene and eggs carrying the normal allele in equal numbers. If such a woman marries a normal man, his Y-carrying sperm-cells fertilizing a haemophilia-carrying egg will produce a man who will suffer from haemophilia because, being a man he has only 1 X-chromosome and therefore no second X-chromosome carrying the normal allele which if present would dominate over the haemophilia gene and prevent it from manifesting its effects. A Y-carrying sperm fertilizing an egg carrying the normal allele will develop into a normal man who in himself and in his progeny will be free from haemophilia.

A X-carrying sperm fertilizing a haemophilia-carrying egg will develop into a woman phenotypically normal but heterozygous for haemophilia, who will therefore transmit the haemophilia gene to half her progeny. A X-carrying sperm fertilizing an egg carrying the normal allele will develop into a normal woman, free from haemophilia in herself and in her progeny. A classic case-history of this condition is provided by Queen Victoria who was heterozygous for the haemophilia gene (Pl. 259, 260).

There are many modifications of the sex-determining mechanism in different types of animals. Here it will suffice to mention the fact that in butterflies and in birds, the mechanism is identical with that described above except that it is the male who has the constitution XX and produces only one kind of sperm, while the female is XY, produces two kinds of eggs, and is therefore the heterogametic sex.

Although sex is determined at fertilization in those organisms possessing the genetic sex-determining mechanism, this does not mean that such determination is necessarily permanent. As has been seen it depends on a balance between the male-inducing and the female-inducing genes, and their rates of activity can change with the result that intersexual individuals can be produced. Furthermore, in long-lived animals such as birds and mammals, the balance of the genes at fertilization determines the sex of the reproductive gland, ovary or testis, which also secretes the appropriate sex-hormones, such as oestradiol or testosterone respectively (Pl. 376). The development of bodily sexual characters depends on the function of these hormones; but the time of their entry into action and the rate at which they are secreted is also under the control of genes other than those responsible for the initial determination of sex, and in some cases aberrations or even sex-reversal can take place.

GENES MUTATE

Mutation is defined as the inception of a heritable variation, the only known way by which such variation can be brought about. It may take the form of a change in a gene, or of an abnormality of the chromosome in the form of a deficiency of a portion of a chromosome, a translocation or an inversion of part of a chromosome, a duplication of part of a chromosome, a duplication of a whole chromosome, or a duplication of a whole set of chromosomes. Such abnormalities are the result of imperfect cell-division. In each case of chromosome abnormality, it is to the change in the genes involved that the effects are due. A striking example of a mutation in man, caused by chromosome abnormality, is the condition known as mongolism, due to the duplication of a whole chromosome with the result that such subjects have 47 instead of 46 chromosomes (Pl. 235).

Gene mutations are chemical changes in the gene-molecule and are the start of the difference between any two allelic genes. After it has mutated, a mutant gene is preserved by replication in its mutant state until it mutates again. In so doing, a gene may mutate in a new direction, or it may mutate back to the condition in which it was before it mutated (reverse mutation). Similar gene mutations at any locus of a chromosome may occur repeatedly.

The frequency with which gene mutations normally occur has been estimated. In organisms as different as a bacterium, a maize plant, a fruit-fly, and man, it is found to be of roughly the same order of magnitude. At each locus in the chromosomes at each generation, a mutation takes place roughly once in every half a million individuals. This may not seem a high rate, but as will be shown later it is sufficient to supply the heritable variation for evolution.

Inversions and translocations of portions of chromosomes may play an important part in genotypic variation by bringing close together in the same chromosomes the loci of genes whose combined effects are particularly beneficial when inherited together. The closer together they are situated in the chromosome, the less frequently will they be torn apart by crossing-over and their combined effect lost. This is the manner in which genotypes controlling special adaptations are built up.

Duplication of chromosomes resulting in *polyploidy* is also of importance, particularly in plants, because this phenomenon leads to reproductive isolation and the formation of new groups (see p. 120).

As mutation is the only mechanism originating heritable variation, is has naturally been subjected to intense study. It has been found that certain physical agents such as ultra-violet light and radioactivity, and some chemical agents such as mustard-gas and its derivatives have the property of accelerating the frequency with which mutations occur. These induced mutations, however, are similar to those that occur and recur normally. The rate of mutation is known to be variable, and the mutagenic agents have merely speeded up the rate, without determining the quality or direction of mutation. As H. J. Muller showed, mutations take place blindly and unpredictably, and are not adaptive (page 98). If only they were adaptive, the problem of the origin of adaptations would be easily solved: the appropriate mutation would be evoked by the environment and produce the beneficial change resulting in adaption to that environment; but the fact, based on countless rigorous experiments, must be faced that organisms are *not* endowed with the providential ability to respond appropriately to the conditions of the environment by producing new mutations resulting in characters adapted to those requirements.

Reference must be made here to the old controversy known as the inheritance of acquired characters. As already explained (p. 71) no character is solely inherited or acquired, but the controversy turns on whether a phenotypic and adaptive change evoked by environment or mode of life in the body of an organism, such as the enlargement of a blacksmith's biceps as a result of wielding a heavy hammer, can induce a mutation producing the same character in the offspring without the environmental factor that originally evoked the character in the parent.

Unicellular organisms like bacteria and protozoa are in a special position because when they reproduce as they do by fission, the body of the old individual is carried over into the bodies of the new, and with it any phenotypic adaptations that the environment had evoked in the old, but this is not genetic inheritance of an acquired character. Bacteria can show remarkable powers of adaptation as a result of which they become able to make use of abnormal supplies of food or resistant to antibiotic and other drugs. Sir Cyril Hinshelwood has shown that this adaptation or training is not the result of the selection of pre-existing mutants, but of a reorganization of the mechanism of synthesis in the cells, which may achieve a high degree of stability. It is however unlikely that the change is permanent and it is not thought that the presence of the substance to which the bacterium becomes adapted plays a part in inducing an appropriate mutation.

When the normal and universal process of sexual reproduction takes place by means of eggs and sperms, heritable characters are coded in the genes, and in spite of repeated attempts, no case is known where an adaptive character impressed phenotypically on the body of a multicellular organism by the environment is genetically so transmitted. The question of how adaptations arise is considered in greater detail later (p. 102). Here it must be noted that there is no basis for attempts

Mitosis, Cell Division in *Vicia faba* (Broad Bean)

237 238 239

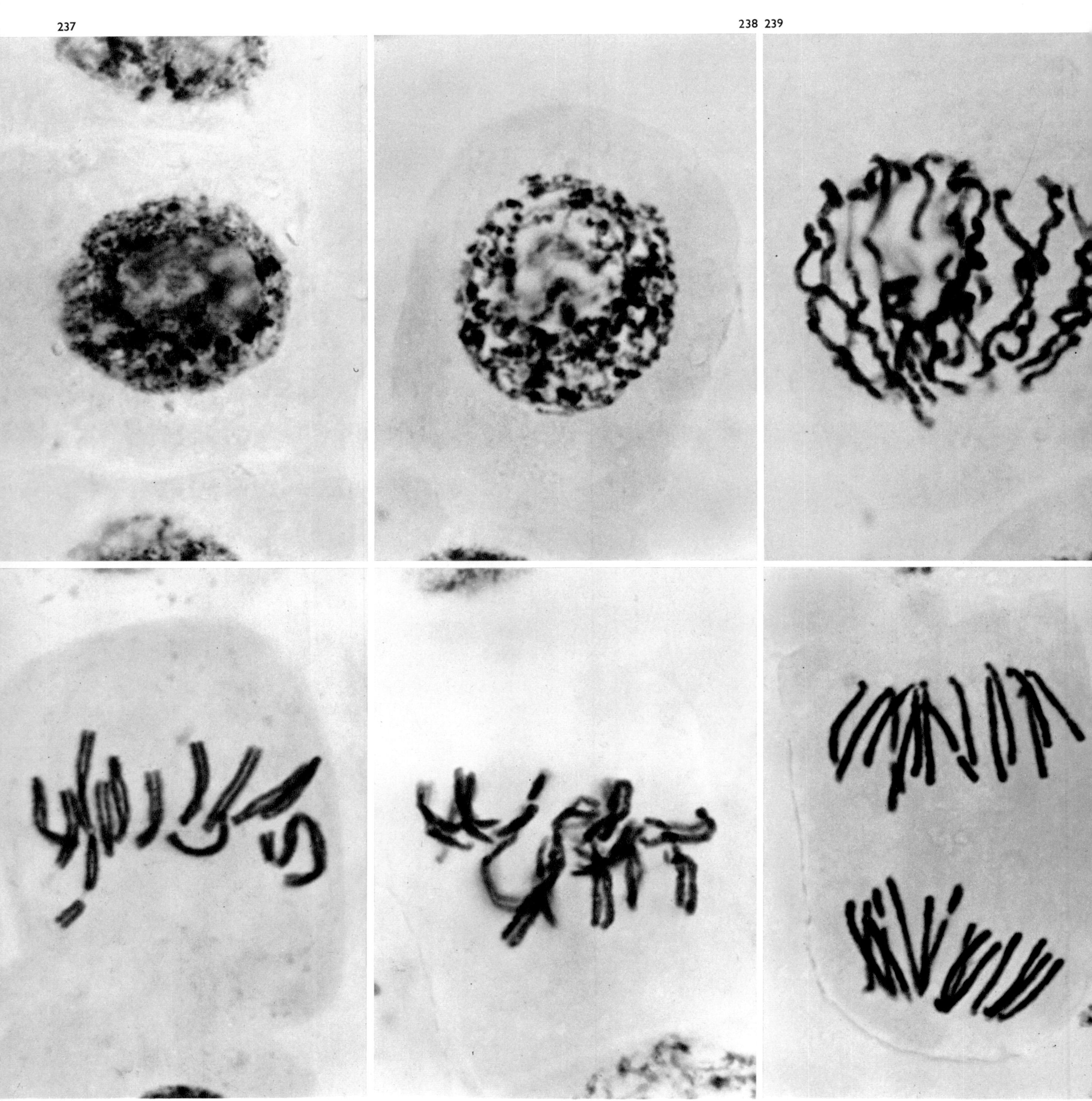

241 242 243

240

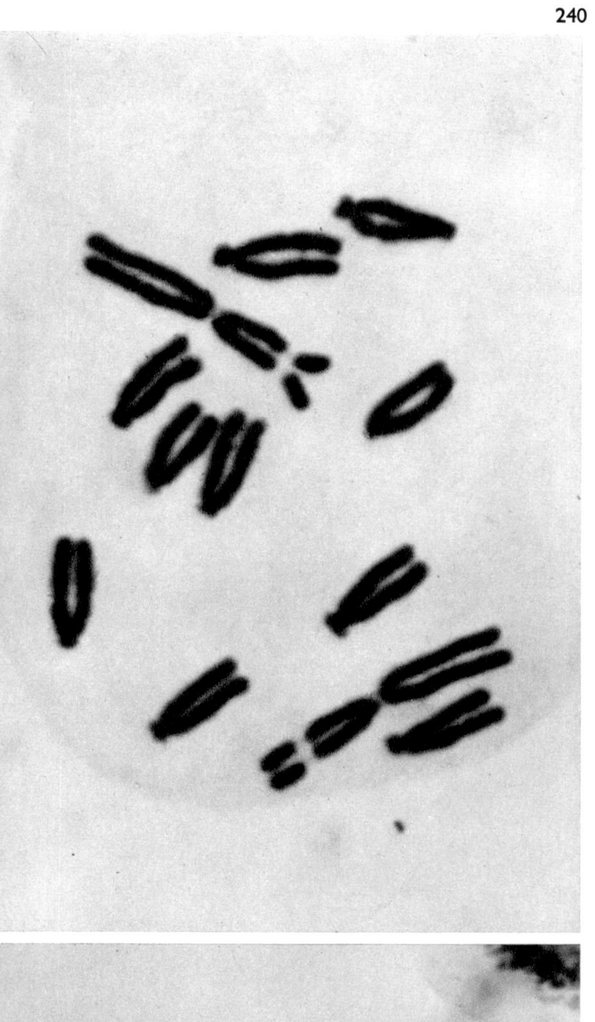

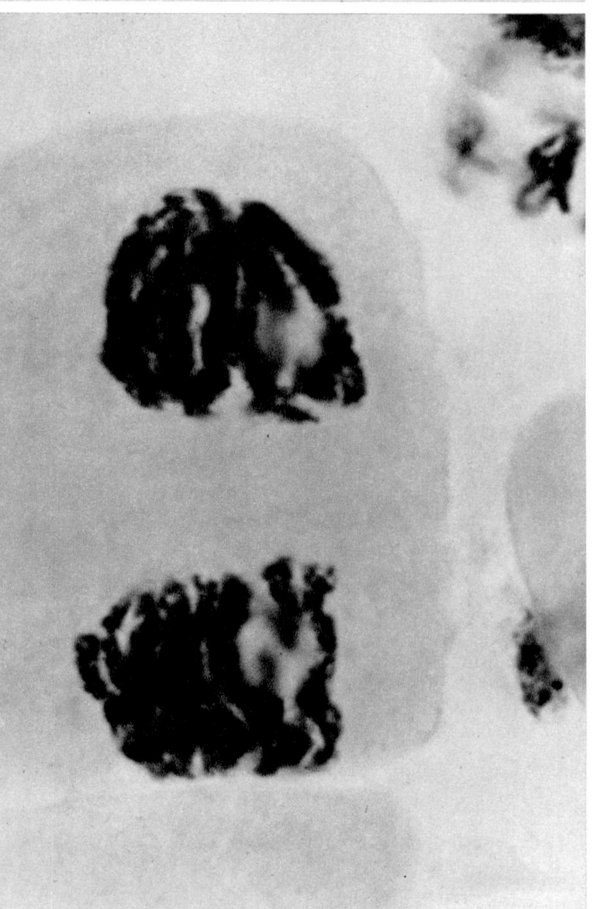

244

237. Resting stage of the cell; the nuclear membrane is present, enclosing granules of chromatin which are stained dark, and the nucleolus, looking like an unstained vesicle. **238.** Early prophase: chromatin granules begin to form visible chromosome threads. **239.** Later prophase: the nuclear membrane is dissolved and the nucleolus is invisible, chromosomes are distinct elongated double threads. **240.** Metaphase: twelve chromosomes spread out in the equatorial plane of the spindle, each split longitudinally except at the centromere or point of attachment to the spindle; ten chromosomes have centromeres near one end, two have them in the middle. **241.** The same chromosomes in a side view of the spindle. **242.** Early anaphase: the centromeres have just divided and begun to pull away from each other. **243.** Late anaphase: the spindle fibres attached to the centromeres have pulled the chromosomes to opposite poles of the spindle, twelve at each end. **244.** Telophase: two nuclei are forming, the chromosomes are losing their distinctness, nucleoli are appearing. **245.** Two nuclei are now completely formed with membrane and nucleolus; the body of the cell has divided between the nuclei and mitosis is complete. Photographs by S. H. Revell.

245

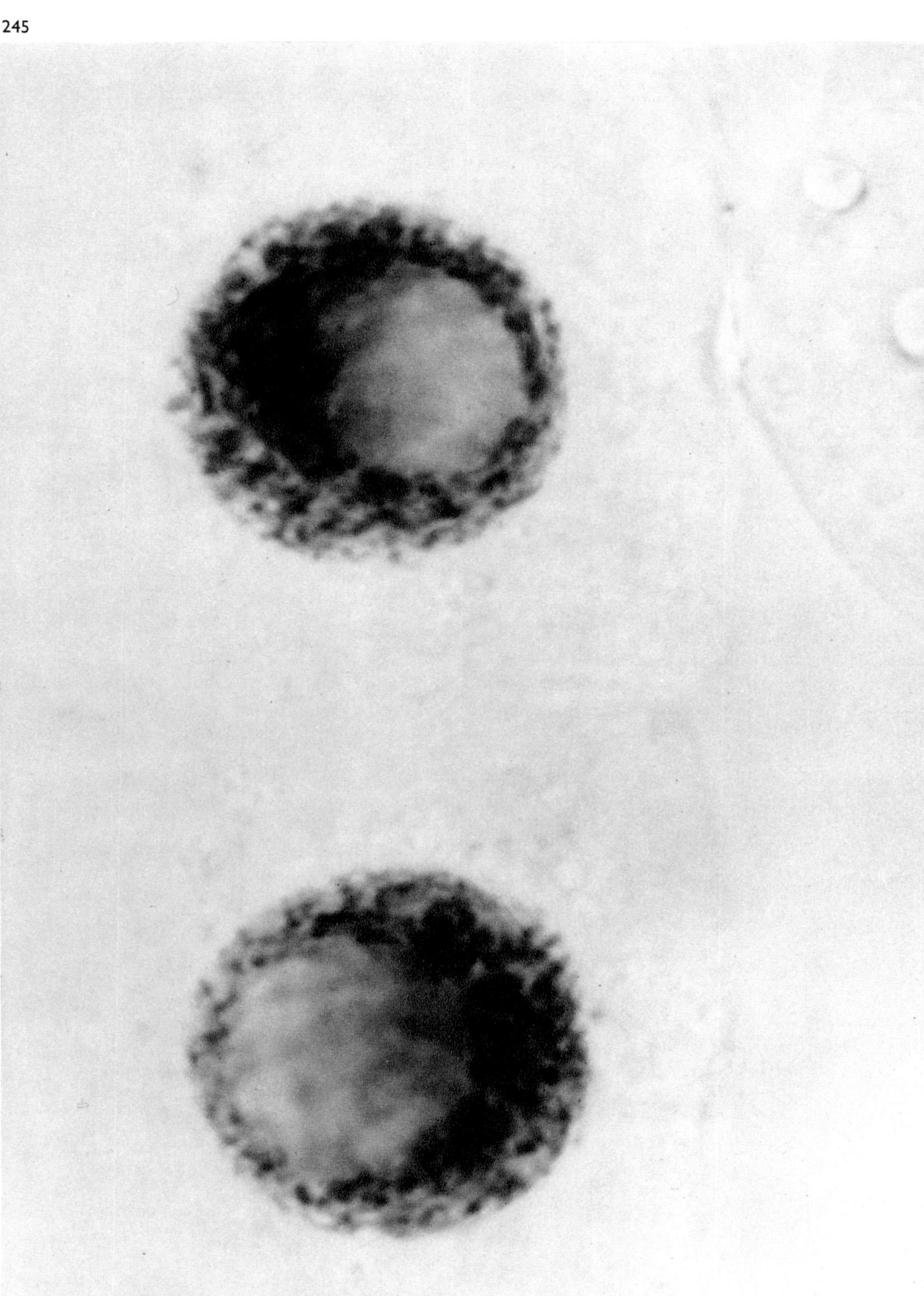

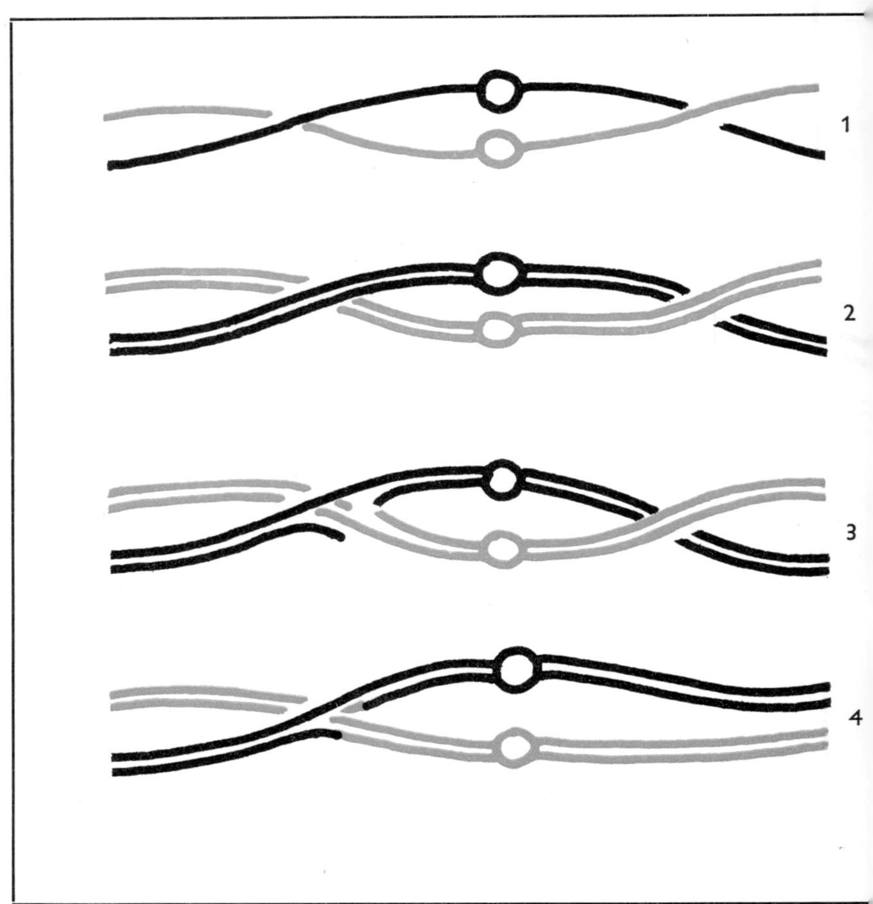

Crossing over in Meiosis

246. (1) Two chromosomes forming one pair; (2), each chromosome split lengthways forming four daughter-chromosomes; (3), breaks in two daughter-chromosomes at the crossing point shown by four loose ends. (4), the loose ends have joined with the 'wrong' partners forming a 'chiasma' or crossing-over; (5), centromeres begin to repel one another and pull the pairs of daughter-chromosomes apart and (6) the chiasma slips towards the end of the chromosomes as (7), the pairs of daughter-chromosomes are pulled apart, one in each pair containing part of one from the other pair; with this phase the first reduction division has taken place and the second reduction division is about to begin. (8) The centromeres have divided and are pulling the daughter-chromosomes apart. (9) Meiosis completed resulting in four haploid germ-cells each with half the number (one) of chromosomes present in the original diploid nucleus (two).

to rely on supposed directive effects of environmental factors if only they were allowed to act for a long enough time: if such effects existed and were powerful enough to affect mutation, they would be detectable during the time required to make the experiments. The fortuitous nature of mutations has to be accepted, and the deeper implications of this fact will be dealt with in the section of this chapter devoted to the consideration of the relations of mutation and selection (p. 98).

Meanwhile, attention may be turned to one further point about mutation which may appear paradoxical. Mutations are almost always unfavourable to the organism in the conditions under which they first occur, and it may be asked if this is so, why mutations are regarded as the source of those heritable variations on which natural selection works to improve the structure, manner of life, and adaptations of the species. The paradox is resolved when it is realized that it is at the moment when they occur and in the environment in which they occur that mutations are usually deleterious. But the conditions of the environment change, what was deleterious may become advantageous, and an example of how this has actually happened will be described in connection with industrial melanism, later in this chapter (p. 93).

WHAT GENES ARE MADE OF

Breeding experiments from the days of Mendel showed that genes are discrete particles that remain unchanged indefinitely until they mutate. When it was proved by T. H. Morgan that genes were carried in chromosomes in linear order, it was possible to make an estimate of the size of genes by calculating the probable number of genes in *Drosophila* and measuring the length of the chromosomes. The estimate worked out at the dimensions of a large chemical molecule. Meanwhile, the chemical composition of the substances contained in the nuclei of cells was investigated; in addition to protein it was found to contain complex substances known as nucleic acids, and these in turn to contain simpler types of molecules called nucleotide bases which belong to the group of compounds known as pyrimidines and purines. With the help of physical methods of investigation, by J. D. Watson, F. H. C. Crick, and M. H. F. Wilkins, far more is now known of the structure of nucleic acid.

The nucleic acid found in chromosomes is composed of long chains made up of an alternating succession of a sugar, deoxyribose, and a phosphate grouping, with the pyrimidine and purine bases attached to the sugar. It is known as deoxyribonucleic acid, conventionally abbreviated to *DNA*. Two of these chains wound spirally round one another form the backbone of *DNA*, like the sides of a spirally-twisted ladder. The rungs of the ladder are attached to the sugar portions of the chains, and the halves of each rung are made up of *one* pyrimidine and *one* purine loosely attached in the middle (Pl. 261-263). The pyrimidine may be *either* a substance known as cytosine *or* a similar substance known as thymine. The purine may be *either* a substance known as adenine *or* a similar substance known as guanine. If cytosine forms one part of a rung, the other part *must* be guanine; nothing else will fit in. Similarly, if thymine forms one part of a rung, the other part *must* be adenine; again nothing else will fit in. It is as if, owing to their different waist measurements, when going down a spiral staircase Sid could walk only with Gwen, and Tim with Anne.

This remarkable structure is nothing less than the physical and chemical basis of the genes. This is shown by the fact that when the *DNA* of one species or variety of bacterium is introduced into another bacterium, that other bacterium is transformed and continues to reproduce in the transformed condition characteristic of the donor bacterium. In other words, a part of the *DNA* functions as a gene and is incorporated in the genotype of the recipient as if it were a normal allele. This was shown by F. Griffith when he injected into mice live naked *Pneumococcus* bacteria together with dead starch-encapsuled *Pneumococcus*. Molecules of *DNA* from the latter must have been introduced into the former, for these thereafter bred true to the starch-encapsuled condition, thus proving that *DNA* molecules function as genes.

Viruses (p. 139) are little more than particles of *DNA*, and when a bacteriophage-virus enters a bacterium, it takes command and synthesizes bacteriophage substance out of the constituents of the body of the bacterium, and even induces the formation of chemical compounds that are not normally present in the bacterium at all (Pl. 363-365). Even more remarkable is the fact discovered by J. Lederberg that a 'temperate' (benign) bacteriophage-virus can be liberated from a bacterium when it takes one of the bacterium's genes with it, and then enters a bacterium of a different strain to which it hands over the gene which becomes part of the recipient's genotype. This process is called *transduction*.

The structure of *DNA* makes it possible to propose a mechanism for two of the most fundamental properties of chromosomes and genes: replication and mutation. Replication is the ability of chromosomes and genes to copy themselves, so that the daughter chromosomes that result from cell-division are qualitatively and quantitatively identical with their parent-chromosomes, and this presumably means that the order in which the pyrimidine and purine bases are arranged in each chromosome is exactly copied. When the cell divides, the two spirally-wound chains of each strand of *DNA* become unwound and each serves as the template for an identical chain to be synthesized beside it out of the soup of chemical substances available in the body of the cell. As for the rungs, if a molecule of cytosine is attached to a sugar molecule of the old chain, a molecule of guanine from the soup, and no other molecule, is fitted between the cytosine and the sugar at the same level of the new chain. Similarly with thymine and adenine. As chromosomes contain a great many strands of *DNA*, the division of the chromosomes involves replication of its contained *DNA* (Pl. 264, 265).

In some cases, the replication of the strands of *DNA* must be supposed to be slightly imperfect, as if the rungs of the ladder were inserted the wrong way round at any one level, or in the wrong order at any successive levels. Since there are two out of four possible nucleotide bases at any single level on the chains of *DNA*, there are four different ways in which a rung at that level can be formed: it could be Sid-Gwen, Gwen-Sid, Tim-Anne, or Anne-Tim. If as a result of ringing the changes on these possibilities the replication of the parent *DNA* is not perfectly identical, it is believed that the result is a mutation. The *DNA* then continues to

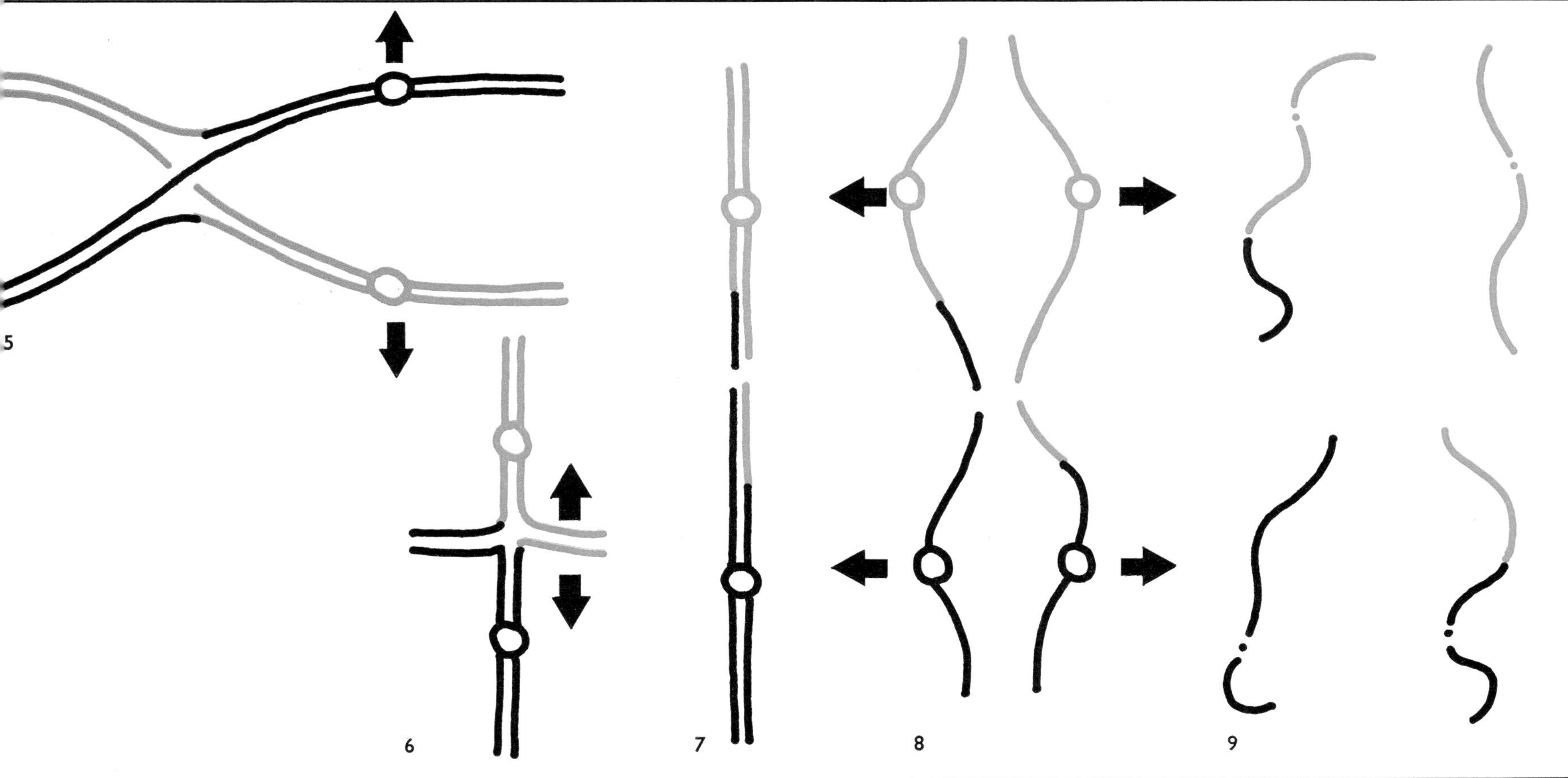

replicate in its mutated condition until it mutates again. As to why radiation should cause mutation (p. 83) and affect the order in which the nucleotide bases are formed, it is significant that the wave-length of maximum light-absorption by *DNA* is in the region of ultra-violet rays. Radiations from radioactivity and cosmic rays have high energy quanta, and although little of this radiation is absorbed, if only one quantum scores a 'direct hit' the energy is sufficient to break chemical bonds and the nucleic acid molecule could then re-form in a different way.

Since there are indications (which will be given later, p. 136) that genes function by guiding protein synthesis with the help of enzymes that activate amino acids, and since the number of amino acids found in living matter of any kind does not exceed twenty four, the code of genetic information embodied in a gene must have the possibility of making at least that number of signals. As just explained, different arrangement on one rung of nucleotide bases can allow four different signals to be made; two adjacent rungs could allow sixteen; and three adjacent rungs could allow sixty-four different signals. The basis of a gene may therefore be a unit of three rungs, or a triplet of three bases, on a strand of *DNA*, and researches by F. H. C. Crick and his colleagues have shown that this is probably correct. As there are sixty-four possible signals and less than twenty-four are required, there would be forty signals to spare, but it is probable that more than one triplet of bases can code the same amino acid. The manner in which the code of genes in DNA is believed to be translated into synthetised proteins in the cell is described later (p. 88) in the section describing how genes work.

The knowledge already obtained makes it possible to make remarkable calculations, as H. J. Muller and T. Dobzhansky have shown. A human germ-cell, whether egg or sperm, contains 4 cubic micra (a micron is one thousandth of a millimetre) of *DNA* and weighs four million-millionths of a gram. If there are 3,000 million people alive on earth today, they are the product of 6,000 million germ-cells, and the total volume of *DNA* that has determined the genotypes of all men living is 2.4 cubic millimetres and its weight is 24 milligrams, about the dimensions of a raindrop.

A single human gamete contains in its *DNA* four thousand million pairs of nucleotide bases (cytosine and guanine, thymine and adenine), and as there are four kinds of these, the number of different possible permutations in which they could be arranged along the length of the *DNA* strands in one gamete is a figure of the order of magnitude of 10 raised to the power of two-and-a-half million. Even if it does little else, an estimate such as this may serve to show something of the enormous potential variability available.

HOW GENES WORK

Genes are the agents by which the hereditary characters are transmitted from parents to offspring in the form of a coded message in which the cipher-groups are chemical molecules. This function, which forms the basis of the science of genetics, is exerted during the formation of the germ-cells with segregation of pairs of alleles, and as a result of random fertilization of eggs by sperms. It occupies two cell-generations immediately prior to the formation of the germ-cells when, as already explained, the cells divide twice while the chromosomes divide only once, thereby reducing their number from the diploid to the haploid state. The genetic aspect of genes is studied by means of the breeding pen and the microscope.

Genes are also the agents by means of which the fertilized egg is directed on its path of development and grows and differentiates into an adult plant or animal. This function which occupies many cell-generations (fifty in the case of man) involves decipherment and expansion of the coded message. It is studied by the techniques of embryology, physiology, and biochemistry. It forms what C. H. Waddington has called the 'epigenetic' system. Both the genetic and the epigenetic functions of genes must be borne in mind when considering how genes work.

Remarkable advances in knowledge have resulted from experiments designed to investigate the manner in which genes exert their first effects. Genes that control the colours of flowers are numerous, and these colours are due to chemical substances of which the composition and structure in many cases are known. Researches in this field have enabled W. J. C. Lawrence and his colleagues to show that the genes that control colours do so by regulating specific chemical processes, such as the attachment of methyl, hydroxyl, or carbohydrate groups to a compound such as anthocyanin. The genes therefore exert their effects through control of particular biochemical processes of synthesis.

A fundamental part in the synthesis of living matter is played by enzymes, protein molecules that have the property of controlling and accelerating the production of specific chemical substances. The relation of enzymes to genes has been shown by the researches of G. W. Beadle and E. L. Tatum on the fungus *Neurospora*, a very suitable organism on which to study the biochemical effects of gene mutations. *Neurospora* can live, grow, and synthesize its own living matter on a basic diet of very simple ingredients such as water, simple salts, sugar, ammonia, and the vitamin biotin. Out of these, it is able to synthesize amino acids and build up the purines, pyrimidines, nucleic acids, and proteins of its body. Mutations can be induced in *Neurospora* by exposure to X-rays, and it is then found that the mutant genes prevent the organism from synthesizing one or other of the amino acids that it requires. It is then unable to live on its basic diet; but by supplying treated organisms with different amino acids, each added to the basic diet one by one, it is possible to identify the one which makes good the deficiency caused by any particular mutation and enables the organisms to live. The synthesis of each amino acid out of simpler substances is carried out by means of a particular enzyme system, and the work on *Neurospora* indicates that the synthesis of each amino acid involves a particular enzyme the production of which is controlled by a particular gene.

The analysis has been carried a stage further by studies on ribonucleic acid, *RNA* a substance similar to *DNA* except that the sugar portions of the spiral chains are ribose instead of deoxyribose and the nucleotide base uracil is present in place of thymine. While *DNA* is found in the nucleus, *RNA* occurs mostly in the surrounding portion or cytoplasm of the cell. It is believed that chains of *RNA* copying the

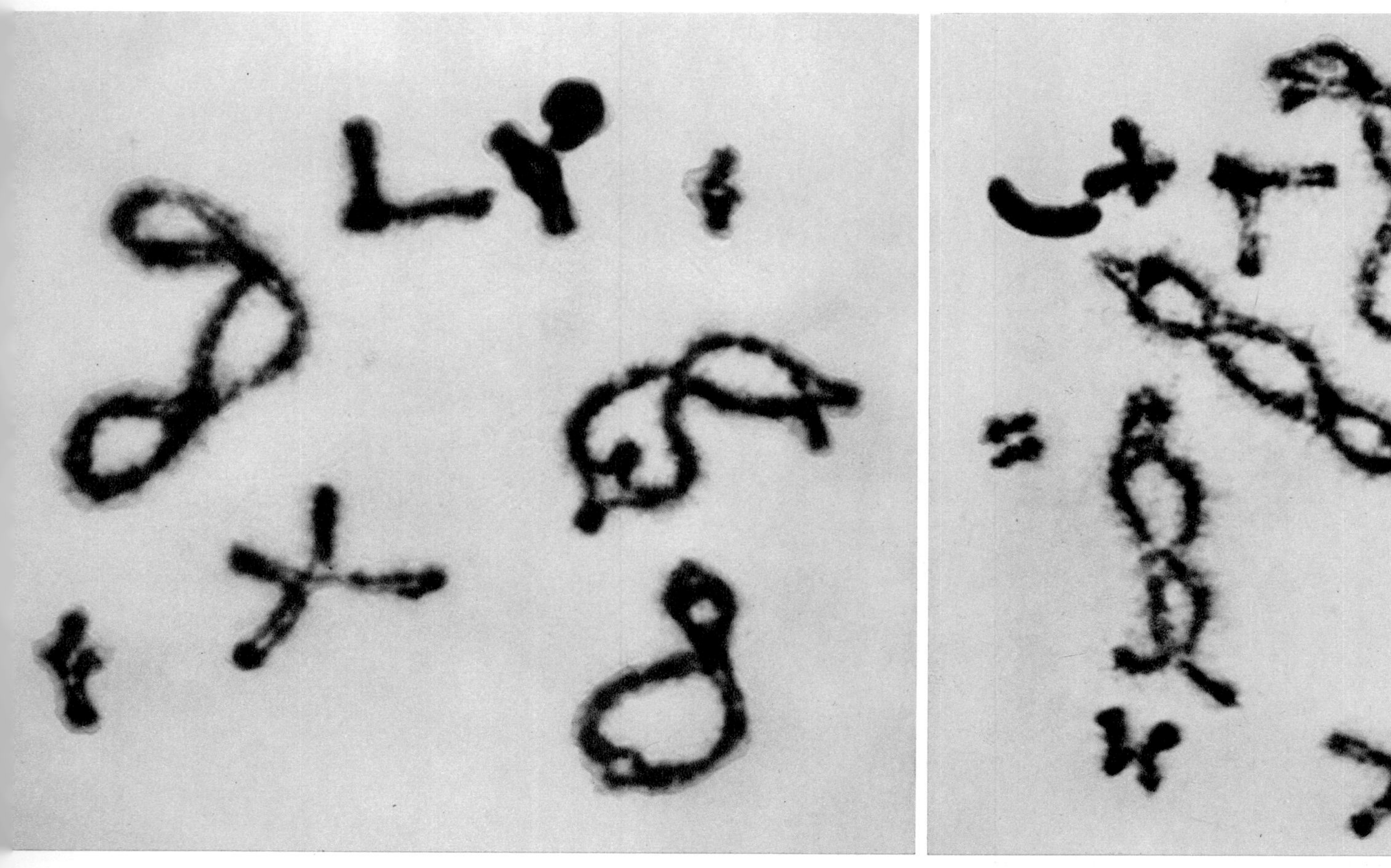

247

247. Photographs of chromosome-pairs in meiosis in the grasshopper *Chorthippus parallelus* showing some with one, two, three, and four chiasmata at each of which crossing-over has taken place.

chains of *DNA* with their genetic code pass out of the nucleus into the cytoplasm as 'messengers' and there out of the soup of available substances join amino acids in the sequence corresponding to the sequence of bases in the *DNA*. This has been shown to happen by M. W. Nirenberg and J. H. Matthaei who introduced synthetic chains of *RNA* in which the identity of the bases was known into a cell-free soup and obtained chains of particular amino acids. Since the properties of proteins depend on the identity of the amino acids they contain and the sequence in which they are arranged, a chemical mechanism is provided for the translation of the inherited code of genes into the synthesis of particular proteins.

In one case it has been possible to follow a causal chain through from gene to amino acid to phenotypic effect. This is the condition in man known as 'sickle-cell' where the red blood-corpuscles contain an abnormal type of the red oxygen-carrying substance haemoglobin, with results of great importance concerning adaptation, described later (p. 93). Here the important point to notice is that sickle-cell is caused by a single gene, and that the abnormal haemoglobin owes its abnormality to the substitution of one amino acid, valine, for another, glutamic acid, which occupies its place in a molecule of normal haemoglobin (Pl. 279-283).

These examples will give an indication of the basic chemical mechanisms by which genes exert their effects.

It has already been mentioned (p. 71) that the particular phenotype which a given genotype produces from among the range of phenotypes that it could produce is determined by the factors of the environment. This fact is well illustrated by the red variety of the garden primrose *Primula sinensis*. If this plant is grown in a hothouse at a temperature of between 59° and 68° F, the flowers are not red but white. This is a matter of chemistry. There is another variety of *Primula sinensis* with white flowers at any temperature from the normal garden temperature up to 68° F. The two varieties differ genetically. At high temperatures therefore the phenotype 'white-flowered primrose' contains two genotypes, and these examples show not only that the phenotypic effect of a gene depends on the environmental factors, but also that genes may differ in the extent to which their effects are subject to environmental factors.

A similar case is the gene which controls the colour of the hair in certain mammals. In the Himalayan rabbit there is a gene responsible for the development of white fur at normal body-temperature of mammals. At lower temperatures, this gene results in the production of black fur, because certain melanin pigments are then not oxidized. This, again is a matter of chemistry. The Himalayan rabbit is born white all over, having been maintained at a high constant body-temperature in the womb of its mother. After birth, however, its extremities, the muzzle, ears, and feet, turn black, and these are the parts of the body most subject to chilling because of their exposure. If the black hair of the ear of such a rabbit is shaved and the rabbit is kept in an artifically high temperature, the newly grown hair is white. The Siamese cat is similar, the beige colour of the body-hair turning black on the muzzle, ears, feet, and the tip of the tail (Pl. 266).

The gene-complex

It is not only with the factors of the environment that genes react; they react with one another to such an extent that the sum total of genes in an organism has to be regarded as a gene-complex in which the effects of individual genes are subject to the modifying effect of others. In *Drosophila* there is a gene that determines the condition known as 'eyeless', which is of course deleterious (Pl. 267). It is nevertheless possible for 'eyeless' flies to mate. The mortality of the offspring is very high, but if breeding from the survivors is continued, after some generations flies with eyes begin to appear among the offspring, and eventually most of the flies have what look like normal eyes. It can be proved that there has been no contamination of the original 'eyeless' gene, by mating these phenotypically 'eyed' but genotypically 'eyeless' flies back with the normal wild type, when it is found that the 'eyeless' gene is present and produces its deleterious effects as regularly as before.

The explanation is that the 'eyeless' gene produces the 'eyeless' phenotype in the particular gene-complex of the normal wild type of fly. During the inbreeding of eyeless flies, the other genes of the gene-complex that were present in the heterozygous condition underwent segregation and recombination; the gene-complex was re-shuffled. Those gene-complexes that reacted with the 'eyeless' gene by means of the effects of modifier genes to produce the 'eyeless' phenotype were extinguished by death. Those gene-complexes, on the other hand, that minimized the 'eyeless' condition by means of the effects of other modifier genes survived and left offspring in which this minimizing of the bad effect was continued. In other words, the phenotypic effect of the 'eyeless' gene was progressively suppressed by the action of the other genes of the gene-complex, and this took place naturally and automatically as a result of the extinction of unsuitable gene-complexes and the survival of the more favourable gene-complexes. In other words again, here is natural selection improving adaptation by gradual change through differential mortality. This is the key to the explanation of evolution by natural selection of genotypes.

The principle of modification of the phenotypic manifestation of a gene, through selection of the gene-complex and re-shuffling of the modifier-genes, has been established by the experiments of R. A. Fisher. In the first place, it has been shown that the difference between dominance and recessiveness in different genes is an effect of the reaction of the other genes of the gene-complex. When a gene first mutates, the usual case is that it is neither dominant nor recessive and that the heterozygote is visibly (phenotypically) different from both homozygotes. If the effect of such a gene is less advantageous than that of the normal allele from which it mutated, which, under the environmental conditions that applied when the mutation occurred, is almost always the case, then in the course of a few generations the re-shuffling of the modifier genes in the gene-complex takes place in the direction of minimizing the phenotypic effects of the mutant gene. What this means is that the gene is gradually *made to become recessive*, and concurrently the normal allele is gradually *made to become dominant*. Most mutations that have been observed to take place in wild forms and in the laboratory are recessive, and the reason for this is probably that these very same mutations have taken place repeatedly before. The gene-complex has had experience of them and is then able to demote such mutants to the recessive condition each time they reappear.

The proof of this principle of the evolution of dominance, for that is what it implies, was provided by E. B. Ford by experiments on the currant moth, *Abraxas grossulariata*. In the typical form of this moth, the pattern is superimposed on a white background. There is a variety, *lutea*, in which the background is suffused with yellow; *lutea* differs from *grossulariata* by a single gene.

When *lutea* and *grossulariata* are crossed, the F_1 heterozygotes are almost intermediate in colour; neither gene is dominant, and there is a certain amount of variability in the depth of the yellow in the background. If the whiter F_1 variants are chosen to breed from, they eventually produce a strain in which the white background of the heterozygotes is almost indistinguishable from the white *grossulariata* homozygote. In this strain the *grossulariata* gene has been made to become dominant and the *lutea* recessive. Conversely, if the yellower heterozygotes are chosen for breeding, they eventually produce a strain in which the yellow background of the heterozygotes is almost indistinguishable from the yellow *lutea* homozygote. In this strain the *lutea* gene has been made to become dominant and the *grossulariata* recessive. These experiments on insects have been confirmed in cotton-plants by S. C. Harland who found that the extent of dominance or recessiveness of any gene is determined by the gene-complex as a whole (Col. Pl. 7).

In the light of these experiments it is possible to see how and why the effects of some genes are dominant and the effects of other genes recessive, and also why some genes are dominant for some of their phenotypic effects and recessive for others. An example of such a case is the gene in poultry responsible for producing the crest of feathers on the head characteristic of Japanese silky fowls, in respect of which it is dominant, and for producing a hernia at the top of the skull in respect of which it is recessive. In the Polish breed of fowls where fanciers have aimed at producing a high-domed skull, the hernia effect is no longer recessive (Pl. 269, 270).

These cases of artificial selection by man producing dominance of some characters controlled by a gene and recessiveness of other characters controlled by the same gene have their precise counterparts in nature. In the moth *Ephestia kühniella* there is a pair of allelic genes controlling brown or red colour of a reproductive organ; but each gene affects several characters, and as E. Caspari showed, each is dominant in respect of the characters it controls which are advantageous and recessive in respect of those which are disadvantageous.

Cases like the foregoing introduce an important consequence which is that where the favourable effects of a particular gene are dominant and the unfavourable effects recessive, the homozygotes will have both advantages and disadvantages while the heterozygotes as P. M. Sheppard showed have advantages only, because recessive effects are not revealed in the heterozygous condition. Where the heterozygote is favoured compared with the homozygotes, the population will contain two phenotypes corresponding to the homozygote and heterozygote genotypes in certain proportions, and this condition is known as balanced polymorphism (p. 95).

Since the very fact that a gene is recessive means that its effects are unfavourable and that its allele without those effects has become dominant, it follows that the heterozygote will not show those unfavourable effects and will mask the presence of the recessive gene. This has many consequences, of which the more important are the following. As has been shown (p. 75), when heterozygotes breed they produce 25 per cent of each kind of homozygotes, and therefore a population cannot avoid containing individuals carrying homozygous recessive genes even if their effects are unfavourable, and this condition is intensified by inbreeding (p. 75). When crosses are made between different strains the recessive genes of the one are masked by the respective dominant alleles of the other with the result that the unfavourable effects are minimized, and the offspring of such crosses show 'hybrid vigour' and are superior to both parent strains.

The second consequence is that dominant genes make it possible for mutant genes to be collected and sheltered in the heterozygous condition even if their effects are unfavourable in the conditions under which the mutations occurred (p. 93); but such genes may become favourable when conditions change (p. 95), and this is how evolutionary novelties arise and are built into the genotype.

In all these experiments involving change of the phenotypic effects of genes by the modifying action of other genes in the gene-complex, an indispensible condition is that these other genes must be present in the heterozygous condition. If they were homozygous, there would of course be no segregative effect producing different genotypes, and the gene-complex would not be re-shuffled. It is therefore of importance to prove that in wild populations in nature heterozygotes are common. The proof was provided by S. S. Tschetwerikoff who found that wild populations of *Drosophila* in nature carried enormous numbers of recessive genes concealed in the heterozygous condition. Very few flies do not carry at least one recessive mutant gene. Other investigations on populations of maize, shrimps, and mice, have revealed a similar profusion of heterozygotes.

Conversely, in order to establish the principle of the modification of the phenotypic effects of genes by the other heterozygous genes in the gene-complex, it is necessary to show that if all the genes in the gene-complex are homozygous, no modifying effect is produced at all. This proof was furnished by W. Johannsen in his experiments on pure lines in beans. In a pure line strain of beans, homozygous for all its genes, as already explained, it makes no difference whether large seeds or small seeds are chosen to breed from; the average size of the seeds produced does not vary at all.

The result of all these experiments has therefore been to show that the phenotypic effects of genes can be and are *gradually* modified, in strict accordance with the Mendelian pattern of distribution of genes, by breeding and continuing to breed from parents with genotypes showing the phenotypic characters that it is desired to accentuate. This is tantamount to saying that choice of parents from which to breed affects the genotype and phenotype of the offspring. Another word for choice is *selection*. These experiments have therefore shown that selection is capable of modifying plants and animals during descent, and that is all that Darwin claimed.

ARTIFICIAL SELECTION

Artificial selection is the deliberate breeding by man from certain variants of his cultivated plants and domestic animals rather than from others, with the object of emphasizing the characters which he wants. It has been practised by man since the Neolithic period some ten thousand years ago, and it has produced the difference between the cabbage and the cauliflower (Pl. 17), the cart-horse and the Shetland pony (Pl. 27), the bloodhound and the pug (Pl. 44). It was by noticing the effects of variation and selection in domestic plants and animals that Darwin was led to look for an analogous kind of selection in nature.

The artificial selection of cereals

The basic distinction between cultivated cereals, such as wheat, barley, oats, and rye, and their nearest related wild species is in the stalk of the ear which holds the ripened grains and is called its axis or rhachis. This is usually tough and retentive in the cultivated forms and fragile in the wild species.

In most wild grasses the axis shatters easily when ripe, scattering the grains, which is an adaptation conferring advantage because it prevents overcrowding of seedlings. From time to time they produce variants with a more retentive axis. This limitation of its means of dispersal is disadvantageous to an annual grass in a wild state; under cultivation, however, forms with an axis that breaks up late or not at all are preferable, because their ears are then easier to harvest without loss of grain. Such variants are automatically better fitted for survival under human care than their fragile ancestors, but would not survive in a natural wild state. A mutation of this kind made possible the perpetuation and development of the basic diploid wheat, einkorn, as a crop.

In common with other grasses, cereals have wind-pollinated flowers, their light dry pollen being air-carried from their well-exposed anthers to their equally well-exposed feathery stigmas. Pollen of different species can thus drift on to the stigmas with the result that a cereal crop may receive new characters by hybridization with related plants growing nearby. The diversity of the cultivated wheats is believed to be partly the result of such hybridization between species which are classified into the related genera *Triticum*, *Aegilops*, and *Agropyron*.

Artificial selection in wheat. The cultivated wheats provide the daily bread and other cereal foods of a great part of humanity. Their cultivation began in Neolithic, if not late Mesolithic, times, at least ten thousand years ago, and on account of this antiquity their origin is obscure. They do not match any known plant in a wild state, but their wild ancestors were evidently grasses native to western Asia. From these, by mutation, by natural hybridization, and by selection to meet human needs over thousands of years, and recently by deliberate controlled breeding, the wheats have evolved into many thousands of kinds, called cultivars and strains.

In western Asia occur species of wild grasses of the tribe Hordeae that are believed to be ancestral to the cultivated wheats. Four of these species are *Triticum boeoticum* (synonym *T. aegilopoides*), *Triticum dicoccoides*, *Aegilops squarrosa*, and a species of *Agropyron*.

Primitive people in various parts of the world gather seeds of wild grasses for food. The discovery by prehistoric men that a seed would produce a new plant, giving seed of the same kind when sown and tended, made civilization possible. To provide a start for a grain crop, the grass must be one that will thrive if accidentally dispersed around human dwellings, and then yield enough to encourage deliberate harvesting, storing, and sowing.

The first accidental cultivation of such grasses may have been near Mount Carmel, where flint sickles have been found, used about eight thousand years ago. Ancient Egyptian tradition relating to the god Osiris also indicates Syria or Palestine as the region where wheat and barley were found wild and first cultivated. In Syria grew up the cult of the Corn God Tammuz, or Adonis (Pl. 271-276).

The production of cultivated wheats, elucidated by H. Helbaek, has involved not only hybridization between different species but also increase in number of the chromosomes, a condition known as polyploidy. As described in a previous section (p. 79), ordinary cells have two sets of chromosomes, symbolized as $2n$. Individuals containing $2n$ chromosomes are called *diploid*, but the reproductive cells (pollen and egg-cell) contain only one set (n), which is called the *haploid* number. Fertilization brings together one set from the male and one from the female; thus the fertilized egg-cell has a double set ($n + n$), and the facts can be tabulated as in Plate 277.

The basic chromosome-set of one species may be represented by the letter A, of another by the letter B, etc. When, through hybridization, a chromosome-set (A) of one species is mated with a set (B) from another species, sterility may result unless, as happens occasionally, both sets are immediately doubled, as a result of a division of the chromosomes without a division of the reproductive cell, resulting in *tetraploid* individuals.

It will be noticed that the suffix *ploidy* is used to indicate the number of basic chromosome-sets in ordinary cells of the plant-body; a *diploid* has 2 sets, a *triploid* 3 sets, a *tetraploid* 4 sets, a *hexaploid* 6 sets, and so on. A *polyploid* is a plant with more than 2 sets.

By their chromosome-numbers the wheats are classified into three main groups:
Diploid or einkorn group ($2n = 14$)
Tetraploid or emmer group ($2n = 28$)
Hexaploid or spelt group ($2n = 42$)

It is believed that groups with high chromosome numbers are descended from groups with lower numbers.

Diploid or einkorn group. The wild *Triticum boeoticum* and the cultivated einkorn (*T. monococcum*) have 7 chromosomes (i.e. set A) in the reproductive cells, and 14 (AA) in the ordinary cells. Einkorn is the most primitive of wheats, closely related to the wild *T. boeoticum* of the Balkan Peninsula and western Asia. It was grown in Neolithic times, but on account of its low yield it has been superseded in most regions, except in barren upland regions and on poor soils where other wheats fail.

Tetraploid or emmer group. Emmer wheats may have been derived from a wild species *Triticum dicoccoides* of western Asia which in turn may have arisen from *T. boeoticum* by hybridization with an *Agropyron* or *Aegilops* species. The wild species *T. dicoccoides*, the cultivated emmer (*T. dicoccon*), and macaroni wheat (*T. durum*) have 14 chromosomes (set AB) in the reproductive cells, 28 (AABB) in the ordinary cells. Of the 14 chromosomes, half (A) correspond to the 7 of the einkorn group. The other half (B) are believed to have come from the weed grass, *Agropyron* or *Aegilops*, hybridization having been followed by chromosome-doubling. In early Neolithic times, wheats of intermediate character, very near the present wild *T. dicoccoides* and much coarser than the oldest emmer known so far, were cultivated at Jarmo in Iraq.

Emmer is one of the oldest cultivated cereals and for thousands of years was apparently the only wheat grown in ancient Egypt, where it is frequently depicted in tomb paintings. The so-called 'mummy wheat' offered to tourists as having kept its viability for thousands of years is really modern-grown wheat. Emmer is not grown in modern Egypt. During Neolithic times, emmer, in association with barley and einkorn, was widely cultivated in Europe and western Asia. Although grown for human food in Abyssinia, India, southern Russia, and here and there elsewhere on a small scale, it is economically unimportant today.

Hexaploid or spelt group. Spelt *(Triticum spelta)* and bread-wheat *(T. aestivum)* have 21 chromosomes (set ABD) in the reproductive cells, 42 (AABBDD) in the ordinary cells. Of the 21 chromosomes, 7 (D) are believed to have come from an otherwise worthless weed grass with hard husks, long beards, and a fragile shattering stem, *Aegilops squarrosa*, through hybridization of this species with a cultivated emmer wheat, followed by chromosome-doubling, whereby the sterile triploid became a fertile hexaploid. This belief is based on the fact that when *T. dicoccoides* is crossed with *A. squarrosa*, a hybrid is produced which resembles *T. spelta* and is fertile with it when crossed.

Spelt is a wheat which apparently originated during the Bronze Age in central Europe, north of the Alps. It was grown by the lakeside people of Switzerland and southern Germany, and was apparently taken by Teutonic tribes to northern Spain. Although yielding less than bread-wheat it is hardier, survives frosts that destroy other wheats, and is more resistant to fungal diseases.

Bread-wheat is the most widely cultivated of cereals, surpassing all other wheats in the suitability of its flour for making light porous bread. To this species belong more than 3,000 cultivars. They exhibit an enormous range of morphological diversity and of suitability to different climatic conditions. Vast acreages of Canada, Australia, and Russia are devoted to bread-wheat. In it the grain is loose within the spikelets of the ear and is thus easily separated from the chaff on threshing; it is, technically, a naked wheat, unlike the more primitive glume wheats such as spelt, emmer, and einkorn, in which the chaff or glume firmly encloses the grains.

Artificial selection in rye. Rye is believed to have originated over 2,500 years ago in Asia Minor from *Secale ancestrale*, a species with a fragile axis but fairly large grains. It grows wild in sandy places, and plants of this species that invaded cultivated areas as weeds among crops of wheat and barley became subject to the same process of selection as the crops. Forms with a more retentive axis were harvested with the wheat crop and threshed and sown with it. These weed ryes of Asia Minor formed the basis of cultivated rye.

When the cultivation of wheat extended northwards, rye accompanied it as a weed, since the two cereals could hardly be separated by primitive agriculturists. In other words, rye seed mimicked wheat seed. The ability of rye to thrive on poor soil and to resist frost and drought better than wheat, oats, and barley, enabled it to yield a crop when these failed, particularly during periods of climatic deterioration. In this condition, natural selection by climatic and soil factors eliminated the other cereals, leaving rye as the sole crop. It was then no longer a weed. Meanwhile, artificial selection by man favoured the forms with the greatest production of grain.

The evolution of rye exemplifies the effect of natural and artificial selection upon mutant genes occurring in man-made conditions unaccompanied by either hybridization or change in chromosome-number. Lacking these causes of increased variability possessed by wheat, the kinds of rye number scarcely more than fifty. Rye (*Secale cereale*) is, however, an important cereal crop in northern upland regions climatically too harsh for the profitable cultivation of wheat. In Scandinavia and central and eastern Europe, it provides flour for bread-making. In Britain it is grown primarily for cattle feeding, but the straw furnishes good thatch, covers for bottles, etc. Even today northern farmers sometimes plant a mixture of rye with other cereals, the relative success of one or the other depending on growing conditions during the year. In the Swiss Alps, rye has been grown at altitudes up to 7,000 feet.

Artificial selection in pigeons

The wild rock-pigeon *Columba livia* is the stock from which many distinct breeds of the domestic pigeon have been obtained by man as a result of selection. When these breeds are crossed the offspring revert to the type of the rock-pigeon.

The variations that breeders have aimed to maintain, or whose features they sought to exaggerate, involve both structure and behaviour. Breeds such as the carrier and racing-homer have been selected for speed of flight and ability to return to their homes; the tumbler for ability to turn aerial somersaults; the pouter and fantail for their remarkable courtship activities; the Russian trumpeter for its voice. It is probable that the earlier domestic breeds came from the east, and some of the present breeds such as barb, fantail, and tumbler can be traced back for three or four centuries.

In some cases this artificial selection by man has produced breeds that could not survive in a wild state. The silver owl breed, for example, has such a short beak that the parents are unable to feed their young, which are fed by foster-parents.

The results of artificial selection in pigeons provided Darwin with evidence that

248

The Habsburg jaw characteristic of kings of Spain, as seen in **248,** Charles II (1665-1700), and his father **249,** Philip IV (1621-1665). **250.** The production of supernumerary teeth is controlled by a dominant gene. **251.** Coloboma of the iris of the eye is controlled by a dominant gene. **252.** The production of supernumerary fingers or toes (polydactyly) is controlled by recessive genes. Consequently, this condition is rarely met apart from a few isolated communities where it may be quite common; in an isolated Spanish village of less than 200 people, almost the whole population has six or seven fingers on each hand.

Some Recognizable Effects of Genes in Man

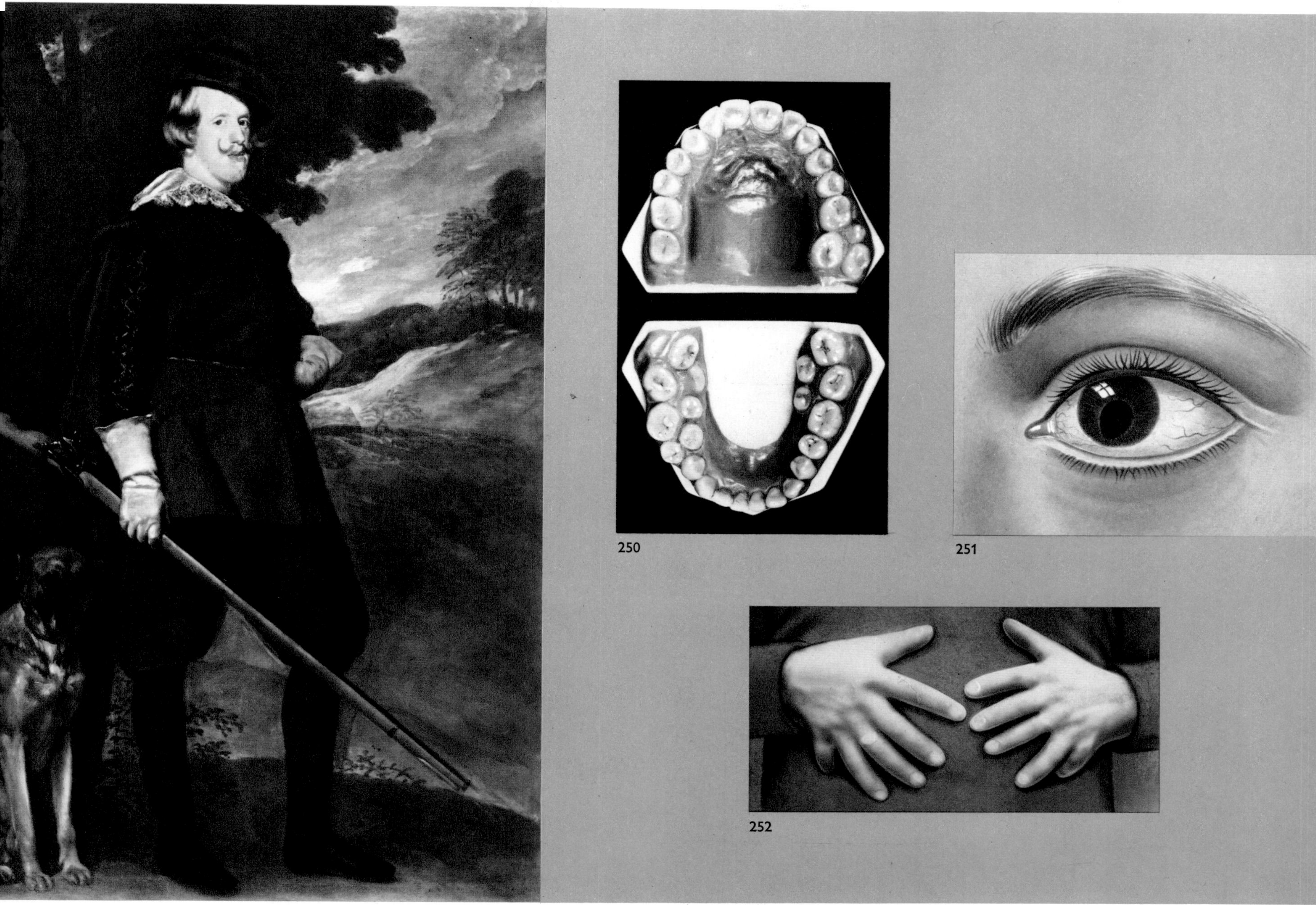

250

251

252

249

variation was fortuitous, for otherwise it would be necessary to believe that those variations that man has used to produce the various artificial breeds of pigeons arose for the purpose of gratifying the tastes and fancies of pigeon-breeders (Pl. 278).

The soundness of the parallel which Darwin drew between artificial selection and natural selection has been substantiated by the results of recent practice in artificial selection. Breeders have discovered that success in building up a breed with the desired qualities depends on the selection of a number of characters in combination. Improvement in the yield of grain in cereals depends on the size of the grain, the number of flowering heads, and so on. The cultivation of melons has involved selection of strains possessing genes that confer resistance to infections by viruses and by fungus. Increased egg-laying in fowls depends on selection for such characters as early time of onset of laying, short periods of broodiness, lateness of cessation of laying, and so on. The combinations of desired characters are obtained by building up a genotype, and this is also how selection operates in nature.

NATURAL SELECTION IN ACTION

Natural selection works on a population showing heritable variation to produce a greater number of surviving offspring by that portion of the variants that is better adapted to its environment. Natural selection works on the phenotype, which means that of the survivors in a population in a given environment, only those that possess the appropriate genotype in that environment will be the parents of the survivors of subsequent generations. As the phenotype is the joint product of a genotype and of variable environmental factors (p. 71), phenotypes corresponding to one and the same genotype can show flexibility and variation on which selection acts. The effects of selection are therefore exerted on the genotype through the phenotype.

Where the environment is stable and an organism is already well adapted to it, natural selection will ensure that variability is reduced to a minimum. This is the principle known as *stabilizing selection*, which may come as a surprise to those who imagine that natural selection necessarily implies evolutionary change. It is in cases where the environment is not stable, or the organism is not yet well adapted to it, that natural selection results in choosing as parents for the succeeding generations those individuals whose genotypes react with the environment to give the better adapted phenotypes. This principle, which may be called *progressive selection*, has been responsible for the production of the plant and animal kingdoms as they are. Its operation, however, requires time. Darwin himself, in conversation with his son Leonard, as reported by E. B. Ford, advanced the opinion that evidence of evolutionary change might perhaps be noticeable over a period of fifty years. As in so many matters, his conjecture was not far from correct, as will be seen.

In all questions of natural selection, the environment is of paramount importance. As Sir James Gray expressed it, the organisms throw the dice of variation, but the environment calls the winning numbers. The truth of this can be demonstrated experimentally. In the fruit-fly *Drosophila* there is a gene that reduces the size of the wings to vestigial size. In the normal environment in which fruit-flies live, any condition in which the flies cannot fly is disadvantageous and penalized by natural selection. But if normal and 'vestigial' flies are exposed together in cages to strong wind, the flies with vestigial wings, not the normal flies, increase in number as L'Héritier and his colleagues discovered. This experiment shows how easily factors of the environment can tip the scales of advantage and disadvantage between a gene and its mutant allele. It also throws light on Darwin's acute observation that insects that inhabit small oceanic islands tend to be wingless. It is therefore clear

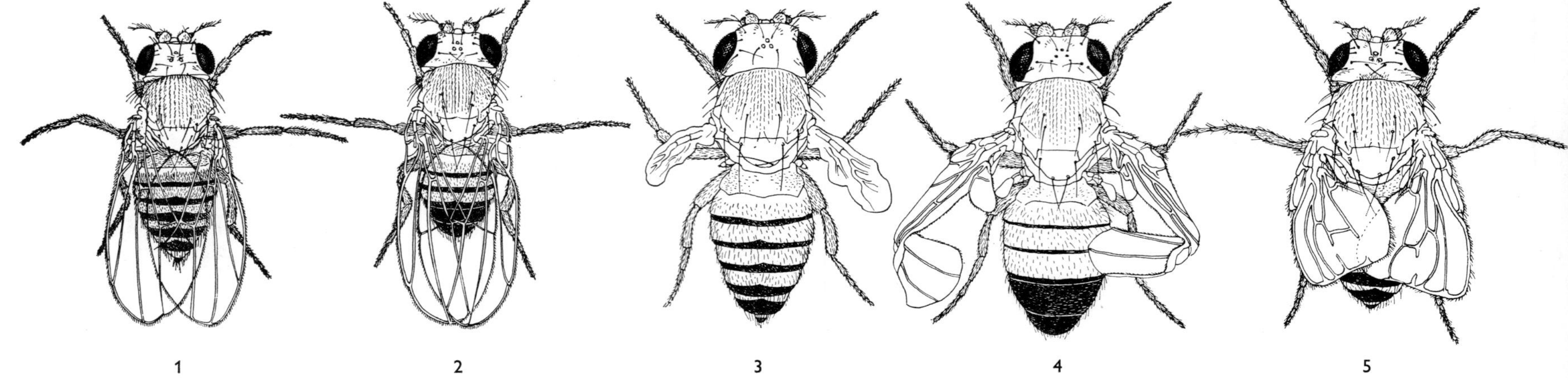

that the relations between organisms and the factors of their environment, living and inanimate, that constitute the science of *ecology*, are of fundamental importance for an understanding of natural selection and evolution.

A simple example of the significance of ecology for evolution is provided by the generalization associated with the name of G. F. Gause, that two different species cannot occupy the same ecological niche in nature, because in such competition they cannot be exactly equal and one will inevitably oust the other. This is why so much of evolution has been a hunt for unoccupied ecological niches, and it is also the explanation of Darwin's principle of divergence: 'the more diversified the descendants from any one species become in structure, constitution, and habits, by so much will they be better enabled to seize on many and widely diversified places in the polity of nature, and so be enabled to increase in numbers.'

The number of individuals in a population fluctuates, as a result of epidemics, food-shortage, or adverse ecological or physical conditions. Periods of low density of population are followed by periods of rapid increase, and at such times the intensity of selection is lowered and outbursts of variation occur. Further, as C.S. Elton showed, when population-pressure again reaches a high level, land animals tend to migrate and in so doing they tend to increase the ranges and the diversities of their habitats, which gives further scope for selection to act and adaptation to be produced. In a sense, the animals may then be said to select their environment.

The study of natural selection in the field therefore involves the collection of information on the incidence of casualties, fertility, evidence that those that do not survive are demonstrably lacking in adaptation, examples of change, and demonstration that such change has been in the direction of more efficient adaptation and brought about by the natural selection of mutant and recombined genes.

Casualties

One of the most striking proofs that the incidence of mortality in nature is high can be obtained from a comparison of the length of life of animals when exposed to the full blast of competition and adverse conditions in nature, and when kept in the shelter of captivity. By the method of ringing and sampling a population of wild birds, it is possible to estimate their average age under natural conditions. For the robin this is under one year, whereas a captive robin can be expected to live for 11 years. For a blackbird the expectation of life in nature is eighteen months; in captivity it is 20 years. For a herring-gull, the comparable figures are 2.8 and 44 years respectively. These figures will suffice to show that Darwin's deduction that there is a high rate of mortality in nature is true.

Next, it is necessary to see whether the incidence of mortality is correlated with imperfection of adaptation. As already mentioned (p. 91), it is an error to think of natural selection solely as an agent bringing about the change of a species. In stable conditions when an organism is well-adapted to its environment, natural selection ensures that variability is reduced to a minimum. That this is a fact is shown by the observations of H. C. Bumpus on the casualties suffered by a population of house-sparrows after a severe snowstorm. The birds found lying on the ground were collected, compared, measured, and weighed. It was found that they were variants that departed from the mean value in both directions, and were lighter or heavier, smaller or larger.

The success with which ducks' eggs hatch is correlated with their medium average size. If the eggs are either larger or smaller than this size, they hatch less frequently. In man, the expectation of life of new-born babies is correlated with the closeness of their approximation to a weight of 8 pounds at birth, and those that are markedly heavier are handicapped no less than those that are markedly lighter. There is therefore definite evidence that *stabilizing selection* results in some genotypes being favoured and others penalized.

The snail *Cepaea nemoralis* is preyed upon by various animals such as thrushes which hunt by sight. The visible appearance of a snail and the type of background on which it lives are therefore important factors in its survival or premature death. The species shows polymorphism (p. 95) and has many distinct varieties differing in the colour of the shell and the absence or presence of dark bands on it, and their number. The ground colour may be brown, pink, or yellow, and the genes concerned are a system of multiple alleles of one locus, yellow being recessive to the other two colours. The presence or absence of dark bands on the shell is controlled by a simple pair of allelic genes, the unbanded condition being dominant.

Thrushes bring snails to anvil-stones to break their shells and eat them. By making inconspicuous marks on the shells of live snails of different colours and placing them on different backgrounds such as brown dead leaves, grass, and coarse vegetation, and by collecting the debris of broken shells near the thrush's anvil-stone, A. J. Cain and P. M. Sheppard were able to determine the exact area over which the thrush had been working and the numbers of snails that it had taken of each variety. These numbers could be compared with the numbers of the total snail population on the particular background where they were taken. Against brown leaf litter, yellow shells are the most easily seen and captured. On the other hand, in grass, the yellow shells (which have a green tinge when the snails are inside them) are less conspicuous and less preyed upon by thrushes than the brown shells. In coarse vegetation, the shells with dark bands are less conspicuous and less preyed upon than unbanded shells.

By this means it has been shown that natural selection is active on populations of *Cepaea* and that the selective agent is predation by thrushes. Furthermore it has been shown that this accounts for the higher proportions of inconspicuously-coloured snails that live on the different backgrounds. By the same token, this experiment shows that the colours of the shells are adaptive.

As the seasons change, the adaptive value of the colour of a shell also changes, and may change from being disadvantageous to advantageous and back again. For instance, in a woodland colony it has been shown that as spring advances, the yellow colour changes from being a handicap to being an asset as the background changes from brown to green. The balance between a species and the various facets of its environment is delicate, variable, and actively maintained.

Batesian mimicry

Batesian mimicry is the name given to the resemblance of individuals of one species to individuals of another species whereby increased probability of survival is obtained. The *mimics* belong to species that are palatable and subject to attacks by predatory birds and other animals, and they acquire relative immunity by imitating as *models* species that are shunned by predators because of their unpalatability as H. W. Bates first suggested. (Col. Pl. 2).

In most parts of its range, females of the species *Papilio dardanus* are polymorphic and present a number of forms, some of which mimic other species very closely and differ greatly from the males and from the non-mimetic females that resemble them in Madagascar and Abyssinia. The different types of females are all genetically controlled. The proof that this type of mimicry is an adaptation that confers survival value and is subject to natural selection was provided by E. B. Ford, who discovered the fact that in those parts of its range where, as at Entebbe, the relative frequency of models to mimics is high, the variability of the mimics is low, not exceeding 4 per cent and the mimicry is almost perfect. On the other hand, in regions where the relative frequency of models to mimics is low and models are rare, as at Nairobi where they are 70 times rarer than at Entebbe, the variability of the mimics is 8 times greater, or 32 per cent. Where the model is rare and therefore relatively unknown to predators, which have not been able to learn to shun it, the survival-value of resembling it is small, and there is less selection-pressure exerted on the mimic towards accurate resemblance of the model.

The genotype of the mimic therefore confers survival-value provided that it does not exceed a certain frequency in the population; above that value resemblance is ineffective, and the frequency of the mimic is therefore automatically kept in balance. There are, however, several different unpalatable species of butterflies that different varieties of *Papilio dardanus* can copy, which they do, each one achieving a numerical balance of its own without upsetting the balance of the others. This is the reason why *P. dardanus* is polymorphic (p. 95) and mimics so many other forms, thereby spreading the risk.

In the early days of Mendelian studies, when it was imagined that the characters now controlled by a mutant gene were identical with those it controlled when it first mutated, an explanation was offered of Batesian mimicry by supposing that parallel mutations had taken place in the models and the mimics, and that the resem-

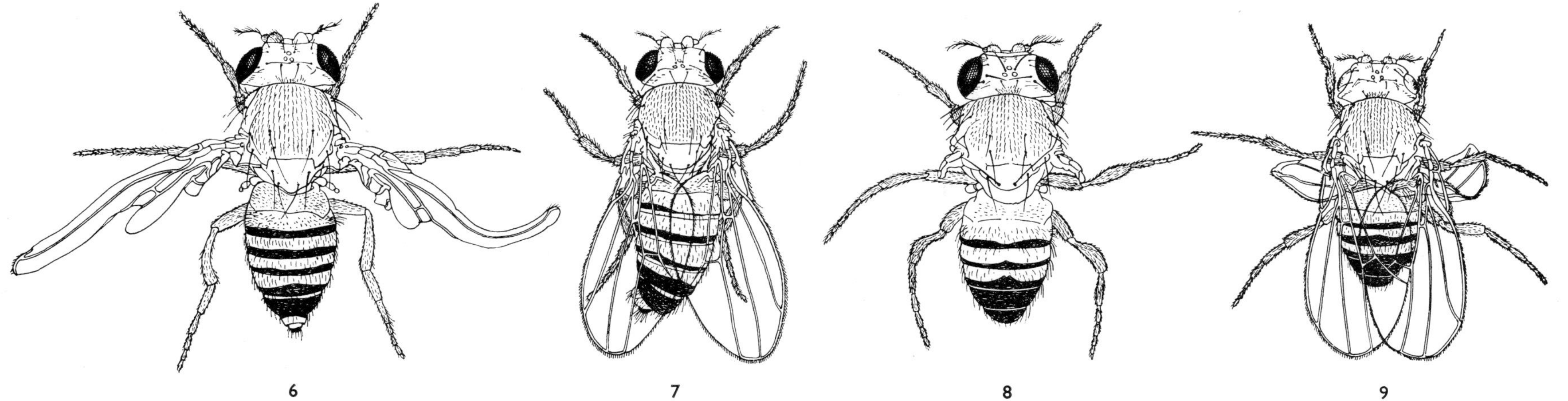

Inherited Abnormalities in the Fruit-Fly

253. Examples of gene-controlled variation in the fruit-fly, *Drosophila*: (1, 2) normal wild-type female and male; abnormal wing structures, (3) 'vestigial', (4) 'antlered', (5) 'strap';(6) twisted abdomen; (7) rudimentary wings; (8) no wings; (9) bithorax, with wing-like structures instead of balancers and an extra thorax-like structure

blance between them was accidental. Since the realization that the phenotypic effect of a gene has become what it is as the result of selection of the other genes of the gene-complex, a facile explanation of this nature cannot suffice, and breeding experiments have definitely disproved it. It is found that the mimetic character of the mimics is not due to a single gene but to the action of several modifier genes that have been collected together to form a switch-gene (p. 97) and have had their effects perfected by selection.

This was proved when specimens from different mimetic forms of *Papilio dardanus* were interbred, or bred with the non-mimetic forms from Madagascar. The offspring showed complete breakdown of the mimetic characters as a result of segregation of the several different genes concerned. This proves that the mimetic characters were the result of a gradual build-up of a gene-complex gene by gene in each mimetic form, under the pressure of selection, as A. C. Clarke and P. M. Sheppard showed.

Sickle-cell

Many natives of western and central Africa have abnormal red blood-corpuscles which instead of being disc-shaped are elongated and look like curved sickles. When such people are out of breath or suffer from oxygen-deficiency, as at high altitudes, their red blood-corpuscles are destroyed and this results in anaemia and, in serious cases, in thrombosis and death.

The sickling is due to a single gene, which directs the formation of an abnormal type of haemoglobin in which the place of the glutamic acid in the molecule is taken by another amino acid, valine. When this gene is present in the heterozygous condition and its normal allele is also present, the pathological effects are produced only under extreme conditions of oxygen-deficiency. The heterozygote is known as sickle-trait. When the sickle gene is homozygous, however, the pathological effects are manifest even under normal conditions.

Death of homozygous sickle-gene carriers removes many genes from the population in every generation, and it might well be asked why the sickle gene has not thus been eradicated altogether. The reason is that the abnormal haemoglobin in sickle red blood-corpuscles is resistant to infection by the malarial parasite, *Plasmodium falciparum*, which enters and feeds on normal red blood-corpuscles until they break down and the parasite is discharged into the blood causing fever. This does not happen to sickle-gene carriers, who are favoured by natural selection if in their environment there is a danger of infection by malaria as A. C. Allison showed.

In an area of given malarial intensity, the proportion of people in a population carrying the sickle gene reaches and maintains an equilibrium when the death-rate from sickle-cell anaemia in sickle homozygotes balances the death-rate from malaria in normal homozygotes who contain no sickle gene. The heterozygote, containing one sickle gene, is thus favoured in a malarial environment, which ensures the preservation of the sickle gene in the population, although the fact that part of the population is heterozygous for this gene necessarily entails the consequence that another part must be homozygous for this gene and suffer for it.

The highest value for the equilibrium-frequency of the sickle gene in West Africa is about twenty per cent of the population. At this value four out of five homozygous sickle children die before they grow up. Among the descendants of this population now represented by the Negroes of the United States where there is no endemic malaria, the sickle gene confers no advantage, and its frequency has fallen to nine per cent in two centuries (Pl. 279-283).

The sickle gene illustrates a number of features of importance. In the first place, it shows that an initially deleterious gene may, nevertheless, confer survival value in particular environments, and that this is brought about by natural selection. Secondly, it shows a condition of balanced polymorphism in which the equilibrium between the selective pressures exerted for and against the normal homozygote and the sickle-trait heterozygote are easy to see. Lastly, it provides an example of a measurable change of frequency of a genotype in a population in a given period of time. This is nothing other than evolution and it has been shown to be due to the action of natural selection.

Industrial melanism

Natural selection can be seen at work here and now actually directing evolution. Modern techniques of study of genetics in populations in the field, developed by T. Dobzhansky and E. B. Ford, have shown that the relative longevities of variants in different environments can be directly measured, and that the effects of such differential mortality have produced evolutionary change. An example of this type of research is that of H. B. D. Kettlewell on 'industrial melanism' in moths.

Up to 1848 the British peppered moth existed in its typical grey form known as *Biston betularia*, which is well adapted to resemble the lichens on the bark of trees. When resting on such a trunk or branch by day it is almost invisible to birds. Soon after 1848, a dark melanic variety appeared, known as *carbonaria*, which is very conspicuous against the natural bark of trees, where birds see them easily and eat them. The *carbonaria* variety differs from *betularia* by a single dominant gene and is slightly more vigorous than the normal grey type. This is an example of a mutation that is not physiologically deleterious. Nevertheless, because of its conspicuous colour the *carbonaria* variety was constantly eliminated, and this variety persisted in populations of the peppered moth only because the same mutation kept on recurring.

Meanwhile the Industrial Revolution brought about a marked change in the environment in many parts of Britain, because pollution of the air by increasing quantities of carbon dust, measured in tons per square mile per month, killed the lichens on the trees and rendered their trunks and branches black. Under these conditions it is the *carbonaria* variety that is favoured and the *betularia* penalized. This has been proved by direct observation of the feeding of birds, and by measurement of the survival rates of the different forms in the different environments. The dark *carbonaria* form survives 17 per cent less well in an unpolluted area and 10 per cent better in a polluted area. One hundred years ago the dark variety of the peppered moth formed less than 1 per cent of the population; in 1900 in industrial areas it was 99 per cent. This represents an overwhelming selective advantage in favour of the *carbonaria* gene in an industrialized environment in the short space of 50 years (Pl. 284–286).

Furthermore, selection in favour of the *carbonaria* gene has accentuated its phenotypic effect. When the mutation first occurred in 1848 the melanic heterozygote was less intensely black than it is today. In other words, the *carbonaria* gene has evolved towards complete dominance.

A map of the distribution of the varieties of the peppered moth shows that today there is a correlation between the industrial areas and a high proportion of the melanic *carbonaria* form. Furthermore, the *carbonaria* form never drops below 80 per cent of the population throughout the eastern counties of England. This is due to the indirect effects of smoke-drift from the industrial areas on the prevailing south-westerly winds. Of the 780 species of Macrolepidoptera in Great Britain, more than 70 are in process of changing by industrial melanism, which is the most striking example of evolutionary change actually witnessed.

It has been objected that while selection of variations due to mutations and recombinations of genes may account for the change of colour in moths from grey to black, such a change is of an order of magnitude much smaller than the changes involved in producing new organs, and that therefore there must have been some

254

Human Phenotypes

Most characters in man are controlled by genes with additive effects and are subject to environmental factors in the determination of their phenotypic manifestation. In the crowd scene, **254,** the different phenotypes shown by every man and woman present is due to their all having different genotypes as well as to differences in upbringing. Identical twins are the product of division of a single fertilised egg and the twins have identical genotypes. If brought up in similar environments they show very similar phenotypes **255, 256,** extending not only to physical features but also to deportment and mental expression.

255 256

more effective agency additional to selection and mutation to account for evolution. Such objection is groundless for two reasons. In the first place it is necessary to consider scales of magnitude of time. The evolutionary change from grey to black in moths has taken less than 100 years; but it took two million years to produce the relatively small evolutionary change amounting to a species in the ancestry of the horse (p. 65), and if plant life began 2,500 million years ago (p. 54), 2,400 million years were required to evolve an oak-tree. It is therefore unreasonable to complain that the amount of evolutionary change observed in 100 years is small.

Secondly, there is no justification for dismissing the selective and genetic mechanism responsible for the change from grey to black in moths as incapable of producing new organs. Genes work quantitatively, and while some determine colour by the speed of the chemical reactions which they control, others determine growth-rates, and therefore sizes and shapes of structures. New structures in evolution are the result of modification of old ones, often with change of function (p. 38). This fact has been stressed by E. Mayr. As there is every reason to believe, with Darwin and with Fisher, that the transformations were gradual, there are no grounds for doubting that the mechanism of selection and mutation that has adaptively turned grey moths black in 100 years has been adequate to achieve the evolutionary changes that have taken place during hundreds and thousands of millions of years.

Melanism in the peppered moth also introduces a principle to which L. Cuénot gave the name of 'pre-adaptation'. The melanic form of the peppered moth happened to be 'pre-adapted' to conditions which were only subsequently realized; in other words, if the industrial revolution had not taken place, the melanic variety would never have become adaptive at all, and would have suffered the same fate as the countless other mutations resulting in variations that have been eliminated because they fell short of the requirements imposed by natural selection.

Here is the explanation of the paradox already alluded to (p. 86) that although genes are usually deleterious to the well-being of the organism when they first mutate, they supply the potential raw material of variation that may be acted upon by natural selection to improve the survival-value of the organism in evolution. The reason is that under the environmental conditions that applied when the gene first mutated, the organism was tolerably well adapted to its environment, and a mutation was more likely to do harm than good. But if the adaptation of the organism to its environment was incomplete, or, more important, if the environmental conditions change, which they inevitably do sooner or later, some one or other of the genes concealed as recessives in the gene-complex produces a phenotype that is better adapted to the new conditions. The enormous reserves of untapped variability in a species in nature, concealed in the form of recessive genes and of polygenes (or multiple factors) will be tapped at some time, in some direction or another, according to the circumstances then prevailing and evolution will occur, but in a manner that cannot be predicted. This is why evolution must be described as opportunistic. If on the other hand, the reserve of potential variability is lacking or insufficient, the species will become extinct.

Polymorphism

It will have been noticed that in the descriptions of cases in which adaptations are proved to have arisen and to be maintained by natural selection, the populations concerned exhibit the phenomenon of polymorphism: colours and banding in snails, mimetic forms in butterflies, sickle-cell in man, and melanic varieties in moths. Polymorphism is a condition in which the species consists not of a single genotype favoured by natural selection, but of two (or more) genotypes producing variant phenotypes each of which is favoured by natural selection under particular conditions of a varied environment and up to a certain numerical extent.

As previously explained (p. 93), the two genotypes are frequently the normal homozygote and the heterozygote where the latter enjoys particular advantages, as in the case of the sickle gene in a malarial environment, but only up to the point at which the advantages of protection from malaria in heterozygotes are balanced by the disadvantages of death from anaemia or thrombosis among the sickle-gene homozygotes in the population.

The two genotypes are maintained in a population under the prevailing environmental circumstances, and neither ousts the other because both are kept in genetical and ecological balance, for which reason this condition is known as *balanced polymorphism*. If the genetical conditions are altered by mutation, or the ecological conditions, for example, by the eradication of malaria from the environment, the balance will be changed, and equilibrium will be reached at a new value for the frequencies of the two genotypes in the population. Such a change in the frequencies of genotypes in a population is evolution by natural selection in its earliest phase.

Industrial melanism provides an illustration of this principle at a further stage, for here, during the past hundred years, the polymorphism that arose when the melanic variety began to be favoured by natural selection in a 'black country' has been *transient polymorphism* under those conditions, and the populations of moths have switched over from grey to black. Such a process may ultimately lead on to a new uniformity. Already, the transient polymorphism exhibited by industrial melanism in moths has shown how the frequencies of different genotypes in a population can be altered drastically, and this, again, is evolution by natural selection.

It may be added that the human species is polymorphic in respect of the blood-groups, as mentioned above (see Chapter Two, p. 40, Chapter Three, p. 81, and Chapter Five, p. 190).

In addition to the ABO blood-group system many others are found in man, of which the Rhesus system is one of the most important. The genetics of this system is very complicated, but there is a polymorphism of rhesus-positive and rhesus-negative groups. They are of clinical importance, particularly because of haemolytic disease of the newborn which threatens one out of two hundred births, and results from the destructive action on the child of the antibodies produced by a rhesus-negative mother in response to the antigens of her rhesus-positive child, whose dominant genes were inherited from its father (p. 101).

It is clear, as E. B. Ford has shown, that the proportions in which the blood-groups are found in different races of man (p. 190) would not remain as constant as they do over considerable periods of time unless, like other cases of balanced polymorphism, they were controlled by natural selection. It is unfortunate that we do not yet know what the conditions are for which they are favourably or adversely adapted, because the little we do know is of great importance. For instance, group O men are most and group B least viable, while the position in women is exactly the reverse; a high proportion of cases of stomach cancer affects group A individuals, while duodenal ulcer is commoner in group O than in other groups.

SEXUAL SELECTION

The theory of *sexual selection* was put forward by Darwin to explain the origin of striking colours, structures, behaviour, and so on, found only in one sex of some animals (usually the males), and used in competition for mates and in the activities of courtship. According to this theory, individuals with such characters well-developed benefit from greater breeding success and more offspring. In the majority of cases, however, these characters are not the result of sexual selection in Darwin's sense, so much as of natural selection favouring general reproductive activity through conspicuous recognition marks, virile behaviour, etc. Characters, structures and activities that result in reproduction are known as *epigamic*, and they include not only the reproductive organs themselves but also sense-organs by means of which the sexes find and recognize each other, structures used in threat or combat

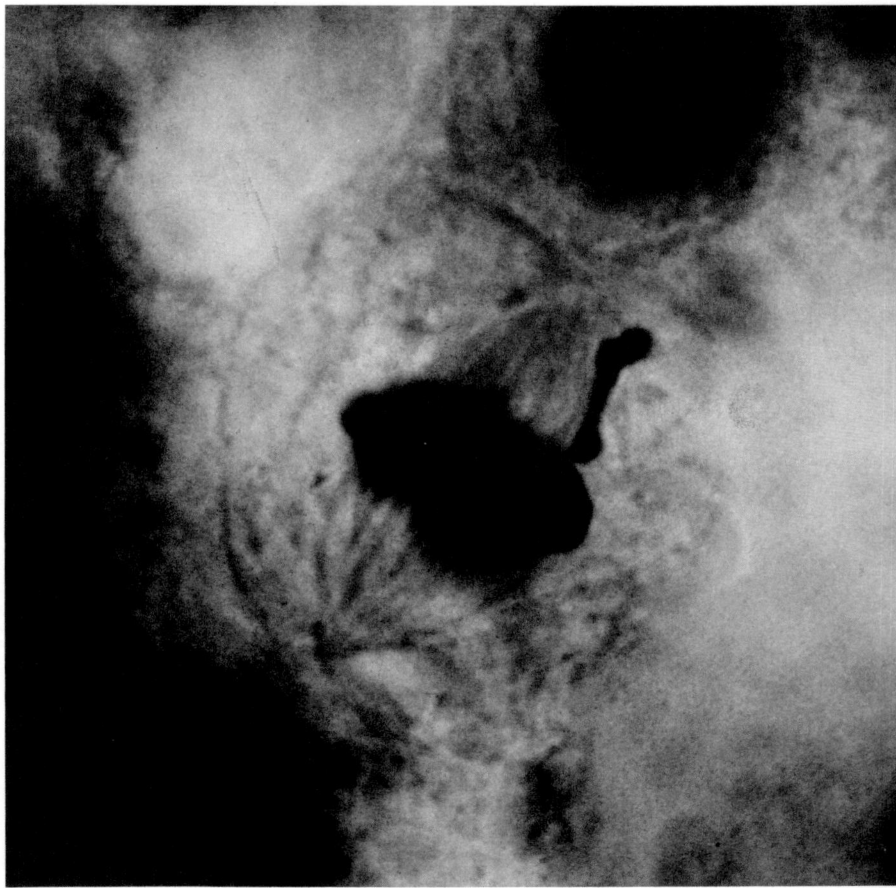
257

The Determination of Sex

257. Photograph of chromosomes during the reduction-division prior to the formation of sperms in man; the autosomes are clumped together at the equator of the mitotic spindle that is plainly visible; the sex-chromosomes have delayed in the process and are situated beside the autosomes, the X-chromosome elongated with a bent outer segment while its inner segment is in contact with the small oval shaped Y-chromosome.

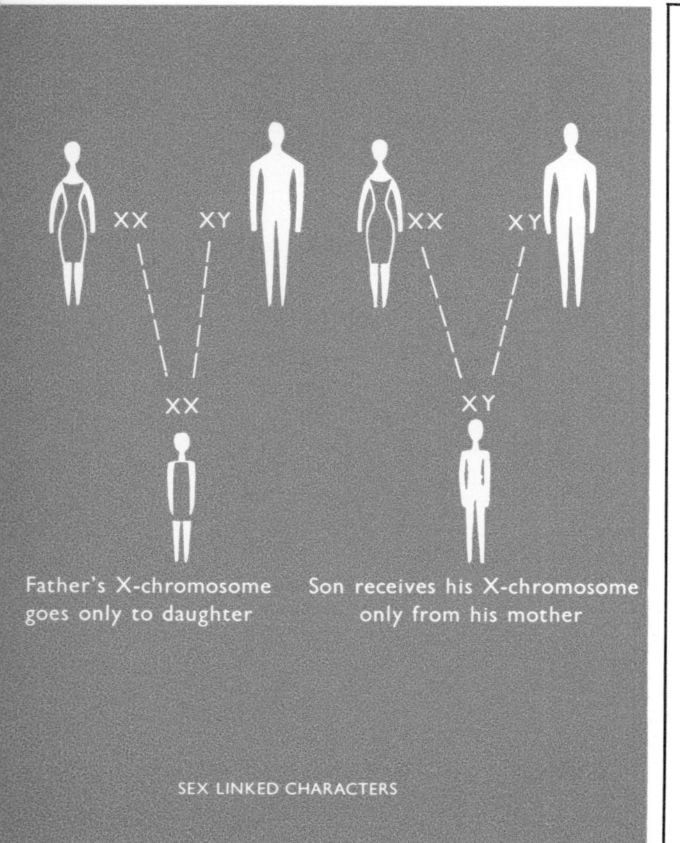

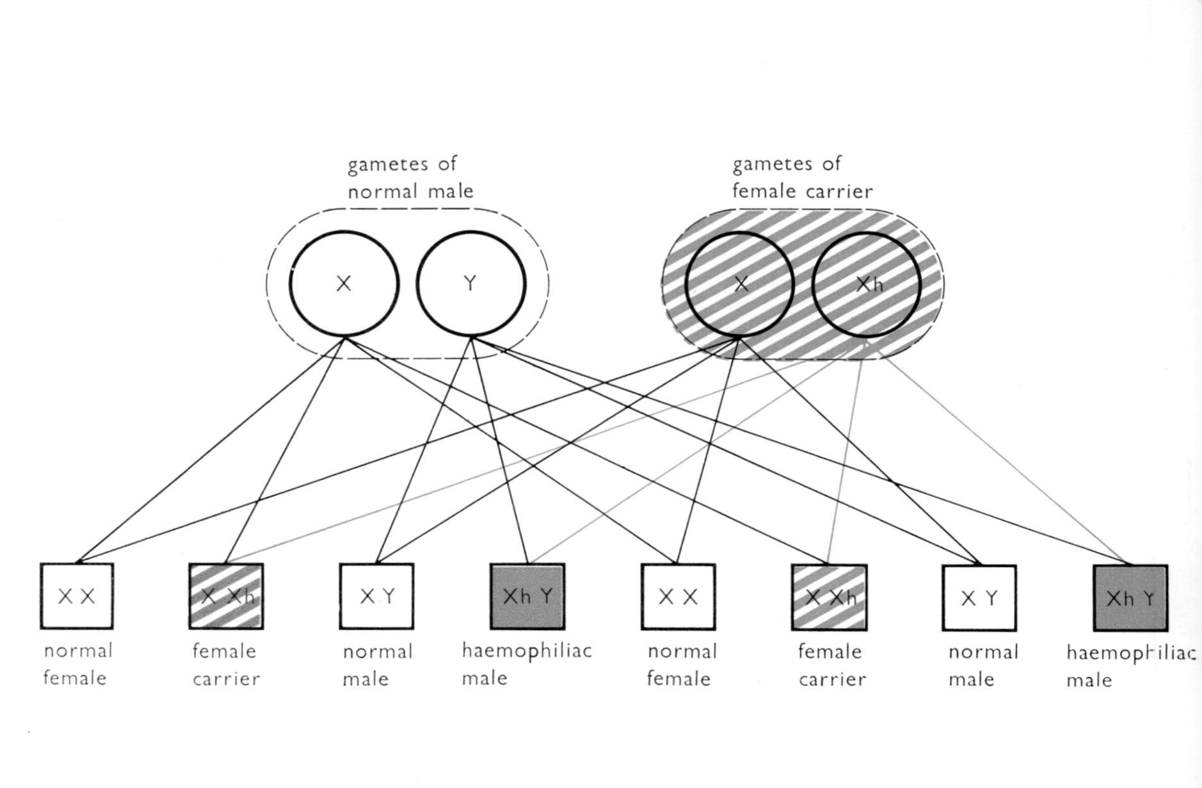

258 259

against rivals, and structures and display-behaviour that initiate, maintain, and complete reproductive activities. Darwin's conception of sexual selection, which holds good in some animals, is a special case of a wider category better called *epigamic selection* that includes examples ranging from intrasexual selection conferring reproductive advantage on successful males especially in polygamous species, to natural selection favouring reproductive activities and conferring advantage on the species (Pl. 287-295).

The ruff is a sandpiper in which the males have frills of conspicuous feathers that they can erect. At the breeding season the males stake out their claims to territory, fight male intruders, and court females with elaborate display. The more active and strikingly-coloured males are the more successful in acquiring mates. The male lyre-bird has a tail made of remarkably specialized feathers. It builds a mound of earth on which it stands and sings, and displays to the female by spreading its tail forward over its head and making the filaments of its feathers vibrate so fast that they look like a shimmering haze of light. The male Amherst pheasant makes a spectacular courtship display in front of females and arouses their interest in him for mating. His display takes special advantage of those plumage areas that are brightly patterned, by which he is distinguished from the female. A similar display before other males serves as a threat towards them and helps to eliminate his competitors. Feathers from the male Argus pheasant show varying degrees of pattern in different feathers from the same bird. They form a gradual series from small simple markings to large and spectacular eye-spots. This indicates the probable transitions through which the more spectacular feathers may be evolved in response to sexual selection.

Sexual selection does not depend on conscious choice by the female, but simply on whether the colour and display of the male has or has not succeeded in stimulating her sense organs sufficiently to induce her to undergo mating. This disposes completely of the objection once raised against Darwin's theory of sexual selection that it presupposed in female birds powers of aesthetic appreciation and choice found in women.

Male elephant seals fight for breeding territories and for possession of the females which are much smaller than the males. Size seems to be a considerable advantage to males of this species in their violent competitions on the beach, and larger males are more successful than smaller rivals. Fighting for territory is usual amongst males of polygamous species. The antlers of male red deer are shed and regrown every year, which causes a heavy drain on the resources of the body. There must therefore be some good reason why they have evolved. They are used for fighting other males, and as deer are polygamous it is believed that they contribute towards reproductive advantage.

These examples are cases in which, as explained on page 102, mere reproductive advantage without effective adaptation to the environment may confer no added survival value on the species, and on the contrary may cause it to become extinct.

In the great crested grebe, courtship activities with display frequently take place after as well as before mating. The sexes are similar in appearance and the display is mutual. One of the most striking examples of this ritual is that whereby both birds of a mated pair dive beneath the surface of the water, collect nesting material in the form of water-weed, bringing it to the surface in their mouths, swim at each other, meet breast to breast and rise up in the water with their bills touching and their ruffs fully spread. Such courtship activities are therefore concerned not with obtaining but with maintaining a mate. Display of this kind keeps the couple together to share the raising of the young, and confers advantage on the species as Sir Julian Huxley showed (Pl. 94).

In the spring, the male stickleback develops a nuptial dress of bluish-white on the back and brilliant red on the throat and belly. It stakes out a territory, builds a nest, fights all other males, and courts and entices females to the nest to spawn (Pl. 132). Turning on its side, the male points its head towards the entrance of the nest. The red colour of the male acts as a threat to other males and an attraction to females; the signal for the male to lead to the nest is given by the female when, heavy with eggs, she points her head upwards. N. Tinbergen who studied this behaviour has shown its importance for the species.

THE GENETICAL THEORY OF NATURAL SELECTION

THE INTEGRATION OF DARWINIAN SELECTION AND MENDELIAN GENETICS

After the foregoing description of the experimental evidence relating to variation, genes, and mutation and selection, it may be helpful to take a view in perspective of the field covered, in order to appreciate the significance of the results achieved from the point of view of evolution as a whole.

The history of the reception of Mendelian genetics by Darwinian selectionists is peculiar. The earliest mutations to be discovered, often called 'sports', were usually deleterious and showed marked discontinuous steps instead of the gradual and continuous variation which Darwinians looked for as the raw material of evolution. They therefore began by rejecting Mendelian mutations as the source of variation. On the other hand, Mendelian geneticists, knowing that their mutations were the only demonstrated source of heritable variation, thought that as they showed wide discontinuous steps and arose suddenly, ready-made and apparently without any selection at all, selection was inoperative in evolution and they rejected it.

With the progress of knowledge it gradually became obvious that each of the two schools of research objected to the other for reasons that were baseless. As more and more genes were identified and their effects studied, the Darwinian selectionists had to learn two lessons. First, it became clear that the wide and discontinuous mutations first observed were the more easily detected extremes of a range in which the majority exert only slight effects. For the same reason, these mutations were deleterious because organisms are delicately adjusted systems, more likely to be upset by large and discontinuous changes than by small and gradual steps.

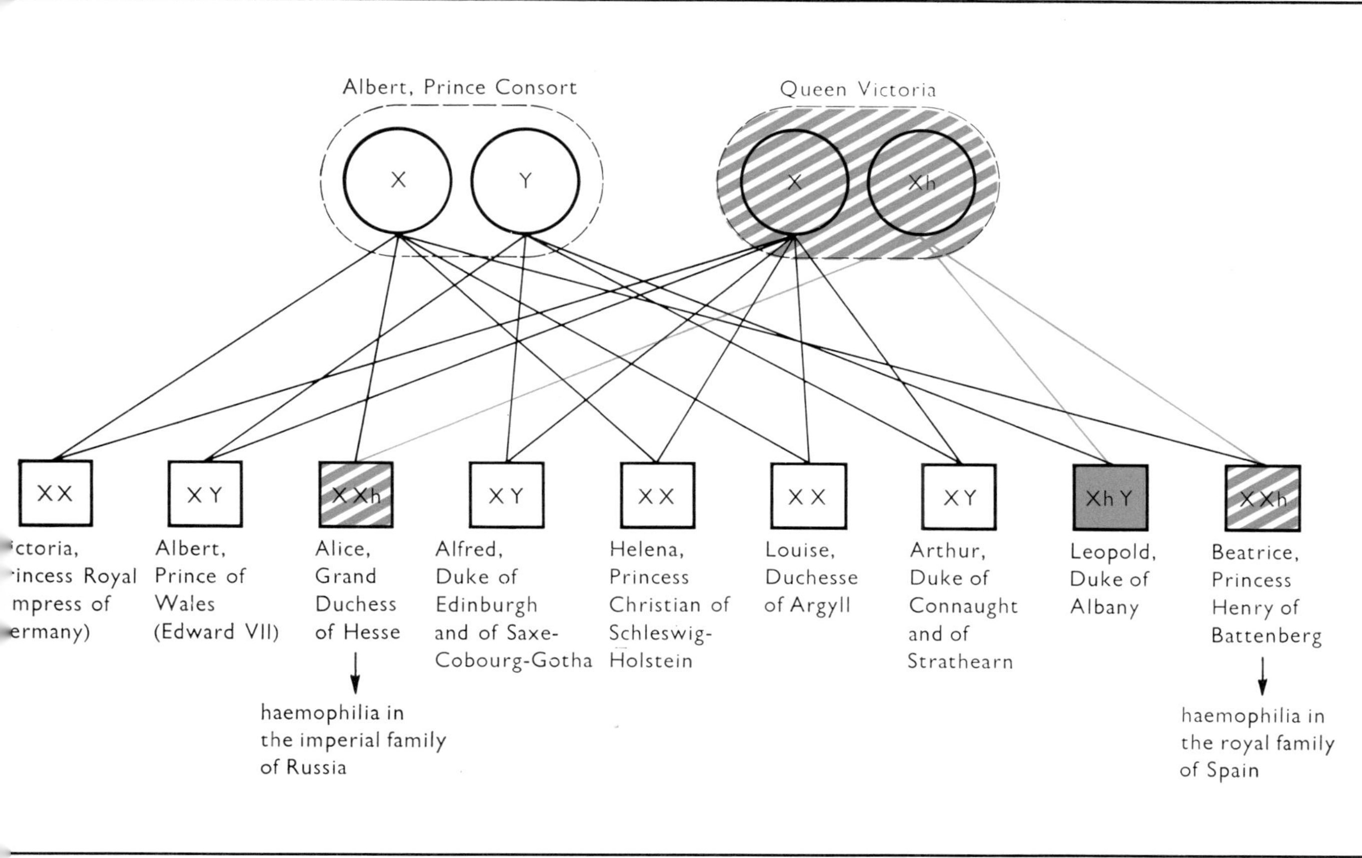

260

The Inheritance of Sex-linked Characters

258. Since a man can receive his X-chromosome only from his mother he can inherit genes carried in the X-chromosome only from her. Since a man can transmit his X-chromosome only to his daughters he can transmit genes carried in that chromosome only to them. A woman can inherit an X-chromosome from both her father and her mother and can can transmit one to her sons and her daughters. Diagrams of the inheritance of a sex-linked character, haemophilia, controlled by a gene carried in the X-chromosome, **259,** in schematic form and **260,** in an actual historical case. The close approximation of the latter to the theoretical probability shown in the former will be noted.

The Mendelian geneticists also had to learn two lessons. On the one hand they discovered that although individual genes are associated with particular characters, their control of those characters is also affected by all the other genes, which constitute an organized gene-complex. As a result of previous mutations, gene-complexes of plants and animals in nature contain many genes and these are sorted out and recombined at fertilization in astronomically numerous possibilities of permutations. These recombinations have been shown to bring about *gradual and continuous* changes in the characters under the major control of individual genes (p. 89).

The Mendelian geneticists' second lesson was the realization that although the effects of the mutations that they first observed appeared to be clear-cut, they were already the results of selection in past gene-complexes. For these mutations have occurred before, and the gene-complexes have become adjusted to them. The fact that a single gene may now act as a switch controlling the production of one or other phenotype does not mean that this phenotype originally arose at one stroke by one mutation of such a switch-gene. It must have been built up gradually as a result of past selection in the gene-complex. Valuable genotypes that depend on certain genes being inherited together are built up when close linkage is established between them on the same chromosome and they are less likely to be separated by crossing-over. This is achieved by translocations and inversions of portions of chromosomes bringing the loci of the genes concerned close together (p. 93).

It is therefore clear that mutations and recombinations of genes provide the supply of variation on which selection acts to produce evolution exactly in the way Darwin's theory requires. Its requirements are exacting, for as T. H. Huxley pointed out, some organisms have evolved slowly and others have evolved fast. The lamp-shell *Lingula* has remained unchanged for 500 million years, while 70 million years were sufficient for an animal like a terrier to evolve into a horse (Pl. 297-299). Huxley saw that natural selection was the only mechanism that could satisfy both those requirements. It is able to do so because Mendelian inheritance is capable of producing both diversity and stability. As E. B. Ford has said, an immense range of types is available for natural selection to act upon, and this is provided by mutation, segregation, and recombination of genes. When a favourable gene-complex has been achieved it is prevented from being dissipated and broken down by the facts that the genes do not blend or contaminate one another, that they mutate only rarely, and that the possibility of genes on the same chromosome becoming separated by crossing-over is minimized by their becoming sited close together.

While a sufficient supply of variation is essential for the survival and evolution of populations exposed to selection in conditions to which they are not completely adapted or in conditions undergoing change, there are circumstances under which variation can be disadvantageous. The gene-complex of a population is the result of selection for living to best advantage in a particular environment that then represents the optimum conditions for that population. If that environment is constant and adaptation to it has been effectively achieved, there is further advantage in reducing the amount of variation that occurs under those conditions, and this may be brought about in many ways. It is usual to find that under optimum conditions, asexual reproduction (p. 148) and parthenogenesis occur frequently, as in plants, protozoa, insects, and several other groups of small animals. Under these circumstances there is no variation between parents and offspring, or between offspring (except insofar as mutations may occur), because asexual reproduction does not allow for any segregation and recombination of genes, and the gene-complexes remain identical. As soon as unfavourable conditions arise, often as a result of seasonal changes, sexual reproduction sets in with its resulting production of variations on which selections acts.

Crossing-over in chromosomes is one of the methods by which variation is produced (p. 79) and the amount of crossing-over that takes place is itself under the control of genes and subject to selection. It has been found in *Drosophila* for example that the amount of crossing-over varies with temperature and is least at the temperature that corresponds to the optimum conditions for the population. This again is the result of selection. Under optimum conditions, therefore, there is a sort of regulator or cybernetic feed-back mechanism that tends to reduce genetic variation to a minimum and keep the genotype constant, which amounts to a natural automatic method of 'leaving well alone'. This is the general principle, discovered by E. B. Ford, in virtue of which *Lingula*, for instance, has not evolved for 500 million years.

Darwin himself never tired of pointing out that without variation, natural selection could achieve nothing. It is now realized, however, that selection can play a part in the promotion of variation. Since it is genes that are selected, the rejection of one gene means that its allele, a gene with more advantageous effects is substituted for it, and this is a positive contribution towards the production of a more advantageous genotype and a better adapted phenotype. Furthermore, since the phenotypic manifestation of the effects of genes is under the control of the entire gene-complex, and these effects can be augmented or reduced in different gene-complexes, the selection that results in the reshuffling of these gene-complexes also contributes towards positive changes in the organisms.

THE SIGNIFICANCE OF PARTICULATE INHERITANCE

At the time when Darwin wrote, nothing whatever was known about the laws of heredity, and all that he had to go upon was the vague notion that offspring tended to strike an average between the characters of their parents, a supposition that went by the name of 'blending inheritance', and occasioned for Darwin the greatest difficulty he had to contend with in formulating his theory. In the first place, if blending inheritance were a fact, it would mean that any new variation that appeared, even if heritable, would be rapidly diluted, and in about ten generations would have been obliterated. To compensate for this it would be necessary to suppose that new variations were extremely frequent and very recent in origin. Since brothers, sons of the of the same father and mother, share an identical heredity, any difference between them would have to be due to new variation that had arisen during their own early lives, and variation would have to affect practically all members of a species. This problem of the supply of variation was a difficulty that

261

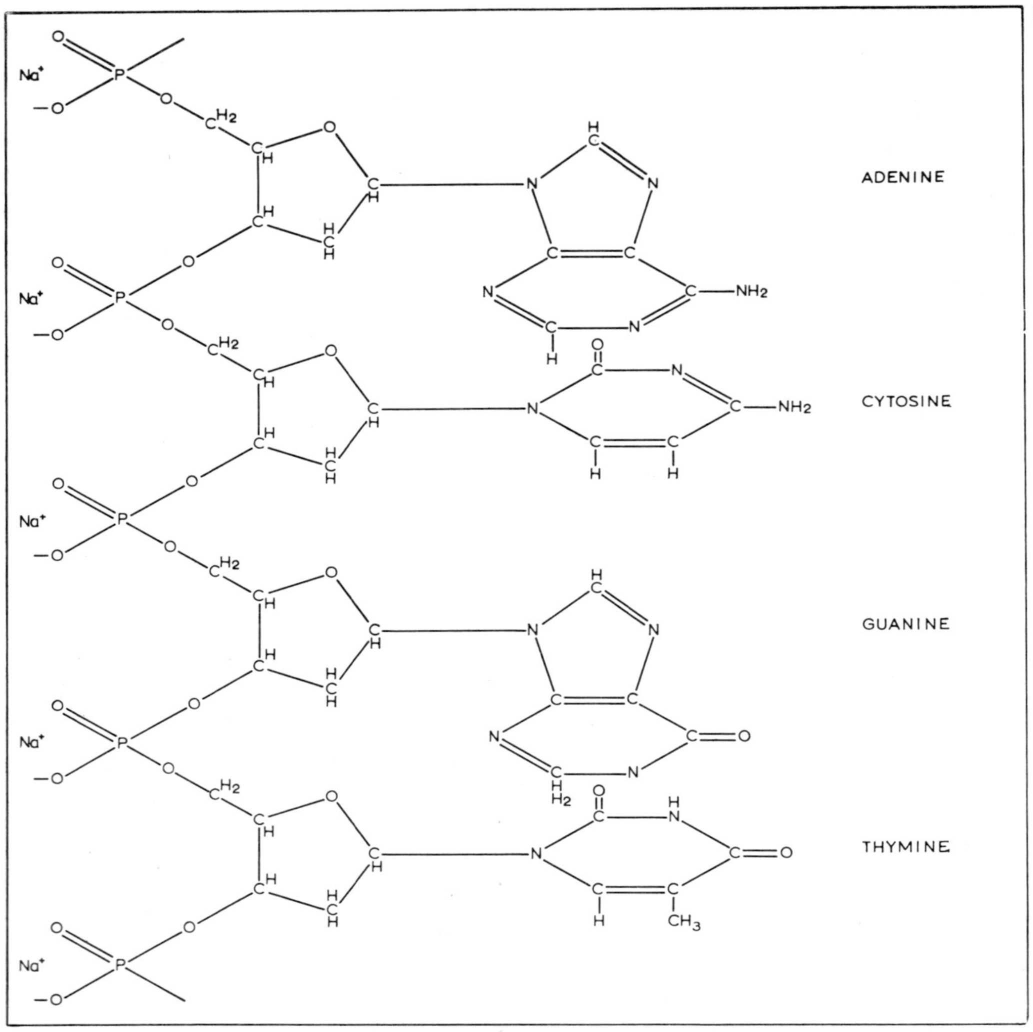

ADENINE

CYTOSINE

GUANINE

THYMINE

The Structure of Deoxyribonucleic Acid

261. The structure of the four nucleotide bases, the pyrimidines cytosine and thymine, and the purines adenine and guanine, linked to the sugar-phosphate chain. **262.** A diagram of the Watson-Crick-Wilkins model of the structure of the molecule of DNA, showing two spiral phosphate-sugar chains wound round each other, inter-connected by horizontal rungs made of two nucleotide bases each firmly attached to a sugar unit. The bases are linked to each other across the rungs by weaker secondary bonds, which permit the two strands of the chain to come apart (→ **264**). **263.** A photograph of a model of DNA, each atom represented by a coloured ball, hydrogen and its bonds are white, carbon atoms are black.

Darwin felt so acutely that it even led him to look for a source of this supply in the supposed hereditary effects of use and disuse.

This reliance on use and disuse as a source of variation, without any effect on his main argument, is the only part of Darwin's demonstration that has had to be abandoned, and he would have welcomed the reasons for it. If only Darwin had realized it, the solution to all these difficulties was being provided by Gregor Mendel, but his results remained unknown until 1900, years after Darwin's death.

The particulate theory of inheritance which Mendelian genetics has established involves a number of consequences of fundamental importance for the problem of evolution. In the first place, the substitution of this quantitative and rigorous science for the vague and baseless notion of 'blending inheritance' completely disposes of the difficulty Darwin met in accounting for the necessary supply of variation on which natural selection could act. The most characteristic feature of the Mendelian gene is that it *never* blends (Pl. 296), but retains its identity and properties intact for long periods of time until it mutates, after which it remains intact in its new condition until it eventually mutates again. This means that the amount of variation, or *variance*, present in a population as a result of previous mutations is conserved. This fundamental fact can be illustrated by the equilibrium that regulates the relative frequencies of the genotypes of a pair of alleles in a natural population, the Hardy-Weinberg law, $p^2{:}2pq{:}q^2$ (p. 81). The homozygous recessive q may represent only 5 per cent of the population, but it will not be swamped by the remaining 95 per cent; instead, it will be maintained at this level until a change in the conditions results in an alteration to the equilibrium. Then the frequency of the homozygous recessive may even be increased.

As a result of the system of particulate inheritance, the variance present in a population is not only *conserved* through generation after generation, but is increased as a result of the recombinations of the gene-complexes in their innumerable possible permutations. This power of increase of variance is one of the most important results of the sexual or bi-parental method of reproduction and is the reason why organisms that possess this mechanism have evolved further than those that lack it.

The conservation of variance is to be considered in relation to the rate at which mutation normally occurs. As mentioned on page 83, it has been calculated in organisms as diverse as a bacterium, a maize plant, a fruit-fly, and in man, that any given gene mutates in about one in half a million individuals. This rate is itself the result of selection, and although it seems slow, it has been adequate to provide the requisite basic heritable variation which the mechanism of germ-cell formation and fertilization has multiplied, and on which selection has worked to produce whatever evolution has taken place. In other words, mutation not only need not but must not be more frequent than this slow rate. The slowness of this rate has a bearing on the relative importance of mutation and selection in evolution.

THE RELATIVE IMPORTANCE OF MUTATION AND SELECTION IN EVOLUTION

Ignorance of the causes that determine the directions in which mutations take place, if such causes indeed exist, is little handicap to the understanding of the mechanism of evolution, because *it is selection, not mutation, that determines the direction of evolution.* This all-important conclusion is based not only on detailed experimental studies on the effects of selection in nature, but also on a very simple demonstration of a general principle by Sir Ronald Fisher. The effect of selection in changing the relative frequency of genes in a population has been calculated for the different benefits in terms of survival-value that such genes confer. At the estimated natural average mutation-rate of one in half a million, no mutant gene has the slightest chance of maintaining itself against even the faintest degree of adverse selection. Furthermore, if the direction of evolution towards favourable adaptations were determined by the direction of mutation, it would be necessary to suppose that such mutations must be predominantly favourable. But the majority of mutations are *unfavourable* when they first arise, and natural selection acts *against* them by converting the resulting mutant genes into recessives or suppressing them into the condition of modifiers; or their effects have been improved by a changed gene-complex produced by a change in the environment and by natural selection, and the genes are then preserved, and become dominant. It is natural selection, not mutation, that has governed the direction and the speed of evolution, and it has been estimated that if mutation were to stop now, there is already sufficient variation in the plant and animal kingdoms for evolution to continue for as long in the future as it has gone on in the past.

The bearing of this demonstration on hypotheses that attempt to explain evolution by postulating the existence of agencies capable of causing mutation in directions advantageous to the organism is plain. It means that all such theories as invoke the effects of use and disuse, inheritance of acquired characters, environmental stimuli, organic selection, inner feelings, inherited memory, momentum along particular directions, orthogenesis (p. 65), and others, including design, which assume that mutation can be made to follow adaptively desirable directions, are not only devoid of any known mechanism by which the direction of mutation might be brought about, and devoid of evidence regarding the existence of such mechanisms, but they involve a cause 'which demonstrably would not work even if it were known to exist', as Sir Ronald Fisher has said. It is therefore not surprising that no evidence has been forthcoming that the effects of use and disuse or adaptive response to environmental conditions are inherited through sexual reproduction or induce appropriate adaptive mutations (p. 83). From the evidence provided by genetics, natural selection is the only mechanism capable of explaining evolution, and it does

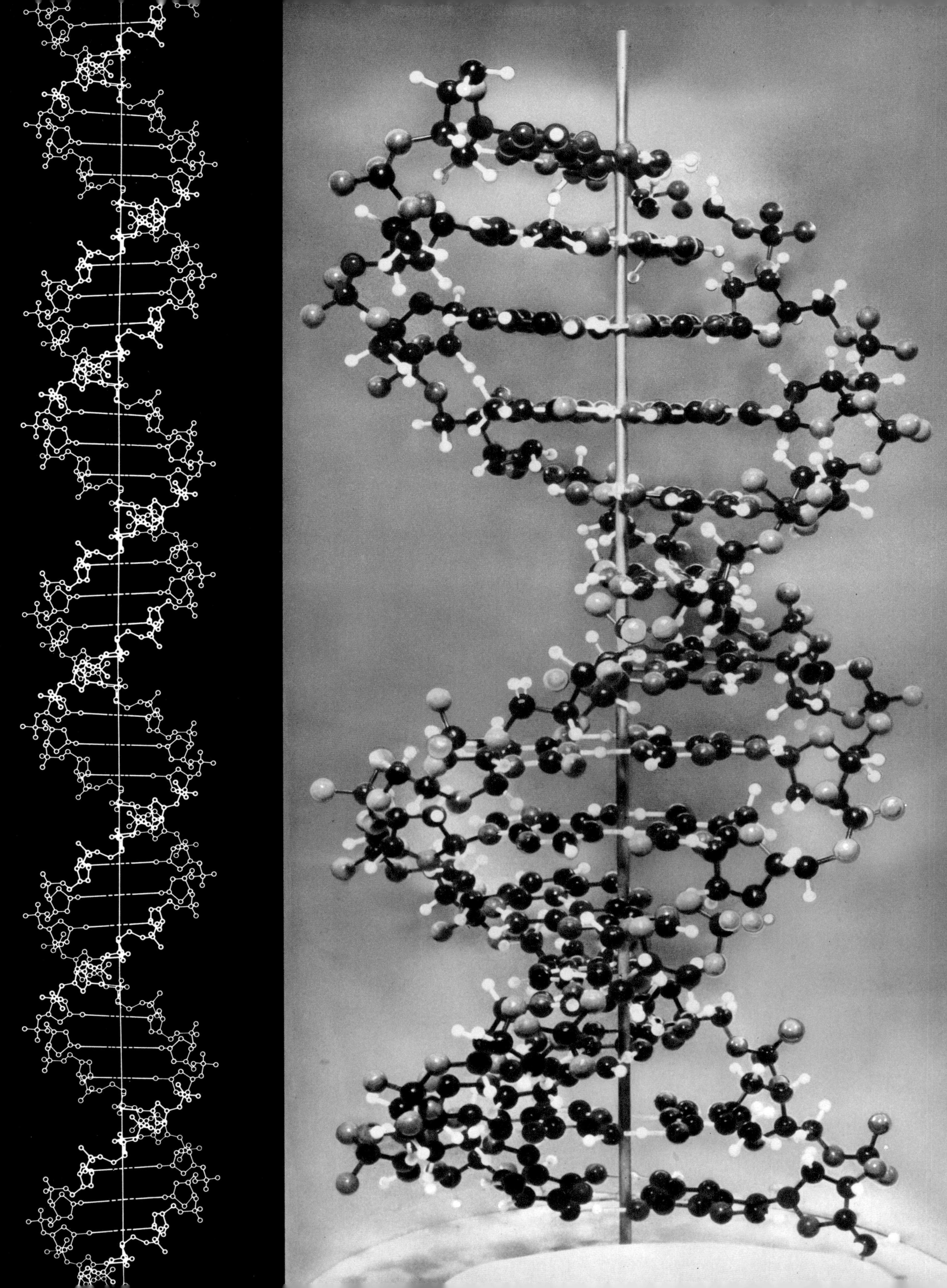

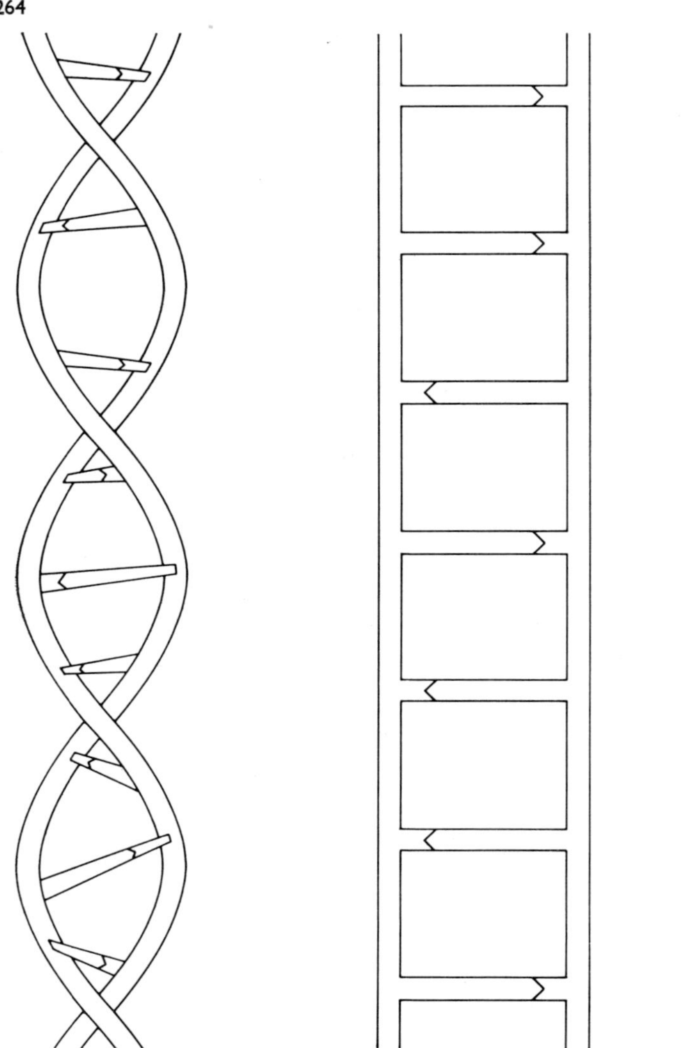

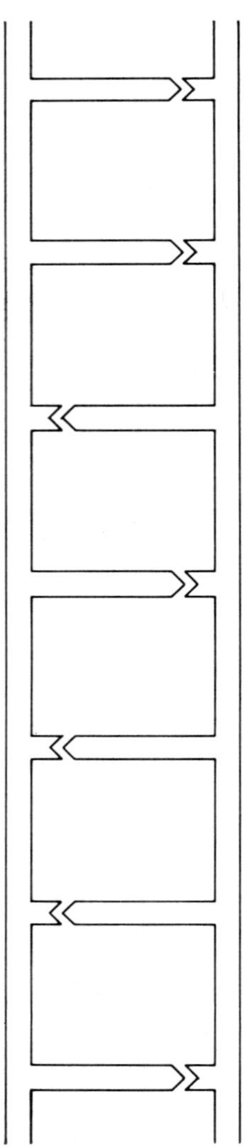

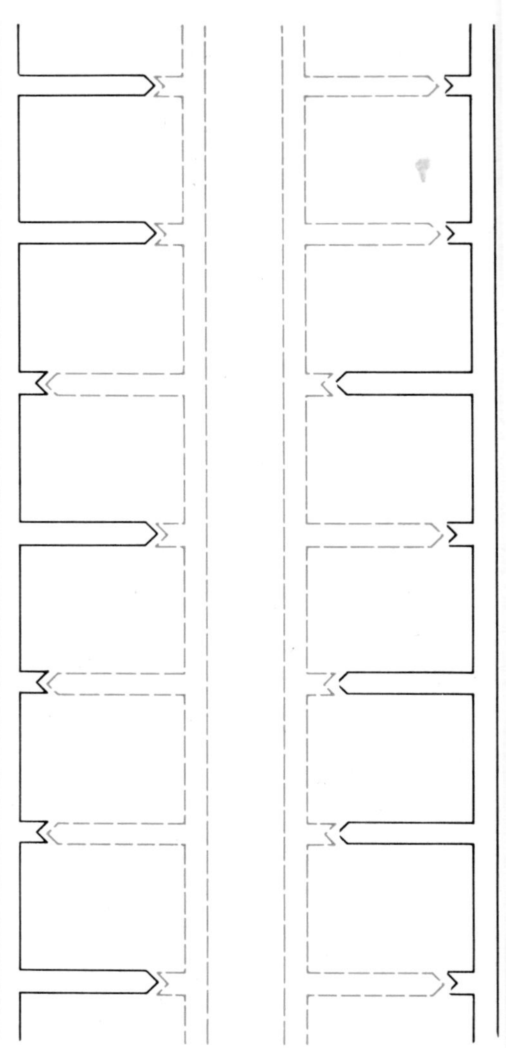

so by making use of such variations as arise, channelling them into directions that are useful to the organism, thereby giving the appearance of having been purposeful in origin.

Palaeontological researches have confirmed the same principle and extended it, for *selection, not mutation, determines the rate of evolution*. The rate of evolution is not correlated with length of life and generation-time. Opossums have short generations, but have not evolved much since *Eodelphys* in the Eocene, 60 million years ago. Elephants on the other hand have long generations, but have evolved sensationally fast since *Moeritherium* in the Eocene. Secondly, rate of evolution is not correlated with variability of the organisms. Teeth were evolving fast in *Merychippus*, but variation in that form was less than in *Eohippus* where teeth were evolving slowly. This leaves only natural selection as the agent capable of controlling the direction, speed, and intensity of evolution as G. G. Simpson showed.

By making use of the ages of geological formations available as a result of the application of radioactive methods of research in geology (p. 49) it i s possible to tabulate the average ages of different categories in different groups of animals, as may be seen in the accompanying table (based on B. Rensch) and Plate 300.

	Average age in millions of years of			
	genera	*families*	*orders*	*classes*
in				
mammals	15	25	65	190
reptiles	50	85	185	310
fishes	50	80	270	450
insects	12	160	180	350
crustacea	—	160	410	540
land-snails	40	65	100	540
sea-slugs	75	125	400	540

Evolution has in general taken place more slowly in marine animals than in related land animals. This is true of fishes as compared with reptiles and mammals, crustacea as compared with insects, and sea-slugs as compared with land-snails. The reasons for this are twofold. First, the marine environment changes less and more slowly, than the land environment, which means that selection has less scope for favouring adaptation to new situations. Secondly, waters in the oceans being continuous, physical isolation of populations which plays so important a part in promoting reproductive isolation (p. 108) and the origin of new species, occurs less frequently and less fast (Pl. 297–299).

The dependence of the speed of evolution on the possibility of exploiting situations in which selections of adaptations can confer marked advantages is well illustrated by the whales. As O. Abel showed, the rate of evolution of whales since the Eocene period showed three periods of acceleration, each of which can be shown to coincide with the adaptation of whales to a new type of food. At the start, whales like *Protocetus* in the Eocene period had dentitions enabling them to feed on large animals, but some took to preying on fish and rapidly evolved teeth like sharks, as in the Squaliodontidae in the Miocene. Next, some whales preyed on small cuttle-fish and evolved a reduced dentition, as in Phiseteridae and Ziphiidae. Finally, the whalebone whales, Mysticeti, having taken to feeding on enormous numbers of small shrimp-like crustaceans (krill), also evolved rapidly.

These and similar lines of evidence are capable of generalization into a principle. The effectiveness with which natural selection can influence the speed of evolutionary change in animals depends not only on the conditions of the environment but also on the position which they occupy in the hierarchy of food-chains, as I. Schmalhausen pointed out. For instance, small organisms that drift about on the sea, or plankton, such as diatoms, protozoa, larvae, and the krill on which whalebone whales feed, are defenceless against their large predators. In their case selection works in favour of high reproductive rate and speeding up of the life-cycle which makes good the losses. Organisms in this category evolve very little further. The same is true of sessile or sedentary organisms that rely on protective colouration or hard shells for their defence. The lamp-shell, *Lingula*, which lives in the comparatively stable environment of the deep sea has scarcely evolved further for 500 million years (Pl. 297, 298). On the other hand, where animals actively resist or accomplish capture by muscular action, evolution has been rapid. In birds and mammals, which are at the tops of their food-chains and in which reproductive rate has been restricted to a comparatively low level (p. 102), natural selection has been most effective and evolution has been most rapid of all.

NATURAL SELECTION WORKS BLINDLY

It has been objected that natural selection cannot explain the evolution of very complex adaptations involving co-ordinated variations in one and the same organism, and even less in two different organisms, such as males and fenales of the same species (p. 27). It has been supposed that such situations argued so high a degree

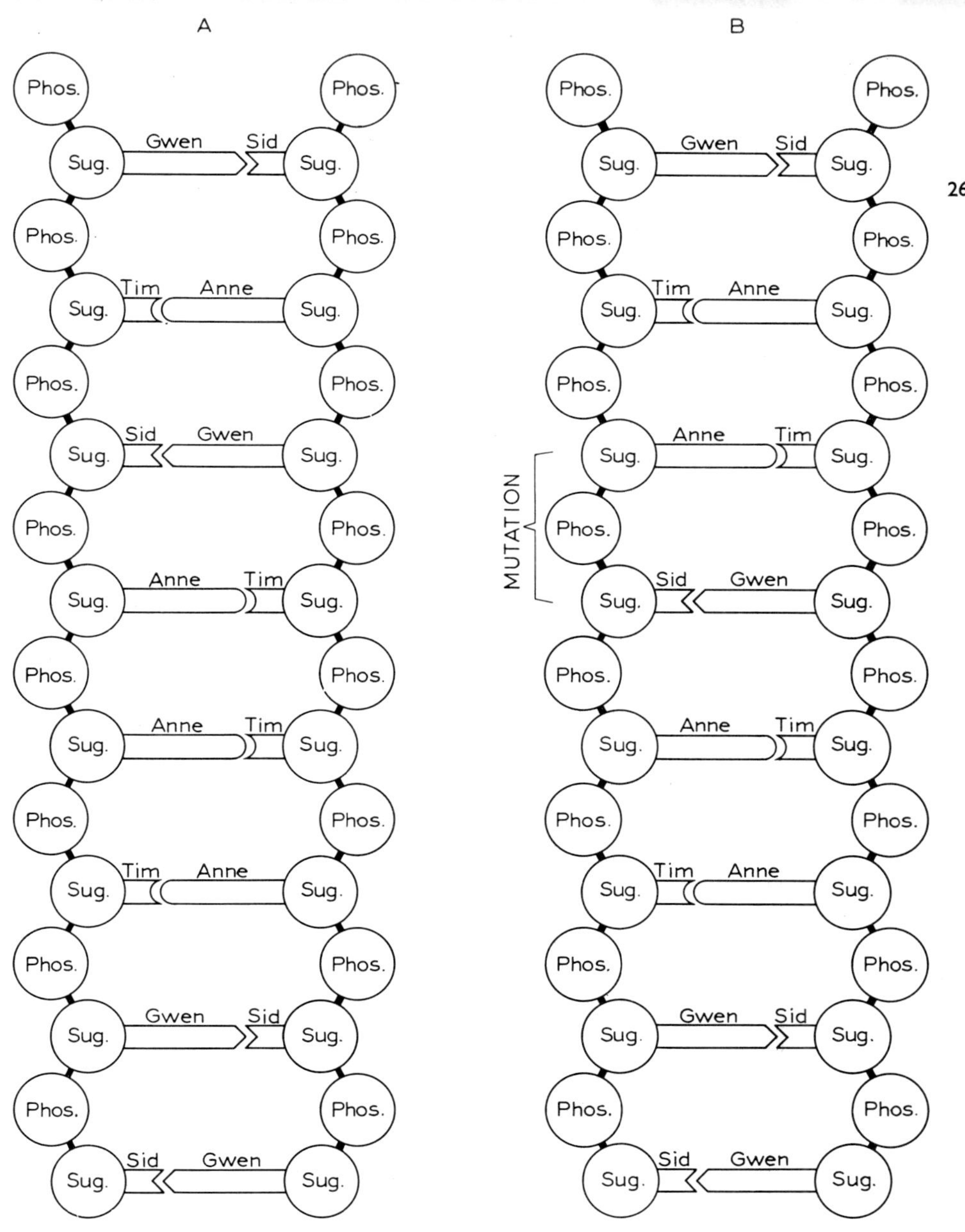

The Reproduction of DNA Chains

264. A diagram of the process of replication of DNA; the phosphate-sugar chains (1) imagined as untwisted (2, 3) the two nucleotide bases of each rung becoming detached in the middle; (4, 5) the separate strands with their bases have split apart and each serves as a template for the reconstitution of a double chain, taking what it lacks out of substances available in the cell; the result is replication. **265.** The mechanism of mutation illustrated by imperfect replication and reversal of the sequence of the nucleotide bases at two adjacent rungs. Three adjacent rungs, or a triplet of bases, are regarded as the basis of a gene.

of mathematical improbability that they could not be explained as a result of natural selection, which was called chance.

In the first place, although variation is haphazard and mutation is fortuitous in frequency and direction, it is neither variation nor mutation but *selection* that determines the course of evolution and produces adaptations. The operation of natural selection is not a game of luck but is governed by rigid conditions.

Adaptations do not arise from a succession of such favourable and providential deviations from the laws of probability as are optimistically devised by patrons of casinos; to use Sir Ronald Fisher's analogy, natural selection produces adaptations by the continuous and cumulative action of the laws of probability over a long period, the process in fact on which proprietors of casinos rely successfully for their prosperity.

It is worth while to study the question of improbability more closely. As Sir Ronald Fisher has also pointed out, improbability bears a different aspect when considered from time before or time after the event. The probability that any one man alive today will have sons, grandsons, and successive descendants in the male line uninterruptedly for one hundred generations, is infinitesimally small. Yet every man today is the living proof that this contingency, so highly improbable as it may have seemed one hundred generations ago, has nevertheless occurred. The property of natural selection whereby only favourable variations are retained has led to the paradox that natural selection is an automatic mechanism for producing results that, considered beforehand, would have seemed to be highly improbable. The effects of natural selection, however, are not those of chance when considered retrospectively; they are rigorously determined and what they have done is to channel fortuitous variation into adaptive directions and thereby simulate the appearance of purposive design.

Mention of purpose introduces the notion of teleology or fulfilment of design, which has been invoked to explain the production of complex adaptations. The argument from design was advanced by Paley in an attempt to prove that adaptations involved design and that design presupposed an intelligent designer. If this were so, then it would be necessary to conclude that the designer designed such adaptations as those of internal parasites to their hosts, or cuckoos to their foster-parents, or even simply of predators to prey. The argument from design is a double-edged weapon when used to attack the problem of evolution, because it can be shown that the more detailed the adaptation, the more unlikely it may appear to be the product of 'chance', the more likely is its possessor doomed to extinction through inability to become adapted to changed conditions, when conditions change. This is what happened to the Huia-bird (p. 27). Excess, even of adaptation, is harmful; and the fossil record shows that the vast majority of lines of evolution have led to extinction, which is a grim comment on the alleged powers of purposeful design.

Adaptations serve useful purposes but this is no evidence that they arose by teleological design to fulfil those purposes. Their usefulness arose by variation and natural selection and such undesigned purposefulness is called teleonomic (C. Pittendrigh). An examples of such accidental 'bonuses' is seen in colour-vision (p. 106).

Furthermore, when examined critically, many adaptations are found to be defective or outdistanced by the evolutionary progress which the species has made. One of the best examples in which this fact can be demonstrated is man. The proneness of the human body to inguinal hernia is a result of the incomplete adaptation of muscles and ligaments to erect stance on two legs. The immunological defence mechanism of the body, which depends on the property of proteins to act as antigens and produce antibodies that neutralize toxic substances, confers great advantages in overcoming infectious diseases, but it is also responsible for the accidents of anaphylactic shock, allergy, and haemolytic disease of the newborn, due to differences between the Rhesus blood-group gene in the pregnant mother and her unborn infant.

This may happen when a rhesus-negative woman, married to a rhesus-positive man, conceives a rhesus-positive child. While in the uterus its rhesus-positive antigens may cross the placental barrier into the mother's blood where she produces antibodies that may cross back into the child, there to react with its antigens to destroy its blood-corpuscles. As P.B. Medawar has pointed out, this last condition is due to the fact that the immunological mechanism in mammals has not yet adapted itself perfectly to the viviparous habit. It means that nature does not always know best, and that it is sometimes possible to improve on nature. It is also possible to deceive it.

Natural selection is a near approach to a fool-proof mechanism. It works inexorably against those strains of organisms whose genotypes do not enable them to produce phenotypes that are adequate to cope with the competitive and difficult conditions under which they live. It works blindly in favour of those organisms that meet these requirements, regardless of whether the direction in which they are selected has long-term prospects or not. Nevertheless, there is one way in which organisms can cheat the action of natural selection, though not for long, as will be seen below. In the majority of cases the highest survival value accrues to the descendants of those individuals that produce not the *largest*, but the *most advant-*

Some Results of Gene Action

266

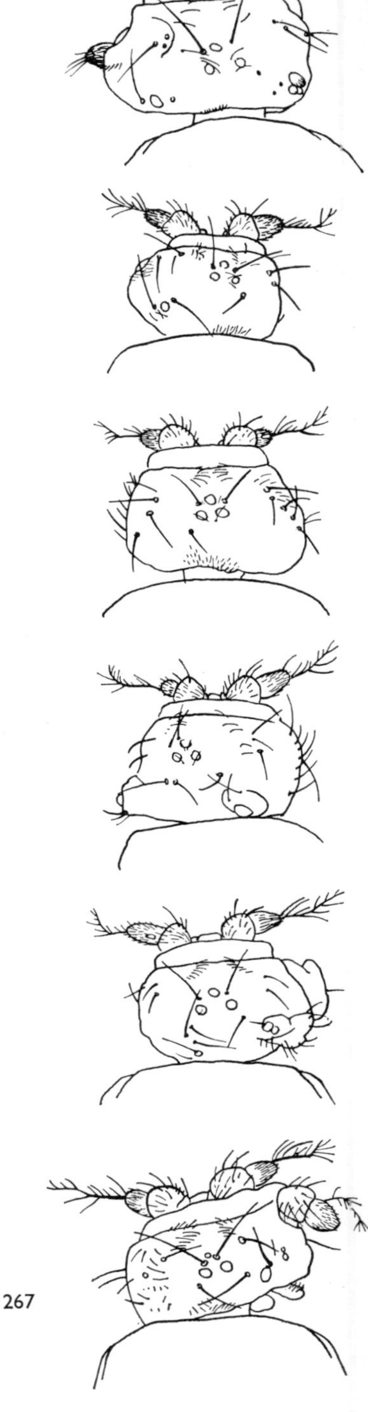

267

ageous number of offspring for the conditions under which they live. This will result in the largest number of *surviving* offspring successfully reaching the age at which they, too, can reproduce. Reproductive rate is itself under the control of natural selection, and in higher animals such as wild birds the number of eggs laid is smaller than the possible physiological limit of egg-production. The number of eggs normally laid is limited by the amount of food which the parent birds can find for the corresponding number of young nestlings in their territory within the necessary time. D. Lack found, for instance, that in some species of birds the greater number of eggs laid, the lower the rate of survival among young birds. On the other hand if the number of eggs laid is too small, although mortality is low, few birds are fledged. It is from nests in which an intermediate number of eggs is laid that most birds are reared.

Selection therefore works against those genotypes that result in the production of more or fewer offspring than the optimum number. Where the conditions are different, as for instance in cuckoos because of the enslavement of foster-parents, the optimum number of eggs laid is higher than in the case of ordinary nesting birds. There are, however, cases in which selection is tricked into working in favour of high reproductive ability instead of efficient adaptation to the environment, with results that may confer a short-term benefit. Examples are the birds of paradise, where the fantastic adornments of male birds may, through preferential sexual selection by the females, result in greater reproductive success of the most extravagantly adorned males, to the detriment and ultimate extinction of the species.

Another example is provided by plants. As J. B. S. Haldane showed, sheer reproductive success may depend on the speed of growth of certain pollen-grains from the stigma of the flower to the ovule, in spite of the fact that these particular pollen-grains may carry otherwise disadvantageous genes. Other pollen-grains carrying genes that control the production of valuable adaptations may lose the pollen-tube race to the ovule and fail to fertilize it.

These examples serve to show that natural selection acts blindly, and that it will make organisms become fitter and better-adapted for the survival of the species only if they are competing with the environment or with organisms of other species. If for any reasons the members of a species compete with their fellow-members of the same species owing to overcrowding or lack of food, or members of one sex compete with one another for mates, the results may be advantageous for the successful individuals, but, before long, disastrous for the species. It is probable that this is one of the important reasons why species have become extinct.

In early days of the study of natural selection, it was imagined by many biologists, including Darwin himself, that nature, red in tooth and claw, strewed death and destruction around and bowled down organisms wholesale like ninepins. This is certainly correct in some cases, but recent research has shown that the most important effects of natural selection are achieved by much subtler means, the essence of which is that some genotypes in a population contribute more to the gene-pool of subsequent generations than others, and they do this without necessarily engaging in mortal combat, but because of the properties of the genes and enzymes that they possess and the efficiency of the phenotypes that they produce.

HOW ADAPTATIONS ARISE

The problem of the origin of heritable adaptations is at the kernel of evolution and deserves the most careful attention. The classic view is, as shown on page 101, that they result from selection of fortuitous variations. Attempts have been made to give greater precision to this concept. At the start it will be well to consider the relations between phenotype and genotype, already described (p. 71).

Since the genotype can produce an organism only by reacting to environmental factors, the genotype can produce any number of phenotypes, normal and abnormal. It is a remarkable fact that genotypes are capable of reacting to certain environmental factors by producing a phenotype which is adaptive, such as the hypertrophied biceps muscles of the blacksmith, although the hypertrophy is not inherited. All that his son inherits (if he does) is the capacity to increase the size of his biceps if he subjects them to the same use as his father did. This is an example of

1

2

3

4

268

Genes react with the environment and one another to produce their phenotypic effects. **266.** A Siamese cat showing blackening of the hairs at the extremities: muzzle, ears, paws, tip of tail, due to the colder temperature to which the chemical reactions controlled by the gene concerned are exposed in those places. This shows that it is impossible to ascribe particular invariable effects to any gene without taking environmental factors into account. Different internal factors must also be taken into account. **267.** Gene-controlled 'eyeless' flies in *Drosophila* (→**253**) lack compound eyes (→**33**) but may show duplications of parts of the head such as antennae. **268.** Different genes may interact in producing phenotypic effects. In poultry 'walnut-comb' (1) is due to the presence together of two dominant genes, of which one by itself produces 'pea-comb' (2) and the other 'rose-comb' (3). Fowls that are recessive for the genes producing 'pea-comb' and 'rose-comb' show 'single-comb' (4). **269.** Japanese silky fowl in which the gene controlling the crest of feathers is dominant, but recessive for the character in which the brain bulges through a hernia in the skull. **270.** Polish fowl in which cerebral hernia is dominant.

269

270

what M. Abercrombie has called Class C adaptation, which is not inherited although the organism's capacity to produce it is.

Next there come cases where in normal development the body gives rise to structures such as the transparent cornea over the eye. No amount of use or disuse by the body or action of environmental factors could produce such an adaptation as this, which is of genotypic origin and is an example of P. B. Medawar's Class B adaptations that are inherited and can only have been produced by fortuitous mutation and selection.

There is a third category in which normal development gives rise to a structure such as the thickened skin of the sole of the foot; but such a structure can *also* be evoked by environmental factors such as use and friction, and give rise to corns or horny palms to the hands. The human infant is born with thickened soles of its feet prefabricated for subsequent use. This is a Class A inherited adaptation that might be thought to have arisen as a Class C non-inherited adaptation, if the so-called inheritance of acquired characters occurred. As, however, all the evidence is contrary, the explanation of such cases must be looked for elsewhere.

There is the possibility that under the cloak of a Class C adaptation, which is not inherited, fortuitous mutation might take place in identically the same direction as the adaptation, which would then become heritable. This is the possibility adopted by Lloyd Morgan in his principle of organic selection. It suffers from the objection that if an organism develops a non-heritable adaptation by the action of environmental factors on its genes, it is difficult to see why a mutation producing the same effect could benefit from selection, since the need is already met.

A second possibility is that when an organism responds to an environmental stimulus by producing an adaptive phenotype, that response, which is due to possession of the necessary genes, is itself variable. C. H. Waddington has shown that in some cases the effects of these genes can be modified as a result of selection. Exposure of fruit-flies to heat-shock resulted in the production of flies that lacked some of the veins of the wing. The extent to which this lack of veins was manifested could be decreased or accentuated by selection. By breeding only from those individuals which showed the effect to the maximum extent, flies were eventually produced with abnormal veins in the wing even without the stimulus of heat-shock. As a result of selection, the gene-complex had been modified in such a way that the phenotypic effect was produced when some other process in the development of the organism was substituted for the environmental stimulus of heat-shock. That this is no case of inheritance of acquired characters but a genuine effect of Mendelian genetic processes is proved by the fact that when pure lines of such flies are selected for increased response, no effect is produced, because in pure lines the genes are homozygous and there is no possibility of re-shuffling the modifier genes to alter the gene-complex. This principle, known as *genetic assimilation*, may have a wide application, but it has been demonstrated only in a few cases.

There is a third possible explanation of the origin of heritable adaptations, which has been suggested by C. Stern. A simple Class C adaptation is possible because the organism possesses a gene which, under certain environmental conditions, reacts in this way. There is, no doubt, a long history behind this capacity, which must reflect the effect of prolonged selection of the gene-complex in the direction of adaptive response to such environmental conditions as are likely to be encountered by the organism. If the adaptive response to the environment is what the gene can ensure when it is present in a single dose, that is, in the heterozygous condition, it is possible that when present in double dose, in the homozygous condition, the gene might produce its effect without the specific environmental stimulus, and, if advantageous, the homozygous condition would be favoured by selection. This hypothesis has the advantage of preserving the principles of fortuitous mutation and selection, while acknowledging a causal connection between the non-heritable adaptive response of an organism during its own lifetime and the eventual inclusion in the genotype of a gene controlling the production of the adaptation. Further research will pronounce on the adequacy of these hypotheses. It should however be remembered that only fortuitous mutation can explain the production of Class B adaptations such as the transparent cornea of the eye, for no specific environmental stimulus can be involved in its origination.

EARLY STAGES OF ADAPTATIONS

An argument sometimes used against the efficacy of natural selection claims that the initial stages in the evolution of adaptations involving complex structures or functions could not confer advantage on their possessors until they had already reached a certain level of perfection. A case in point is that of the electric organs of certain fish.

Electric organs
Such organs are developed out of muscles and are capable of electric discharges of two or three hundred volts, strong enough to catch prey and defend the fish against its enemies. They are clearly adaptive and confer survival-value on their possessors, but the question arises what functions they could perform in the initial stages of their evolution when it must be supposed that their power was too weak to kill prey or to deter predators. Darwin himself was well aware of this problem, and he met the argument by pointing out that 'it would be extremely bold to maintain that no serviceable transitions are possible by which these organs might have been gradually developed'. He has been proved to be right, because of the discovery by H. W. Lissmann that weak electric discharges given off by certain fish function in a manner analogous to radar and serve to convey information of the proximity of objects in the water (Pl. 302). Electric organs can therefore be adaptive even when they are too weak to kill prey or deter predators.

A gradation can therefore be made out, starting from the simple muscle, contraction of which is always associated with a weak electric discharge. This can be strengthened by disposing the insulated muscle-plates in series like an electric battery, and the organ can be used like radar. Any strengthening of the power of of the discharge confers advantage from the outset of the improvement, until the discharge is strong enough to kill prey and deter predators. In some fish the electric organs are formed from glands instead of muscles, but the principles are the same. The key to the problem is the fact that the functions which adaptive organs now perform may be quite different from those which they formerly performed and because of which they were at the outset favoured by selection.

Substitution of function, illustrated by the evolutionary history of electric organs, is very common. The most primitive vertebrates obtained their food by means of a structure known as the endostyle, which caused a current of water to flow into their mouths bringing food-particles and it secreted a sticky substance to which the food-particles stuck. When the vertebrates had evolved biting jaws, the endostyle became converted into the thyroid gland. The hindmost pair of gill-pouches of the early fish became adapted to contain air and were converted into swim-bladders in some fish and into lungs in other fish and in their descendants the land vertebrates. Other examples we have already met: the fins of fish became the five-toed limbs of land vertebrates; and the bones forming the hinge of the lower jaw in fishes, amphibia, and reptiles, have become intercalated in the chain of auditory ossicles in mammals (Pl. 97, 303).

Flight in birds
A stumbling block for many is to understand how natural selection can account for the initial stages of the production of wings in flying birds, because in order to fly a bird requires an outfit of feathers, wing-bones, breast-bone, muscles, and nerve-centres capable of co-ordinating movement, the initial stages of which would confer no advantage. The difficulty vanishes as soon as it is realized that it was not for the purpose of flying that these structures were first evolved. Feathers began as heat insulators when the ancestors of birds became warm-blooded, and conferred advantage by minimizing heat-loss from the start of the improvement. The ancestors of birds, like *Archaeopteryx*, lived in trees, as is known from the structure of their feet, and leaped from branch to branch. Increase in stiffness and in the area of the vane of the feathers on their forelimbs produced a gliding surface which enabled the birds to make longer and longer glides and conferred advantage from the start of the improvement. The structure of the muscle-crests on the forearm-bone, the breast-bone, tail, and brain of *Archaeopteryx* show that it glided and was incapable of active flight; but any increase in the firmness of the wing-skeleton, the strength of the breast-bone, and the size of the pectoral muscles enabled the bird to supplement its gliding by flapping action, however feeble at first, and conferred advantage from the start of the improvement. Finally the tail shortened, enabling the bird to make aerobatic flights, and the cerebellum of the brain increased as a direct embryological result of the more numerous nerve-impulses discharged by the active muscles, joints, and sense-organs of balance. Here again, the key to the problem is that selection was at the start directed towards efficiency of functions different from that which the wings of flying birds now perform: namely heat-insulation and gliding (Pl. 304–310).

Orchids and moths
Darwin undertook his classic studies on fertilization in orchids to show that in plants, just as in animals, there are structures that confer advantage on the species and represent adaptations produced and maintained by natural selection.

In Madagascar, an orchid (*Angraecum sesquipedale*) was found in which the nectary takes the form of a spur eleven and a half inches long. Darwin therefore predicted that in Madagascar there must be a moth whose proboscis when extended was capable of reaching a length of eleven and a half inches. Such a moth was in fact found: *Xanthopan morgani praedicta*.

As the detachment of the pollinia from the flower and their attachment to the insect depend on the moth inserting its proboscis up to the hilt into the flower (p. 27), the full advantages of cross-pollination are likely to accrue to those plants whose flowers have the longest nectaries. Conversely, as the supply of nectar at the bottom of the nectary is of importance to the moth, advantages will accrue to those moths whose proboscis is long enough to reach to the bottom of the nectary. In this manner, natural selection will promote lengthening of both nectary and proboscis, and bring about this adaptation gradually and increasingly, conferring advantage from the start (Pl. 91).

Cuckoos' eggs
All cases of parasitism are examples of adaptation. The parasitic habits of the cuckoo are well known and of particular interest because it can be shown not only how they arose but that they were produced by natural selection.

It is quite common for birds to use the disused nests of other birds as a foundation on which to build their own. Falcons use the old nests of ravens, crows, magpies, rooks, or herons. Wagtails, flycatchers, and tits can build their own nests, but occasionally place them inside the nests of other species. These examples represent different degrees in the first stage in the evolution of breeding parasitism.

The second stage is reached when a bird occasionally lays an egg in the nest of another species; kestrels, starlings, rollers, and especially ducks have evolved this habit.

The transition from the second to the third stage of breeding parasitism is illustrated by the South American cow-birds of the genus *Molothrus*. Some species of this genus build nests and incubate their own eggs, though at the same time frequently using the nests of other birds. Other, closely allied species of *Molothrus*, are habitually parasitic on other birds and have abandoned the habits of building nests and incubating their eggs. This stage has also been reached by the cuckoos of the Old World and some finches in Africa.

The selective agent in the breeding parasitism practised by the cuckoo is the power of discrimination possessed by the foster-parent, which may desert the nest after the cuckoo's egg has been laid in it, or eject the cuckoo's egg.

Non-parasitic cuckoos generally lay white eggs of a fair size, but there is variation in the colour which may be blue, green, or spotted. The eggs of the species of foster-parents parasitized by cuckoos are usually coloured, smaller than those of the cuckoo, and characteristic for each of the species involved. If a cuckoo's egg is laid in any of their nests it will stand a higher chance of avoiding detection if it approximates in size and colour to the eggs of the foster-parents. There is great variation in the size and colour of birds' eggs, and selection is exerted in favour of those cuckoos whose eggs most effectively mimic the eggs of the foster-parent species to which they have attached themselves.

Three grades in this mimicry can be discerned: (1) elementary, in which there is rough approximation in size but no resemblance in colour, as in chiffchaff-cuckoo and wood warbler-cuckoo eggs, which are usually rejected; (2) advanced, in which size and colour show approximation so that a considerable proportion of the eggs is accepted; (3) perfected, in which the resemblance in size and colour is complete and the eggs of the host and the parasite can be distinguished only by slight differences. Here belong the eggs of the orphean warbler-cuckoo, the great reed warbler-cuckoo, and the brambling-cuckoo, which are accepted in the great majority of cases by the foster-parents. When this stage of adaptation has been reached, the cuckoo can lay more eggs with the probability of their being hatched than if it laid in its own nest. The evidence is therefore complete that the adaptation of cuckoos to their hosts was produced by natural selection and conferred advantage from the start (Col. Pl. 8).

The adaptation of whales to deep sea
The adaptation of whales to life in deep water are numerous and striking, and among the most remarkable are those concerned with the structure and functions of the ears, revealed by the researches of F.C. Fraser and P. E. Purves. For animals in deep water, unable to use the senses of sight, smell, taste, or touch to find their food or

Selection on Colour-Genes of the Moth

Colour Plate 7
Result of selection on colour genes in the currant moth. *Grossulariata* gene produces white, its allele *lutea* yellow. Neither is normally dominant. Breeding from whitest heterozygote variants gives a strain in which the *grossulariata* gene becomes dominant, while it becomes recessive if the yellowest variants are selected, in both cases as a result of reshuffling of the other genes in the gene-complex. Sometimes genes are dominant for some of their effects and recessive for others.

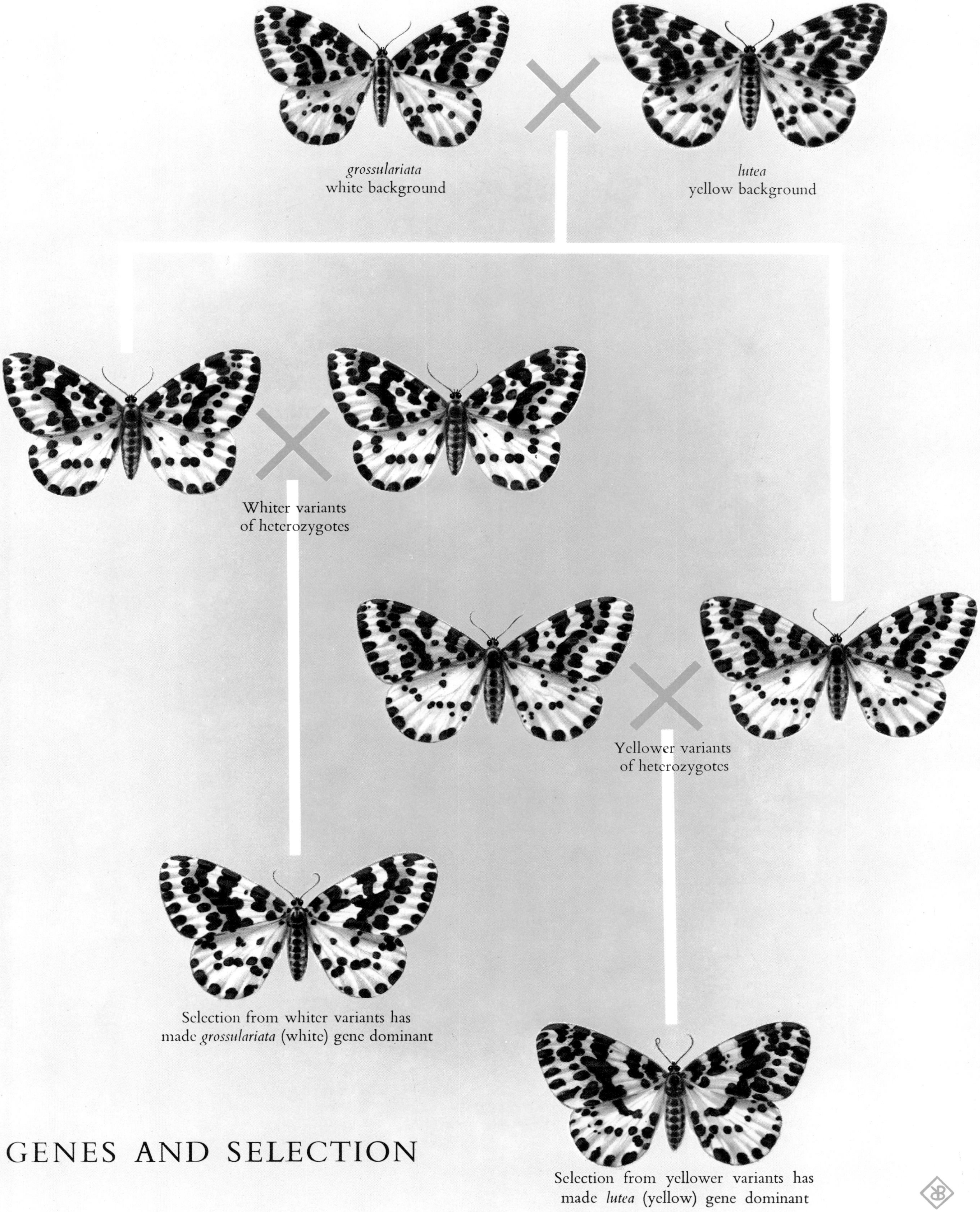

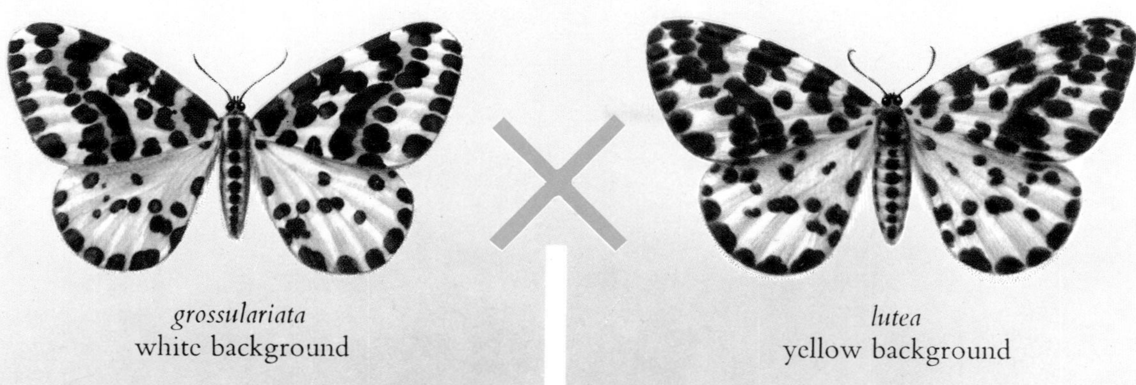

grossulariata
white background

lutea
yellow background

Whiter variants
of heterozygotes

Yellower variants
of heterozygotes

Selection from whiter variants has
made *grossulariata* (white) gene dominant

GENES AND SELECTION

Selection from yellower variants has
made *lutea* (yellow) gene dominant

1

2 3

4

5 6

7

8 9

10

11 12

13

MIMICRY IN CUCKOO'S EGGS

their mates (without which there would be no breeding), there remains only the sense of hearing. When sound waves pass from one medium to another of different density (e.g. from air to water) they are deflected or in some cases reflected. Thus an animal in air disperses the energy of sound-waves falling anywhere on its body which is a different, mainly liquid medium, so that they become insignificant compared with the waves impinging on its ear-drums. Since there are two of these, an appreciable distance apart, and since the animal can move its external ears and its head, it is possible for it to determine the direction from which the sound comes.

Transmission of sound-waves in water is similar to transmission through a living body, so that the sound-energy penetrates into the body of the whale all over its surface with little diminution. Therefore the whale's ears can appreciate the direction from which sound comes only if they are accoustically isolated from the rest of its body and receive stimuli solely through their ear-plugs and ear-drums. This is achieved by means of outgrowths of the air-containing cavities of the middle ear, corresponding to the Eustachian tubes, which surround the auditory organs. The auditory isolation is increased by the secretion into these air-spaces of an albuminous oily foam. These air-spaces conferred advantage by improvement of directional hearing from the start of their development (Pl. 311). The air-spaces also serve a second function. As the whale dives, the pressure of the water on the outer side of the ear-drum increases, and the ear-drum cannot function to receive and transmit sound vibrations unless the pressure in the airspaces on the inside is adjusted. This is achieved by a roundabout method.

Outgrowths from the air-spaces invade and take the place of some of the bones of the skull, such as the pterygoid, which do not ossify. Bone is a tissue which contains well-developed blood-vessels in addition to spicules of calcium phosphate. Indeed, it is in the hollow shafts of the long bones that marrow is situated and red blood-corpuscles develop. In the case of the whale pterygoid bone, although the hard bony spicules are not formed the blood-vessels are, and they give rise to a fibrous network of veins in contact with the outgrowths of the air-spaces. When the whale dives and the external hydrostatic pressure rises, blood is injected into the vessels of the fibrous network which thereby increase in volume and correspondingly diminish the volume of the air-spaces, the pressure of which therefore goes up. Advantage was conferred from the start of the development, since the initial stages progressively enabled the whales to dive a little deeper.

The structure of the ear in whales probably explains a further adaptation. At the pressure of great depths, there is a danger experienced by divers, that the nitrogen in the air in the air-spaces may be forced into the blood in the blood-vessels lining them and give rise to embolisms. The oily albuminous foam that is contained in the air-spaces is an absorbent of gaseous nitrogen six times more efficient than blood, and it is believed that the spout of a whale after breaking surface is the exhalation of the foam containing absorbed nitrogen. Here again, advantage would have been conferred from the start, by enabling the whales to dive to progressively greater depths. This case, however, introduces a new principle; for if the increased development of foam was favoured by selection because of its function in improving directional hearing, the part which it plays in protecting the whale from nitrogen-embolism, which is dependent on the accidental fact that foam is an efficient absorbent of nitrogen, may be regarded as an adaptational bonus.

The human eye

Of all the structures developed by the animal kingdom, the one which presents most difficulty is the human eye, unless it is understood how it is possible for the initial stages of complex structures to confer immediate advantage. We may take comfort from the fact that Darwin himself recognized that it was his most difficult problem. Since his day, however, microscopical study of the fine structure of some of the most lowly members of the group to which the vertebrates and therefore man belong have revealed stages in the evolution of the human eye that show how even the initial stages conferred progressive improvement at each step.

Before describing the simplest forms of eyes, a few words should be said on the ingredients, as it were, available to the ancestors of the vertebrates, out of which they developed paired eyes, at least 500 million years ago. In the first place, sensitivity to light is a property of primitive living matter, for it is found in one-celled plants and animals. It depends on the presence in the cell of a pigment, such as a carotenoid derivative that absorbs light-energy, for a perfectly transparent cell would be incapable of absorbing light, receiving stimulation or transmitting an impulse from such stimulation. In primitive animals, including all invertebrates, the site of light-sensitive cells is on the outer surface of the outer layer or epidermis, which is, of course, where rays of light first impinge on the animal. This is also where pigment-cells are found. In addition, the outermost layer of cells gives rise to two other types of tissue that are intimately involved in the production of an eye: nerve cells and nerve-fibres that transmit nervous impulses, and black melanin pigment, which is opaque to light. Transparent cells, or secretions of cells of a convex or spherical shape, form simple lenses that can concentrate the rays of light. Lenses are found even in one-celled organisms. With these ingredients, the following stages can be recognized in the evolution of paired eyes.

At the start of the evolution of vertebrates, the central nervous system was sunk beneath the surface of the skin. This takes place in embryonic development by the depression of a groove between a pair of longitudinal folds all the way along the back of the animal, and the fusion of the folds above the groove, which thereby becomes converted into a hollow tube, the neural tube, or spinal cord. By the formation of the neural tube, the outermost cells that were originally on the surface become enclosed within the tube and line its cavity; that is to say, these cells, which include the light-sensitive cells, lie on the *inner* edge of the neural tube, furthest from the outer surface of the body.

The condition just described is that of the lancelet, *Amphioxus* (*Branchiostoma*), where the light-sensitive organs are large single cells, each with a pigment-cell in the form of a hollow cup plastered on to it. The result is that each light-sensitive cell is insulated from light falling on to it from one side, and is therefore capable of receiving light only from the opposite side. As some of the light-sensitive cells face the dorsal side, and others face ventrally, the animal is capable not only of perceiving light but also the direction from which it comes. It should be added that the body of the animal is transparent and that the rays of light travel through it to reach the light-sensitive cells in the neural tube.

The next stage is shown by ascidians. The adults of these animals are sessile and degenerate, but the larvae, so-called ascidian tadpoles, have an eye developed out of the foremost part of the neural tube which is the brain. The eye is composed of a number of light-sensitive cells forming a cup-shaped layer that can be called a retina. The cavity of the cup is occupied by three vesicular cells forming a lens which concentrates the rays of light on the retina. The advantage, which consists in greater sensitivity and the possibility of spatial discrimination, accrues from the start of the improvement, when two sensory cells are grouped together. Furthermore, the sensitivity of the organ is further increased by the presence of a lens, which confers this advantage even when it consists of only a single cell (Pl. 312-314).

In the earliest true vertebrates beginning with the lampreys, there are two pairs of eyes, the foremost being the true paired eyes, and the hindmost the pineal eyes, on the top of the head. The paired eyes are lateral outgrowths from the wall of the brain on each side, projecting sideways as so-called optic vesicles, the outer surface of which comes into contact with the inner surface of the epidermis. At the point of contact the outer half of each optic vesicle folds inwards, like a deflated football squashed in. The optic vesicle is thereby converted into the optic cup consisting of two layers, an outer and an inner layer, connected with the brain by the optic stalk, the mouth of the optic cup being directed outwards, towards the epidermis.

The inner layer of the optic cup is the retina and contains the light-sensitive cells that become differentiated into so-called rods and cones, containing carotenoid derivatives such as visual purple which absorbs light-energy. These cells, it must be remembered, line the cavity of the neural tube, and when its side wall is pushed out to form the optic vesicle, these cells lie on the inner surface of the inner layer of the vesicle; that is to say on the side of that layer turned towards the brain and away from the outer surface of the animal. The remainder of the inner layer of the optic cup produces the nerve-fibres that connect with the rods and cones and conduct nervous impulses from them along the optic stalk, now the optic nerve, to the nerve centres in the brain. The inner layer of the epidermis immediately overlying the optic cup develops into a vesicle which sinks into the mouth of the optic cup, becomes detached from the epidermis, and gives rise to the lens. That the lens fits exactly into the mouth of the optic cup is the result of the fact that in embryonic development, the optic cup produces a chemical substance (a so-called organizer) that induces the epidermis to produce the lens. The outer layer of the epidermis remains thin and transparent and gives rise to the cornea. Here again, in embryonic development, it is the optic cup that produces a substance that makes the epidermis remain thin and transparent. Rays of light therefore have to pass through the cornea, through the lens, and through the nerve-fibres of the retina before they strike the sensitive elements in the rods and cones. For this reason, the retina of the paired eyes of vertebrates is described as inverted (Pl. 315-319).

The outer layer of the optic vesicle develops black pigment which backs the

Mimicry in Cuckoos' Eggs

Colour Plate 8

Cuckoos' eggs showing different grades of perfection in this adaptation to deceive foster-parents. In each case the cuckoo's eggs are shown *on the right* of its fosterer's. 1, Siberian blue robin *Luscinia cyane*. 2, redstart *Phoenicurus ph.* some difference in size and colour. 3, reed-warbler *Acrocephalus arundinaceus*. 4, whitethroat *Sylvia communis*. 5, pied wagtail *Motacilla varrellii*. 6, meadow-pipit *Anthus pratensis*, all similar in size and colour. 7, bunting *Emberiza fucata*. 8, bunting, *E. ciopsis*. 9, magpie *Pica pica*. 10, stonechat *Saxicola stejnegeri*. 11, shrike *Lanius collurio*. 12, robin *Erithacus rubecula*. 13, warbler *Prinia flavirostris*. Almost perfect resemblance.

271 272 273 275 276

retina and not only prevents the rods and cones from receiving light-rays from any other direction than through the mouth of the optic cup, but also prevents internal reflection. The pigment-layer is strengthened by connective tissue and forms the sclerotic or white of the eye-ball.

Further refinements found in different vertebrates consist of the attachment of muscles to the lens, which in some is moved bodily backwards or forwards, resulting in a focusing mechanism concentrating the rays of light on the retina; in others the lens is elastic and changes its shape and degree of curvature, which produces the same effect of accommodation. The rim of the mouth of the optic cup may develop a diaphragm with pigment, the iris, capable of enlarging and contracting its aperture which is the pupil. Finally, the muscles of that part of the body where the eye is situated become attached to the eyeball and rotate it backwards or forwards, upwards or downwards.

There can be little doubt that the series of stages just described through which the eye passes in embryonic development, is a repetition of the manner in which it evolved. That it is a complex structure cannot be denied, but it is equally clear that each stage was an improvement conferring advantage from the start, and was therefore accessible to the action of natural selection (Pl. 320–325).

Finally, it must be realized that wonderful as the structure of the eye is, it is not a perfect optical instrument. Helmholtz drew attention to its physical imperfections, particularly in regard to its failure to correct for chromatic aberration. Its imperfections, moreover, including the inverted retina, are living witnesses to the stages through which it passed in evolution.

Colour-vision

Colour-vision is another case in which an adaptive result may be achieved without itself being a direct object of selection. Colour-vision has been evolved independently in many groups of animals: some insects, fishes, birds, and mammals. Among the light-sensitive elements in the eye, some (low-threshold rods, most sensitive in blue light) are specially sensitive in dim illumination; others (cones, most sensitive in red light) confer acuteness of vision in bright light when they are innervated one by one so that light-stimuli are perceived separately by very small areas of the retina. In each of the two functions of seeing in the dark and seeing accurately in the light, increased efficiency confers survival-value from the start of the improvements. But when both these functions have been achieved in the same eyes, as E. N. Willmer has indicated, a mechanism is automatically produced in which the visual elements are differentially sensitive to light of different wave-lengths, and this is the basis of colour-vision. The emergence of colour-vision as an unexpected bonus resulting from the perfection of two other functions is an example of the principle to which Lloyd Morgan applied the term emergent evolution (Col. Pl. 9).

THE ORIGIN OF SPECIES

In previous sections, examples have been given of the way in which natural selection, acting on the results of mutations and recombinations of genes, changes the genotype in a population, and this process is none other than evolution. Closely related but not identical is the phenomenon of the origin of species, conveniently referred to as *speciation*. The production of differences between populations recognized as differences of the rank of species is a by-product of the processes whereby the populations become better adapted to their respective environments. It is therefore necessary to begin with a consideration of the definition of species.

What species are

Since different species differ not only in the precise conditions of their origins but also in the times since they originated, they also differ in the degrees of difference which distinguish them from other species. This is the explanation of the curious fact that although species are the units in which all living organisms are grouped, the status of the species is difficult to define.

There is first the criterion of structure: members of a species visibly resemble each other more closely than they resemble members of any other species. This criterion, which is frequently the only one that can be applied, as for instance to preserved specimens and fossils, suffers from the criticism that the attribution of specific rank to a population is an arbitrary act at the discretion of the taxonomist,

274

Artificial Selection of Cereals

271. An ear of *Triticum boeoticum*, wild ancestor of einkorn. **272.** An ear of *T. monococcum*, einkorn, the most primitive haploid wheat, cultivated extensively in the Neolithic period, and einkorn growing at high altitude in Switzerland. **273.** *T. dicoccoides*, wild emmer. **274.** *T. dicoccon*, emmer, tetraploid wheat and emmer growing in ancient Egypt where for thousands of years it was the only wheat; it is still grown today in Abyssinia, India, and south Russia. **275.** An ear of *T. spelta*, hexaploid wheat, grown by Bronze Age lake-side dwellers and in Roman Britain, and spelt growing at a high altitude in Germany. **276.** An ear of bread-wheat and bread-wheat, the main source of bread, growing in Saskachewan, is grown in Canada, Australia, and Russia. **277.** Diagram illustrating how tetraploid and hexaploid wheats arise from diploid wheats by hybridisation followed by chromosome doubling resulting in polyploidy.

The Production of Tetraploid and Hexaploid Wheats

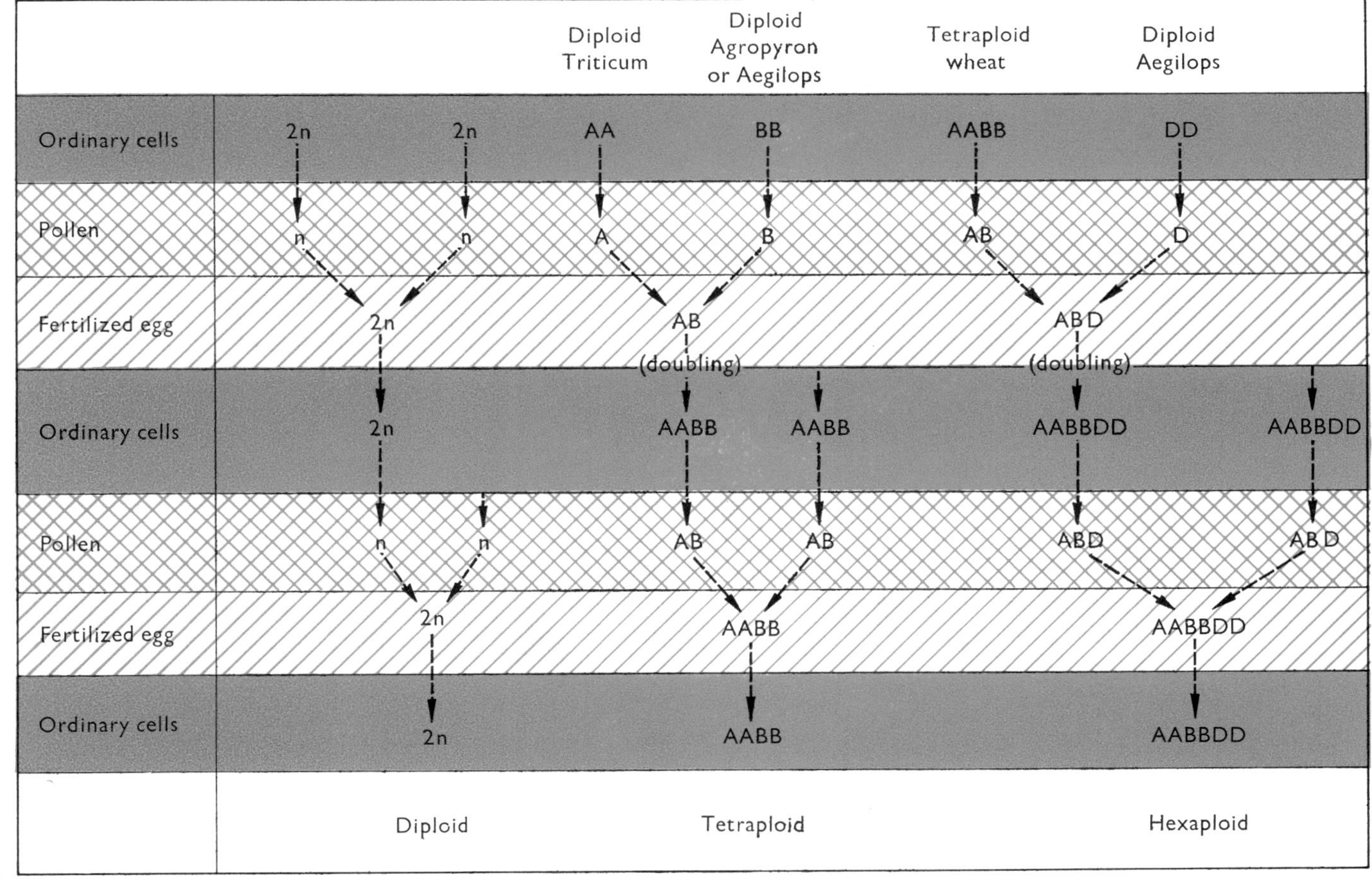

277

and this has led to the reproach that such species are subjective concepts and have no existence outside the mind of the scientist who described them.

This criticism cannot be levelled at the biological criterion of the species, which is that of a group of organisms reproductively isolated from other organisms under natural conditions. Whether a population does or does not interbreed with another population is a matter of fact which can be proved or disproved by observation and experiment on living populations in nature, and a species defined in this manner is not arbitrary but has objective reality and existence.

The corollary to the biological criterion of reproductive isolation of a species is that of fertility between the various populations within the species, even if these populations are distinguishable geographical races. This is the concept of the species as a community that shares a common pool of genes, a gene-pool, of such a kind that an hereditary character of any member of the species may potentially be transmitted to any other individual of a later generation in any part of its range; a process called gene-flow. Some idea of what a gene-pool means in practice can be obtained by considering that everybody alive today in England has during the past twenty generations had over one million ancestors, although some of them will have been the same people. In the fourteenth century, which is roughly twenty generations ago, the total population of England did not exceed two million. Most English people today have therefore inherited genes from half of the population of England six hundred years ago.

The reason why the species is difficult to define is because species are not static units, nor are they necessarily the end-products of finite changes, but rather stages in a continuous process of potentially infinite change, in which they may be at any level, as H. W. Parker has pointed out. Like stars at different stages of their evolution, species must be the object of research to determine the status of each.

An additional difficulty arises from the fact that different species need not be visibly distinct from one another. Among examples of such so-called *sibling species* may be mentioned the mosquitoes that used to go under the name of *Anopheles maculipennis*, which is now known to cover six species, indistinguishable by visual inspection, but which differ in geographical distribution, feeding and mating habits, breeding places, and ability to transmit malaria. Millions of pounds were wasted on malaria research before the existence of these sibling species was realized.

Evolution can take place up to a point without the production of new species, but if evolution continues beyond that point the time must come when reproductive isolation occurs and new species originate. New species can be seen originating in nature here and now, and new species have been artificially produced in the laboratory.

Speciation takes place when, for various reasons, populations cease to breed with neighbouring populations and, under different conditions of selection, accumulate different heritable variations by mutation and recombination of genes. As E. Mayr has shown, some form of biological isolation between portions of populations is probably a necessary condition for divergence leading to the formation of new species and higher groups.

The essential feature of biological isolation is the reproductive isolation of a population, and the operative factors may be *geographical*, when portions of populations are separated by physical barriers such as seas, deserts, or mountain ranges; *ecological*, when populations live in the same geographical area but in different habitats or niches, or breed at different times; or *genetic*, when portions of a population are prevented from interbreeding because of incompatibilities resulting from changes in the chromosome mechanism.

GEOGRAPHICAL ISOLATION

The accidents of geology can, of course, separate portions of a population that are genetically similar at the time of their separation. More important, however, are the results of separation and isolation of portions of a population that have already undergone some divergence as a result of the play of local factors of selection in different parts of the geographical range. Variation of this type is known as geographical variation and leads to the formation of geographical races of a species,

278

Artificial Selection in Pigeons

278. Artificial selection in pigeons. 'The diversity of the breeds is something astonishing. Compare the English carrier (A) and the short-faced tumbler (B). The carrier is also remarkable from the wonderful development of the carunculated skin about the head. The short-faced tumbler has a beak in outline almost like that of a finch; and the common tumbler has the singular inherited habit of flying at a great height in a compact flock and tumbling in the air head over heels. The runt (C) is a bird of great size, with long massive beak and large feet. The barb (D) is allied to the carrier, but, instead of a long beak has a very short and broad one. The pouter (E) has a much elongated body, wings, and legs; and its enormously developed crop which it glories in inflating. The trumpeter (F) and laugher utter a very different coo from the other breeds. The fantail (G) has thirty or even forty tail feathers, instead of twelve or fourteen. At least a score of pigeons might be chosen which, if shown to an ornithologist and he were told that they were wild birds, would certainly be ranked as well-defined species.' (Darwin) The results of artificial selection, practised by man on cultivated plants and domestic animals since Neolithic times (p. 185) have been so effective in changing breeds as in cereals (→ **271**), often in different directions as in horses and dogs (→ **26, 44**), that Darwin recognized selection as the means of change in species under natural conditions. It was important for him to prove that the amount of change obtained by artificial selection, which can be measured by the amount of difference between breeds of the same animal, could be as great as the differences between different species. Here, in pigeons, he found this evidence. He also found that when breeds were crossed their offspring often reverted to the simple blue rock-pigeon (H) which he rightly recognized as the single ancestral stock from which variations had been selected in different directions by man.

frequently described as sub-species. Geographical races are the commonest source from which new species arise.

Geographical variation introduces the problem whether adjacent populations in different geographical areas qualify for the status of species or not. In considering this problem it is helpful to introduce two terms: *allopatric* and *sympatric*, which simply mean, respectively, residing in different areas and in the same area. If adjacent populations in neighbouring areas show differences, but grade into one another in their zones of contact, the intergradation is evidence of interbreeding and the populations are held to belong to one species with allopatric geographical races or sub-species. On the other hand, if adjacent allopatric populations show differences but do not grade into one another or show very rare hybrids in their zones of contact, it is to be concluded that they interbreed very rarely or not at all and are separate species. In some cases, however, the ranges of two populations may overlap, when they are said to be sympatric. If they fail to grade into one another it is evidence that they do not interbreed and are fully separate species.

It is difficult for the initial divergence that will lead to two separate species to arise sympatrically from a population interbreeding freely, whereas the difficulty is resolved by the reproductive isolation of allopatric populations that geographical isolation produces. Examples of allopatric speciation will be given below.

Geographical variation within a species frequently takes the form of continuous gradients of change in characters such as size, colour, breeding-times, adaptation to habitats, speed of embryonic development, etc. Such gradients are usefully called *clines*, a term introduced by Sir Julian Huxley; there are size-clines, colour-clines, etc. There are clines in the number of vertebrae in species of fish. A cline in a character of a population may extend with gradual change over a considerable area, to the ecological conditions of which the gene-complex of the population is adjusted.

An example of a size-cline is provided by the puffin, *Fratercula arctica*. If comparison is made between the sizes of full-grown specimens from populations living in the Balearic Islands, the British Isles, Norway, and Spitzbergen, it is found that there is a steady increase in body-size from temperate to arctic latitudes. Using the length of the wing as a standard of measurement, the following variation is found.

Locality	*Length of wing in mm*
Spitzbergen, North Greenland	175–194
Norway, Bear Island Iceland, South Greenland	158–177
British Isles	155–166
Balearic Islands	135–145

This size-cline is an illustration of 'Bergmann's rule', which applies to warm-blooded animals. The source of heat in these animals is proportional to the muscles in their bodies, or to the cube of their linear dimensions. The loss of heat is proportional to the area of their outer surface, or to the square of their linear dimensions. At large sizes the ratio of surface to volume is small and the heat-loss relatively small. At small sizes, on the other hand, the ratio of surface to volume is high, and the heat-loss great. In a cold climate this becomes a serious handicap to the animal and a limiting factor to the permissible degree of smallness. In the puffin the size-cline shows an increase in linear dimensions of 1 per cent for every 2° of latitude north (Col. Pl. 10).

Bergmann's rule also applies to different but related species, as is illustrated by penguins. The emperor-penguins of the Antarctic continent reach a height of 120 cm, the Adelie penguin of the South Orkneys a height of 75 cm, the penguin of the Cape of Good Hope a height of 55 cm, and the penguin of the Galápagos Islands (on the Equator) a height of 44 cm.

POLYTYPIC SPECIES

Species that are split up over their range into a number of geographical races or sub-species are called polytypic species. There is a simple reason why species undergo such geographical variation. It is because in any area the environment is extremely complex and the habitats are numerous and changing. A species is not adapted to one 'environment' but to a great many, and its adaptation is a com-

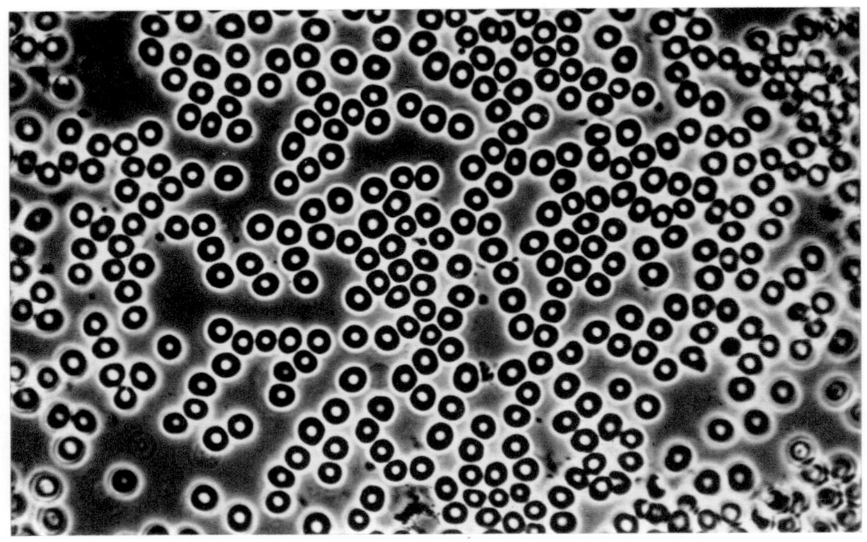

279

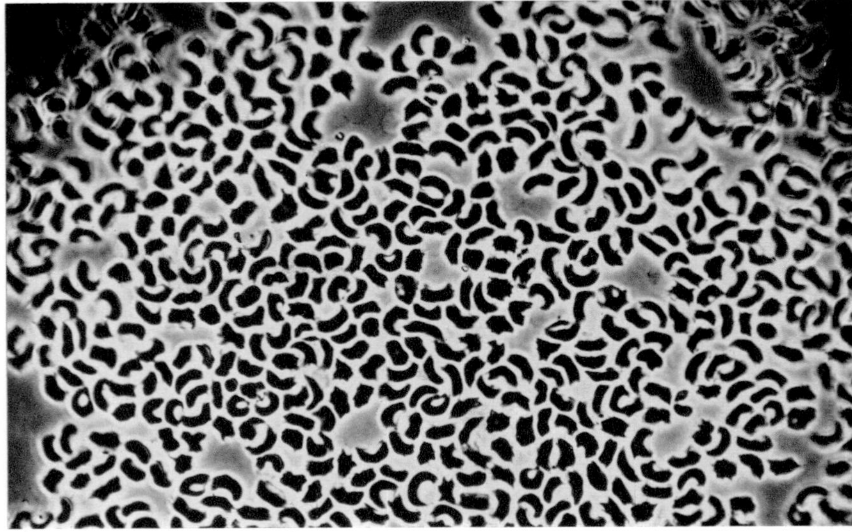

280

promise of adjustment to as many of them as possible. If a portion of a population of a species becomes restricted in range, however, its adaptation need no longer take account of those habitats from which it is cut off and to which it need no longer adjust itself. Geographical races are locally adapted, and this means that their genotypes are slightly different since they have been acted upon by different factors of natural selection.

It sometimes happens that allopatric geographical races at different extremities of the range of a species may become sympatric as a result of geographical overlap. It may then be found that the individuals of the two populations in the sympatric area do not interbreed but behave as if they were separate species. Examples are the great tits, the gulls, and the Californian salamanders.

The great tit

The great tit, *Parus major*, variety *major*, with its green back and yellow belly, has a range that extends all the way from western Europe across central and eastern Europe and Siberia to the Pacific Ocean north of Japan. It also extends across Asia Minor and Persia to India, but with geographical variation affecting the colour of the back, which becomes grey, and the belly, which becomes white in the Indian form *Parus major* variety *cinereus*. The intergrades between European and Indian great tits show that they interbreed from link to link of the chain and still belong to the same species.

Further intergrades connect *Parus major cinereus* of India with the geographical races of *Parus major* variety *minor* in China and Manchuria, which have a green back but a white belly. In the region of the Amur river, between Manchuria and Siberia, the range of *minor* overlaps with that of *major*, but the two do not interbreed. Instead, they behave as if they were separate and different species, in spite of the fact that they still belong to one and the same gene-pool, since *minor* in China is connected by interbreeding populations with *cinereus* in India and this, again, with *major* in Europe. During the course of their geographical variation in different directions, therefore, the populations of *major* and of *minor* now living sympatrically in the same area on the Amur river, have undergone divergent differentiation of their genotypes. If it were not for the connecting populations in India and Europe, *major* and *minor* would have to be regarded as separate and distinct species. They have not yet reached this state, but are incipient species. A comparable area of overlap between *major* and *cinereus* without interbreeding is found in Central Asia (Col. Pl. 11).

The herring gull and the lesser black-backed gull

The lesser black-backed gull and the herring gull occupy a range shaped like a ring round the North Pole. The British lesser black-backed gull, *Larus fuscus graellsii*, has a dark mantle of feathers and yellow legs. This grades into the very similar Scandinavian lesser black-backed gull, *Larus fuscus fuscus*. Continuing in an easterly direction along the range of the species, this geographical race grades into the Siberian Vega gull, *Larus argentatus vegae*, with its lighter grey mantle and dull flesh-coloured legs. The Siberian gull grades into the American herring gull, *Larus argentatus smithsonianus*, and this, in turn, into the British herring gull, *Larus argentatus argentatus*, which has a light grey mantle and pinkish legs.

In the British Isles where they live sympatrically, the lesser black-backed gull and the herring gull differ not only in colour and appearance but also in their habits. The former tends to breed inland on moors and is often migratory in winter; the latter prefers to nest on cliffs and is resident. The former is more a bird of the open sea than the latter; the latter gives the extreme alarm-call less frequently than the former, and there is a difference of pitch in their calls. These differences show the extent to which geographical variation can result in the alteration of the genotype of two portions of one and the same species under different conditions of natural selection when semi-isolated at the extreme ends of the range. Now that they overlap in their range they behave as different species, and this is shown in the different specific names they are given. Actually, they will acquire full species-status only when the ring of interbreeding forms connecting them round the world is broken, and the gene-pool is divided into two (Col. Pl. 11). It is to be noticed that in the case of the gulls, as in that of the tits (above), the acquisition of the status of separate species does not depend on the populations that are candidates for this status. They have already undergone sufficient evolution to produce non-interbreeding sympatric populations. Their promotion to species-status depends on fortuitous events elsewhere: as just explained, a rupture in geographical continuity of the gene-pool will confer this status. In the next example, Californian salamanders, this event is in process of happening.

Californian salamanders

Ensatina eschscholtzi is a species of salamander that has moved southwards since the Ice Age along the Pacific coast into California. When it came to the Central Valley of California, which is hot and dry and unsuitable for newts, the migrants split, one branch passing south along the Coast Range, the other inland along the range of the Sierra Nevada. Although they grade into one another smoothly and are linked by interbreeding populations, several geographical races have been made out, varying in the colour of the body, and the size of the eye. As the researches of R.C. Stebbins have shown, the characters that distinguish the races are adaptive and have been produced by the selection of different variants in different climates. The amount of black pigment in the skin, which is more plentifully present in the races that live in the northern and elevated parts of the range, is concerned with heat-regulation, for black absorbs light, and dark colouration in hot climates leads to over-heating in animals lacking heat-regulating mechanisms. At the same time, dark colouration is adaptive in the dim light of dark forests because of the high degree of background-matching that it produces.

The development of yellow lipophore pigment is associated with the water-balance of the animal, for it controls the rate of water-absorption through the skin. Water is abundant in the northern part of the range, but scarce in the south. The eyes of the different races vary in the quantity of guanophore pigment found in the iris; this protects the eye in bright light and is lacking in races of nocturnal habits. The spotting and blotching of the animals is an adaptation to background-matching in those races which live generally on a variegated background, and is characteristic of those inhabiting the Sierra Nevada. The races of the coastal strip are uniformly coloured without blotches. The size of the body varies as a size-cline connected with heat-regulation and water-loss.

The southernmost variety of the coastal strip races is called *eschscholtzi* and is uniform orange-red in colour with no blotches and very little black pigment. The southernmost variety of the Sierra Nevada group of races, called *klauberi*, is heavily mottled black and yellow. Its range overlaps that of *eschscholtzi*, with which it lives sympatrically but does not interbreed. There is an intermediate form between *klauberi* and its next northern neighbouring race of the Sierra Nevada group, *croceator*, but there is a geographical discontinuity in the range; *klauberi* is out of touch with and isolated from *croceator*. The geographical race *klauberi* is therefore cut off from the remainder of its former gene-pool by geographical isolation, and should strictly be accorded the status of a separate species. Here, therefore, is evidence of the production of a population that breeds only within the circle of its own members, and has evolved out of a geographical race that differs from the other races of the species to which it belonged by characters that are adaptive and therefore under the control of natural selection exactly as Darwin claimed (Col. Pl. 12).

That reproductive isolation confers advantage on two species living sympatrically is shown by the conditions in the cotton plants studied by S. G. Stephens. The ranges of *Gossypium barbadense* and *G. hirsutum* overlap in the West Indies and the northern part of South America. Hybrids between strains of the two species living sympatrically in these areas are weak and inferior, with a bushy habit and the stem,

Natural Selection in Action

279. Normal red blood cells and **280,** the red blood cells of a man homozygous for the sickle gene that produces abnormal haemoglobin molecules and distorted blood cells. **281.** The malarial parasite in a normal red cell - it cannot enter a sickle-cell. **282.** Distribution of sickle-cell gene in Africa. **283.** Distribution of malaria in Africa. The grey peppered moth is almost invisible on a background of lichen in regions unpolluted by smoke, against which the mutant black variety *carbonaria* is conspicuous (→ **69, 70**). Conversely the grey form is conspicuous against soot on trees in industrial areas where the *carbonaria* form is almost invisible. Birds mostly see and catch the conspicuous forms and miss those that match their background. **284,** robin on unpolluted tree with *carbonaria* in its mouth. **285,** redstart on soot-covered tree with a grey moth in its mouth. Predation is selective and colouration adaptive. A century of selection in favour of blackness in polluted areas has increased the black effect of the *carbonaria gene* **286.**

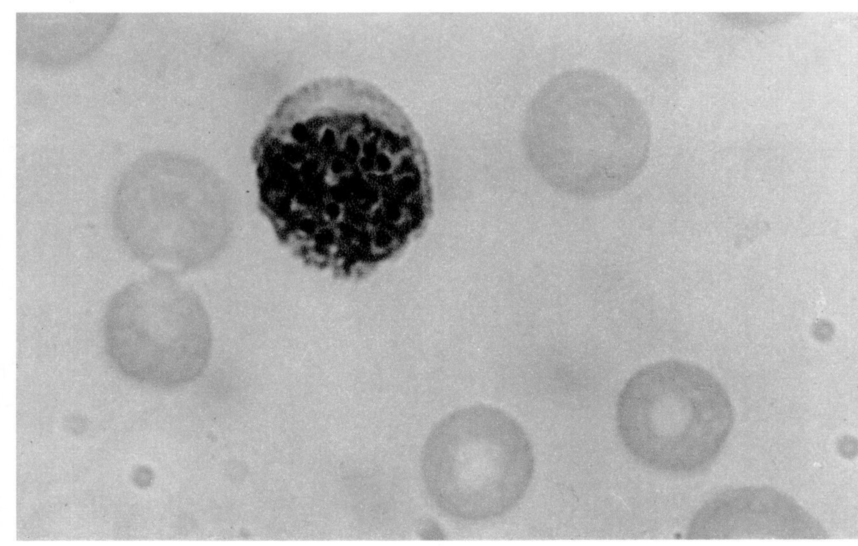

281

282

15-20%
10-15%
5-10%
5%

FREQUENCY OF SICKLE-CELL GENE IN AFRICA, ARABIA

283

284

285

286

287 288

290
291

292
293

289

Sexual Selection

Sexual selection in Darwin's original sense involves possession by one sex, usually the male, of structures and behaviour used for threat or combat against rivals or display before females, resulting in greater reproductive success for the winners. **287.** Display of the white peacock. **288.** The 'eyes' in the feathers of the train of the common peacock. **289.** Lyre-bird on its mound dancing and displaying with its specialised tail feathers shaking and shimmering over its head. **290.** Reeve and **291,** Ruffs. The Ruff shows sexual selection in Darwin's sense. The males are larger, strikingly coloured; more numerous than females, and polygamous. They fight and the winners get reproductive advantage. **292.** Elephant-seals, a polygamous species showing the greater size of the bulls. **293.** Red deer males and **295,** fallow deer males fighting. **294.** A mated pair of great-crested grebes engaged in the ritual of presenting each other with nest-building material, an example of display and courtship activities taking place after mating, the sexes similar in appearance and the display mutual.

294 295

Deep Sea

296

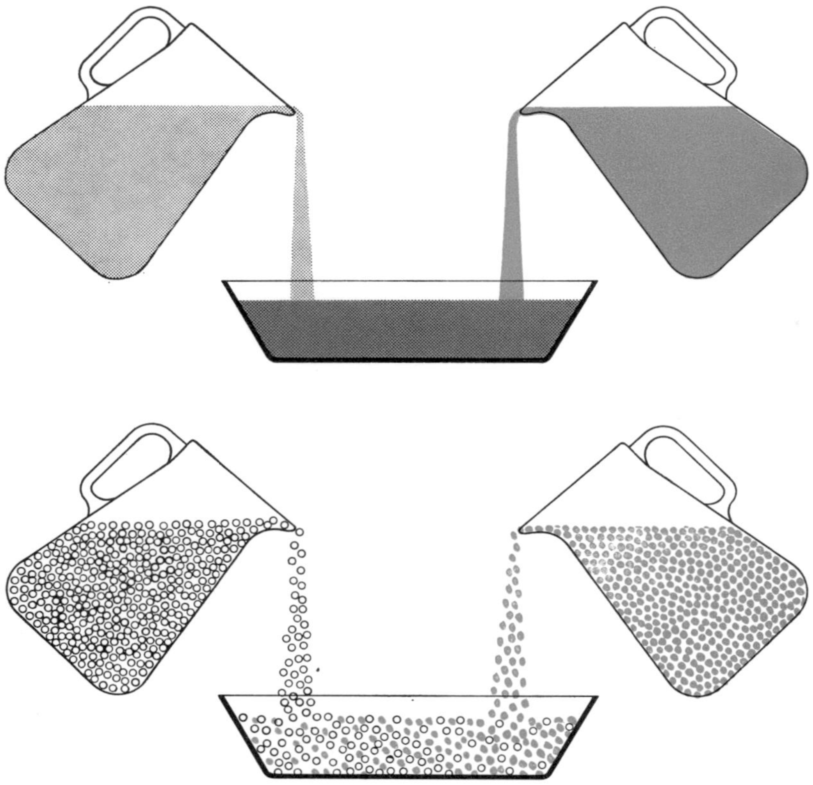

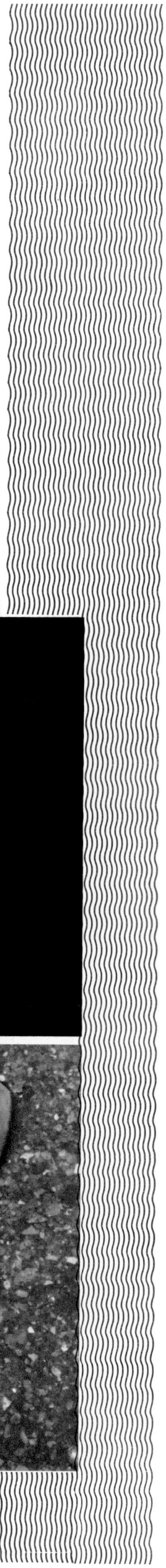

(Particles) Particulate Inheritance (Liquids) Blending Inheritance

One genus persists through 500 million years.

Particulate Inheritance and Speeds of Evolution

Mendelian inheritance is particulate, the discrete self-copying genes never become contaminated or blend, and variance is conserved. The difference between 'blending' inheritance and particulate inheritance may be shown diagrammatically **296,** the former by *yellow* and *black* liquids poured into a dish where they mix intimately and permanently, the latter by *yellow* and *black* seeds that can be separated out again. Just as both these mixtures produce a superficially similar *cream* colour, so particulate genetic inheritance may produce a phenotype that *looks* like, but is not, a blend between the parental characters. The speed of evolution is controlled by the pressure of selection which, in turn depends on environmental change. In the constant conditions of the deep sea, the lamp-shell *Lingula* **298** has remained in the same genus for 500 million years, as shown by fossils of this age **297.** In the changing environment on dry land the ancestry of the horse has passed through 8 genera in 70 million years **299. 300.** The higher rate of evolution on land as compared with that in water is shown by the average ages of genera, families, orders, and classes in mammals and reptiles compared with fishes, insects compared with crustacea, and land-snails compared with marine gastropods. **301.** Rensch's diagram of systematic categories showing roughly to scale their average ages in mammals.

297

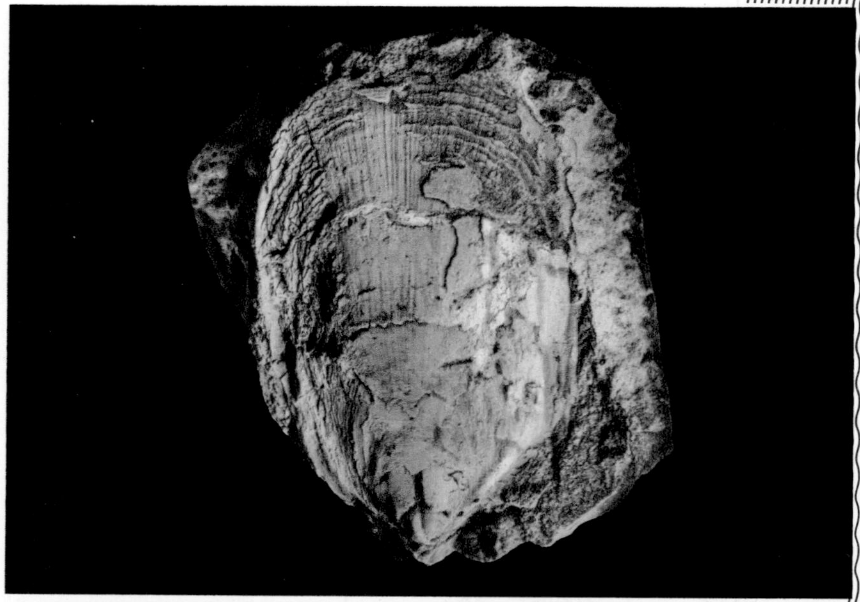

298

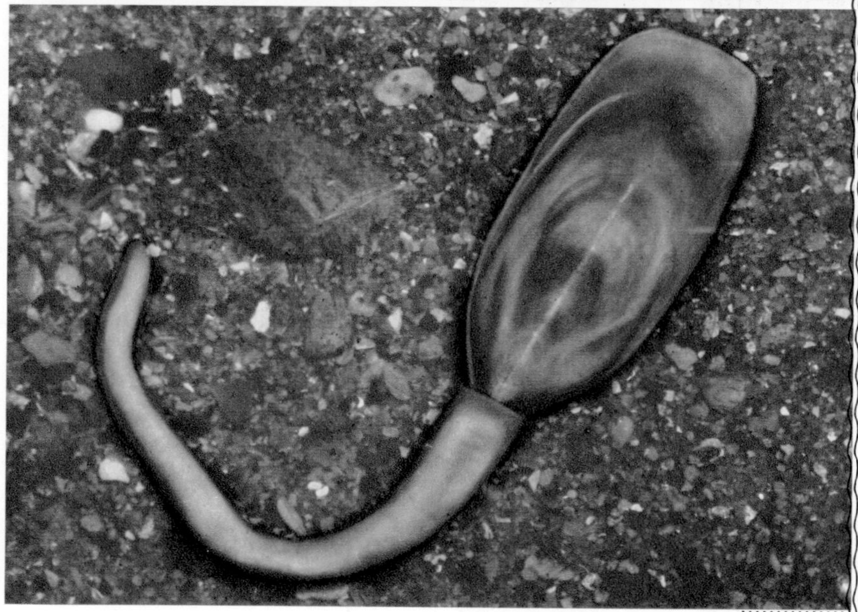

Lingula

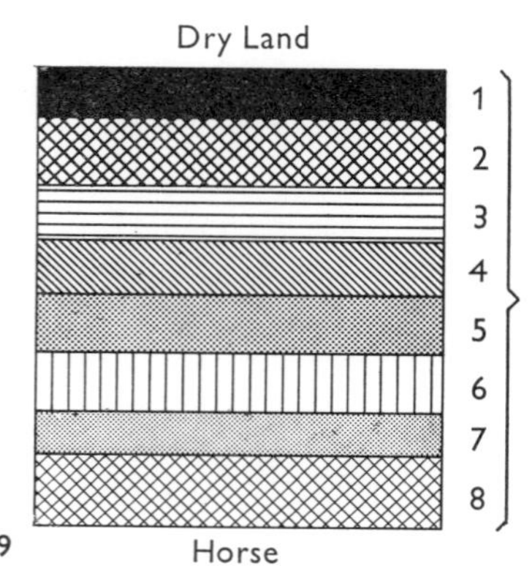

299

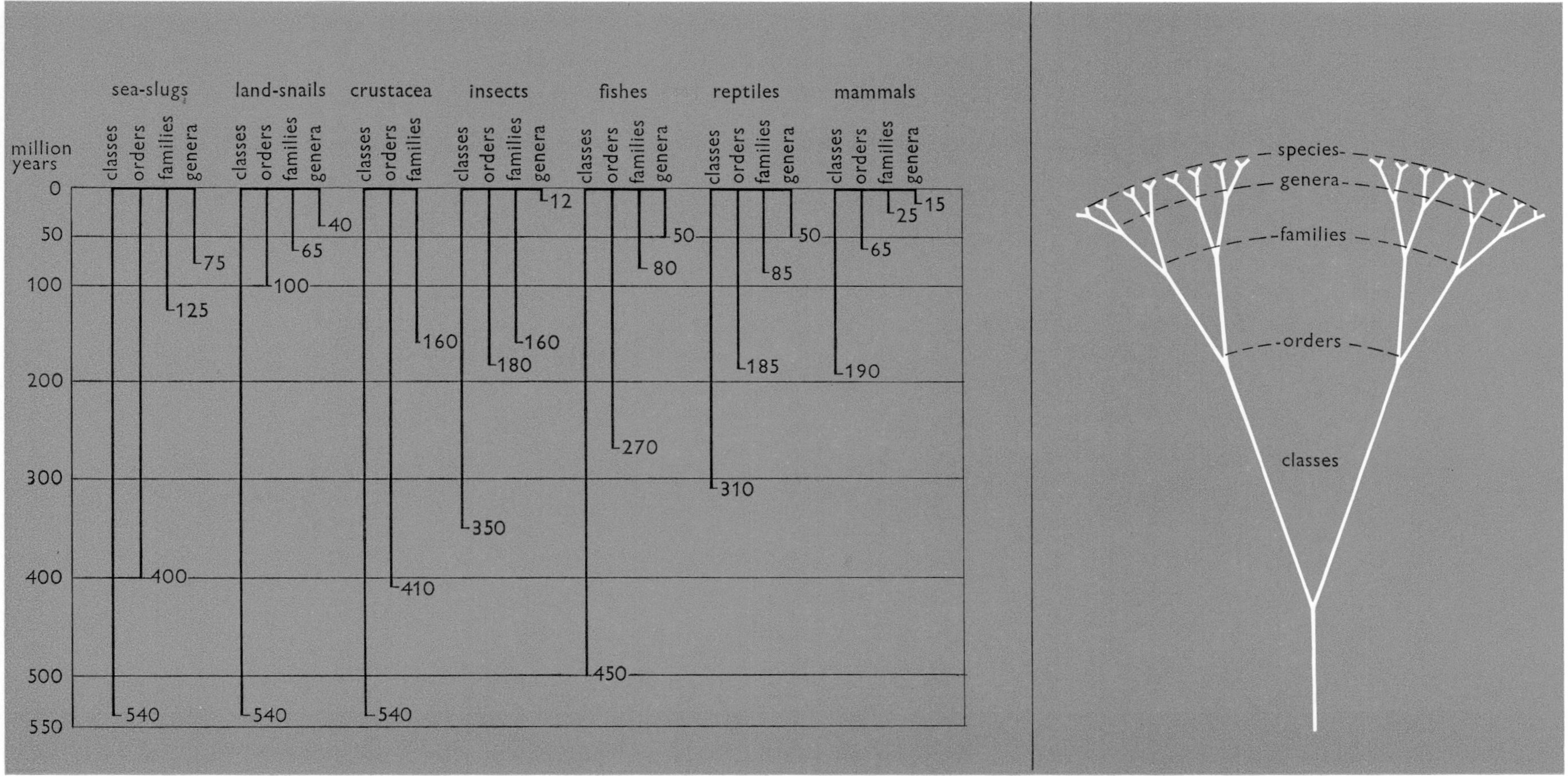

300 301

Relative Ages of Categories of Animals

petiole, and midribs of the leaves covered with a layer of cork. Hybrids between strains of these two species living allopatrically, outside the zone of overlap, do not, of course, arise in nature but they can be bred artificially and are vigorous without any of the 'corky' characters of the sympatric hybrids. It has been found that the genotypes of the sympatric strains, but not of the allopatric strains, of the two species contain genes which complement one another and produce 'corky' characters. Each species breeding within itself produces normal offspring: it is the hybrids that are penalized, and whatever the reason for the original appearance of the 'corky' genes may have been, the restriction of the genes concerned to the geographical zone of overlap, which is the only one where they confer advantage, indicates that they have been preserved by natural selection.

In addition to these observations in the field, there is experimental evidence to show that once reproductive isolation has been started, natural selection may accentuate it until it is complete. *Drosophila pseudoobscura* and *D. persimilis* are two species of fruit-flies whose reproductive isolation is not complete so that they can interbreed, particularly at low temperatures. K. F. Koopman found that matings between flies of the same species leave more offspring than matings between flies of different species. Natural selection thus favours species-specific mating and produces inter-specific sterility. This is the very evidence which T. H. Huxley said was necessary for Darwin's theory of evolution by natural selection to receive its final confirmatory proof.

ECOLOGICAL ISOLATION

In Europe there are two species of edible frogs. One, *Rana esculenta*, inhabits central Europe. The other, *R. ridibunda*, is found in Spain and also in eastern Europe, and Asia Minor, having come north from Africa on each side of the Mediterranean. The range of *R. esculenta* overlaps that of *R. ridibunda* on each side, but reproductive isolation between them is maintained because *R. ridibunda* normally breeds three weeks earlier than *R. esculenta*, and the two gene-pools are thereby kept separate even where the forms are sympatric. This is an example of ecological isolation. But occasionally, local climatic conditions may delay the breeding season of *R. ridibunda*, and then hybridization with *R. esculenta* can occur, as H. W. Parker showed (Map 7).

An example of how the divergent effects of ecological isolation may begin, is furnished by the butterfly *Colias philodice* studied by W. Hovanitz. In this species the female is typically yellow, but mutation gave rise to a white form which is physiologically adjusted to live at a lower temperature than the other. For this reason, the white form is more frequently found flying in the early morning and in the evening than the yellow form, from which it is not separated by any geographical barrier. The species therefore has the potentiality for the development of two races and the establishment of polymorphism, based on physiological and ecological differences. From this condition, further evolution is possible.

The best examples of ecological isolation, however, are furnished by the finches of the Galápagos Archipelago, as shown in the map (Pl. 41) and diagram (Pl. 328).

The Galápagos finches

The evolution of the finches of the Galápagos Islands, which started Darwin on his doubts about the fixity of species (see p. 16), has been analysed in the light of modern knowledge of genetics and ecology by D. Lack. Both geographical and ecological isolation have played their part in this evolution.

The Galápagos Islands, which arose volcanically from the sea 600 miles off the coast of South America, must have been uninhabited by birds when they were first colonized by a species of small South American finch of the genus *Geospiza*, living on the ground and feeding on seeds. All the ecological niches were untenanted and available. At the present time, there are fourteen species of finch in the Archipelago. Of these, three species still live on the ground and feed on seeds, but are differentiated into large *(G. magnirostris)*, medium-sized *(G. fortis)*, and small *(G. fuliginosa)* forms feeding on seeds of different sizes. Two species *(G. scandens* and *G. conirostris)* live on cactus plants. One species *(G. difficilis)* combines ground and cactus-feeding and eats leaves.

Another six species, which differ from *Geospiza* by having abandoned the ground or cactus plants to live in trees, are included in the genus *Camarhynchus*. Of these, one species *(C. crassirostris)* has remained vegetarian and feeds on buds and fruit. The remainder feed on insects and show a differentiation into large, medium, and small forms *(C. psittacula, C. pauper, C. parvulus)*, which eat insects of different sizes. One species *(C. heliobates)* eats insects in wood. Another *(C. pallidus)* has made itself into a sort of artificial woodpecker, for it uses a spine of a cactus to probe into holes in trees and to dig out the grubs.

A thirteenth species resembles a warbler and eats soft small insects *(Certhidea olivacea)*. Resembling it is the fourteenth species *(Pinaroloxias inornata)*, which lives also on Cocos Island 500 miles distant to the northeast.

The geographical isolation of the Galápagos Archipelago as a whole has enabled these finches to pursue their local evolution along ecological lines without the complication of possible crossing with other South American species. In addition, the geographical isolation of some of the outlying islands of the Archipelago has enabled some species to exploit ecological niches not otherwise open to them. For example, on Hood Island, the large ground finch, *Geospiza magnirostris* is absent, but the cactus finch *G. conirostris* is present, and occupies the ecological niche of a large ground finch in addition to its own; its beak there is larger than it is elsewhere except on Culpepper Island, where it has become a purely ground finch in the absence of *G. magnirostris* and its beak is largest. Similarly on Culpepper Island, the small ground finch *G. fuliginosa* is absent, and its niche has been occupied by the ground-and-cactus species *G. difficilis*, whose beak is correspondingly enlarged as compared with the same bird on other islands.

Early Stages in Adaptation:

Weak electric discharges given off by fishes act like radar and inform the fish of proximity of objects. **302.** Graphic record of discharges of *Eigenmannia virescens*: the origin of electric organs giving discharges strong enough to kill prey and deter predators. **303.** The origin of the 5-fingered limb of land vertebrates, forelimbs of (1) *Sauripterus*, a primitive fish showing numerous radials supporting the fin, (2) a primitive amphibian, (3) a reptile, the radials reduced to 5 while the other bones correspond with those of the fish. The origin of flight in birds. Feathers arose as heat-insulators when birds became warm-blooded.

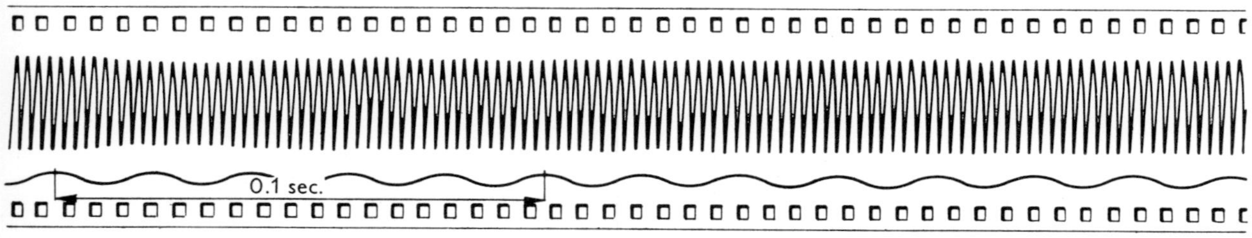

302

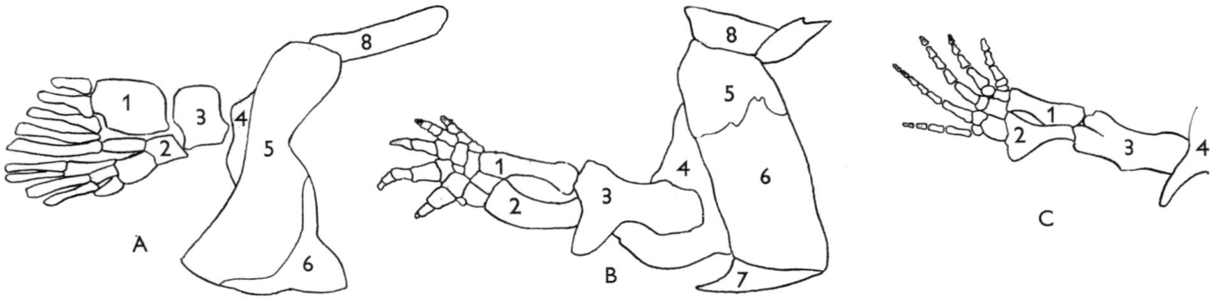

0.1 sec.

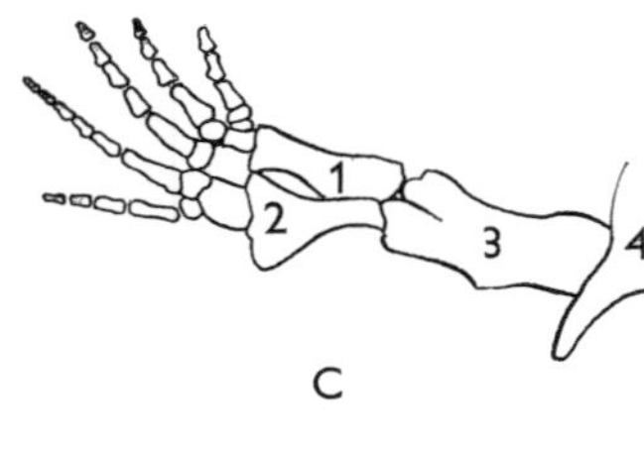

A. Sauripterus
B. Primitive tetrapod (Amphibian)
C. Seymouria

1. radius
2. ulna
3. humerus
4. pectoral girdle (scapula and coracoid)
5. cleithrum
6. clavicle
7. interclavicle
8. supracleithrum

303

304

305

306

307

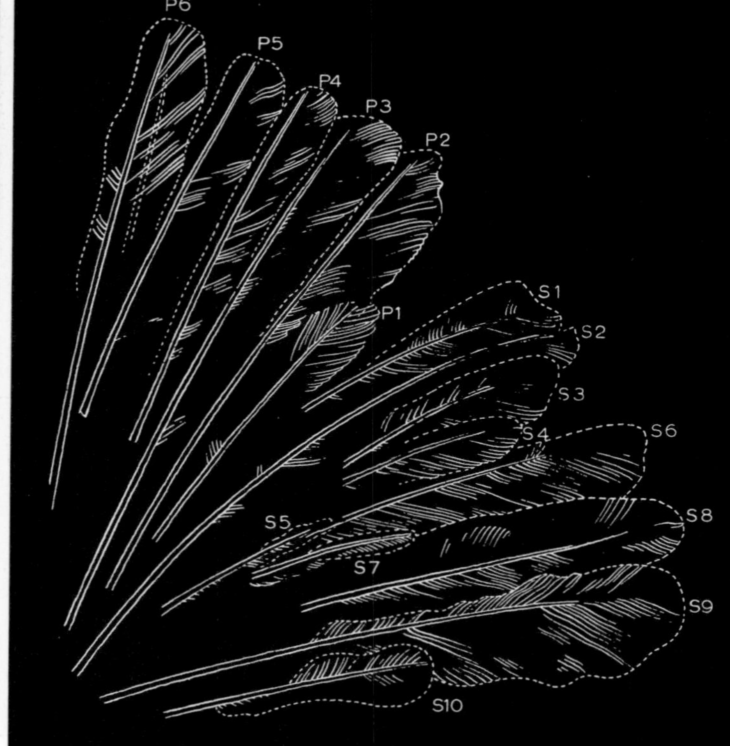

308

Wings

304. Body-feather of a Jurassic bird, **305.** of a modern bird. **306.** Feather with stiff vane giving air-resistance in a Jurassic bird. **307.** Right wing of *Archaeopteryx* showing impression of feathers enabling it to glide **308,** key to feathers of *Archaeopteryx*. **309.** Brain of *Archaeopteryx* showing the small size of its cerebellum, incapable of 3-dimensional co-ordination required for active flight. Superior musclepower converted gliding into active flight. **310.** Radiogram of a flying bird showing that the feathers are arranged on the wing as in *Archaeopteryx*.

310

309

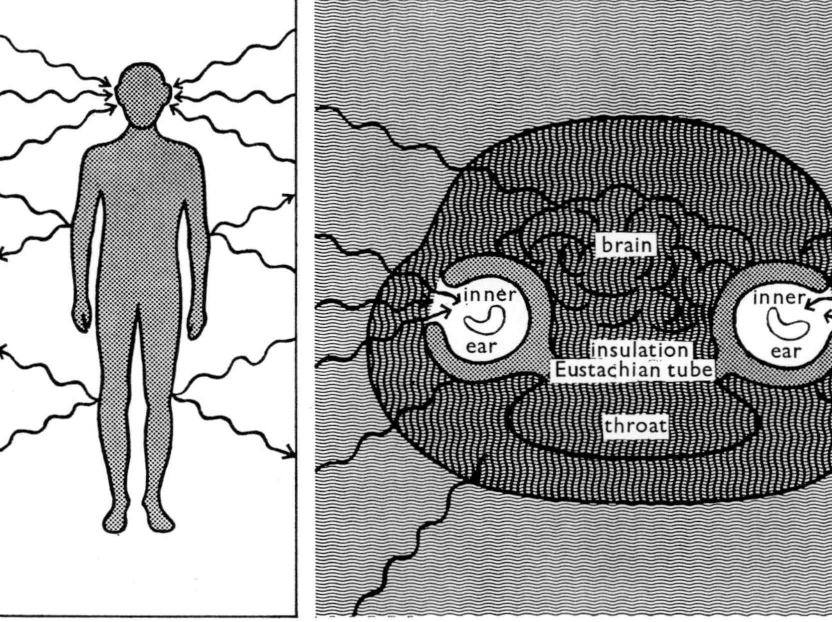

A. Sound absorbed only by eardrums and reflected by other parts of the body, because density of air and body are very different

B. Sound absorbed all over the body because density of water and body are similar; but insulation of inner ear permits directional hearing 311

Directional hearing

311. Diagram of sound-conduction in air and in water to illustrate the adaptation of whales to directional hearing. Man in air reflects or deadens sound-waves falling on his body except on the eardrums, the diaphragms are a distance apart by which the direction whence sound comes can be appreciated. A whale in water absorbs sound waves all over its body and the direction whence sound comes can be appreciated only if the ears are acoustically insulated. This is achieved by outgrowths from the Eustachian tubes and tympanic cavities forming sacs containing oily foam. This, further, absorbs nitrogen and protects the whale from embolism when deep. It is evacuated after diving by 'blowing'. (F.C. Fraser and P. E. Purves).

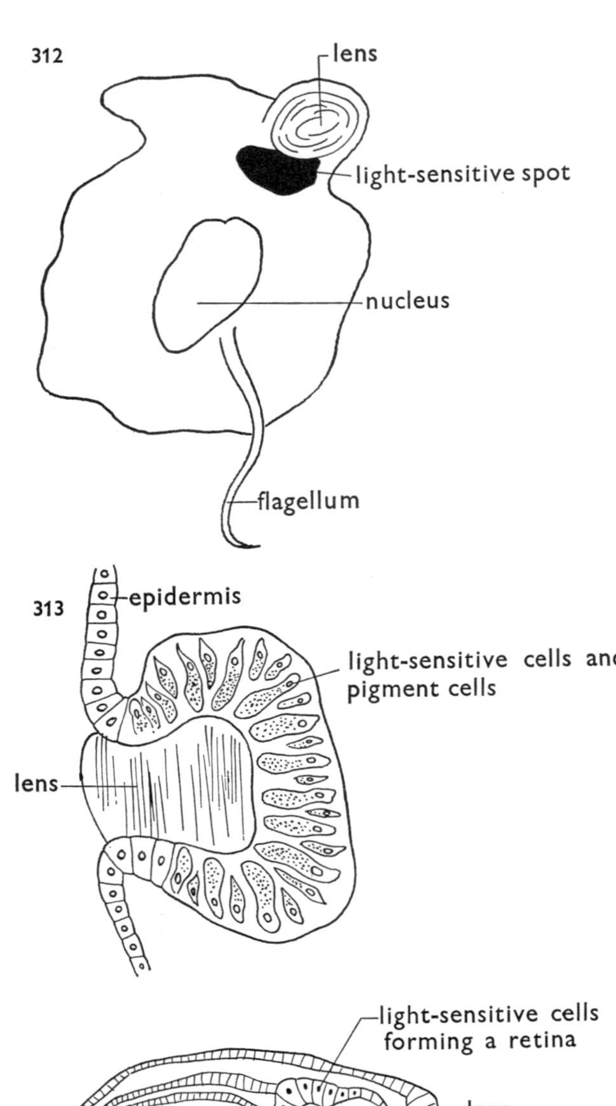

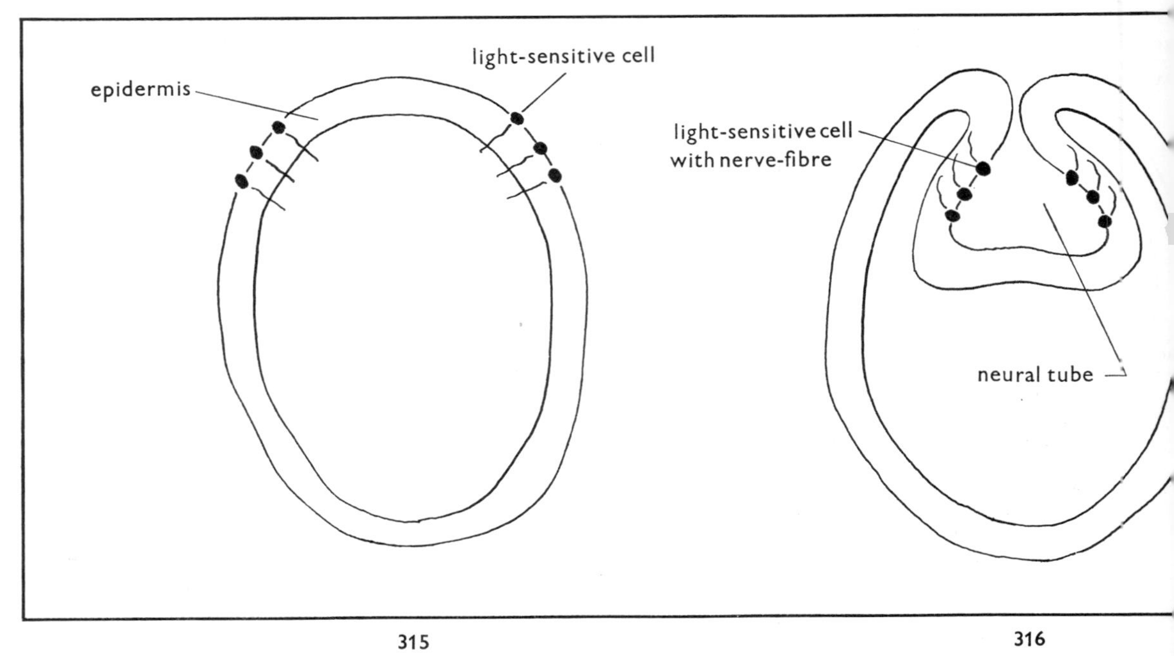

The Evolution of the Eye

312. A one-celled organism with light-sensitive spot covered by a simple spherical light-concentrating lens. **313.** Section through the eye of a jelly-fish showing a cup-shaped layer of light-sensitive cells forming a retina. **314.** Ascidian tadpole showing the retina formed from the lining of the brain-cavity. **315.** Primitive condition in vertebrates in which the light-sensitive cells are on the outer surface of the epidermis. **316.** With infolding of the neural tube to form the brain and spinal cord the light-sensitive cells come to line the inside of its cavity. **317.** Section through the lancelet *Amphioxus* in which the light-sensitive cells are in this condition and line the cavity of the neural tube. **318.** An early stage in development of the eyes in vertebrates showing optic vesicles bulging from the sides of the brain. **319.** Optic vesicles converted into eye-cups consisting of retinal layer and pigment layer, the lens developing from the epidermis opposite the mouth (future pupillary opening) of the cup; the light-sensitive cells are on the side of the retina away from the light, which is why such a retina is called inverted.

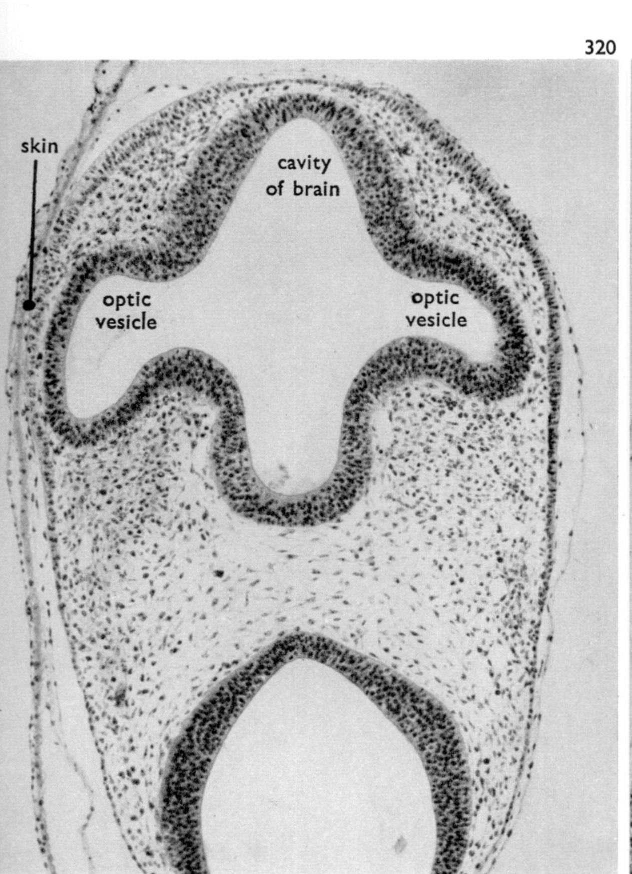

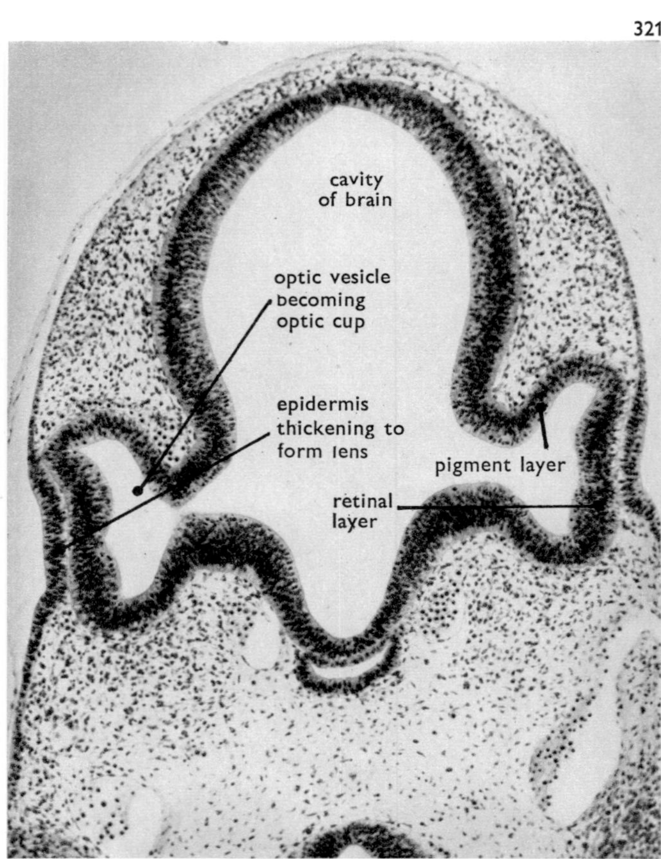

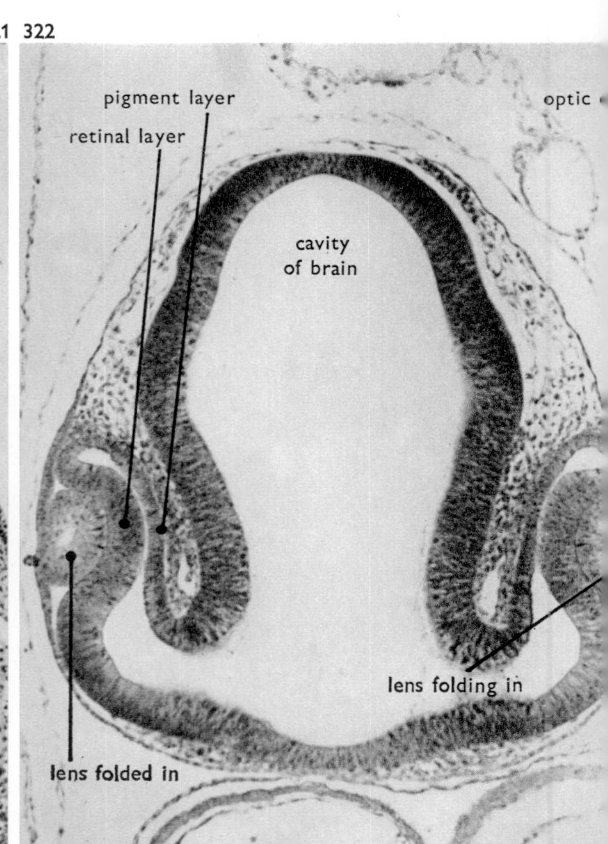

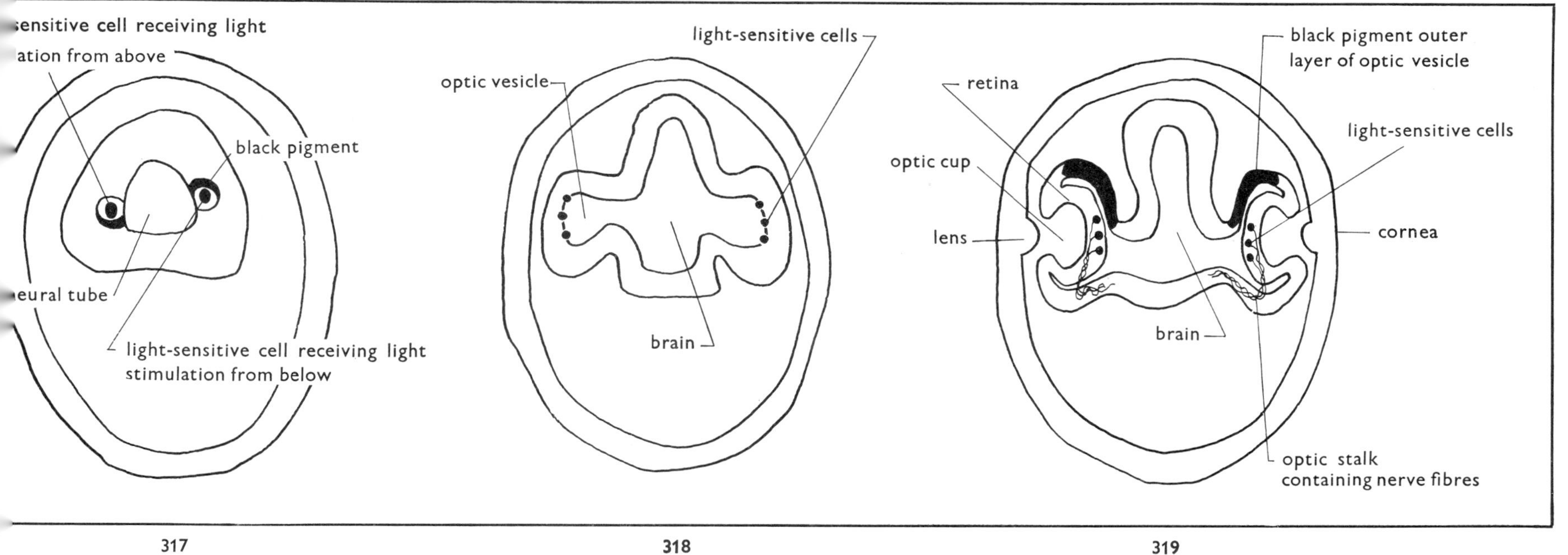

317 318 319

Development of the Eye in Vertebrate Embryos

320. The side walls of the brain are pushed outwards towards the skin forming optic vesicles. **321.** The optic vesicles flattened against the skin which is thickening and will form the lens. **322.** Optic cups now formed with inner retinal and outer pigment layers, the lens fitting into the mouth of the cup. **323.** The optic cup taking shape with thick retinal and thin pigment layers connected with the brain by the optic stalk, still hollow. **324.** Lens now 'lens-shaped' by elongation of its inner layer of cells to form lens-fibres. **325.** Late stage showing the eye with differentiated retinal layer with light-sensitive cells (rods and cones) and nerve-cells surrounded by the protective sclerotic layer, large space occupied by the vitreous humour, lens in position beneath the iris diaphragm, separated from the cornea by the aqueous humour **326** (*overleaf*). The eye is protected by eyelids, eyelashes, and eyebrows. It serves not only as an organ of vision but also as a means of expression in human beings.

Evolution in a contrary direction is found on Charles Island, which is inhabited by *Camarhynchus pauper* and *C. parvulus*. Both these species are insect-eaters, but possible competition between them has been minimized by *C. parvulus*, the smaller form, concentrating on still smaller insects for its food, in consequence of which it has evolved a smaller beak. These examples illustrate Gause's principle (p. 92) of competitive exclusion of more than one species from any one ecological niche.

In the Galápagos Islands, therefore, geographical and ecological isolation of portions of the population of finches has proceeded far enough to result in the divergence of four *genera* as well as fourteen species.

These birds and these islands, as Darwin showed, provide the classical example of adaptation to different ecological conditions leading to the origin of different species.

GENETIC ISOLATION

Genetic isolation can occur by a sort of trick, whereby reproductive isolation can be acquired by individuals suddenly, as a result of changes in the number of chromosomes in their cells. The changes concerned are special cases of doubling, trebling, or some higher multiplication of the normal diploid number of chromosomes, resulting in triploid, tetraploid, hexaploid, octaploid, or, more generally, *polyploid* races.

323

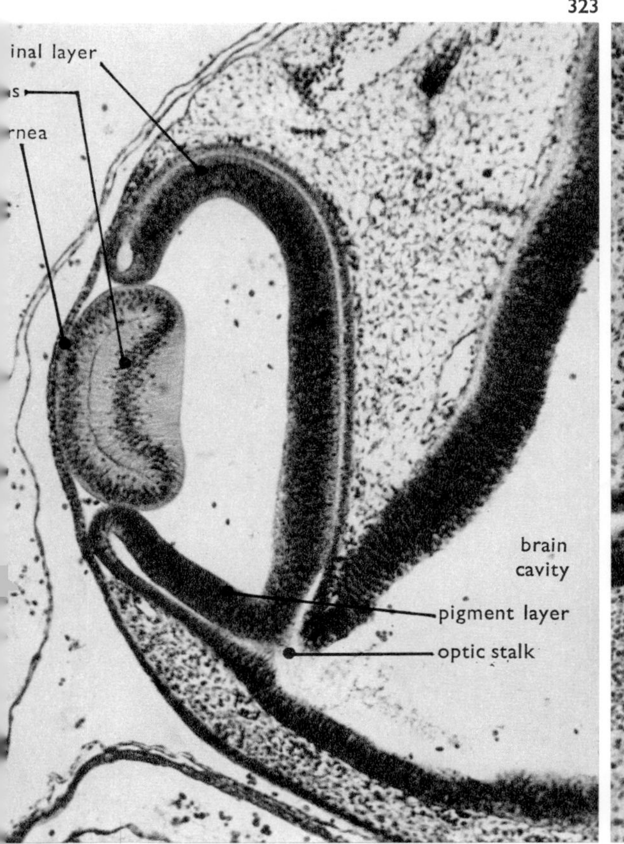

324 325

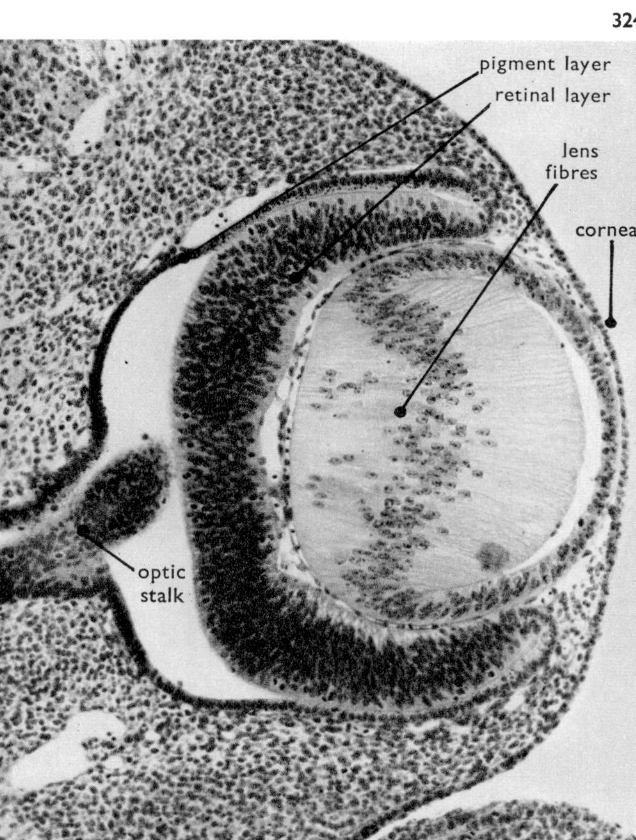

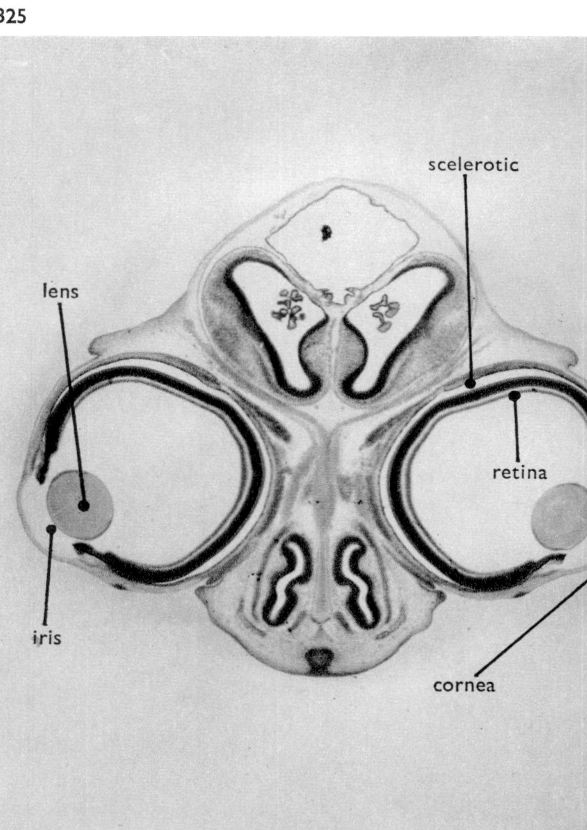

326

Colour Vision and Complementary Colours

Colour Plate 9
Diagram based on E. N. Willmer showing how colour-vision probably arose. A, visual elements in the retina of a primitive vertebrate eye, showing rods with rhodopsin most sensitive in blue light, and cones with iodopsin most sensitive in orange light; nervous impulses are conveyed away by 'mop' nerve-cells serving several rods and cones along a single pathway of nerve-fibres. B, adaptation to efficient vision in dim light by development of low-threshold rods with large quantities of rhodopsin, impulses from which are conveyed away by a second separate pathway of nerve-fibres. C, adaptation to increased acuteness of vision by development of midget bipolar nerve-cells each receiving impulses from one single cone, enabling localised light-stimuli to be perceived separately by very small areas of retina, impulses from which are conveyed away by a third separate pathway of nerve-fibres. The three pathways conduct impulses from low-threshold rods, mixed rods and cones, and single cones, maximally sensitive respectively to blue, green, and orange light. Colour-vision is then a 'bonus'. Many organisms make use of their enemies' colour-vision, which is the basis of Müllerian (Col. Pl. 1) and Batesian (Col. Pl. 2) mimicry and warning colouration. D, *Anophylla magnifica* with disruptive pattern like excreta on a leaf. E, *Trosia dimas*, conspicuous. F, *Ophthalmoria claudiaria*, with 'eye-marks' as deterrents. G, *Laternaria phosphorea*, with 'horror mask' like an alligator head and 'eye-marks'. H, Persons with normal colour-vision can obtain the sensation of colours complementary to the original in an after-image if they fix their vision on the black cross on the mast of the ship in bright light for a few minutes and then look at a white background. The effect is attributable to temporary fatigue of the elements in the retina sensitive to light of different wave-lengths.

Polyploidy

Polyploidy is almost restricted to the vegetable kingdom, in which it is very common. It has been found in all groups except the Fungi. In the flowering plants, it has been estimated that one-third of known species are polyploid, a condition especially frequent among perennials, as G. L. Stebbins found. Examples are many races of dahlias, chrysanthemums, and paeonies (Col. Pl. 13, 14).

The case of the paeony illustrates the way in which the geographical distribution of the diploid and tetraploid species provides evidence of the evolutionary history of the genus. In Europe and western Asia, as Sir Frederick Stern has shown, the diploid species are confined to southern Spain, the Balearic Islands, Crete, Rhodes, the Crimea, and the Caucasus region. The tetraploid species, which in each case have a wider range of distribution, occupy central Europe and Asia Minor, regions which they appear to have colonized by emigration as the climate became warmer after the Ice Age. The facts that such emigration was performed by tetraploid species and that their ranges became greater than those of the diploid species that gave rise to them, illustrates a general principle which will be referred to again below.

The size of the cells in an organism is dependent on the number of chromosomes that they contain, and it is common to find that polyploids are giant forms. It is therefore not surprising that the cultivated forms of wheat, oats, cotton, tobacco, potato, banana, coffee, and sugar-cane, which have been artificially selected for size, are polyploids.

There are two kinds of polyploidy, depending on whether hybridization has been involved. A plant that has simply multiplied the number of its chromosomes, by a division of the chromosomes without a corresponding division of its cells, is known as *autopolyploid*, or self-polyploid. Polyploidy occurs spontaneously in nature and can be obtained experimentally by such agencies as cutting-back and regeneration, and by the use of certain substances such as colchicine.

Autopolyploids such as tetraploids can with difficulty be crossed with their related diploids, but the resulting hybrids, being triploids, are sterile because at meiosis (p. 79), preparatory to the formation of germ-cells, the chromosomes are unable to execute the normal manoeuvres on which the successful outcome of the cell-divisions depend. They therefore fail to produce germ-cells or to set seed. This is why the cultivated banana, the fruit of which is technically a berry, contains no seeds. Autopolyploidy therefore confers reproductive isolation on the polyploid plants.

There is another kind of polyploidy which results from hybridization. *Primula floribunda* and *P. verticillata* are two species of primrose which can interbreed and give rise to hybrids, but these are sterile because the chromosomes derived from one parent are incompatible with those derived from the other in meiosis. Occasionally, however, the chromosomes of the hybrid become doubled and it is then a tetraploid, half of the chromosomes having been derived from one parent and half from the other. This condition, known as *allopolyploidy*, allows the plants to produce fertile germ-cells that give rise to fertile offspring, because each chromosome then has a compatible partner at meiosis. These allopolyploid hybrids are constant, fertile, and breed true. They are different in form and habit from either of the parent-species, and are sterile with both of them. In other words, under the eyes of L. Digby at Kew Gardens, a constant, fertile new type, reproductively isolated from all other species was produced by genetic isolation, fulfilling all the requirements of a species. It was accordingly called *Primula kewensis* (Pl. 330).

The origin of *Primula kewensis* by allopolyploidy was no unique phenomenon. An allopolyploid from the mint plants *Galeopsis pubescens* and *G. speciosa*, each of

COLOUR VISION, WARNING AND COMPLEMENTARY COLOURS

portion containing rhodopsin; maximum sensitivity 507 m μ

portion containing iodopsin; maximum sensitivity 570 m μ

rod

cone

nucleus

'mop' bipolar nerve cell

flat bipolar nerve cell

e fibres lucting ulses along pathway

nerve cell

(A) SIMPLE PRIMITIVE EYE

ow ireshold od

nucleus

e fibres lucting ulses along pathways

APTATION TO DIM LIGHT BY DEVELOP– NT OF LOW THRESHOLD RODS ABLE TO CUMULATE RHODOPSIN IN LARGE ANTITIES

imum sensitivities ie sensory cells esponding ie three ways

blue 460 m μ

green 540 m μ

orange 580 m μ

violet

midget bipolar nerve cell

e fibres lucting ulses along e pathways

DAPTATION TO INCREASED ACUTENESS OF SION BY PROVISION OF MIDGET BIPOLAR ERVE CELLS, EACH RECEIVING IMPULSES OM A SINGLE CONE

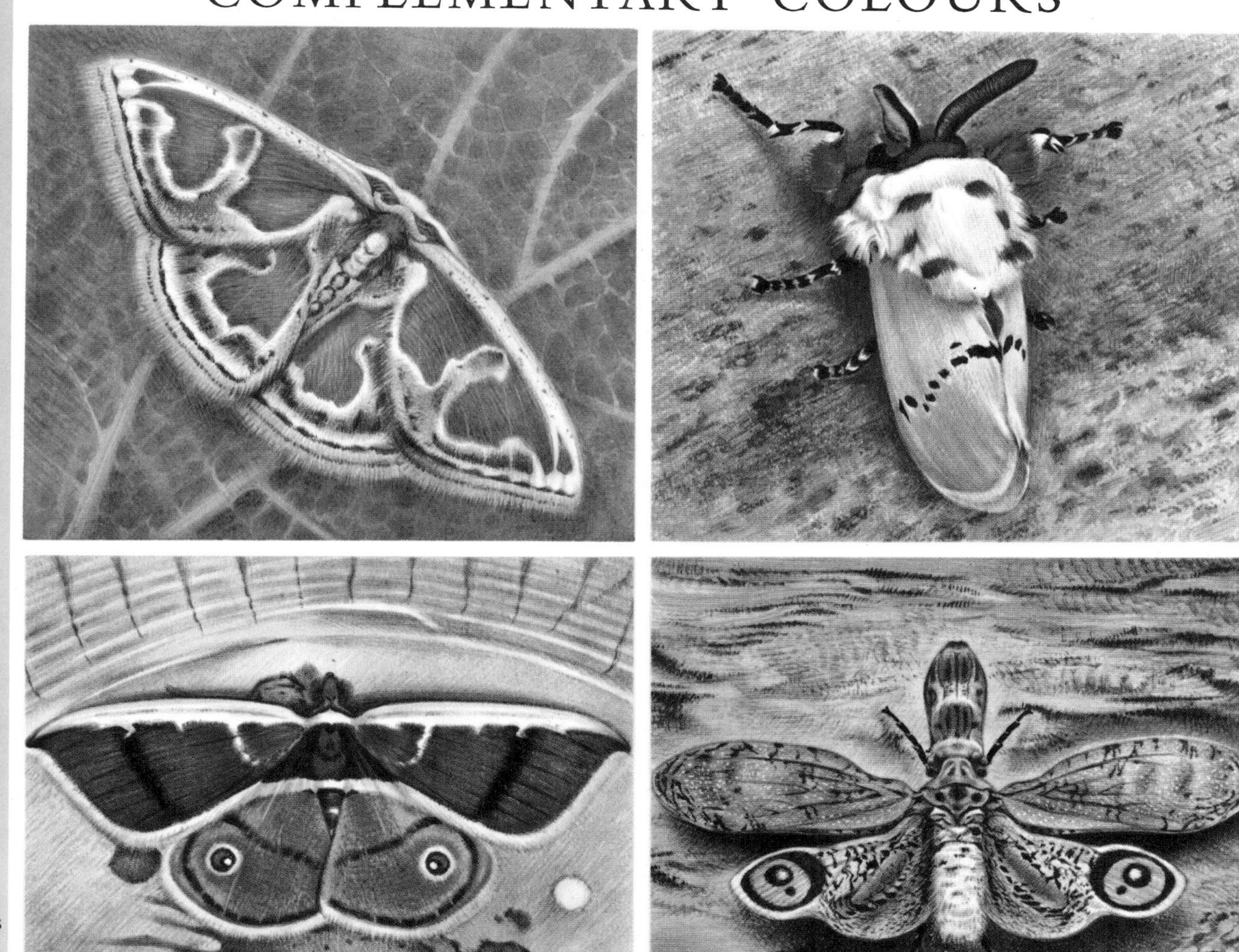

(D,E,F,G) WARNING COLOURS OF INSECTS IN THE BRAZILIAN FORESTS.

(H) COMPLEMENTARY COLOURS

GEOGRAPHICAL VARIATION: THE SIZE-CLINE OF PUFFINS

Length of wing in mm

Colour Plate 10. In different parts of the range of a species, populations may become locally adapted and give rise to geographical variation. This frequently takes the form of continuous gradients of change, or *clines*, in characters such as size, colour, breeding-period etc. This plate shows the size-cline of the puffin *Fratercula arctica* measured in average wing-length of specimens from the Balearic Islands to Spitzbergen.

SPITZBERGEN
175 – 194
158 – 177
SOUTH GREENLAND
BEAR ISLAN
ICELAND
NORWAY
BRITISH ISLES
155 – 166
135 – 145
BALEARIC ISLANDS

SPECIATION IN THE GREAT TIT

Colour Plate 11A. This map shows the distribution of the great tit, *Parus major*. The variety *major* with green back and yellow belly extends over Europe, Asia Minor, and Siberia to the Pacific Ocean. In Persia, variety *major* grades into the Indian variety *cinereus* with grey back and white belly. This in turn grades into the Chinese variety *minor* with pale green back and white belly. In the region of the Amur river, the ranges of *major* and *minor* overlap and the varieties are sympatric but do not interbreed. Instead, they behave as if they were separate species although they belong to the same gene-pool through the interconnecting and interbreeding populations in India, Europe, and Siberia. A comparable region of sympatric overlap without interbreeding between varieties *major* and *cinereus* occurs in central Asia.

SPECIATION IN GULLS

Colour Plate 11B. The lesser black-backed gull *Larus fuscus graelsii* in Britain has a dark mantle and yellow legs. It grades into the Scandinavian *L.fuscus fuscus*, which in turn grades into the Siberian Vega gull *L. argentatus vegae* with lighter grey mantle and dull flesh-coloured legs. This grades into the American herring–gull *L.argentatus smithsonianus* and this in turn into the British herring-gull *L.argentatus argentatus* with light-grey mantle and pink legs. There is thus a continuous gene-pool of gulls round the North Pole in a range forming a ring overlapping in Britain where the lesser black-backed and herring-gull live sympatrically. Geographical variation has affected not only their colour but their habits. (Inset: island of Skokholm). The lesser black-backed gull breeds inland and is migratory in winter, the herring-gull nests on cliffs and is resident. They do not interbreed but behave like distinct species.

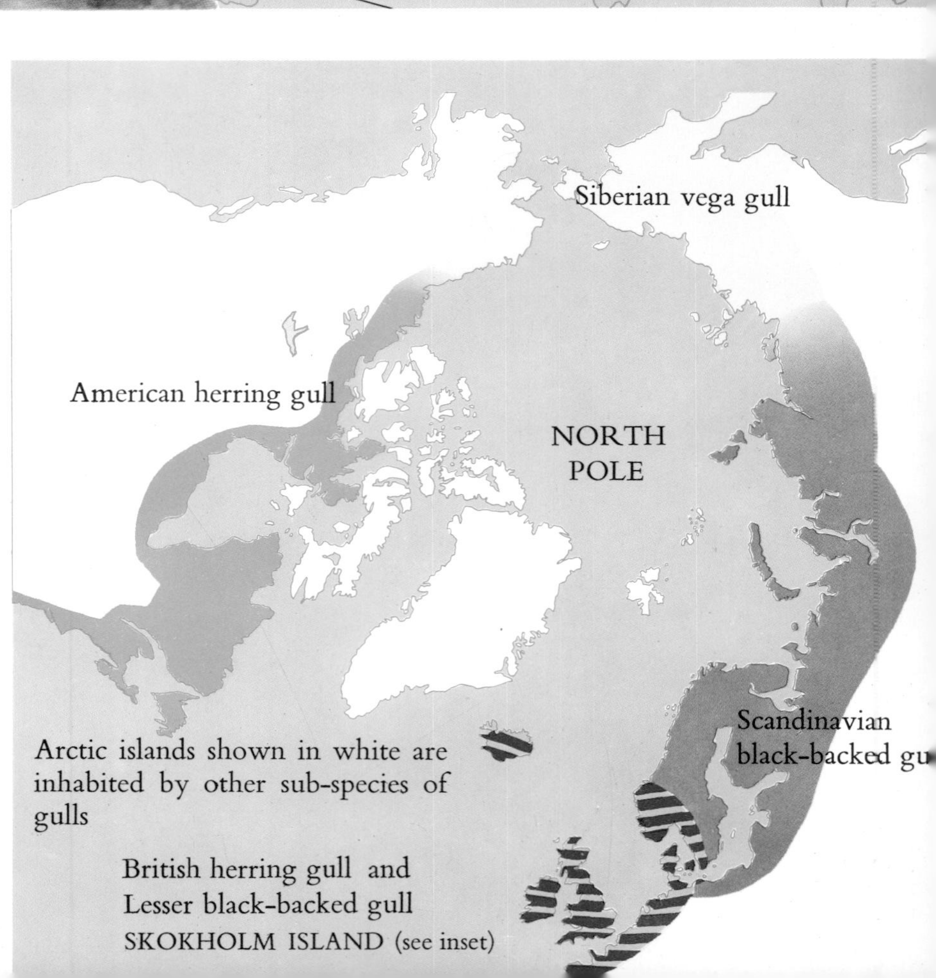

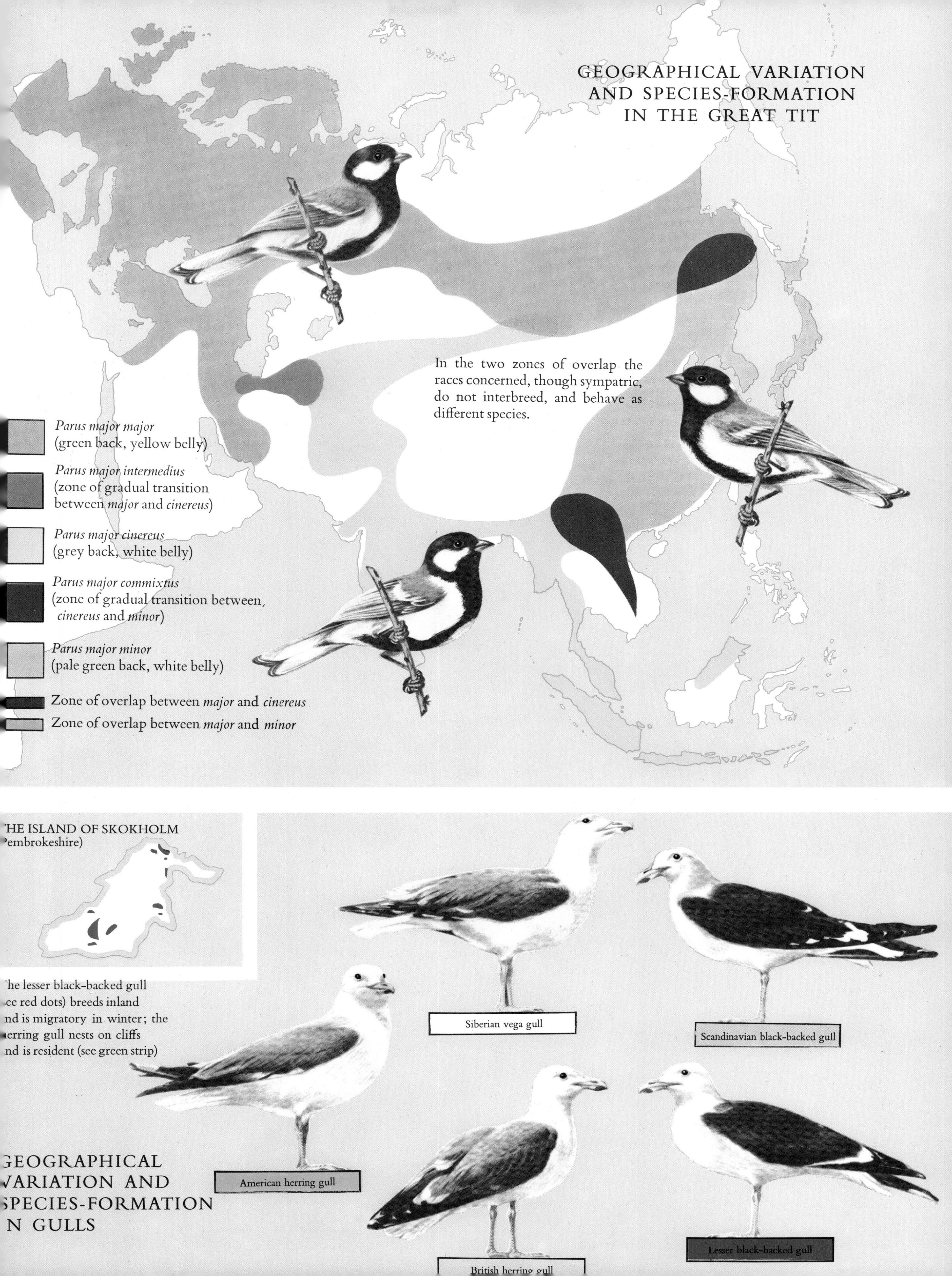

GEOGRAPHICAL VARIATION
AND SPECIES-FORMATION
IN THE GREAT TIT
In the two zones of overlap the races concerned, though sympatric, do not interbreed, and behave as different species.
Parus major major
(green back, yellow belly)
Parus major intermedius
(zone of gradual transition between major and cinereus)
Parus major cinereus
(grey back, white belly)
Parus major commixtus
(zone of gradual transition between cinereus and minor)
Parus major minor
(pale green back, white belly)
Zone of overlap between major and cinereus
Zone of overlap between major and minor
HE ISLAND OF SKOKHOLM
embrokeshire)
he lesser black-backed gull
ee red dots) breeds inland
nd is migratory in winter; the
erring gull nests on cliffs
nd is resident (see green strip)
Siberian vega gull
Scandinavian black-backed gull
American herring gull
Lesser black-backed gull
British herring gull
EOGRAPHICAL
ARIATION AND
PECIES-FORMATION
N GULLS

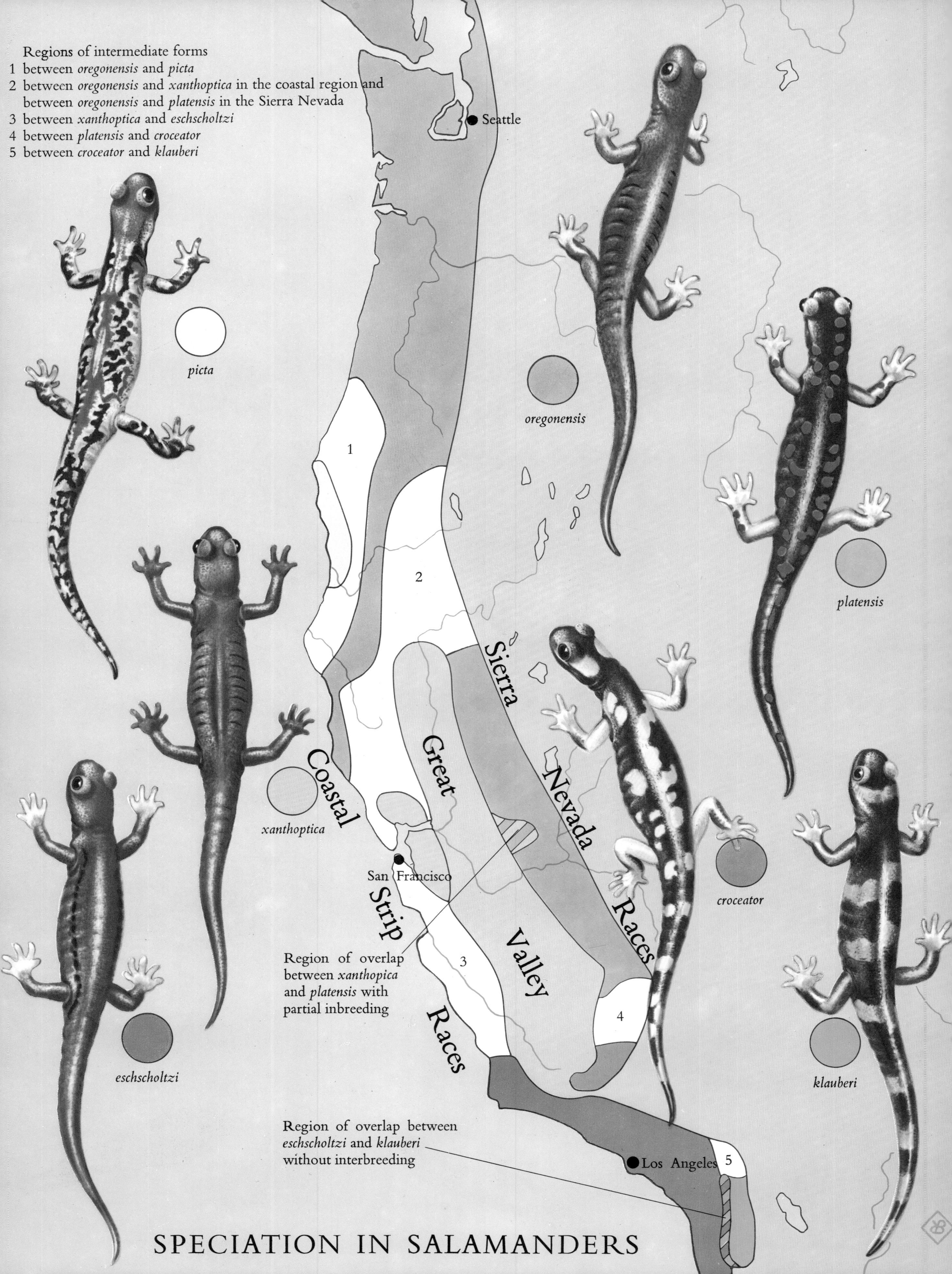

SPECIATION IN SALAMANDERS

Geographical variation and species formation

327. Colour-cline in the deer-mouse *Peromyscus maniculatus*. Along an axis from the coast inland in Florida the colour grades in a cline from very pale on an island reef of pure white sand (*leucocephalus* sub-species), through pale (*albifrons*) on the beach of the mainland, to dark inland (*polionotus*) where the soil also is dark. This colour-cline is related to humidity and other climatic factors as well as the colour of the soil. The same three mice are shown against a background of dark soil where *polionotus* (3,6) is found, and of light soil where *albifrons* and *leucocephalus* (2,5 and 1,4) are found.

which has 16 chromosomes, gives a resulting allopolyploid with 32, and it is not only similar to the wild natural species *G. tetrahit* but fertile with it. This is the proof that *G. tetrahit* arose in nature by hybridization and allopolyploidy from *G. pubescens* and *G. speciosa*. This natural species was therefore duplicated synthetically in the laboratory by G. Müntzing (Pl. 331).

A number of other natural allopolyploid species have been synthesized among which are the following:

Rubus loganobaccus (loganberry) from *R. idaeus* x *ursinus*.
Nicotiana digluta (tobacco) from *N. glutinosa* x *tabaccum*.
Brassica napus (swede) from *B. campestris* x *oleracea*.

Cultivated allopolyploids that have been synthesized include the following:

Gossypium hirsutum (cotton), and *Triticum aestivum* (bread-wheat). This last case is of particular interest because it shows that the valuable bread-wheats originated as allopolyploids after hybridization between the emmer, or hard wheat *T. dicoccoides*, and the worthless grass *Aegilops squarrosa* (p. 90).

Cases in which the allopolyploid origin of species has been indirectly proved include *Spartina townsendi* (cord-grass), *Penstemon neotericus*, *Iris versicolor*, *Prunus domesticus* (plum), *Poa annua*, *Nicotiana arentsii*, *Artemisia douglasiana*, *Oryzopsis aperifolia*, and *Bromus marginatus*.

Polyploidy is therefore an important method by which in nature reproductive isolation is suddenly conferred. Polyploids contain a larger number of genes for each locus and can be more variable than their diploid relatives, as C. D. Darlington showed. It is frequently found that plants spreading into fresh areas and newly opened habitats at the edges of the range of their species, are polyploids. It is believed that the existing families and genera of woody flowering plants, which can be traced back to the beginning of the Tertiary era, seventy million years ago, originated from polyploid ancestors in the Cretaceous period or earlier, when new habitats were released by the extinction of the Gymnosperms.

It is clear that polyploidy has played an important part in evolution and it may also supply the reason why the classification of the flowering plants has so far defied taxonomists to produce a scheme describing their descent on the principle of divergence, which is universally applicable in all other groups of living organisms. If allopolyploidy has played an important part in the evolution of flowering plants, it means that hybridization has occurred frequently in their ancestry, and their characters, instead of showing clear-cut divergence, would be expected to show mixture throughout the group. Their recent evolutionary history would therefore have been reticulate, like the strings of a net that diverge and converge again, and cannot be expressed by a simple branching tree (Pl. 392).

HOW MANY SPECIES ARE THERE?

Previous sections of this chapter have provided evidence that natural selection, working on heritable variation due to mutation and recombination of genes, has resulted in evolution and adaptation, and under conditions of reproductive isolation, in the origination of new species. It may be of interest to give an indication of the magnitude of the phenomenon of speciation. At the present time, it is estimated that the number of species of plants and animals alive amounts to some 1,400,000, distributed as shown on the accompanying table.

It would be useful to know the average numbers of individuals in a species, but at present little more can be said than that they are enormously variable. *Homo*

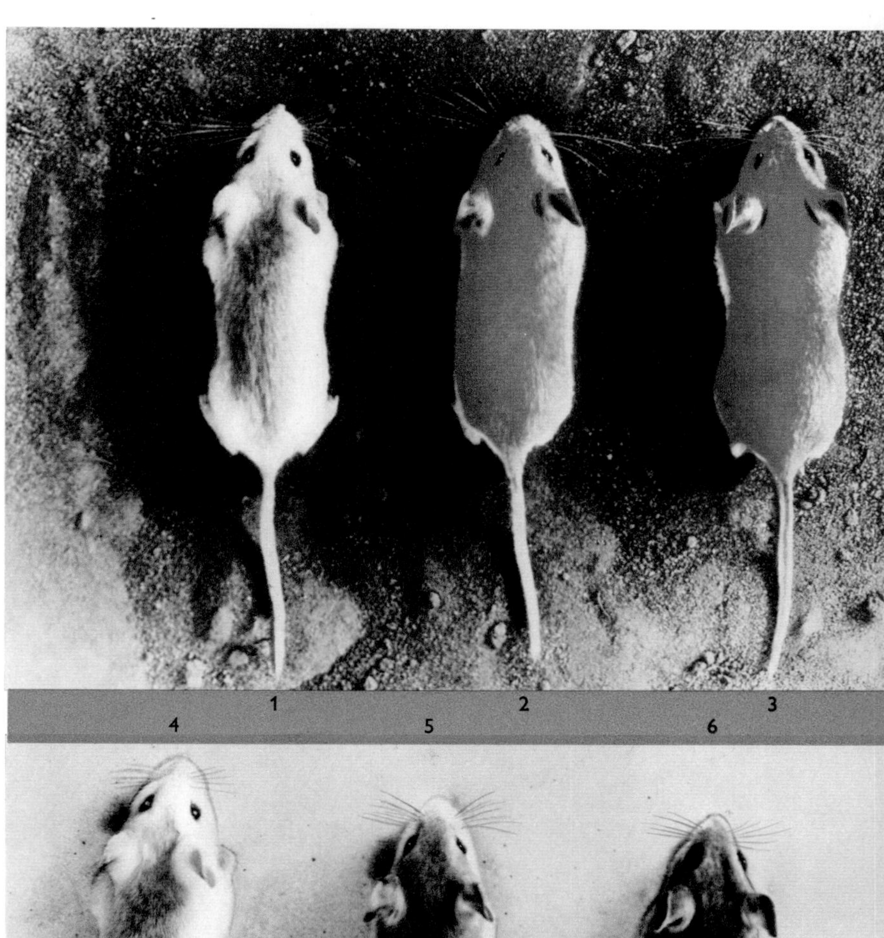

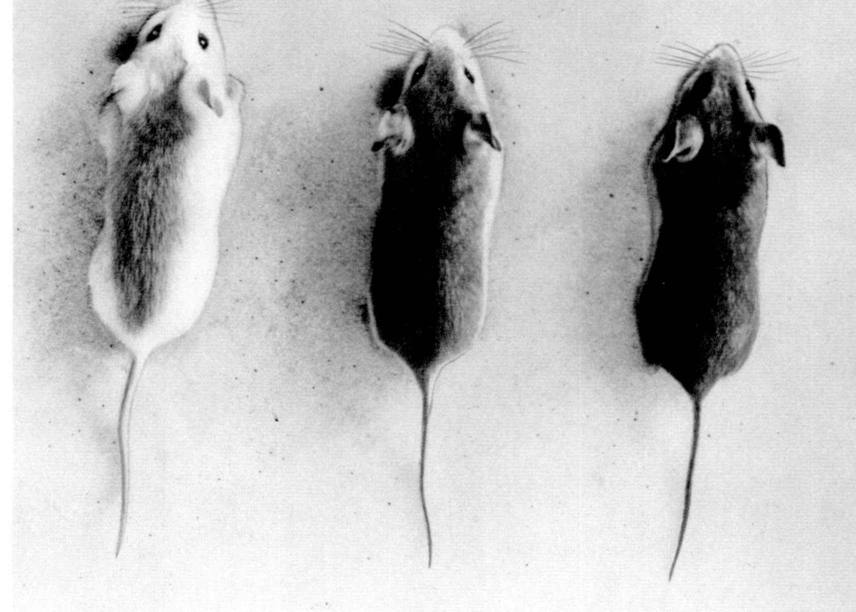

327

Geographical variation and species-formation in salamanders

Colour Plate 9
Map of western North America showing the ranges of geographical races of *Ensatina eschscholtzi* and the intermediate regions where they intergrade. The species appears to have migrated southward and to have become split by the dry Great Valley of California into coastal strip and Sierra Nevada groups of races differing in characters some of which are adaptive, varieties *oregonensis*, *picta*, *xanthoptica* of which a small population has crossed the Great Valley to the Sierra Nevada where it intergrades partially with the local race, *platensis*. This in turn intergrades with *croceator* and the latter with *klauberi*, the southernmost inland race. There is, however, a gap in the modern range of *croceator* as a result of which *klauberi* is discontinuous and isolated, *eschscholtzi* the southernmost coastal race the range of which overlaps that of *klauberi* with which it does not interbreed. These two races therefore behave as distinct species, and as *klauberi* is cut off from the rest of the gene-pool it can be regarded as a new and recently formed species.

Geographical and ecological isolation

Map 7. The geographical distribution of edible frogs, *Rana esculenta* and *R. ridibunda*. The range of the latter overlaps that of the former on both sides but reproductive isolation between the species is normally maintained because *ridibunda* breeds earlier than *esculenta*. **328.** The evolution of finches in the Galàpagos Islands. Of the fourteen species three live on the ground and eat seeds: large, *Geospiza magnirostris*; medium, *G. fortis*; small, *G. fuliginosa*. Two, *G. scandens* and *G. conirostris* live on cactus plants; one, *G. difficilis* combines ground and cactus feeding and eats leaves. Six species of another genus, *Camarrhynchus*, live in trees. *C. crassirostris* eats buds and fruits; the remainder eat insects: large, *C. psittacula*; medium, *C. pauper*; small, *C. parvulus*. *C. heliobates* feeds on insects in wood. *C. pallidus* is an artificial woodpecker and uses cactus spines held in its beak to dig out grubs. *Certhidea olivacea* resembles a warbler and eats small soft insects. *Pinaroloxias inornata* is similar.

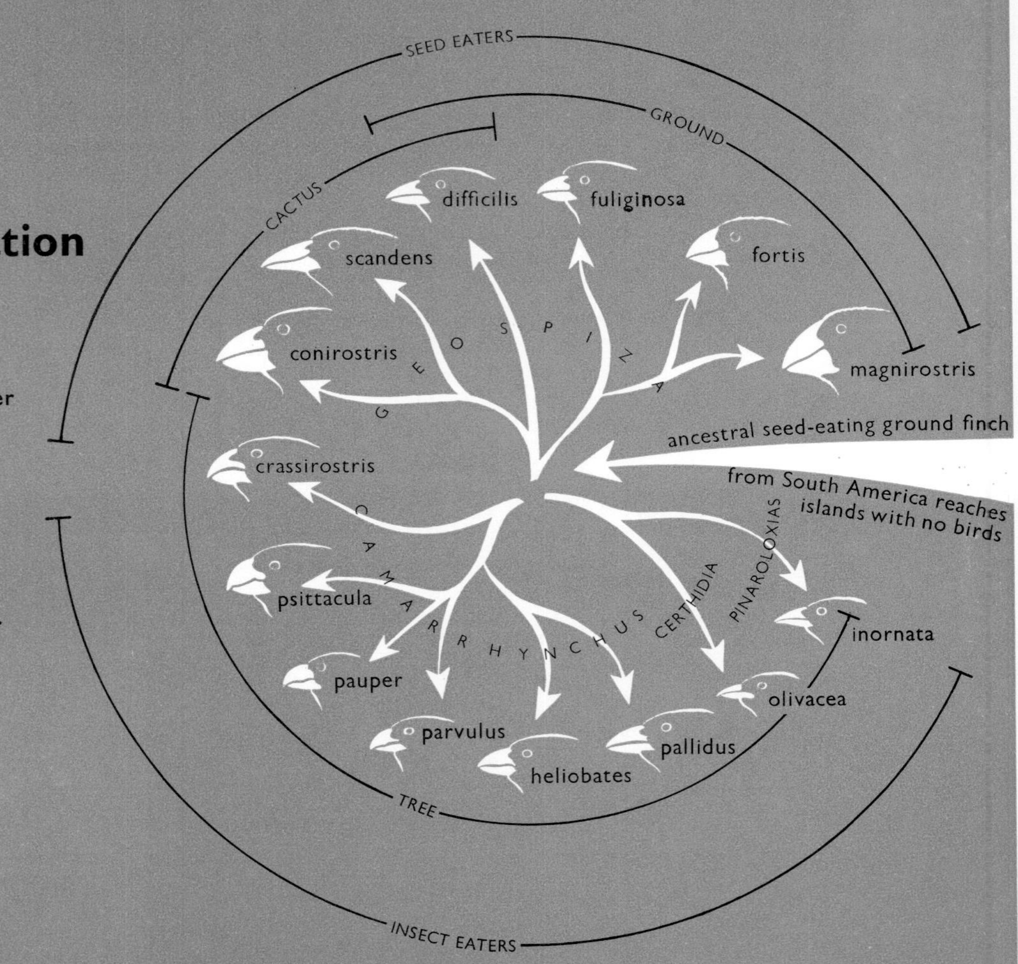

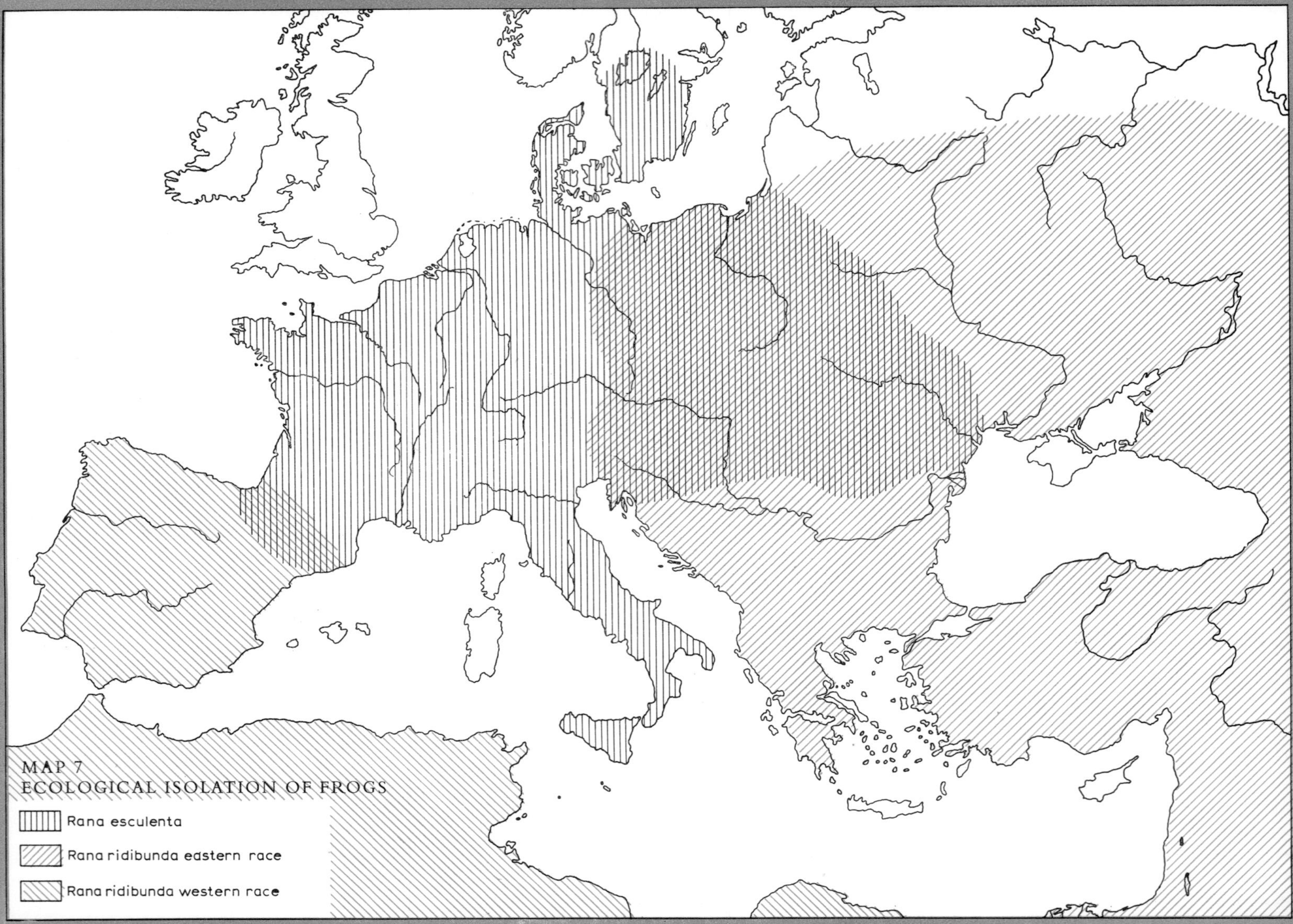

MAP 7
ECOLOGICAL ISOLATION OF FROGS

Rana esculenta

Rana ridibunda eastern race

Rana ridibunda western race

Industrial melanism

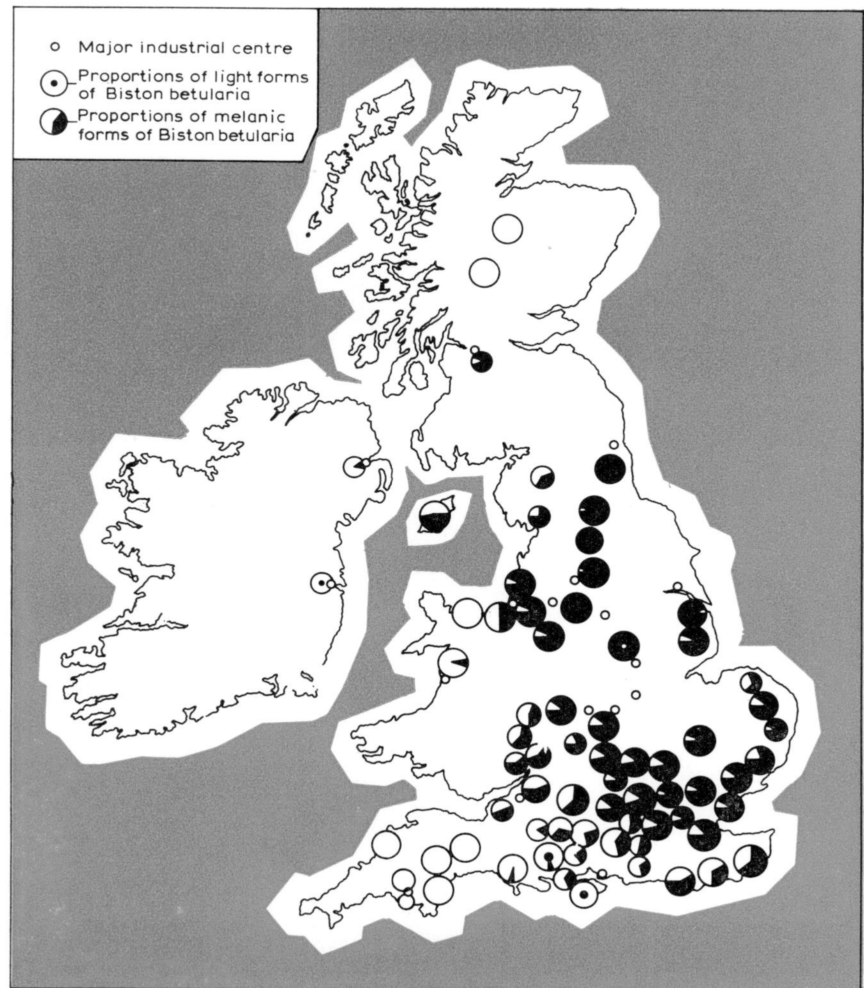

Map 8
The spread of industrial melanism in the Peppered Moth in various locations in the British Isles is shown in this map. The proportion of the original light form *Biston betularia* as compared with the mutant black form *carbonaria* in various localities is indicated by the relative areas of white and black shown in the large circles. The position of major industrial centres is indicated by small circles. It will be seen that the melanic form has spread and almost supplanted the original light form in areas where industrial development has polluted the countryside with soot, and that these areas are chiefly in the central and eastern parts of Britain, a distribution for which the prevalent westerly winds are partly responsible. (→ 69,284).

sapiens is estimated to number 3,000 million individuals. An estimate by E. S. Deevey of the population of man's ancestors one million years ago, when man-like apes were turning into ape-like men (p. 174) is 125,000. In the trumpeter swan, the number of individuals known to be alive a few years ago was about 47. In 1960, thanks to protective measures of conservation there were estimated to be 1,500. The wood bison of northern Canada is not known to consist of more than 200 head of cattle. Père David's deer is represented by 456 animals distributed between 31 zoological gardens and parks.

ESTIMATED NUMBERS OF LIVING SPECIES, 1960

	Plants		
Bacteria	1,350	Liverworts	9,000
Blue-green Algae	1,000	Mosses	14,000
Slime-fungi	450	Ferns	9,500
Flagellates	2,000	Horsetails	25
Diatoms	5,000	Club-mosses	1,000
Green algae	6,000	Psilotums	4
Brown algae	900	Quillworts	70
Red algae	2,500	Cycads	80
Moulds	1,000	Conifers	500
Cup fungi	2,400	Gnetums	80
Mushrooms	7,500	Maidenhair trees	1
Other fungi	27,000	Monocotyledons	50,000
Lichens	18,000	Dicotyledons	200,000
			359,360
	Animals		
Protozoa	30,000	Linguatula	70
Mesozoa	50	Onychophora	65
Porifera	4,500	Chelicerata	35,000
Platyhelminthes	6,000	Crustacea	25,000
Coelenterata	9,000	Insecta	850,000
Ctenophora	90	Other arthropoda	13,000
Acanthocephala	300	Mollusca	80,000
Rotifera	1,500	Bryozoa (Ectoprocta)	3,300
Gastrotricha	175	Brachiopoda	250
Kinorhyncha	100	Chaetognatha	30
Nematomorpha	100	Echinodermata	4,000
Nematoda	10,000	Phoronidea	5
Priapulida	5	Pogonophora	45
Nemertina	750	Hemichordata	80
Entoprocta	60	Tunicata	1,500
Annelida	7,000	Cyclostomata and Fishes	20,000
Echiuroida	60	Amphibia and Reptilia	6,000
Sipunculoidea	250	Birds	8,600
Tardigrada	180	Mammals	3,200
			1,120,365

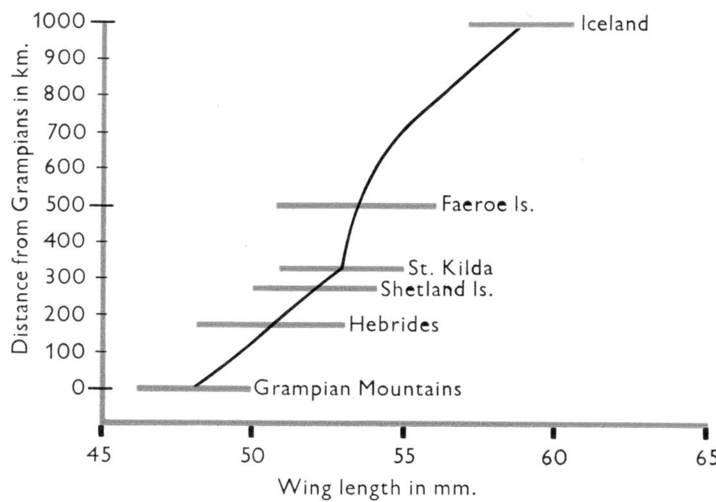

Size-cline of the wren

329. The wren increases in size with increasing latitude from the Grampian Mountains of Scotland to Iceland, and this size-cline is shown by measurements of wing-length. The horizontal lines show the extent of local variation.

330

THE ORIGIN OF GENERA AND HIGHER CATEGORIES OF CLASSIFICATION

The species is the basic category of classification because the species, and only the species, is the breeding unit of living things. It follows that every organism alive now and every organism that has ever lived belongs or belonged to some one species or other. The manner in which species arise from other species has been described earlier in this chapter.

When a species has split into two or more different species it gives rise to a genus, containing species, and by continued evolutionary divergence a genus becomes a family containing genera. Similarly, a family becomes an order containing families, and an order becomes a class containing orders. Whether any given line of evolution will blossom out into a higher category, remain as it was, or become extinct, can be known only by the event. If birds had been no more successful in multiplying their species than pterodactyls, they would, like them, have remained an order of reptiles. It is because they have been so successful that birds are regarded as a separate class of vertebrates. As will be shown later, there are reasons for believing that some modes of evolution are more likely than others to give rise to higher categories. For the moment, the important point is that all higher categories, be they genera, families, orders, classes, or even phyla, started by being species, and are products of successful species. Genera, families, orders, classes, and phyla originated by the same machinery that leads to the production of new species.

Attempts have occasionally been made to contest the truth of this statement and to claim that while species may arise through the natural selection of mutant and recombined genes, the higher categories came into existence by a different process, involving large-scale sudden changes to which the names 'macromutation' and 'saltation' have been given. Agencies of this kind have been appealed to for an explanation of the apparently sudden appearance of fossils in geological formations, by supposing that new genera or families, or even higher categories might arise 'ready-made' without going through the mill of natural selection of mutant and recombined genes. Such a possibility was considered and rejected by Darwin. 'Why should not Nature take a sudden leap from structure to structure?' he wrote; and continued: 'On the theory of natural selection, we can clearly understand why she should not; for natural selection acts only by taking advantage of slight successive variations.'

Recent research has confirmed Darwin's argument in every respect. In the first place, Sir Ronald Fisher has shown that the average immediate selective value of mutations is inversely related to the magnitude of their phenotypic effects. This is only what would be expected from the fact that organisms are complex and delicately adjusted systems, more likely to be damaged than improved by abrupt changes.

When it is appreciated that a process of macromutation is purely hypothetical, that nothing is known on which it could be based, that it is opposed to everything that is known about evolution, and that the sudden appearance of new types in geological formations is simply explained by their having migrated into the region where they are found from somewhere else, while their immediate ancestors have not yet been found, there is little to be said in favour of such a process. Furthermore, the conditions for the origin of higher categories are that higher categories arise by the normal processes of natural selection working on mutant and recombined genes from species that have come to occupy new zones to which they have become adapted and which offer them scope for further rapid evolution by adaptive radiation. When the fresh adaptive zone is a new medium, hitherto unoccupied or inefficiently occupied, as was the land when first flowering plants, insects, and reptiles colonized it, or the air when it was invaded by insects, pterodactyls, birds, and bats, the result is bouts of rapid evolution equivalent to 'break-throughs'. The successful species then speedily give rise to other species in such numbers that the category containing them becomes one now recognized as of higher rank, as G. G. Simpson and B. Rensch have shown.

CENTRES OF EVOLUTION

In all the cases in which the geographical distribution of living forms and of fossils is adequately known, as in the classes of vertebrates, it is noteworthy that the centre where they successively emerged and evolved and from which they dispersed was the tropical zone of Asia. Thence the fishes, amphibia, reptiles, birds, and mammals spread fitfully, as climatic and ecological conditions allowed, to Africa, to the Americas across the Bering and Panama Isthmuses by land, and across water-gaps to Madagascar and Australia, to oceanic islands, and to other continents (Map 9).

Not all groups spread equally or everywhere. Spread in one direction might be balanced by retreat or extinction in others, while the chance finding of suitable conditions in newly occupied regions led in some cases to successful colonization and intensive evolution in areas quite different from that where the group originally evolved. This is an important caveat against the danger of concluding that a group originated in the area where its species today are most numerous. Only the evidence provided by the distribution of fossils is valid for the discovery of the centre of origin of a group. It shows for instance that horses evolved in North America, spread to the Old World, and then went extinct in North America (Map 23). Camels evolved in North America, spread to South America, Asia, Europe, and Africa and went extinct in North America. These examples will suffice to show how dangerous it is to draw conclusions on the cradle of a group of organisms from the geographical distribution of its living representatives without knowing their fossil history.

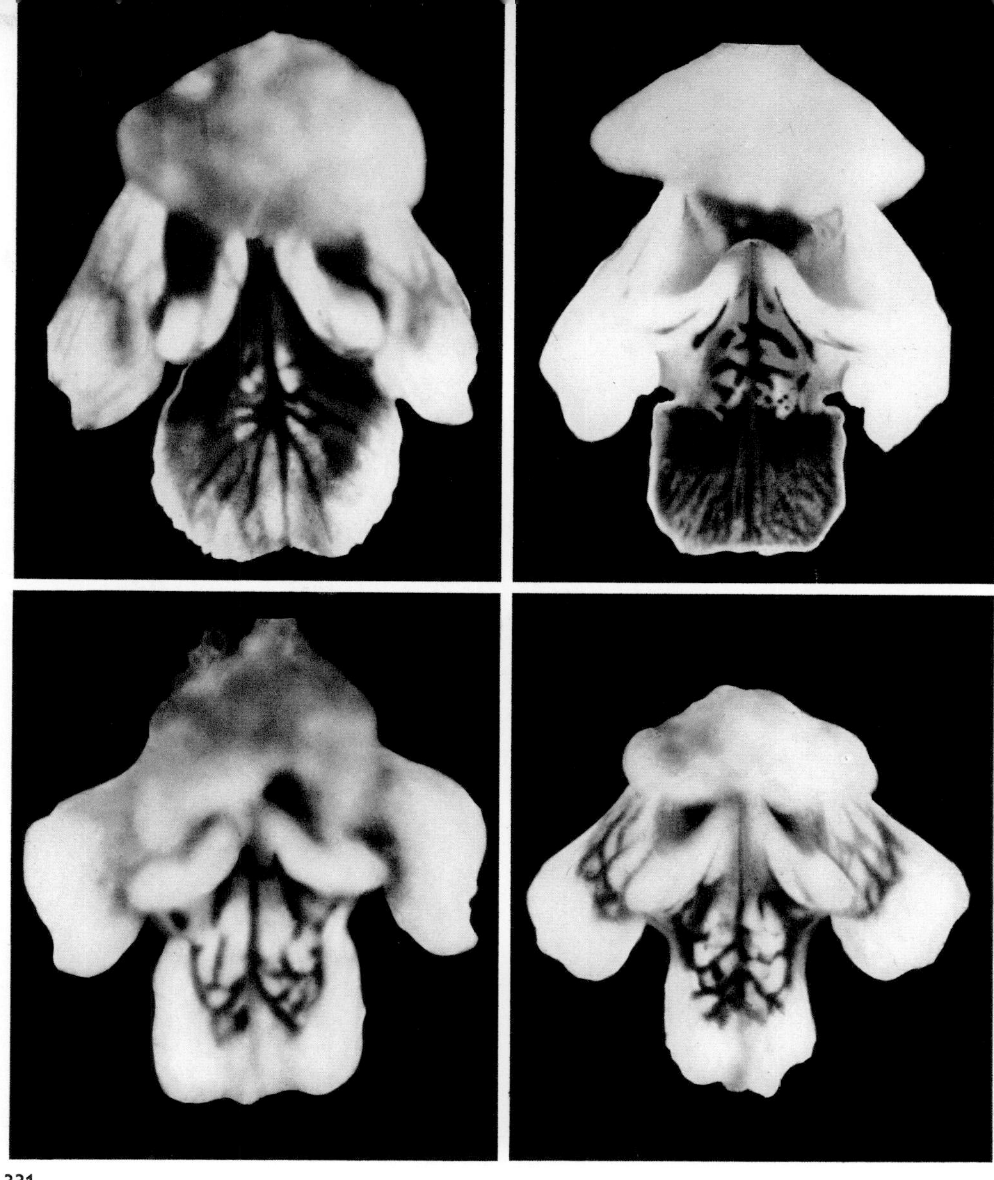

331

Polyploidy, genetic isolation

330 (*left*), *Primula floribunda*, a species of primrose with diploid chromosome number 18, (*centre*) *P. verticillata*, likewise with 18 chromosomes. Hybrids can be formed between these species but they are sterile unless their chromosomes undergo doubling in which case a tetraploid with 36 chromosomes results, *P. kewensis* (*right*) true-breeding, different from and sterile with each parent species. *P. kewensis* is therefore a new species formed by allopolyploidy. Proof that this is a method by which species are formed in nature is provided by **331,** the mint, *Galeopsis*; flower of *G. pubescens* (*top left*) and flower of *G. speciosa* (*top right*), both with diploid chromosome number 16. Allopolyploid with chromosome number 32 (*lower left*), formed from these two species by A. Müntzing and not only similar to, but fertile with, the natural species *G. tetrahit* (*lower right*) which must therefore have originated in the same way. Comparison between flowers and chromosomes of diploid and tetraploid plants: **332,** flower of diploid *Tradescantia* with its chromosomes; **333,** flower of tetraploid *Tradescantia* with its chromosomes.

332
333

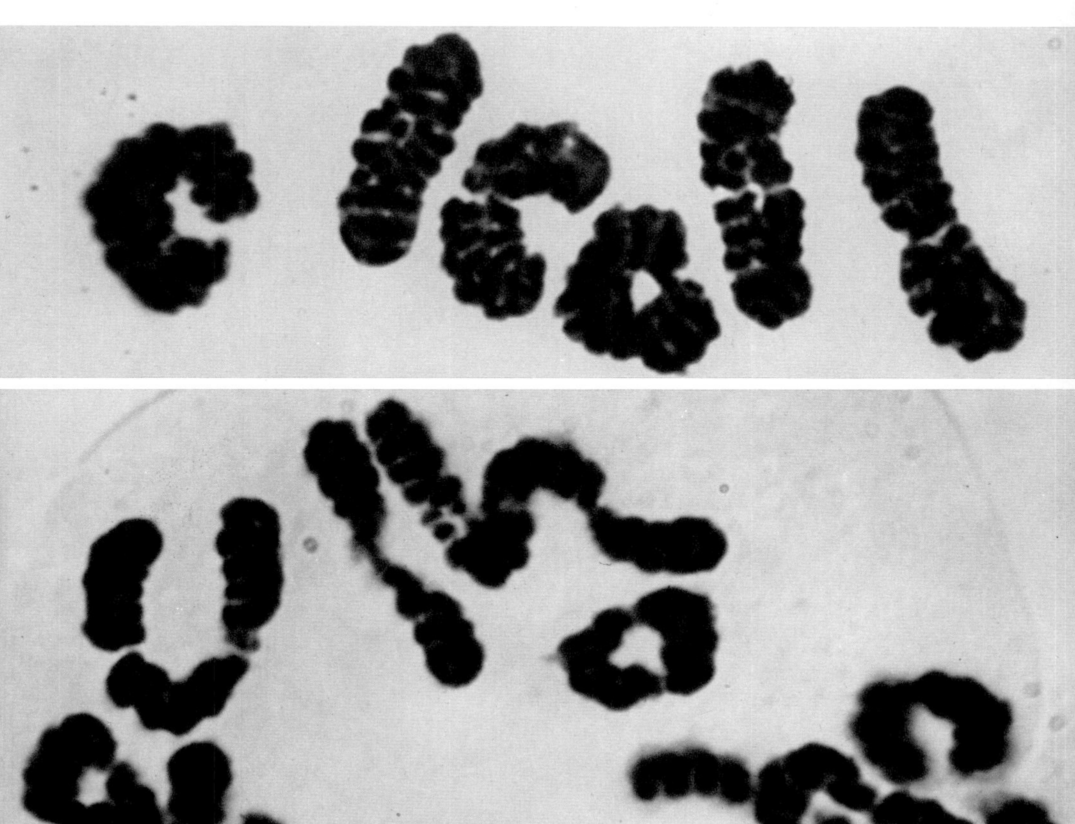

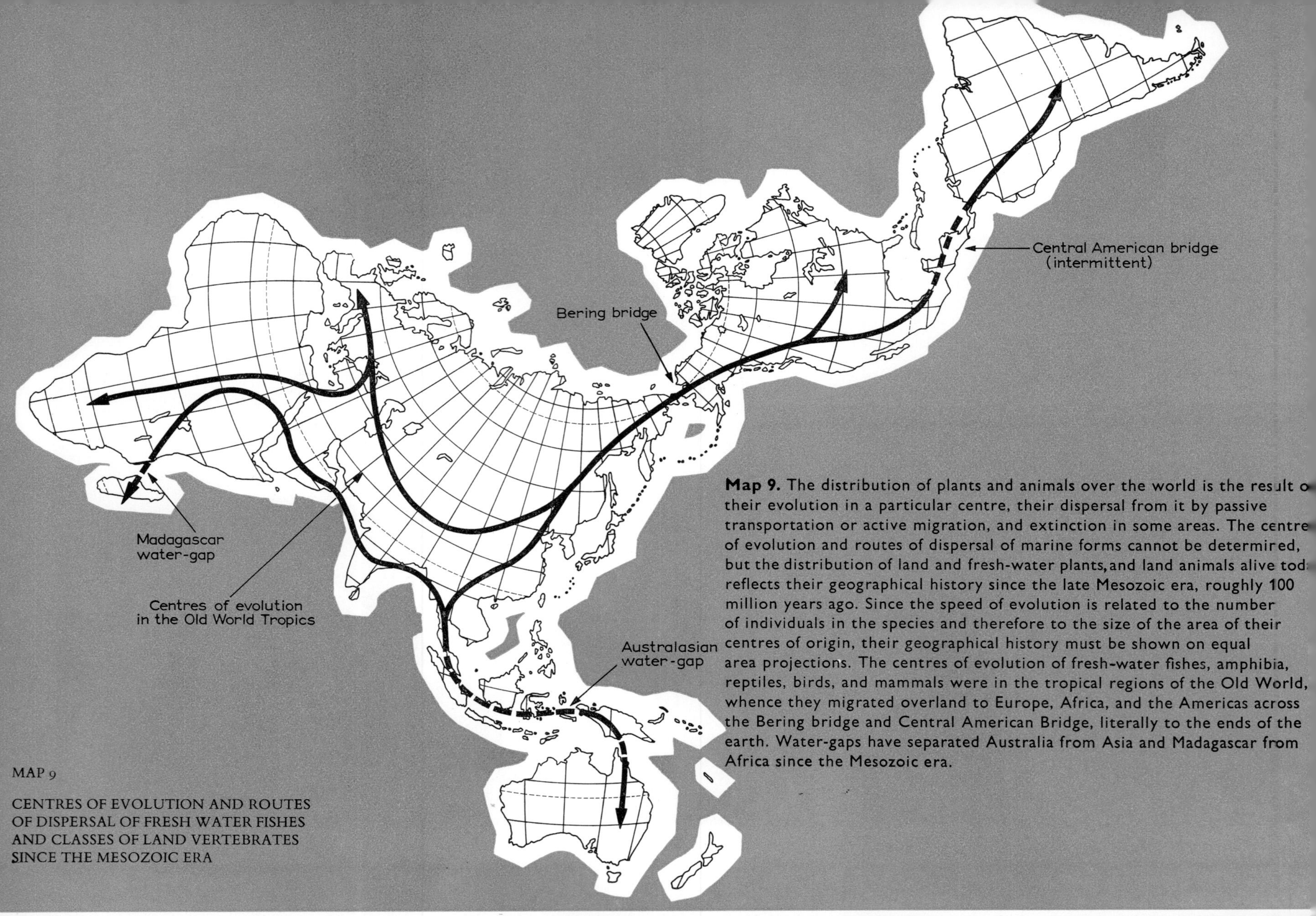

Map 9. The distribution of plants and animals over the world is the result o their evolution in a particular centre, their dispersal from it by passive transportation or active migration, and extinction in some areas. The centre of evolution and routes of dispersal of marine forms cannot be determined, but the distribution of land and fresh-water plants, and land animals alive tod reflects their geographical history since the late Mesozoic era, roughly 100 million years ago. Since the speed of evolution is related to the number of individuals in the species and therefore to the size of the area of their centres of origin, their geographical history must be shown on equal area projections. The centres of evolution of fresh-water fishes, amphibia, reptiles, birds, and mammals were in the tropical regions of the Old World, whence they migrated overland to Europe, Africa, and the Americas across the Bering bridge and Central American Bridge, literally to the ends of the earth. Water-gaps have separated Australia from Asia and Madagascar from Africa since the Mesozoic era.

MAP 9

CENTRES OF EVOLUTION AND ROUTES OF DISPERSAL OF FRESH WATER FISHES AND CLASSES OF LAND VERTEBRATES SINCE THE MESOZOIC ERA

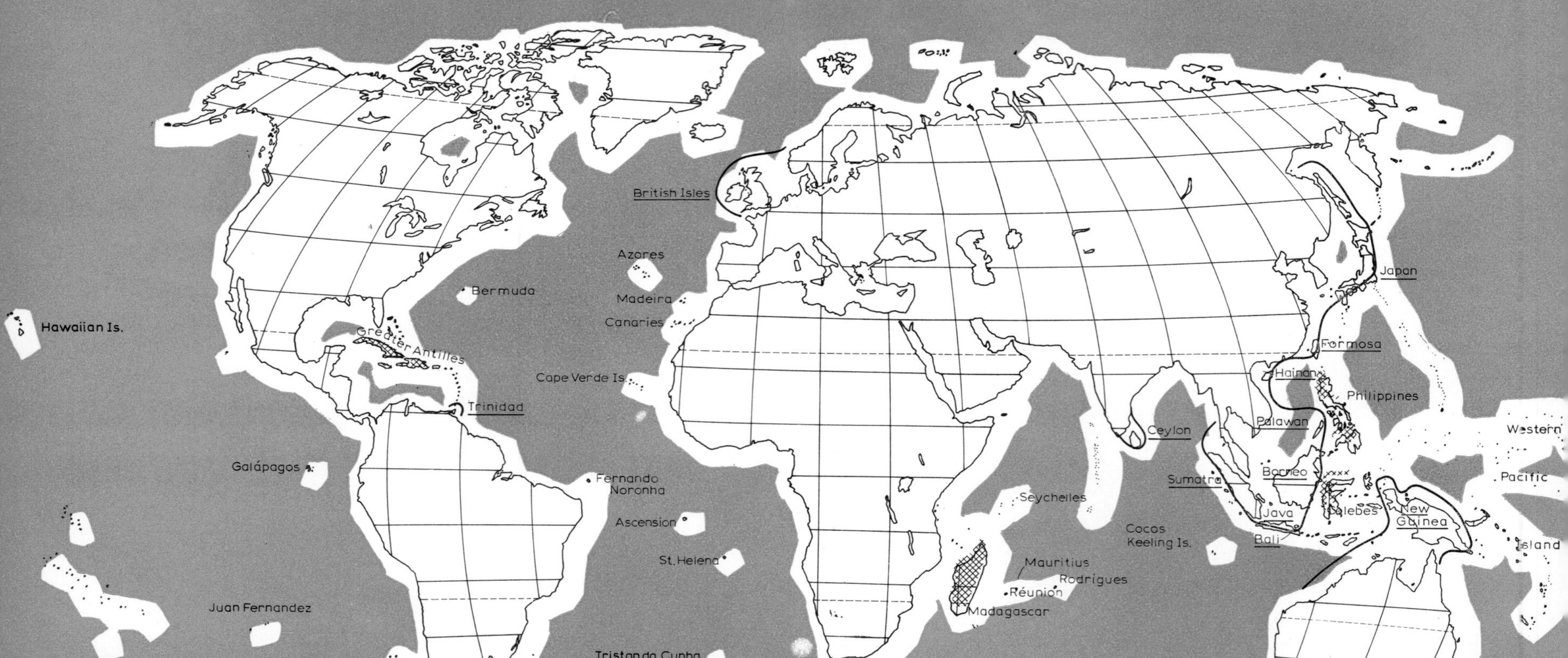

MAP 10

CONTINENTAL AND OCEANIC ISLANDS

Azores	oceanic islands
Trinidad	continental islands
Madagascar (shaded)	ancient islands

Map 10. *Oceanic islands* owe their formation to recent volcanic or coralline action and have never been connected with any continent. Their flora and fauna of land-animals is the result of fortuitous dispersal and accidental transport by ocean currents and prevailing winds (→ Map 14). *Ancient islands* have not been connected with any continent since early geological times. Their isolation for at least 100 million years means that their present flora and fauna must have reached them across a water gap. When a fauna spreads over a land-mass the ecological balance between prey and predator is preserved. This is exactly what has not happened in ancient islands: Madagascar, Philippines, Celebes, New Zealand, and the Greater Antilles. *Recent continental islands* are fragments detached from the nearest continent in recent times.

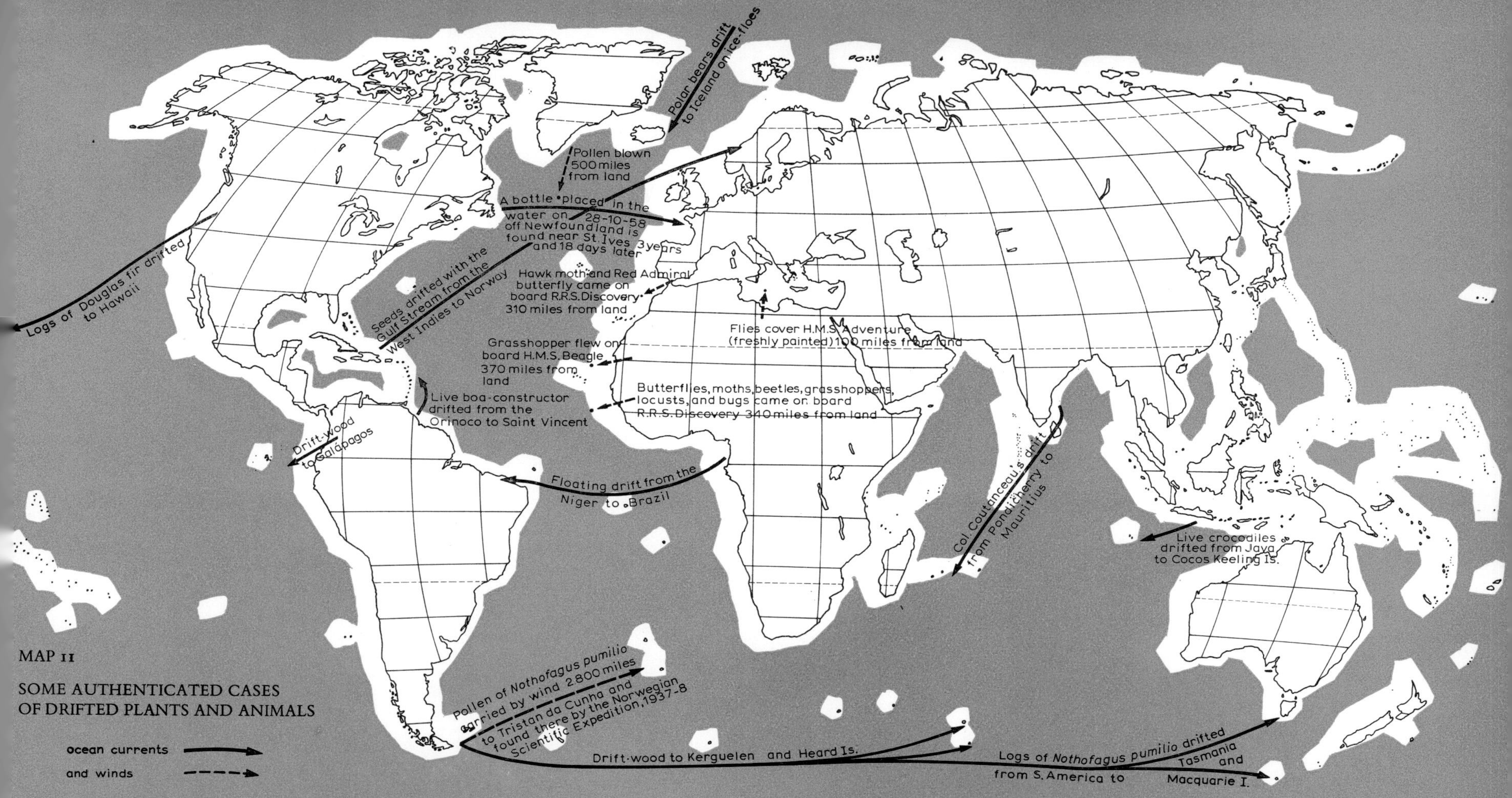

MAP 11

SOME AUTHENTICATED CASES OF DRIFTED PLANTS AND ANIMALS

Map 11. Oceanic islands (Map 10) have never had land connections with any continent and therefore their original populations of land plants and animals must have reached them by means of transport due to drifting in ocean currents and strong winds. Darwin showed that the hypothesis of land-bridges connecting oceanic islands with neighbouring continents was untenable, and he experimented on the time that seeds could withstand immersion in sea water without losing their viability. He also studied the prevailing ocean currents and winds in different parts of the world and showed how the populations of oceanic islands could have reached them by accidental dispersal through drifting. In this map a few historically authenticated cases of drifting are indicated which provide the evidence that Darwin's explanation was correct.

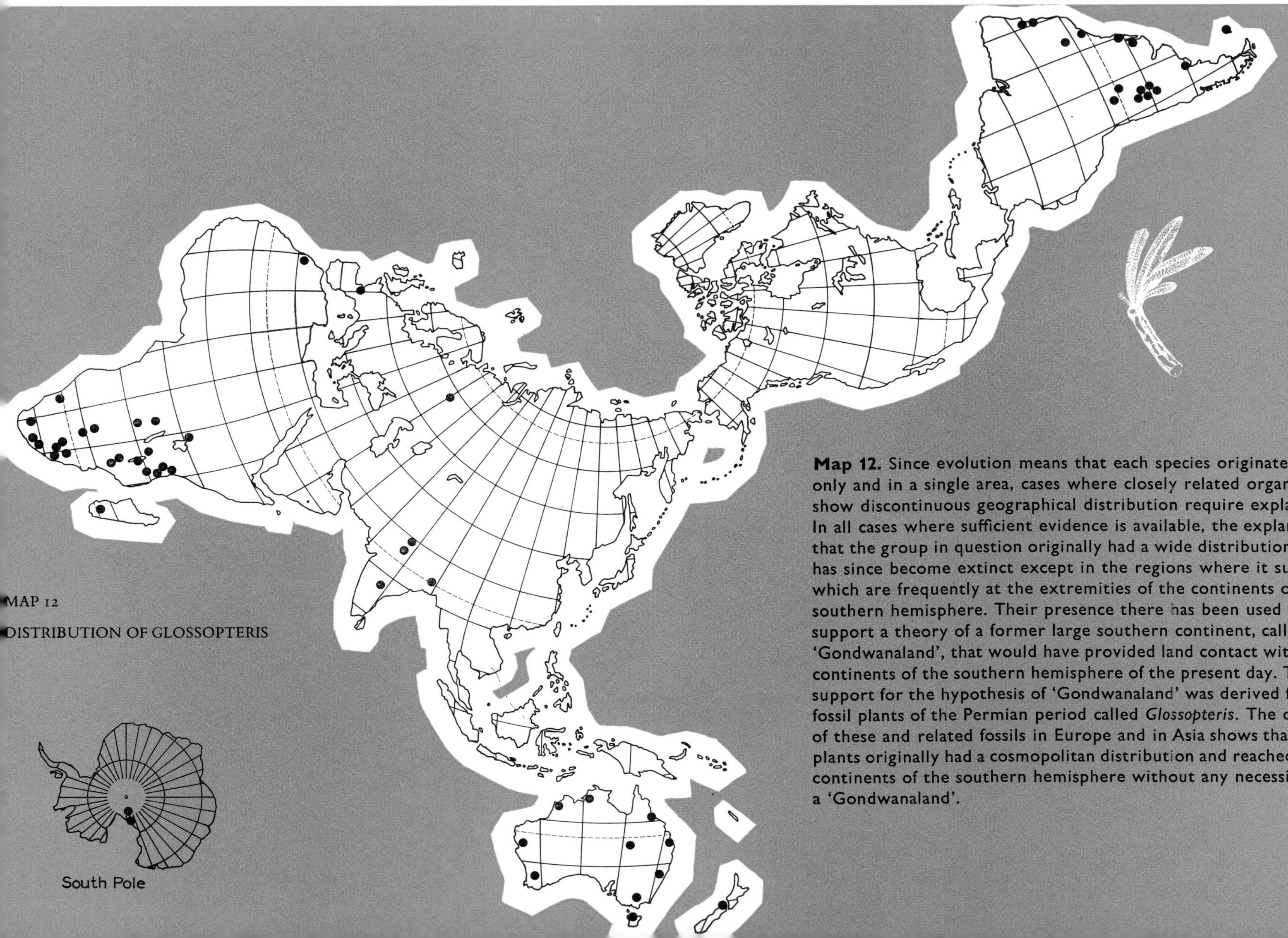

MAP 12

DISTRIBUTION OF GLOSSOPTERIS

Map 12. Since evolution means that each species originated once only and in a single area, cases where closely related organisms show discontinuous geographical distribution require explanation. In all cases where sufficient evidence is available, the explanation is that the group in question originally had a wide distribution and has since become extinct except in the regions where it survives, which are frequently at the extremities of the continents of the southern hemisphere. Their presence there has been used to support a theory of a former large southern continent, called 'Gondwanaland', that would have provided land contact with the continents of the southern hemisphere of the present day. The chief support for the hypothesis of 'Gondwanaland' was derived from fossil plants of the Permian period called *Glossopteris*. The discovery of these and related fossils in Europe and in Asia shows that the plants originally had a cosmopolitan distribution and reached the continents of the southern hemisphere without any necessity for a 'Gondwanaland'.

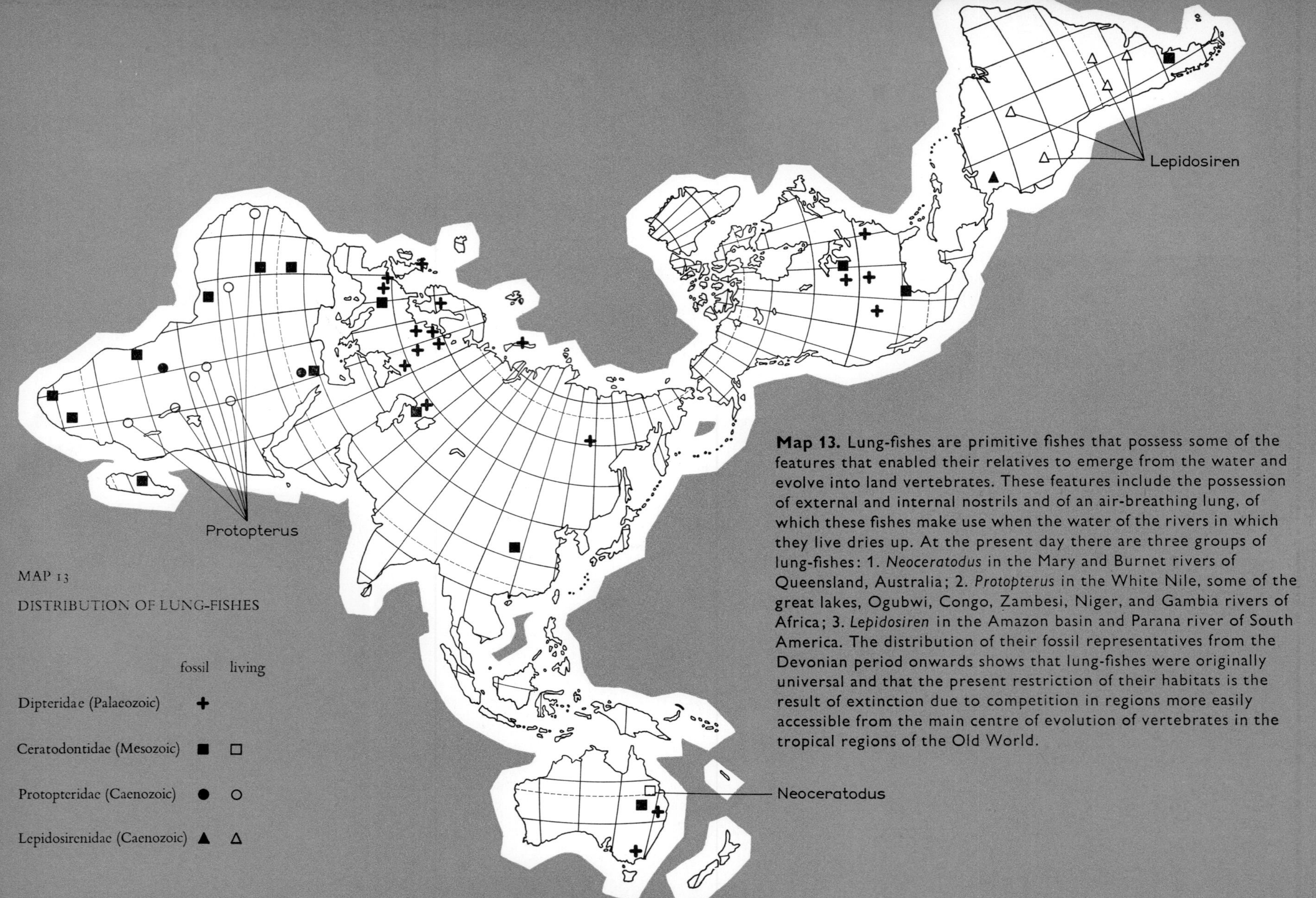

Map 13. Lung-fishes are primitive fishes that possess some of the features that enabled their relatives to emerge from the water and evolve into land vertebrates. These features include the possession of external and internal nostrils and of an air-breathing lung, of which these fishes make use when the water of the rivers in which they live dries up. At the present day there are three groups of lung-fishes: 1. *Neoceratodus* in the Mary and Burnet rivers of Queensland, Australia; 2. *Protopterus* in the White Nile, some of the great lakes, Ogubwi, Congo, Zambesi, Niger, and Gambia rivers of Africa; 3. *Lepidosiren* in the Amazon basin and Parana river of South America. The distribution of their fossil representatives from the Devonian period onwards shows that lung-fishes were originally universal and that the present restriction of their habitats is the result of extinction due to competition in regions more easily accessible from the main centre of evolution of vertebrates in the tropical regions of the Old World.

In the case of each of the classes of vertebrates, the centre of origin and dispersal was the tropical Old World, the largest existing land mass, and this fact illustrates a principle first enunciated by Darwin. He started from the proposition that variation would be expected to be greatest in a species the individual members of which are most numerous, and this hypothesis has been confirmed by Sir Ronald Fisher and E. B. Ford, who showed that the larger the number of individuals in a population the greater the number of mutations and recombination of genes, and the wider the variability. Numerous species cover more area and evolve faster, while the competition of natural selection is more intense and the survivors become dominant groups. This is why placental mammals are biologically superior to the marsupials. It is also the reason why the less efficient groups have been successively driven away from the centre of dispersal in the Old World to the extremities of South America, South Africa, and Australia, where they persist as relicts showing discontinuous geographical distribution (Maps 4, 5, 12-24).

Since the size of the area in which evolution has occurred is important, maps constructed on equal-area projection are used, as in Maps 4, 5, 9, 12, 13 and 15-24. Such maps have the advantage of emphasizing that the 'ends of the earth', at the southern extremities of Africa, South America and Australia, are at the greatest distances from the major centre of evolution in the tropical Old World (Map 9). This is the explanation of the persistence in those extremities of primitive species, now isolated, shown on maps by K. Ander, exhibiting what has been called extreme southern distribution (Maps 13, 15 and 17-22). The existence of living or fossil representatives of such species in Europe is the evidence that their distribution was once world-wide and that they have become extinct elsewhere. As J. Millot has stressed, there is no need to imagine any disappeared southern continent of 'Gondwanaland' to explain their distribution.

While the spread of plant or animal populations over land masses is easy to explain, the origin of populations of isolated islands presents a problem. Once the fact of evolution had been realized, the discontinuous distribution of species of plants and animals acquired a new importance. Evolution means that each species arose once only, under particular and unique conditions of selection, from an interbreeding population that occupied one continuous area. When similar or related forms are found in discontinuous areas, the fact requires explanation in each case. Some of the facts of discontinuous geographical distribution are astonishing. A species of liver-wort, *Marchasta areolata*, has been found in New Zealand and Tristan da Cunha. A species of *Daphnia* has been found in Greenland and the Lake of Locarno. *Pachyglossa* is a genus of moss found in New Zealand and in Patagonia. Tapirs are mammals of fair size found in South America and the East Indies (Map 16). This case is particularly instructive because it introduces the type of explanation that has been advanced time and again to explain discontinuous geographical distribution. This has been the supposition that the areas in question had previously been connected by land-bridges that extended right across the oceans and since then have sunk without trace beneath the sea. To explain the distribution of tapirs it has been supposed that there was a land-bridge right across the Pacific Ocean. As fossil tapirs have been found in Europe and North America their distribution was once world-wide and no Pacific land-bridge is necessary at all. Madagascar was supposed to have been joined by a land-bridge to India to explain a slight resemblance between the lemurs of the two countries, and South America by another land-bridge to Australia because Marsupials live in both (Map 4). When a fauna spreads over a land mass it does so respecting the biological balance of prey and predators; herbivores are followed by carnivores. This is exactly what has not happened in Madagascar and Australia, the fauna of which can only be understood if there was a water gap

Polyploidy and geographical distribution

Colour Plate 13
Chromosome numbers of different species are significant not only for distinction between them when the plants are similar in appearance but also because their geographical distribution gives indications of their lines of migration. A flower and chromosomes of *Paeonia cambessedesii*, diploid, indigenous to Balearic Islands, B flower and chromosomes of *P. russi*, tetraploid, found in Corsica, Sardinia, and Sicily, C flower and chromosomes of *P. mlokosewitschi*, diploid, confined to a small area of the Caucasus Mountains east of Tbilisi, D flower and chromosomes of *P. wittmanniana*, tetraploid, widely distributed in Transcaucasia. In each case, the diploid species have restricted and the tetraploid species wider ranges. The tetraploid species of *Paeonia* colonised central Europe and Asia by emigration when the climate became warmer after the Ice Age. This is an example of the principle that plants spreading into fresh areas and newly-opened habitats on the edges of the ranges of their species are mostly polyploids.

POLYPLOIDY AND GEOGRAPHICAL DISTRIBUTION

Paeonia cambessedesii (diploid)

Paeonia mlokosewitschi (diploid)

Paeonia russi (tetraploid)

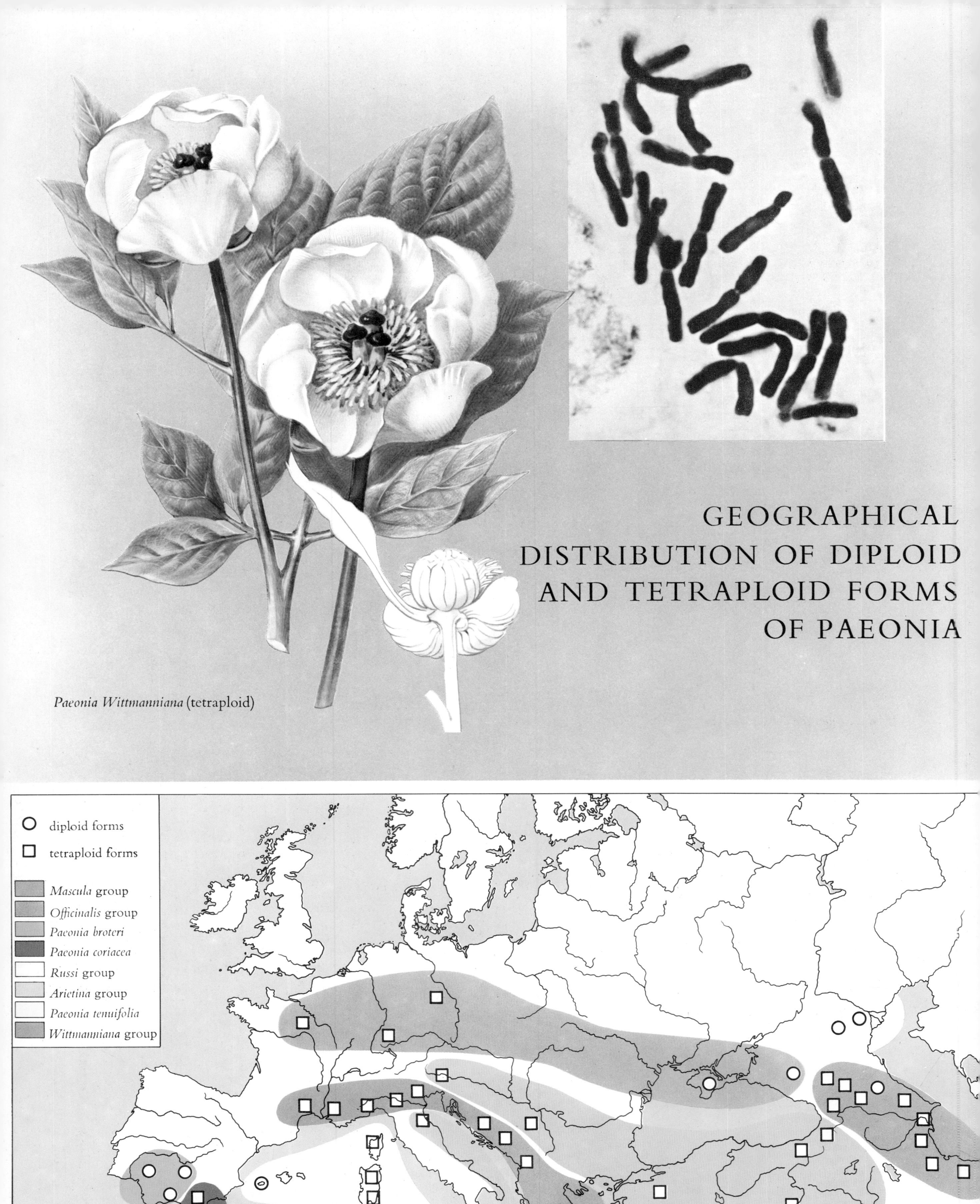

Paeonia Wittmanniana (tetraploid)

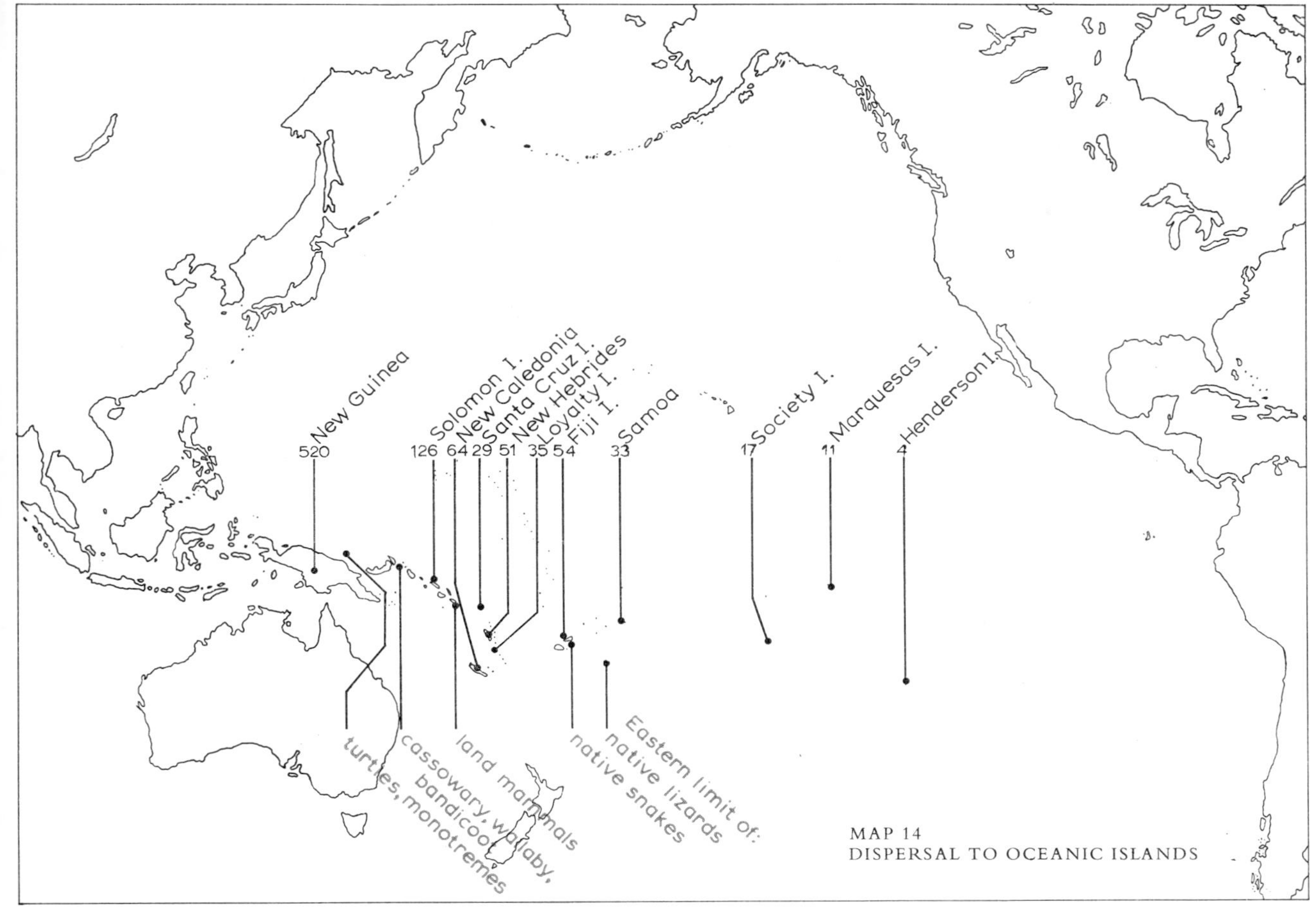

Map 14. The numbers of species of land mammals, birds (of which the figures are shown), and reptiles on oceanic islands in the Pacific show a gradual decrease with increasing distance from the land-areas of Australia and New Guinea. The size of the islands and their proximity to other islands are also factors which cause a certain amount of variation in the regular decrease in number of species. While some of the birds may have been blown to their destinations by strong winds during flight, the dispersal of land reptiles and mammals can only have resulted from flotation on timber, or from swimming. This distribution shows that the populations of the Pacific Oceanic islands is the result of fortuitous eastward spread and 'island-hopping', which is the normal mode of origin of the populations of islands that have never formed part of any continent (after E. Mayr, and P. J. Darlington, simplified).

between them and Africa and Asia respectively since Mesozoic times (Map 9).

To explain the presence of animals on oceanic islands like the Azores or the Galàpagos, it has been supposed that the continents of Europe and South America previously extended to them. There are no continents between which imaginary land-bridges have not been invoked to explain discontinuous geographical distribution. Such facile explanations were firmly rejected by Darwin who showed that this reckless appeal to land-bridges was absurd. Modern research in geology has fully endorsed Darwin's view because the evidence from mineralogy, stratigraphy, seismology, and gravity anomalies leaves no escape from the conclusion that the floor of ocean basins has never been part of the continental crust.

The hypothesis of land-bridges is also untenable for another reason. If a land-bridge is invented to explain why 5 per cent of the species of an island or continent is closely related to those of another continent, no explanation is possible of why the remaining 95 per cent of the species are different. There are related fresh water fishes in Africa and South America, but if there had been a land-bridge between these continents, countless other animals would have made use of it even more easily and the existing distinction between the characteristic forms of life in Africa and South America would be inexplicable. This argument also applies to the possibility that continents now separated were once in contact before continental drift (if it occurred) tore them apart. The only requirements for the explanation of the distribution of the living floras and faunas of the continents, which are the result of their divergent evolution since the Mesozoic era, are the isthmuses of Suez, Bering, and, intermittently, Panama. Any other continental contacts since the Mesozoic era would make the present distribution inexplicable.

To the continents belong the continental shelves, now largely submerged, but which previously connected the continents with the continental islands (Map 10): the British Isles with Europe; Ceylon, Sumatra, Java, Borneo, Formosa, and Japan with Asia; Newfoundland and Greenland with North America; South America with the Falkland Islands and perhaps with Antarctica via the South Shetlands; New Guinea with Australia. Madagascar and New Zealand are ancient islands that have had no connexion with any continent at least since the Mesozoic era. The remaining islands of the world have arisen in the oceans without connexions with any continent at any time. The question therefore arises how these oceanic islands have been populated.

To solve this problem without recourse to land-bridges, Darwin experimented on how long seeds or snails could remain viable after immersion in sea water. Of 87 species of seeds immersed for 28 days 64 germinated. Nuts germinated 90 days and some seeds after 137 days immersion. West Indian seeds are drifted across the Atlantic Ocean by the Gulf Stream and land in North western Europe. Another possibility is that seeds are eaten by fish and the fish by birds that fly long distances and vomit the seeds in pellets or pass them out with excrement. From a ball of earth on a bird's foot Darwin raised 82 seedlings. Birds' feet can also carry larvae of freshwater molluscs and spawn of fish. Even if the bird dies its body can float and its crop containing seeds be thrown up on shore. There is also the possibility of plants and animals being floated on rafts of drift wood or matted weeds and carried out to sea. Some historically authenticated cases of drifting are shown in Map 11.

Wind has astonishing powers of transportation. Locusts, beetles, bugs, flies, and of course birds, have been taken on ships hundreds of miles from land. In the air, moths have been found at a height of 700 metres, seeds at 2500 metres, and leaves at 5000 metres. Fish have been carried in tornados across desert regions in Australia. These are the means by which oceanic islands have been originally populated, by accidental dispersal from land masses.

Geographical distribution of diploid and tetraploid forms of *Paeonia*

Colour Plate 14
The ranges of related groups are enclosed within boundary lines. The tetraploid forms range over wider areas than their related diploid forms, from which they evolved and spread when the climate improved after the Glacial Period. After Sir Frederic Stern.

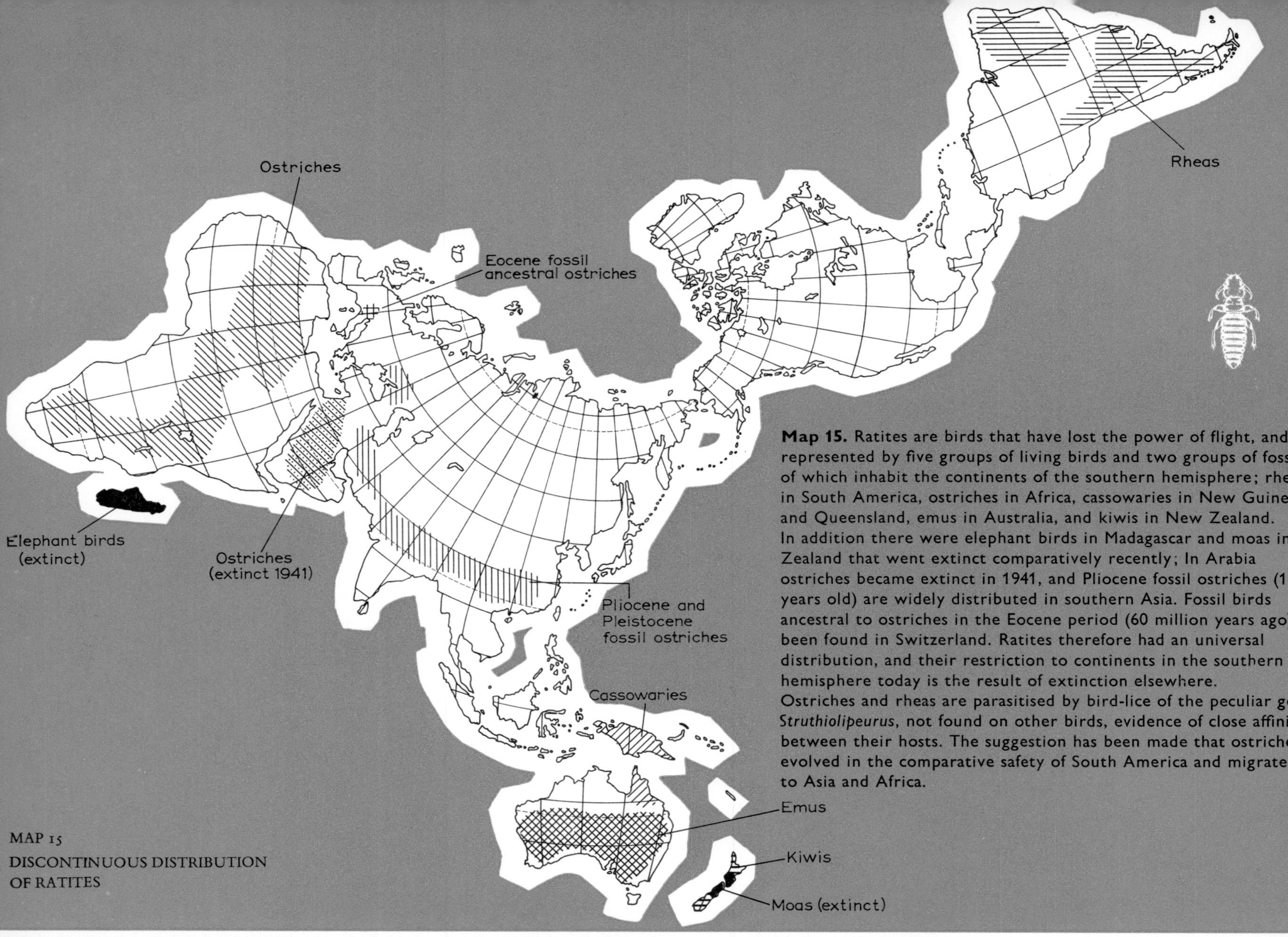

Ostriches

Eocene fossil
ancestral ostriches

Rheas

Elephant birds
(extinct)

Ostriches
(extinct 1941)

Pliocene and
Pleistocene
fossil ostriches

Cassowaries

Emus

Kiwis

Moas (extinct)

Map 15. Ratites are birds that have lost the power of flight, and are represented by five groups of living birds and two groups of fossils, all of which inhabit the continents of the southern hemisphere; rheas in South America, ostriches in Africa, cassowaries in New Guinea and Queensland, emus in Australia, and kiwis in New Zealand.
In addition there were elephant birds in Madagascar and moas in New Zealand that went extinct comparatively recently; In Arabia ostriches became extinct in 1941, and Pliocene fossil ostriches (10 million years old) are widely distributed in southern Asia. Fossil birds ancestral to ostriches in the Eocene period (60 million years ago) have been found in Switzerland. Ratites therefore had an universal distribution, and their restriction to continents in the southern hemisphere today is the result of extinction elsewhere.
Ostriches and rheas are parasitised by bird-lice of the peculiar genus *Struthiolipeurus*, not found on other birds, evidence of close affinities between their hosts. The suggestion has been made that ostriches evolved in the comparative safety of South America and migrated to Asia and Africa.

MAP 15
DISCONTINUOUS DISTRIBUTION
OF RATITES

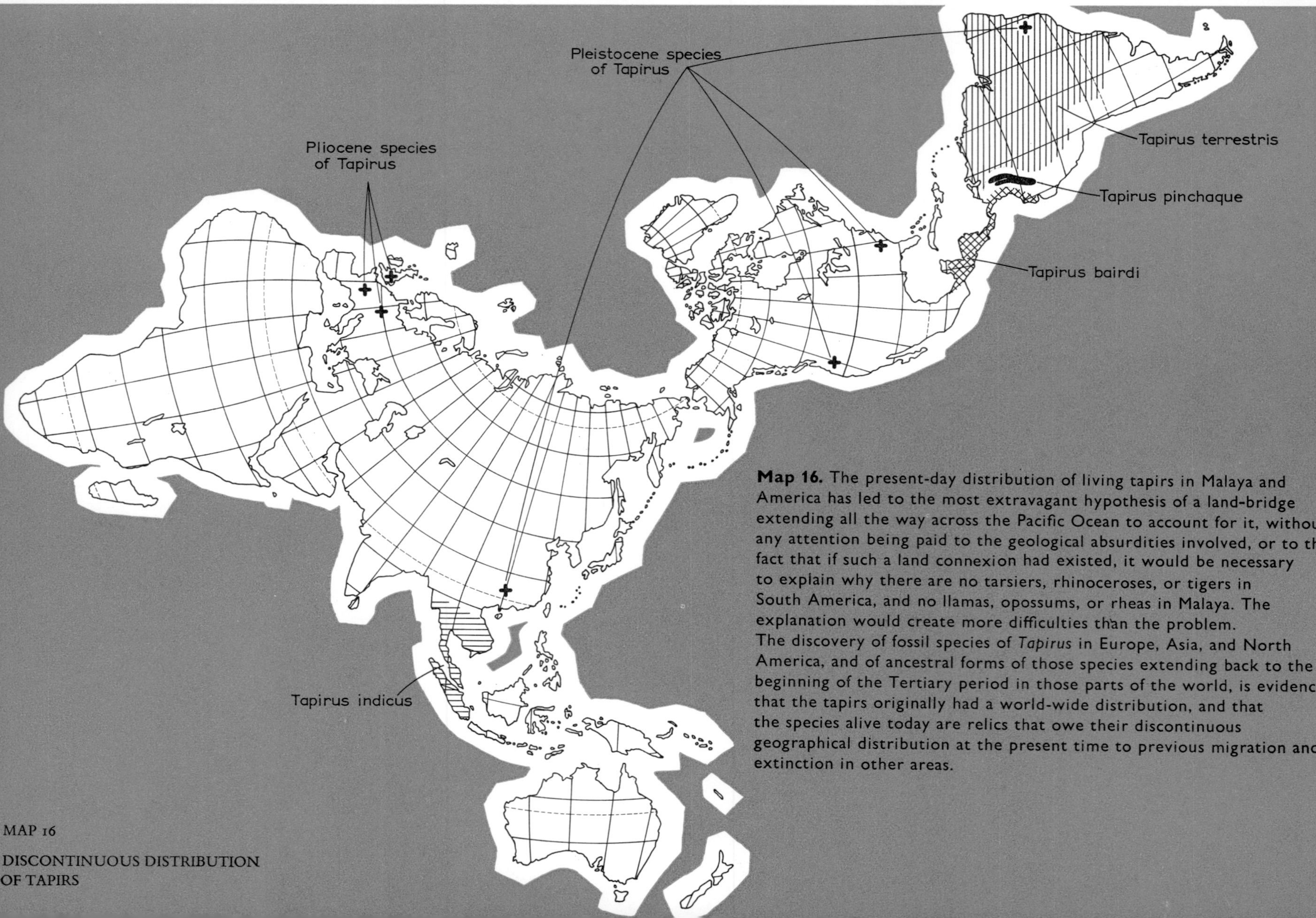

Pleistocene species
of Tapirus

Pliocene species
of Tapirus

Tapirus terrestris

Tapirus pinchaque

Tapirus bairdi

Tapirus indicus

Map 16. The present-day distribution of living tapirs in Malaya and America has led to the most extravagant hypothesis of a land-bridge extending all the way across the Pacific Ocean to account for it, without any attention being paid to the geological absurdities involved, or to the fact that if such a land connexion had existed, it would be necessary to explain why there are no tarsiers, rhinoceroses, or tigers in South America, and no llamas, opossums, or rheas in Malaya. The explanation would create more difficulties than the problem.
The discovery of fossil species of *Tapirus* in Europe, Asia, and North America, and of ancestral forms of those species extending back to the beginning of the Tertiary period in those parts of the world, is evidence that the tapirs originally had a world-wide distribution, and that the species alive today are relics that owe their discontinuous geographical distribution at the present time to previous migration and extinction in other areas.

MAP 16
DISCONTINUOUS DISTRIBUTION
OF TAPIRS

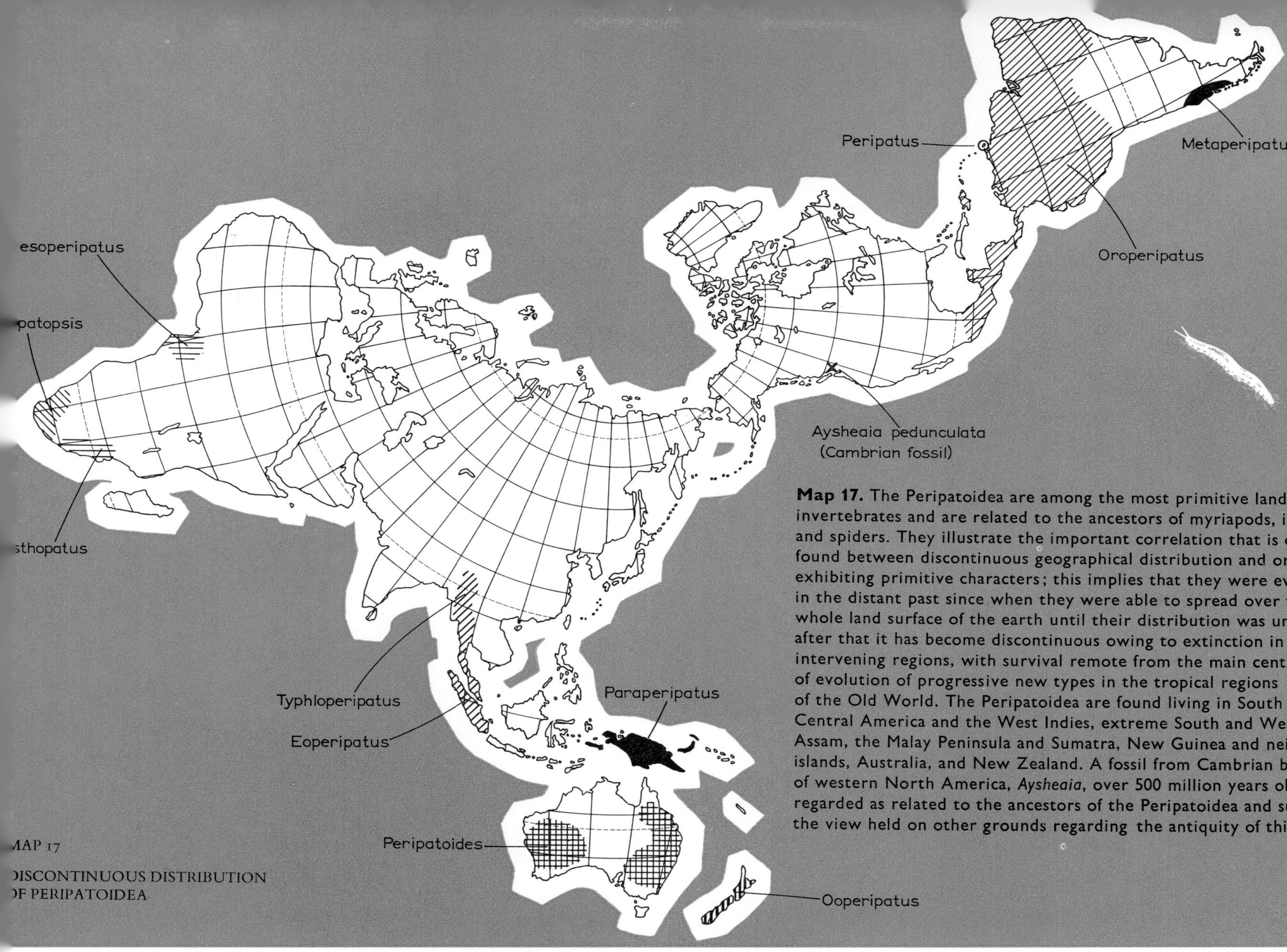

Peripatus

Metaperipatus

Oroperipatus

esoperipatus

patopsis

sthopatus

Aysheaia pedunculata
(Cambrian fossil)

Typhloperipatus

Paraperipatus

Eoperipatus

Peripatoides

Ooperipatus

Map 17. The Peripatoidea are among the most primitive land invertebrates and are related to the ancestors of myriapods, insects, and spiders. They illustrate the important correlation that is commonly found between discontinuous geographical distribution and organisms exhibiting primitive characters; this implies that they were evolved in the distant past since when they were able to spread over the whole land surface of the earth until their distribution was universal; after that it has become discontinuous owing to extinction in intervening regions, with survival remote from the main centre of evolution of progressive new types in the tropical regions of the Old World. The Peripatoidea are found living in South and Central America and the West Indies, extreme South and West Africa, Assam, the Malay Peninsula and Sumatra, New Guinea and neighbouring islands, Australia, and New Zealand. A fossil from Cambrian beds of western North America, *Aysheaia*, over 500 million years old, is regarded as related to the ancestors of the Peripatoidea and supports the view held on other grounds regarding the antiquity of this group.

AP 17

DISCONTINUOUS DISTRIBUTION
OF PERIPATOIDEA

Miocene fossils

Oligocene fossils

Miocene fossils

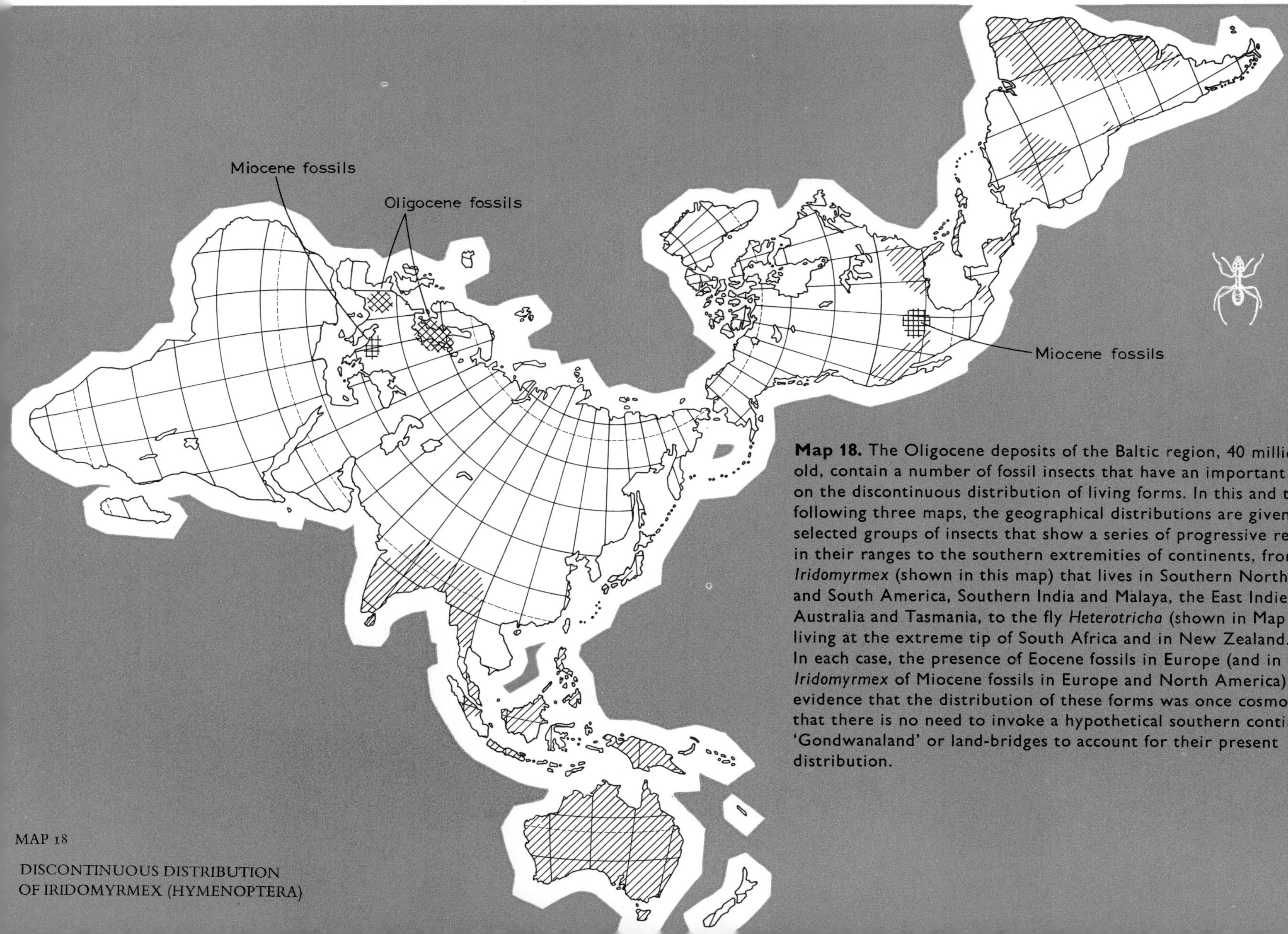

Map 18. The Oligocene deposits of the Baltic region, 40 million years old, contain a number of fossil insects that have an important bearing on the discontinuous distribution of living forms. In this and the following three maps, the geographical distributions are given of four selected groups of insects that show a series of progressive restriction in their ranges to the southern extremities of continents, from the ant *Iridomyrmex* (shown in this map) that lives in Southern North America and South America, Southern India and Malaya, the East Indies, Australia and Tasmania, to the fly *Heterotricha* (shown in Map 21) now living at the extreme tip of South Africa and in New Zealand.
In each case, the presence of Eocene fossils in Europe (and in the case of *Iridomyrmex* of Miocene fossils in Europe and North America) is evidence that the distribution of these forms was once cosmopolitan, and that there is no need to invoke a hypothetical southern continent of 'Gondwanaland' or land-bridges to account for their present distribution.

MAP 18

DISCONTINUOUS DISTRIBUTION
OF IRIDOMYRMEX (HYMENOPTERA)

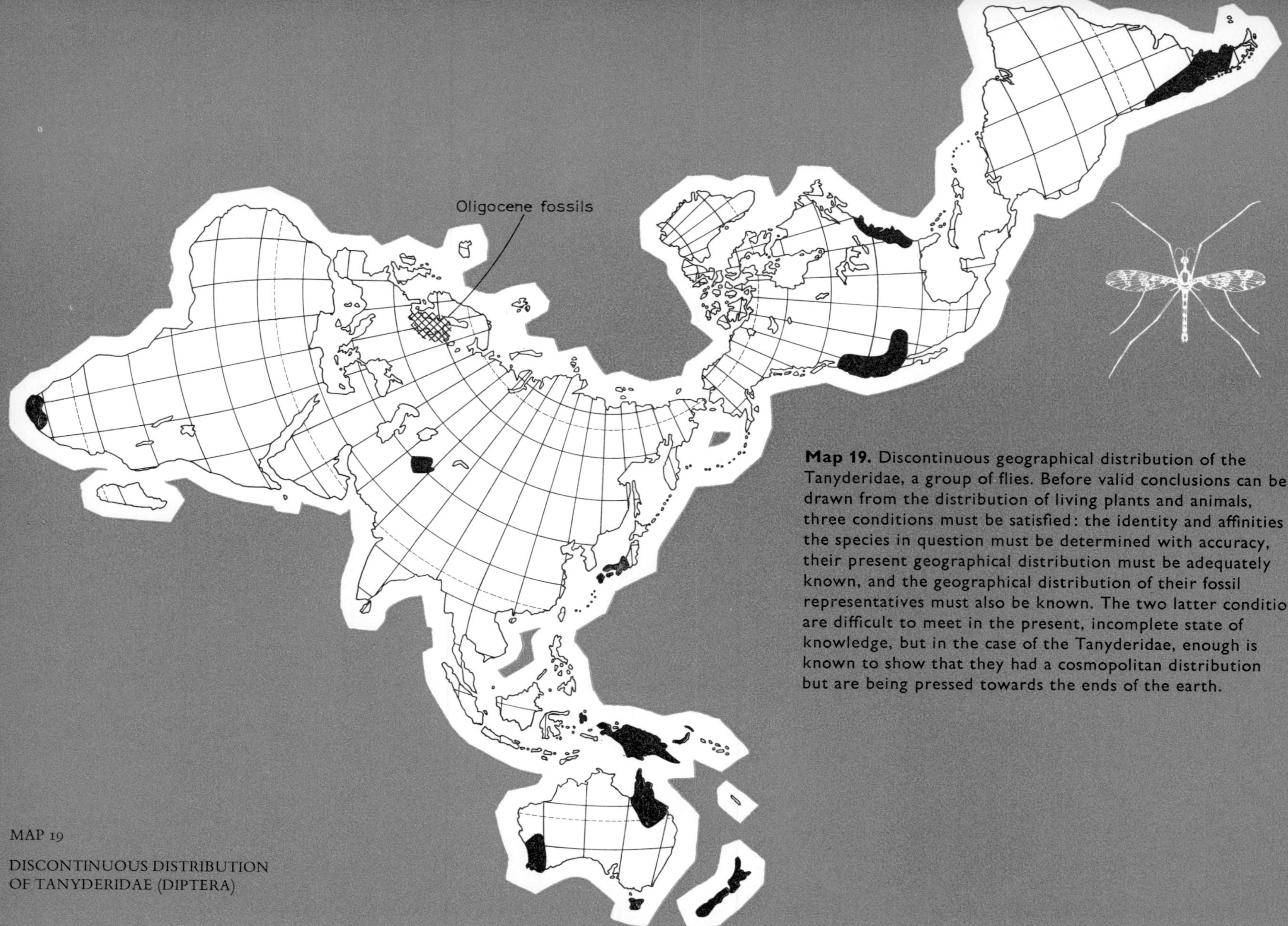

Oligocene fossils

Map 19. Discontinuous geographical distribution of the Tanyderidae, a group of flies. Before valid conclusions can be drawn from the distribution of living plants and animals, three conditions must be satisfied: the identity and affinities of the species in question must be determined with accuracy, their present geographical distribution must be adequately known, and the geographical distribution of their fossil representatives must also be known. The two latter conditions are difficult to meet in the present, incomplete state of knowledge, but in the case of the Tanyderidae, enough is known to show that they had a cosmopolitan distribution but are being pressed towards the ends of the earth.

MAP 19

DISCONTINUOUS DISTRIBUTION OF TANYDERIDAE (DIPTERA)

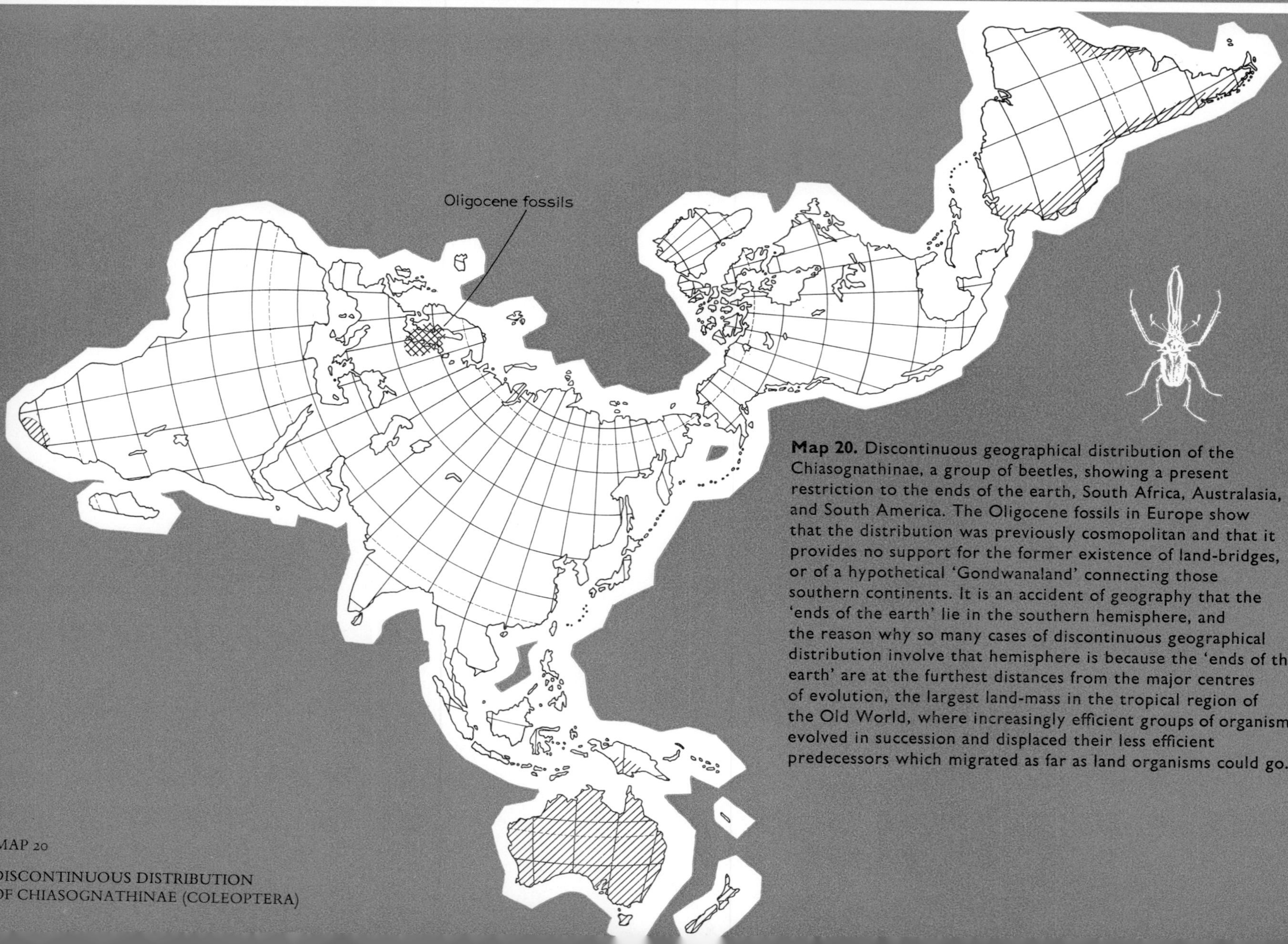

Oligocene fossils

Map 20. Discontinuous geographical distribution of the Chiasognathinae, a group of beetles, showing a present restriction to the ends of the earth, South Africa, Australasia, and South America. The Oligocene fossils in Europe show that the distribution was previously cosmopolitan and that it provides no support for the former existence of land-bridges, or of a hypothetical 'Gondwanaland' connecting those southern continents. It is an accident of geography that the 'ends of the earth' lie in the southern hemisphere, and the reason why so many cases of discontinuous geographical distribution involve that hemisphere is because the 'ends of the earth' are at the furthest distances from the major centres of evolution, the largest land-mass in the tropical region of the Old World, where increasingly efficient groups of organisms evolved in succession and displaced their less efficient predecessors which migrated as far as land organisms could go.

MAP 20

DISCONTINUOUS DISTRIBUTION OF CHIASOGNATHINAE (COLEOPTERA)

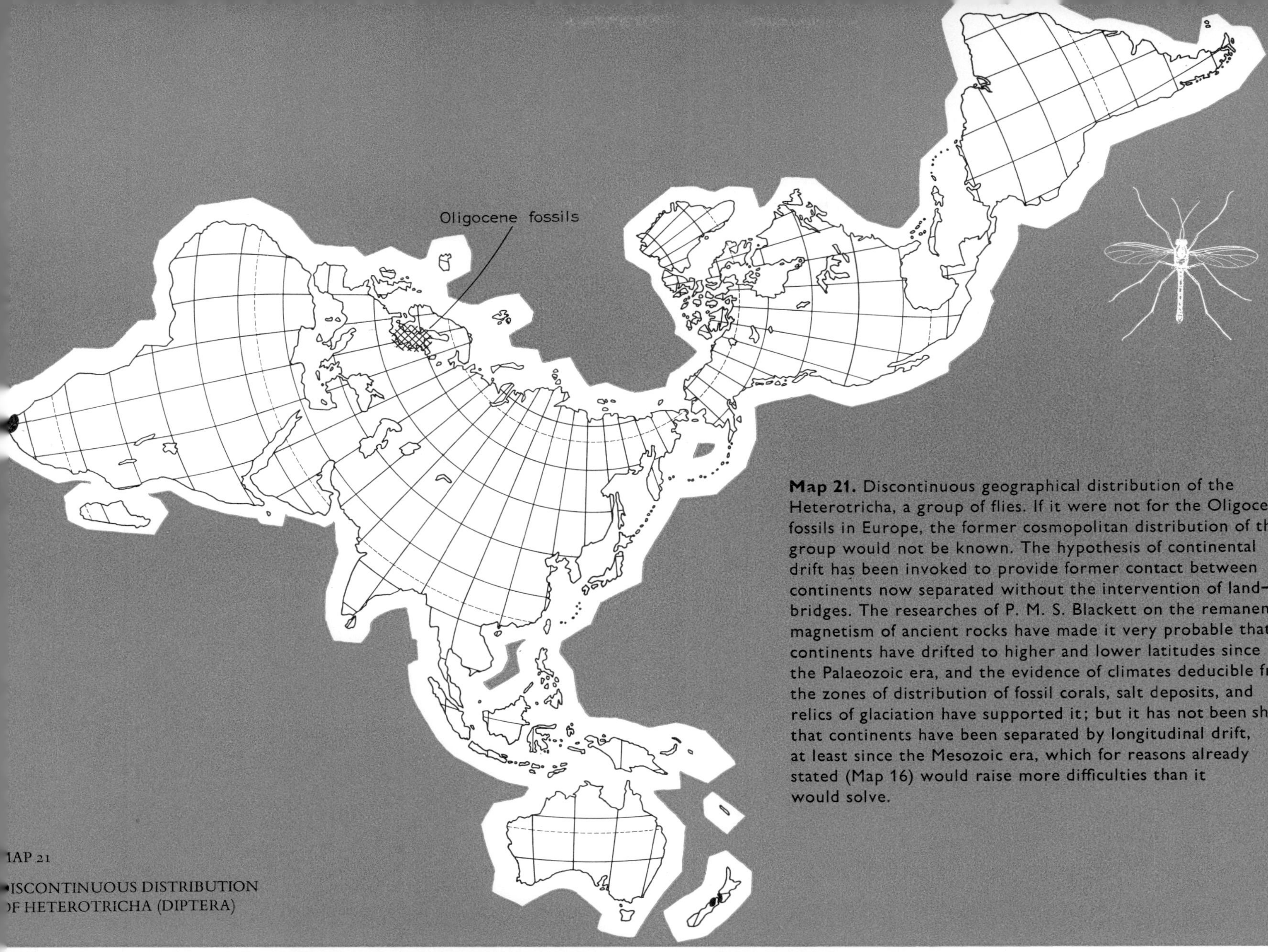

Oligocene fossils

Map 21. Discontinuous geographical distribution of the Heterotricha, a group of flies. If it were not for the Oligocene fossils in Europe, the former cosmopolitan distribution of the group would not be known. The hypothesis of continental drift has been invoked to provide former contact between continents now separated without the intervention of land-bridges. The researches of P. M. S. Blackett on the remanent magnetism of ancient rocks have made it very probable that continents have drifted to higher and lower latitudes since the Palaeozoic era, and the evidence of climates deducible from the zones of distribution of fossil corals, salt deposits, and relics of glaciation have supported it; but it has not been shown that continents have been separated by longitudinal drift, at least since the Mesozoic era, which for reasons already stated (Map 16) would raise more difficulties than it would solve.

IAP 21

ISCONTINUOUS DISTRIBUTION
)F HETEROTRICHA (DIPTERA)

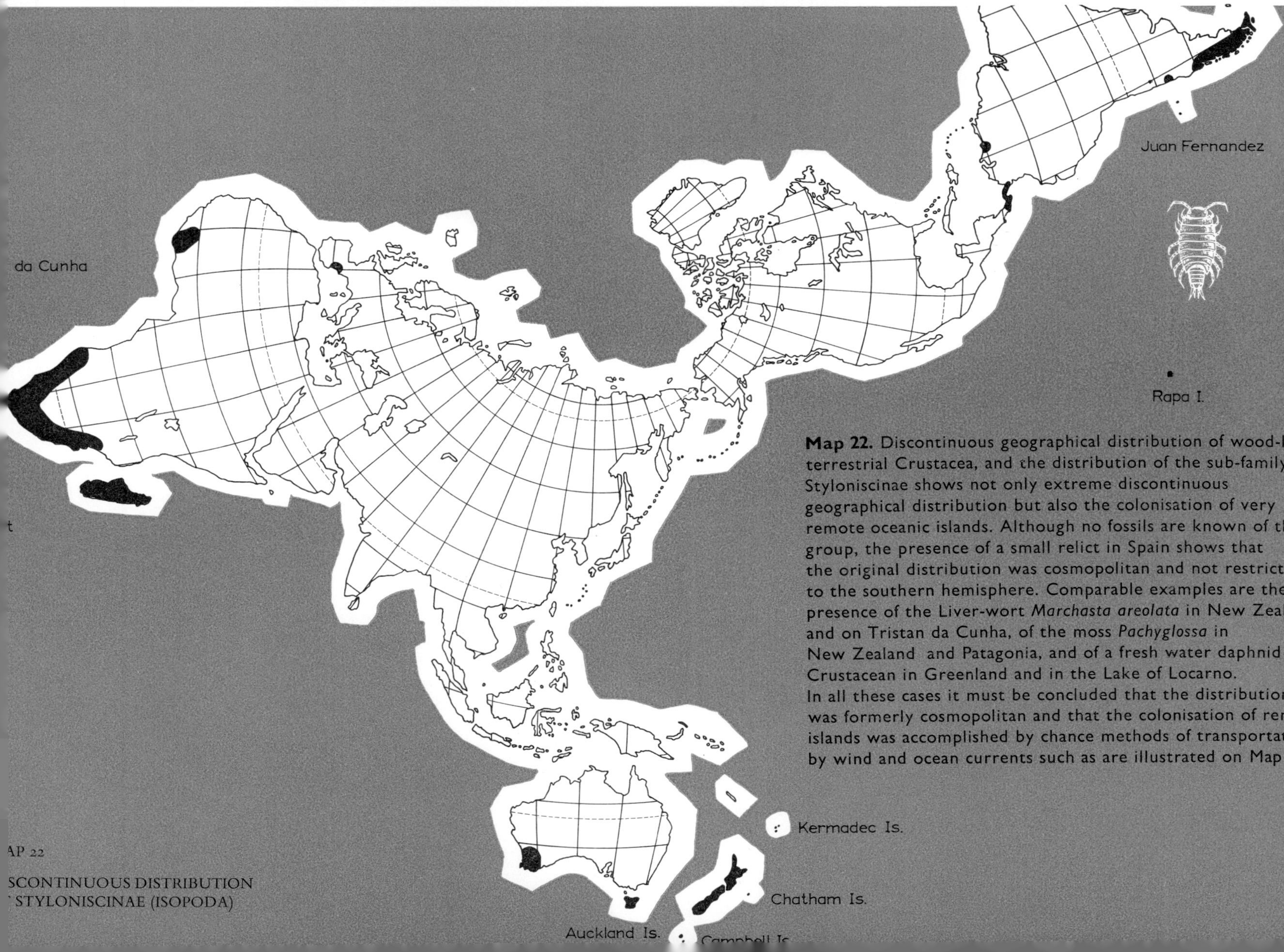

Juan Fernandez

da Cunha

Rapa I.

t

Map 22. Discontinuous geographical distribution of wood-lice, terrestrial Crustacea, and the distribution of the sub-family Styloniscinae shows not only extreme discontinuous geographical distribution but also the colonisation of very remote oceanic islands. Although no fossils are known of this group, the presence of a small relict in Spain shows that the original distribution was cosmopolitan and not restricted to the southern hemisphere. Comparable examples are the presence of the Liver-wort *Marchasta areolata* in New Zealand and on Tristan da Cunha, of the moss *Pachyglossa* in New Zealand and Patagonia, and of a fresh water daphnid Crustacean in Greenland and in the Lake of Locarno. In all these cases it must be concluded that the distribution was formerly cosmopolitan and that the colonisation of remote islands was accomplished by chance methods of transportation by wind and ocean currents such as are illustrated on Map 11.

Kermadec Is.

AP 22

SCONTINUOUS DISTRIBUTION
STYLONISCINAE (ISOPODA)

Chatham Is.

Auckland Is.

Campbell Is.

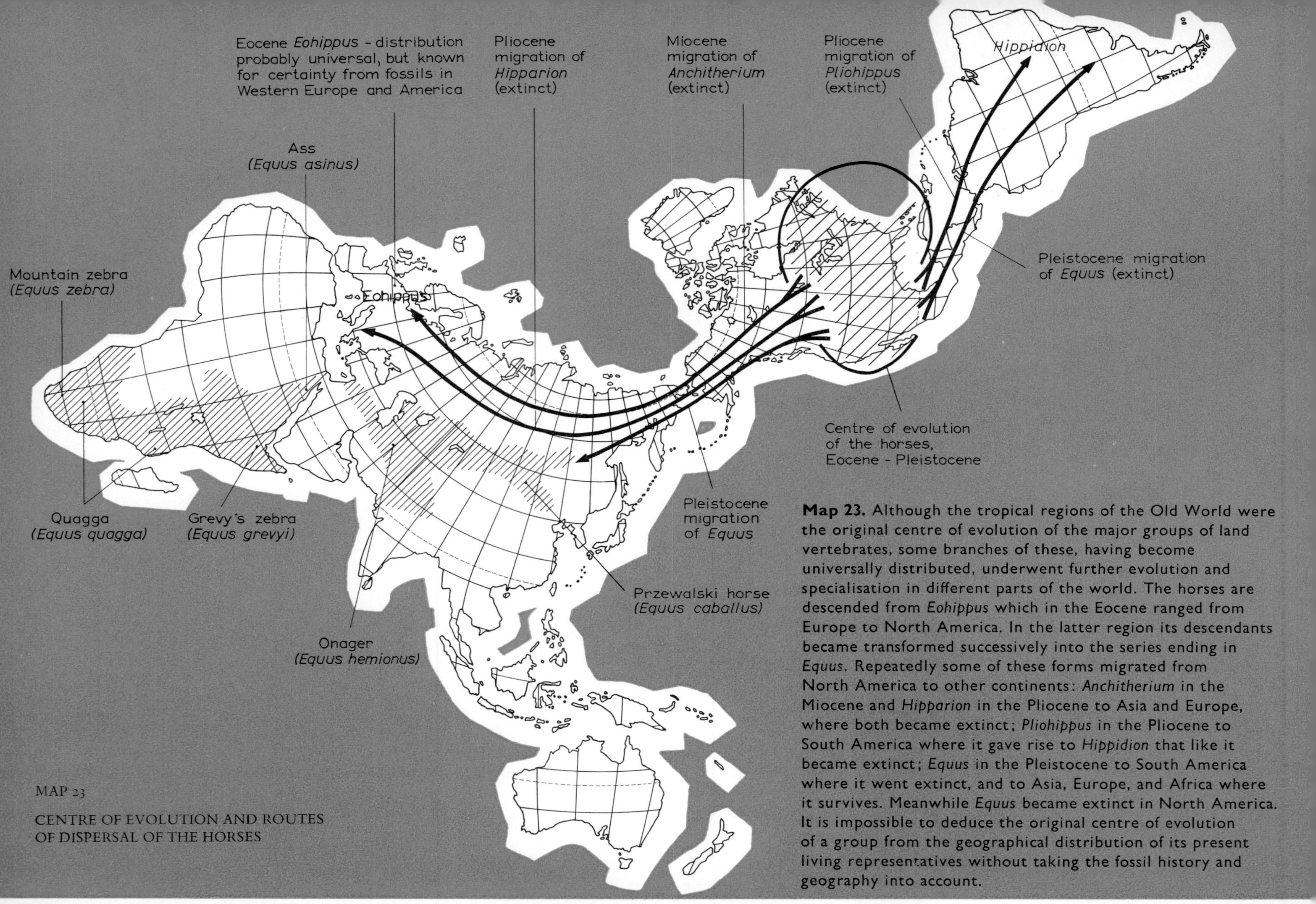

Eocene *Eohippus* - distribution probably universal, but known for certainty from fossils in Western Europe and America

Pliocene migration of *Hipparion* (extinct)

Miocene migration of *Anchitherium* (extinct)

Pliocene migration of *Pliohippus* (extinct)

Hippidion

Ass (*Equus asinus*)

Mountain zebra (*Equus zebra*)

Eohippus

Pleistocene migration of *Equus* (extinct)

Centre of evolution of the horses, Eocene - Pleistocene

Quagga (*Equus quagga*)

Grevy's zebra (*Equus grevyi*)

Pleistocene migration of *Equus*

Przewalski horse (*Equus caballus*)

Onager (*Equus hemionus*)

Map 23. Although the tropical regions of the Old World were the original centre of evolution of the major groups of land vertebrates, some branches of these, having become universally distributed, underwent further evolution and specialisation in different parts of the world. The horses are descended from *Eohippus* which in the Eocene ranged from Europe to North America. In the latter region its descendants became transformed successively into the series ending in *Equus*. Repeatedly some of these forms migrated from North America to other continents: *Anchitherium* in the Miocene and *Hipparion* in the Pliocene to Asia and Europe, where both became extinct; *Pliohippus* in the Pliocene to South America where it gave rise to *Hippidion* that like it became extinct; *Equus* in the Pleistocene to South America where it went extinct, and to Asia, Europe, and Africa where it survives. Meanwhile *Equus* became extinct in North America. It is impossible to deduce the original centre of evolution of a group from the geographical distribution of its present living representatives without taking the fossil history and geography into account.

MAP 23

CENTRE OF EVOLUTION AND ROUTES OF DISPERSAL OF THE HORSES

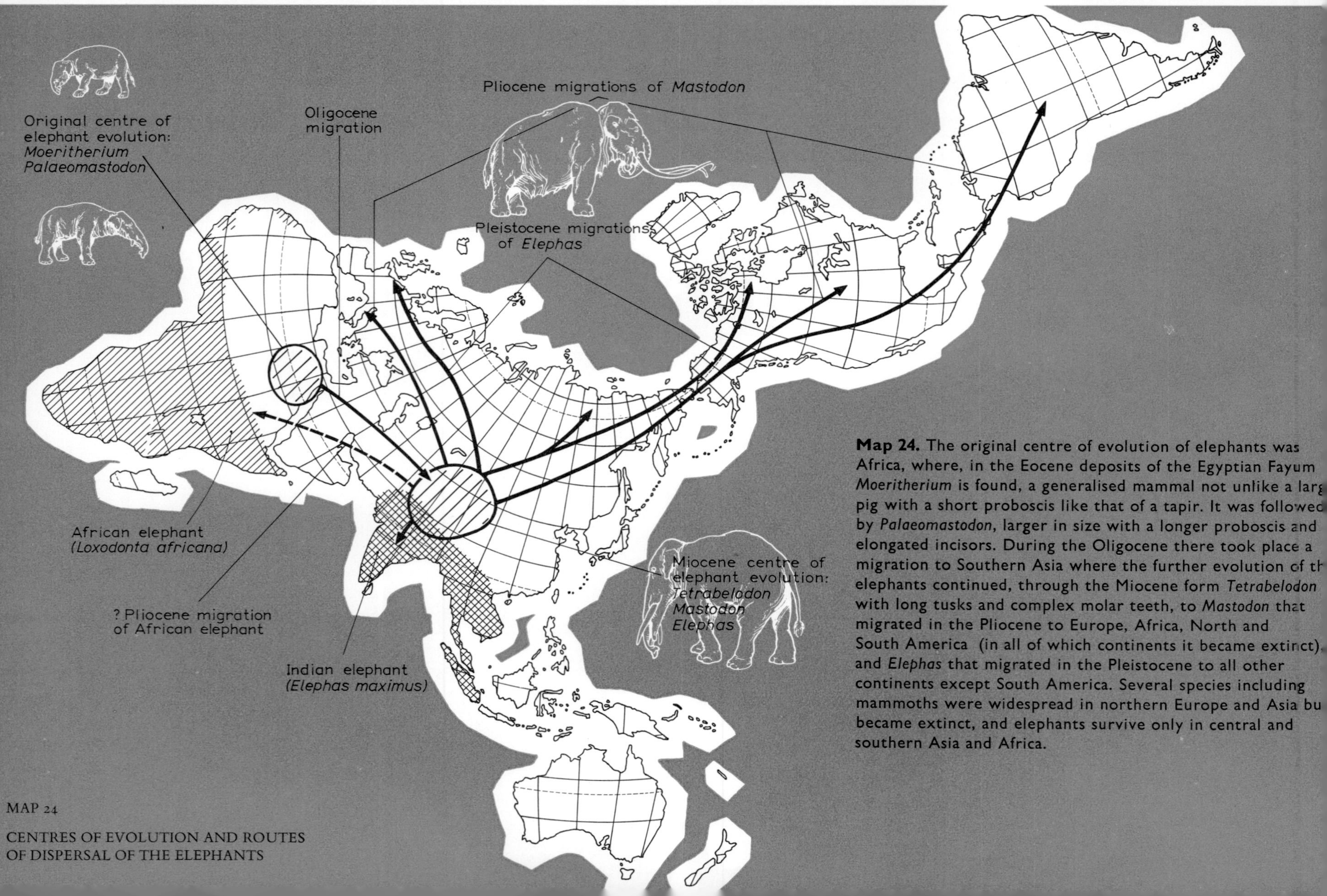

Pliocene migrations of *Mastodon*

Original centre of elephant evolution: *Moeritherium* *Palaeomastodon*

Oligocene migration

Pleistocene migrations of *Elephas*

African elephant (*Loxodonta africana*)

Miocene centre of elephant evolution: *Tetrabelodon* *Mastodon* *Elephas*

? Pliocene migration of African elephant

Indian elephant (*Elephas maximus*)

Map 24. The original centre of evolution of elephants was Africa, where, in the Eocene deposits of the Egyptian Fayum *Moeritherium* is found, a generalised mammal not unlike a larg pig with a short proboscis like that of a tapir. It was followec by *Palaeomastodon*, larger in size with a longer proboscis and elongated incisors. During the Oligocene there took place a migration to Southern Asia where the further evolution of th elephants continued, through the Miocene form *Tetrabelodon* with long tusks and complex molar teeth, to *Mastodon* that migrated in the Pliocene to Europe, Africa, North and South America (in all of which continents it became extinct), and *Elephas* that migrated in the Pleistocene to all other continents except South America. Several species including mammoths were widespread in northern Europe and Asia bu became extinct, and elephants survive only in central and southern Asia and Africa.

MAP 24

CENTRES OF EVOLUTION AND ROUTES OF DISPERSAL OF THE ELEPHANTS

Chapter IV THE MAJOR STEPS OF EVOLUTION

THE ORIGIN OF LIFE

Darwin intentionally left the question of the origin of life untouched in his books, and assumed the existence of one or a few original living germs from which as the result of variation and natural selection the vegetable and animal kingdoms evolved. The reason for Darwin's reticence was that the state of knowledge in his day made it unprofitable to come to any conclusions regarding the origin of life; but the problem interested him greatly. In 1871, with remarkable insight he wrote: 'It is often said that all the conditions for the first production of a living organism are now present, which could ever have been present. But if (and oh! what a big if!) we could conceive in some warm little pond, with all sorts of ammonia and phosphoric salts, light, heat, electricity, etc. present, that a protein compound was chemically formed ready to undergo still more complex changes, at the present day such matter would be instantly devoured or absorbed, which would not have been the case before living creatures were formed.' In this striking passage Darwin expressed with accuracy a point of view that represents the most informed opinion on the subject today. Darwin's 'warm little pond' is now taken quite seriously as a result of advances in knowledge of chemistry that show that complex so-called 'organic' compounds can be formed in nature without the agency of living organisms.

The problem of the origin of life should be approached from the fact that at early stages of the earth's own evolution, life was impossible. Whether the earth cooled out of a molten state or condensed out of cold dust, the physical and chemical conditions that then prevailed must have been totally incompatible with life. Life must therefore have arisen on earth at some time since its formation. The course of evolution from chemical molecules to living matter can, even in the light of many striking recent discoveries, only be conjectured, and many more discoveries will be required before the certainty that this evolution has taken place can be clothed with firm details as to how it happened.

Living matter is associated with complex chemical compounds, of which proteins are among the most important. Proteins are very large molecules, and are only beginning to yield up the secrets of their structure. They are built up from many molecules of smaller, simpler substances, known as amino acids, which contain carbon, oxygen, hydrogen, and nitrogen, and occasionally sulphur and the specificity of the proteins depends on which amino acids they contain and on the order in which they are arranged. Infinitely great as the possible number of different proteins may be, it is a remarkable fact that throughout the realms of living beings, the number of different amino acids that can enter into their composition is just over twenty. Here, at any rate, is a simplicity underlying the complexity of proteins (Pl. 336, 338).

No less important a constituent of living matter is deoxyribonucleic acid or *DNA*, which numerous experiments have shown to be the chemical basis of genes, as already described (p. 86). *DNA* is also the fundamental agent of replication and of the synthesis of more material like itself. Finally *DNA*, through the genes that it contains, and their action on ribonucleic acid (or *RNA*) in the body of the cell, determines the synthesis of further proteins which act as enzymes and, in turn, accelerate the synthesis of other substances. And yet, the effective part of *DNA* in determining which particular synthesis shall take place depends on the order in which four substances, the nucleotide bases, two purines and two pyrimidines, are arranged (see p. 86). Here is another case of simplicity at the base of complexity.

Chlorophyll, the substance by means of which green plants capture carbon from the carbon dioxide in the air, and haemoglobin, the red substance that transports oxygen in the blood of animals, are closely similar derivatives of porphyrin, the former containing magnesium and the latter iron. Porphyrins are found in all living cells, and although they cannot be described as 'simple' substances, they are uniform in chemical structure (Pl. 343, 344).

Energy for the chemical processes that take place in living organisms is stored and released by means of a simple compound of phosphoric acid, adenosine triphosphate or *ATP*. It is the same substance, whether it furnishes energy used in the contraction of muscles, electrical discharges from electric organs in fish, production of light in fireflies, or the synthesis of complex chemical substances (Pl. 345).

In spite of the complexity of the composition of living organisms, there is therefore a basic simplicity in the nature and structure of substances concerned with many of the fundamental functions of life such as the utilization of raw materials and oxygen, and the production of energy. On the chemical plane, as in the structure of organisms, 'Nature is prodigal in variety, but niggard in innovation.'

Since acetic acid and other simple carbon compounds were synthesized in the middle of last century, and Marcellin Berthelot and others synthesized chains of carbon atoms forming hydrocarbons and built up derivatives from them, it has gradually become clear that the so-called organic chemical substances found in living organisms can be prepared in the laboratory from their constituent elements. Chemists can now synthesize fatty acids, amino acids, sugars, purines, and many vitamins. Chains of amino acids known as peptides have been synthesized from simple amino acids, P. Doty has shown that they form spirals and the complexity and size of these artificial compounds may equal those of natural proteins (Pl. 336, 338).

The next question was whether organic substances could be built up in nature without living organisms. In considering such a possibility, an important factor is whether gaseous oxygen was present in the earth's atmosphere, because free oxygen would break down complex compounds. When protected from oxygen, organic compounds can keep indefinitely, as in the case of oil in the earth's crust or amino acids in flinty chert that have been preserved for 1,700 million years (see p. 54). The conclusion to which A. I. Oparin, J. B. S. Haldane, and H. C. Urey have come is that early in the earth's history, the atmosphere contained no free oxygen, but hydrogen, water vapour, ammonia, and marsh gas.

A flood of light was thrown on the possibilities of natural synthesis of organic compounds when S. L. Miller subjected a mixture of these four gases to electric discharges and ultra-violet light at temperatures slightly below the boiling point of water. In other words, energy was applied to this little artificial atmosphere. The result was the production of formic, acetic, propionic, lactic, and glycollic acids, and of no less than twenty-five different amino acids; acetic acid and glycine were obtained in large quantities (Pl. 335). These two compounds are just the substances that can combine and condense to form porphyrins, as D. Shemin showed. In view of these results, it is less surprising that meteorites, extra-terrestrial material from the remnants of shattered planets, have been found to contain hydrocarbons, amino acids, and substances similar to cytosine, which is one of the pyrimidine components of *DNA*. Of the nucleotide bases, the pyrimidines can be formed from carbon dioxide, urea, and succinic acid, the purines from carbon dioxide, formic acid, glycine, aspartic acid, and glutamic acid. These are the kinds of substances produced in Miller's experiments.

The conclusion is inescapable that the chemical substances essential for life – by means of which the organism is able to ingest and convert substances outside the organism into the organism itself, and to replicate its like – were built up in the world and synthesized by energy from the sun in the form of ultra-violet light, electric discharges, chemical reactions, and perhaps the heat associated with volcanic eruptions, before living organisms ever appeared on earth at all. There must have been chemical evolution before biological evolution could begin; but Darwin's principle of variation and natural selection was also applicable to chemical evolution. Variation took the form of the formation of new compounds. Natural selection favoured those that possessed chemical stability, and this is probably the explanation of a curious fact of chemical structure found in all living organisms. Every atom of carbon has four chemical bonds by which it is attached to other atoms or groups of atoms. When all four of these atoms or groups are different, the carbon atom to which they are attached is asymmetrical, and the molecule containing it exists in two forms, mirror-images of each other and comparable to the right hand and left hand of a pair of gloves (Pl. 335 (7), 337). When a compound containing an asymmetric carbon atom is produced synthetically in a laboratory, equal quantities of the right-hand (DEXTRO-) and left-hand (LAEVO-), or D and L forms are obtained, and no chemical means of separating them is known unless other asymmetric substances are used. Living organisms can achieve separation by this method; one of Pasteur's most striking discoveries was that micro-organisms, which contain many asymmetric centres, consume L molecules of tartaric acid but never D molecules in a mixture of both forms. The astonishing fact is that of compounds with asymmetric molecules, living organisms synthesize and use one form exclusively, D or L. Thus, in general, only D sugars and only L amino acids enter into the chemical reactions that living organisms perform.

It is easy to understand that once a system using exclusively one asymmetric form has become established it will be perpetuated, because mirror-image parts cannot take each other's places in any mechanism. The difficulty is to explain how such exclusiveness originated, and a manner in which this problem could be solved in principle has been suggested by George Wald. It is only necessary to suppose that originally organisms synthesized both D and L forms of asymmetric molecules and that such synthesis of mixed forms results in products that are less efficient and stable in the system than pure D or pure L forms. Doty found evidence of this in spirals formed by synthetic peptide chains. It would then have been for physical and chemical reasons that in the course of time, pure D or pure L forms and their methods of synthesis were naturally selected and thereafter persisted.

H. Gaffron has calculated that when chemical evolution had resulted in the synthesis of the necessary organic compounds in the oceans, the soup formed by these compounds could have represented a ten-per-cent solution. This is regarded as a favourable concentration in which organisms could have arisen. If groups of molecules of proteins, nucleic acids, phosphates, and so on, were then surrounded with a semi-permeable membrane or fence composed of other molecules, the result would have been the production of organized isolated systems giving rise to simple cells. Evidence of the origin of cells in the sea is provided by the fact that even today, after thousands of millions of years, the composition of the body fluids, including those of man, is basically similar to that of sea water.

The first cells must have maintained and fed themselves by simply drawing on the 'soup' in which they were bathed. Systems that obtain food by taking it ready-made are called *heterotrophic*. The *DNA* that these primitive cells contained would have enabled them to synthesize more of themselves, to grow, and, by division of the cells into two when they had reached a certain size, to reproduce. Such cells were endowed with what is called life.

This primitive condition can only have been transitory, because, as Darwin foresaw, the earliest heterotrophic organisms would ultimately have exhausted all the supply of essential chemical substances in the soup in which they were bathed. The next step was the evolution in heterotrophic cells of the chemical processes of synthesis by which essential chemical substances could be made from simpler substances in and by the cells themselves. Such synthesis requires the presence of enzymes, which are proteins with the property of accelerating the production of specific compounds. This is the function that the genes in *DNA* perform: one gene determines the production of one enzyme, which catalyses the formation of one intermediate or end-product (p. 87). In some such manner the food-taking heterotrophes eventually became converted into food-making *autotrophes*. This probably took place gradually, gene by gene and enzyme by enzyme, and even today there are organisms that can manufacture some but not all of their requirements.

In the autotrophic stage, the organisms became independent of the supply of ready-made compounds in the soup, and were able to survive when this supply became exhausted. Already at this stage natural selection must have been effective, for those organisms that failed to evolve the necessary enzyme-system before the supply of complex compounds was exhausted must have perished.

The action of ultra-violet rays from the sun, which was probably originally responsible for building up the complex compounds in the soup, must also have been transitory, because when gaseous oxygen first appeared in the atmosphere from the utilization of water and carbon dioxide, some atoms of oxygen would combine to form ozone, which absorbs ultra-violet light, as a result of which little ultra-violet light then reached the surface of the earth. This must have had two consequences. The first was that the enzyme-systems and compounds built up by organisms in their autotrophic stage were protected from the destructive effects of light of short wave-length (ultra-violet) on the delicate chemical bonds that kept them together. The second consequence was that living organisms must have come to depend on a new source of energy, other than ultra-violet light. This was probably light of visible and longer wave-lengths, the energy of which produces photo-chemical effects on coloured substances like compounds of iron or copper, particularly in conjunction with porphyrins.

The next stage in the evolution of autotrophic organisms was the development of *photosynthesis* by means of chlorophyll. This green substance, based on a porphyrin containing magnesium, absorbs the energy of sunlight and provides this energy for chemical synthesis. Along with enzymes that fix carbon from the carbon dioxide in the atmosphere, it builds up carbohydrates (sugars and starches), which are essential raw materials for living matter and for further supplies of energy. Furthermore when an enzyme system containing manganese is present together with chlorophyll, the process of photosynthesis also results in the liberation of free gaseous oxygen in the atmosphere. The onset of this process, which has persisted up to the present day in the life of all green plants, was of enormous importance, because most of the oxygen in the atmosphere is regarded as the product of photosynthesis by green plants (Pl. 341).

The world is so big, the sky so wide, and the atmosphere so high, that it is difficult to realize that the oxygen which it contains could be the product of the life of green plants. As an illustration of the fact that the dimensions of the atmosphere and of a living organism are not incommensurable, it may be remembered that with every second breath that a man takes into his lungs, there passes on the average one molecule that has already passed through the lungs of Newton, or Shakespeare, or Julius Caesar, or anybody distant enough in time for rediffusion of the atmosphere to have taken place, as Harlow Shapley said.

As long as free oxygen was unavailable as a source of energy, life was *anaerobic*, a condition found in many micro-organisms such as bacteria, yeasts, and protozoa today. They obtain their energy from chemical reactions (chemosynthesis) but may actually be killed by exposure to gaseous oxygen.

When free oxygen became available, life could become *aerobic* and obtain energy from that source by oxidation. This new step made possible the evolution of plants and of animals.

The foregoing sketch of the course of evolution from molecules to living organisms in the form of cells is necessarily conjectural in many places, although it accords with a solid and rapidly increasing basis of experimentally verified facts. There is no doubt that as these increase still further, the picture will be corrected, modified, and provided with more detail. Already, nevertheless, one conclusion can be drawn, which is that the conditions necessary for the origin of life on earth were peculiar, transitory, and past. Life with the properties it is known to have is no longer originating from inorganic matter now. Pasteur's disproof of 'spontaneous generation' is endorsed by general principles.

The pageant of evolution on Earth naturally prompts the question whether life exists on other planets. It is of little use to speculate on this subject on grounds of probability, and in view of the distance separating Earth from even the nearest planets, evidence is difficult to obtain. Nevertheless there is some. Dark patches on Mars's surface change colour with the Martian seasons from greenish grey in spring to brownish lilac in autumn. Spectroscopic analysis of the light reflected from these regions, carried out by W. M. Sinton, shows that light of certain wave-lengths is absorbed, which agree with the wave-lengths of infra-red light absorbed by organic molecules. These absorption-bands are not found in light reflected from the lighter areas of Mars's surface. These findings suggest that plants of some kind live on Mars and show seasonal variation. The absence of atmospheric oxygen on Mars makes it impossible for animal life, as known on Earth, to exist on Mars.

THE KINDS OF LIFE

Bacteria

The simplest living cells existing today are bacteria, but for all their simplicity relative to an oak tree or a man, they are equipped with most of the chemical machinery found in higher organisms. Spherical or rod-shaped, they may be as small as one ten thousandth of a millimetre in diameter or as big as six hundredths of a millimetre in length, and may live singly or grouped into chains or clusters. The cell-wall is composed of protein, carbohydrate, and teichoic acid, and the surface may be drawn out into numerous hair-like fimbriae or a small number of whip-like filaments. These filaments, which consist of single fibrils, can move and impart a feeble power of locomotion to the bacteria in the fluid in which they live (Pl. 347, 348).

Inside the cell, the bulk of the contents is composed of so-called cytoplasm containing all the complex chemical compounds whose reactions constitute the processes of replication, growth, utilization of energy, and ultimate breakdown. In the cytoplasm are a small number of bodies containing deoxyribonucleic acid *(DNA)* representing the genes, which in bacteria are not organized into an unitary nucleus. Cell-division does not involve the complicated processes of mitosis, for which reason the bacteria are ascribed to a group called Procaryota. Reproduction, which can be very rapid, is by means of fission and can take place every half hour. This means that thirty minutes is sufficient time for the *DNA* to replicate the substances necessary to construct two cells out of the original one. Simple sexual processes take place, as will be described below (p. 143).

The food-requirements of bacteria vary greatly. Some, like the so-called purple bacteria, are anaerobic and require no atmospheric oxygen. They are *photosynthetic autotrophes*. The pigment they contain enables them to use the energy of sunlight to reduce carbon dioxide and to oxidize substances such as hydrogen sulphide and sulphur by a primitive method of photosynthesis; and they can serve as a possible model of an early stage in evolution representing the transition from the primitive heterotrophic to the autotrophic condition at a time before atmospheric oxygen was available, since they contain a magnesium porphyrin pigment that absorbs light energy, very similar to the chlorophyll of plants. Other bacteria are *chemosynthetic autotrophes* and possess the necessary chemical synthesizing enzyme-systems that enable them to build up their complex compounds from simple inorganic substances such as carbon dioxide and nitrates using atmospheric oxygen for oxidation.

Energy is derived in some soil bacteria *(Thiobacillus thio-oxidans)* from oxidation of sulphur. In another species *(Leptothrix ochracea)* from oxidation of ferrous salts of iron to ferric salts. Another *(Hydrogenomonas)* oxidizes hydrogen to water. Others *(Nitrosomonas)* oxidize atmospheric nitrogen or ammonia to nitrites, and others again *(Nitrobacter)* oxidize nitrites to nitrates. This is a process of fundamental importance because nitrates are an essential food-component of plants, which are unable to fix and make use of atmospheric nitrogen. Leguminous plants have nodules on their roots in which nitrogen-fixing bacteria live. It is for this reason that a crop of leguminous plants in a field is equivalent to a dressing with nitrates.

The ability of bacteria to break down complex chemical compounds into simple substances, especially carbon dioxide, makes them the chief agents in the processes of putrefaction and decay. When a plant or animal dies, complex compounds of carbon would keep the carbon locked up if bacteria did not break them down to carbon dioxide, which is the only form in which carbon can be used by plants.

In addition to this vital role that bacteria perform in maintaining the carbon cycle, they also play a more sinister part because of the toxins which they produce when parasitic and pathogenic. Diphtheria, pneumonia, botulism, tuberculosis, scarlet fever, plague, and cholera, are among the infectious diseases that bacteria cause in man.

The Invasion of Land

334. Life originated in water and emerged onto land as in plants, worms, snails, woodlice, centipedes, insects, spiders, and amphibia like this marsh-frog.

Blue-Green algae

The Procaryota contain another group of organisms besides the bacteria, the so-called 'blue-green algae' or Myxophyta. They consist of single cells or linear colonies in which formed nuclei, mitotic divisions, sexual processes, and whip-like flagella have never been observed; their cell-walls are chemically similar to those of bacteria, and they appear to represent an early branch of organisms on the way to becoming plants which have never got further than the stage of evolution represented by bacteria. Their requirements are simple and some of them can fix atmospheric nitrogen. That they are a primitive group is shown by the fact that the earliest known fossils, 1,700 million years old, belong to this group (p. 54, Pl. 355).

Plants

One of the most important events in the history of the world was the evolution of the green pigment chlorophyll by means of which solar energy is used to build up complex compounds from carbon dioxide, water, and simple salts such as nitrates and phosphates with liberation of oxygen. This mode of nutrition is called *holophytic* and the only organisms that can do this are *plants*, which are the supreme autotrophes (Pl. 341). The process is the same whether they are single cells like green algae or multicellular giants with green leaves, like sequoia trees (Pl. 339).

It is clear therefore that plants are a stage in evolution superior to that of bacteria. They are uniform in their possession of chlorophyll and in the fact that the walls of all plant cells are composed of cellulose, a substance similar to starch. Sexual processes take place and the cells of plants contain *nuclei*, in which the *DNA* takes the form of linear strings of genes, chromosomes, which are accurately replicated and equally divided between daughter cells when cell division occurs by mitosis.

Mitosis is the characteristic method of division of the nucleus in all plants (and animals), which for this reason are distinguished from Procaryota and included in the group called Eucaryota (see chapter III p. 78).

The holophytic method of nutrition has directly influenced the pattern of evolution of the entire vegetable kingdom. The raw materials out of which they build up living matter are to be found everywhere in the sea and on the land, and the source from which they derive their energy penetrates wherever light shines from the sun. Plants thus live in the midst of their requirements and do not need to go in search of them. The result is that they have evolved into organisms that are stationary and rooted to one place, all higher plants spreading green leaves into the air (which contains carbon dioxide) and sending roots into the soil (which contains a solution of salts). Some plants are parasitic on others, on which they are dependent for part, like mistletoe, or all of their food supplies, like broom-rape, which has gone so far as to lose all its chlorophyll and is completely degenerate (Pl. 135, 136).

A few plants, such as Venus's fly trap, sun-dew, and pitcher-plants have evolved the curious adaptation of catching insects, which they digest with enzymes and absorb (Pl. 407, 409).

Fungi

Yeasts, moulds, and mushrooms have usually been included in the plant kingdom, under the name *Fungi*, but they show a number of features which in the view of many scientists entitle them to rank as a group on their own. Whether they are unicellular like yeast cells or multicellular like mushrooms, fungi possess no chlorophyll, cannot perform photosynthesis, and are dependent for some at least of their food supplies on complex chemical compounds produced as a result of the life or decomposition of other organisms. This mode of nutrition is known as saprophytic and classes the fungi among the secondary heterotrophes. Many fungi are parasitic, such as *Tinia* which penetrates into the skin in man and causes the condition known as athlete's foot. Fungi undergo sexual processes which differ considerably from those of other organisms (p. 143, Pl. 372). The multicellular fungi develop from a network of fine threads called a *mycelium* made up of a number of *hyphae* which ramify in timber or underground in the soil and send up the visible part of the fungus as toadstools or mushrooms (Pl. 356).

Among the moulds are the yeasts, which perform chemical reactions by fermentation, the results of which are familiar, for they split sugar into carbon dioxide and ethyl alcohol. Different species of yeasts are responsible for the different flavours of fermented liquors and different species of mould for different cheeses. Some moulds produce substances that are toxic to bacteria and these include antibiotics such as penicillin, chloromycetin, and aureomycin.

Lichens

Lichens are composite organisms consisting of a particular species of fungus living in intimate association with a particular species of alga. The two components can be dissociated and cultivated separately, though the alga then fares better than the fungus. The unicellular algae, in large numbers in the lichen, being blue-green algae or green algae, perform nitrogen-fixation and or photosynthesis from nitrogen and carbon dioxide in the air, and draw water and salts from the fungus in which they are embedded. The fungus provides the water and salts from the substratum and benefits from the products of the algae. Such an association of two different species of organisms that benefits both is called *symbiosis* and presents a case of mutual adaptation. In the case of lichens it enables both partners to live together in environments where for reasons of desiccation or excessive exposure to sunlight neither could live separately, such as bare rocks that afford no sustenance to any other forms of life (Pl. 357, 358). At the present day it is probable that the chief form of life in Antarctica is represented by lichens. In some environments, however, the balance of

335

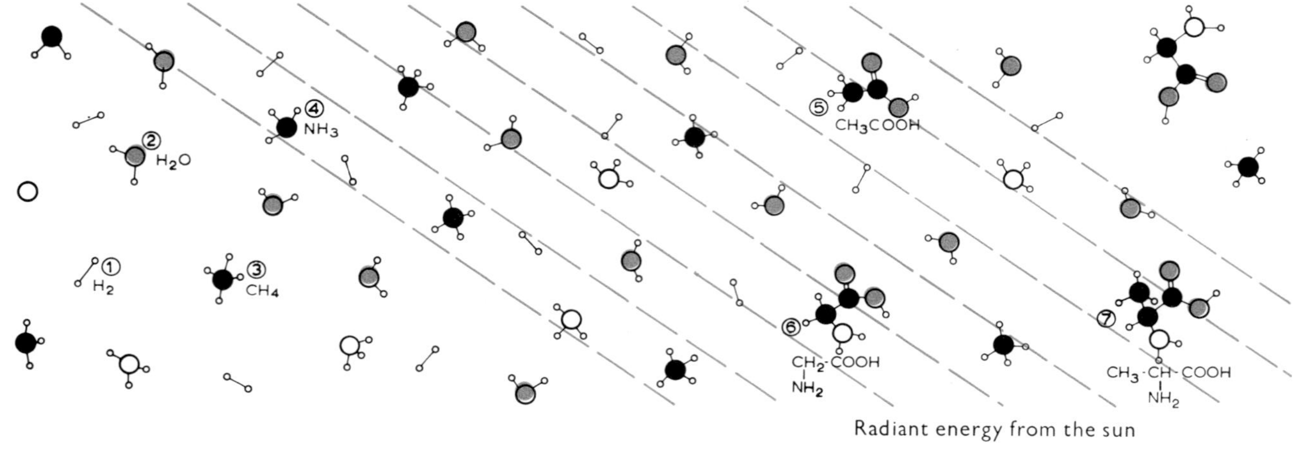

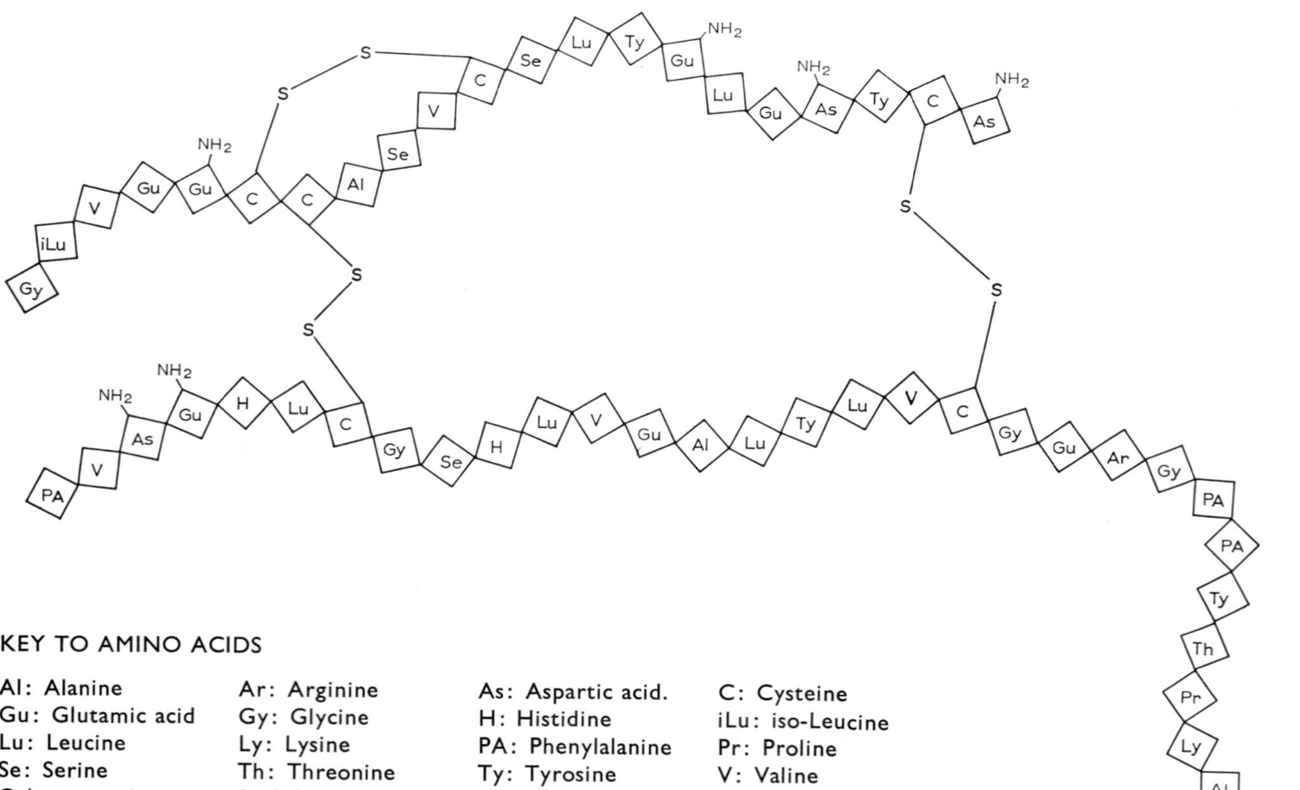

336

335. Chemical formulae of simple compounds important in the evolution of life: (1), hydrogen, H_2; (2), water, H_2O; (3), methane, CH_4; (4), ammonia, NH_3. A mixture of these substances subjected to electrical discharges or ultra-violet light produces more complex molecules, including (5), acetic acid, CH_3COOH, and amino acids such as (6), glycine, $CH_2(NH_2)COOH$, and (7), alanine $CH_3CH(NH_2)COOH$. Amino acids can become aggregated to proteins; **336,** insulin, a small protein molecule, the first to have the order of amino acids completely established, by F. Sanger; **338,** part of a stretched (*right*), and contracted (*left*), protein fibre such as hair or wool, showing how aminoacids are joined into long chains which can fold in different ways. Alanine, **335** (7) contains an asymmetric carbon atom; **337,** crystals of D and L forms of sodium ammonium tartrate, show an effect due to asymmetric carbon atoms.

advantage in the association is tilted markedly against the alga which the fungus may even destroy and feed on saprophytically. The association between the two species is then no longer symbiosis but parasitism. The alga does not seem to be modified by its association with the fungus, but the habit of growth of the fungus appears to be markedly altered as a result of the presence of the alga, in a manner analogous to that by which a plum tree is led to produce a gall when a gall-wasp lays its eggs in its tissues.

Animals

At an early stage one group of organisms solved the problem of food-supply by actively taking it ready-made from living plants. Having discarded such enzyme-systems as they previously possessed, they were and are unable themselves to perform the necessary synthesis of complex compounds from simple substances, and require proteins, carbohydrates, and fats in order to live. This method of nutrition is called *holozoic* and the organisms that use it are animals; whether unicellular like an amoeba or multicellular like man, they are identical in respect of requiring food that is available to them only in the bodies of other living organisms. Animals are the supreme secondary heterotrophes. Some animals eat other animals, but ultimately the food-chain of all animals is traceable back to plants. With few exceptions animals are aerobic and breathe oxygen, which is used to produce energy. It follows that animals could not have come into existence before plants had provided free oxygen as a result of photosynthesis, and had also provided their living bodies for animals to eat. It also follows that the entire animal kingdom is dependent on the vegetable kingdom for its continued existence (Pl. 342).

The method of nutrition practised by animals has had a profound effect on the evolution of the animal kingdom. Since the essential constituents of their food, proteins, carbohydrates, and fats, are only to be found in the bodies of other living organisms, and are not universally distributed in water or air like carbon dioxide and simple nitrates and phosphates, animals have to take steps to obtain their food and even to go hunting in search of it. Except for sessile animals and degenerate parasitic animals, typical animals must have powers of locomotion in order to live. Very small animals move by means of whip-like flagella or hair-like cilia, or by the flow of protoplasm known as amoeboid movement, characteristic of amoebae and other one-celled animals or Protozoa (Pl. 410, 411). Larger animals move by mechanical power of muscular contraction, and this ultimately entails skeletal structures that provide fixed points from which the muscles contract and nerves that co-ordinate the contractions. Movement is most efficient when the body is elongated and symmetrical, the same end always pointing forwards. A result of this adaptation is the development and concentration at the end that moves first, the front end, of the sense organs receptive to light, touch, taste, smell, balance, and hearing, and of the nerve centre that co-ordinates the impulses received from these sense organs, in other words, the brain. The adaptive value of sense organs and brain at the front end of animals enabling them to find food and mates and to recognize danger, resulted in the specialization of that end into a head.

Another result of the holozoic method of nutrition is the necessity for chemical treatment of the captured food. The proteins, carbohydrates, and fats that an animal devours are not in a condition in which they can be incorporated into the animal's own living substance, because each species builds up its own specific substances. The animal's food has to be chemically broken down or digested, into simpler compounds: proteins into amino acids, carbohydrates into soluble sugars, fats into

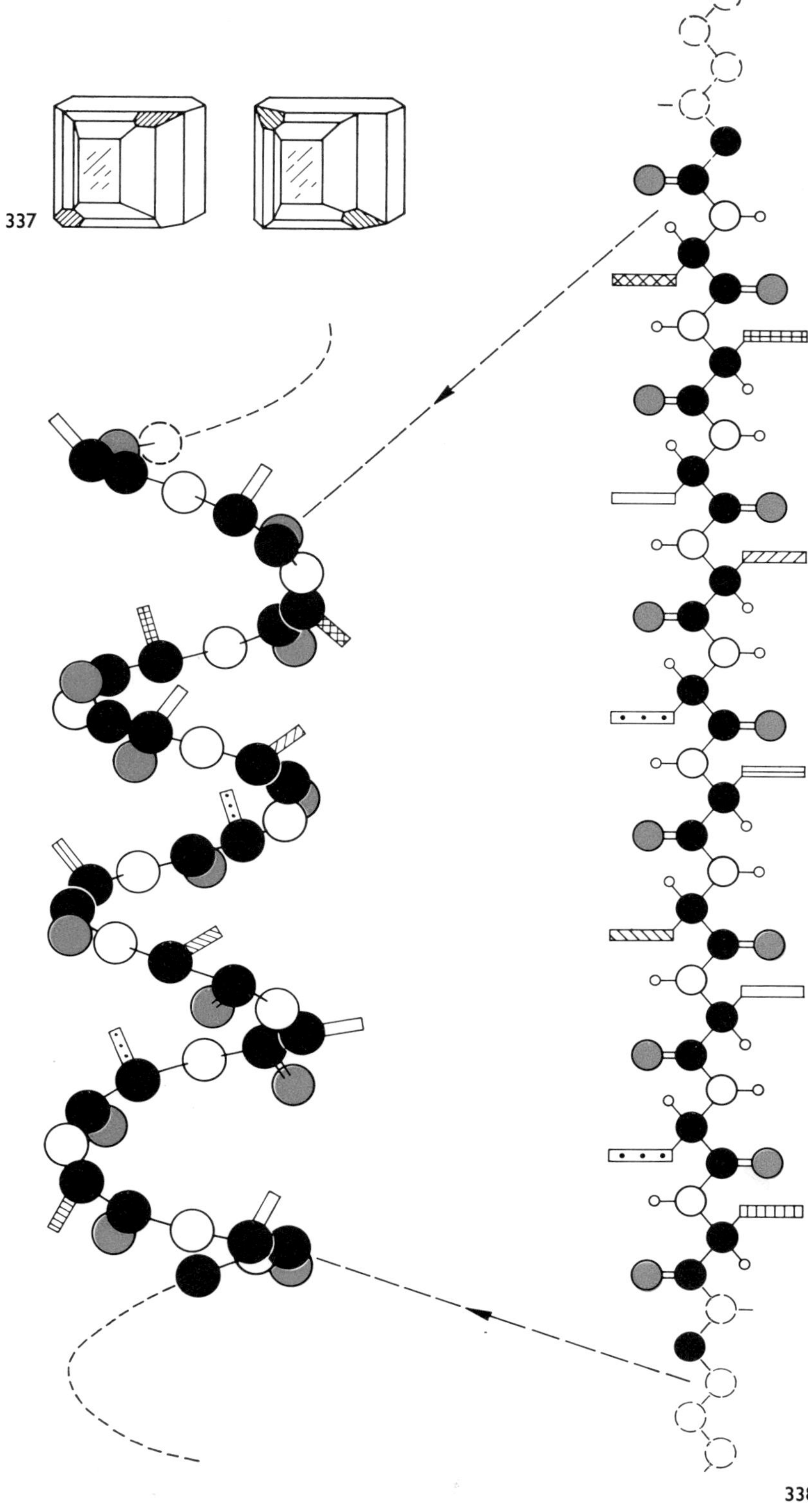

glycerol and fatty acids. This digestion takes place in closed chambers. Amoebae and other unicellular animals ingest their food anywhere on the surface of their bodies and enclose it in a vacuole in which digestion takes place. Higher animals have a special place where food is taken into the body, the mouth, leading into an alimentary canal where glands secrete enzymes that digest the food, which is then diffused in a soluble state into the body fluids or blood stream and so transported all over the body. It may therefore be said that animals are mobile test-tubes.

Some animals that live in water have degenerated and have adopted sedentary or sessile habits, waiting for food materials to be wafted to them in currents of water propelled by movement of cilia, as in sponges and ascidians. Such animals in the adult stage have lost their bilateral symmetry, power of locomotion, and special sense organs. Still more degenerate animals, such as tape-worms, live as parasites inside other animals from which they derive all their nourishment (Pl. 140). Some parasites (e.g. *Sacculina)* have lost all their special structures and are simply absorbent sacs producing germ-cells. Their nature is discernible only from their development.

Viruses

Viruses are very minute particles sometimes as small as 1/100,000th of a millimetre in diameter, which can multiply only within the living cells of susceptible hosts which they parasitize. Examples are the viruses of smallpox, measles, influenza, and poliomyelitis in man, distemper in dogs, foot-and-mouth disease in cattle, psittacosis in birds, mosaic disease of tobacco, and so-called bacteriophages of bacteria (Pl. 359-367).

Viruses consist of little more than particles of protein combined with nucleic acid. These nucleoproteins, like genes, induce the formation of molecules similar to themselves out of the materials of the host cells even if the host cells have never produced those molecules before. This shows the replicating power of the nucleic acids and suggests that viruses are little more than genes. In the case of some plant viruses it has been shown that the virus contains only one kind of protein. Viruses vary by mutation (which is why the nature of influenza changes), and are acted upon by natural selection resulting in adaptation. Viruses which kill their hosts are imperfectly adapted; those which do not are well adapted.

There is no information about the time when viruses first appeared, but monkeys and men must have got their herpes viruses from their common ancestor, 40 million years ago, as Sir Macfarlane Burnet showed.

The nature of viruses presents a problem. The definition of living organisms is that they take into themselves food-substances which they build up into their own bodies with the result that they grow and reproduce their like by division. Viruses on the other hand cannot synthesize their own substance out of anything but the contents of the living cells of the bacteria, plants, or animals that they parasitize, and their multiplication is not the result of division but of the multiple replication of their substance for which the parasitized host-cell is forced to provide the material.

For these reasons it is difficult to regard viruses as survivors from the pre-cellular stage of evolution or as examples of the transitional stage from non-living to living matter. More probably they should be regarded as parasites descended from what were originally portions of the cells of other organisms, bacteria, plants or animals, perhaps a few molecules of *DNA*, or genes, that have acquired partially separate existence. This view receives strong support from the fact discovered by J. Lederberg that in some bacteriophages the *DNA* is identical with part of that of the bacterium that it parasitizes and can take its place.

THE EVOLUTION OF SEX

Syngamy and meiosis

In the simplest organisms, consisting of a single cell, fusion between two individuals can take place, especially when environmental conditions become adverse. This process, which is a form of mutual ingestion, increases vigour and confers survival value. It is really nothing other than fertilization. The two cells fuse together, and their two nuclei combine into one. By this means the hereditary units in the nuclei, the genes of the two original individuals, are pooled. This process, known as *syngamy*, is the basis of sex, regardless of whether the individuals that fuse are similar or different in structure.

Subsequently the fused individual reproduces by simple fission of the body into two. The descendants will eventually fuse with the bodies of others and then reproduce by fission again.

Since all eucaryote organisms possess a definite quantity of DNA, which means a definite number of chromosomes and of genes, the fusion of two individuals immediately doubles that number. Before fusion, each individual possessed the *haploid* number of chromosomes, designated by the symbol n. After fusion the combined individual, known as a *zygote* has the *diploid* number of chromosomes, or $2n$. This process of doubling is then reversed by the reduction division or *meiosis* (Pl. 236) which is a delayed type of mitosis (Pl. 237-245) in which the chromosomes divide once but the cell divides twice, so that each of the four granddaughter cells contains the haploid number of n chromosomes. These are germ-cells or gametes that can then fuse with other cells, thereby bringing about syngamy.

The fundamental feature of meiosis is that the chromosomes pair up, one partner of each pair having been derived from one of the two original individuals that fused. Each chromosome then divides so that there are four chromosome strands lying coiled round each other. It is at this stage that breakages in the strands take place, and the free end of one strand becomes attached to the free end of another strand. In other words, the strands 'cross over', and this is the physical basis of genetic 'crossing over' of groups of genes. The centromeres of the two original chromosomes remain undivided and repel one another, pulling apart the pairs of daughter chromosome-strands but because of the crossing-over of strands they are interlocked, the interlocking forming what is called a *chiasma*. The result is that the two pairs of daughter chromosomes are not completely parted until the chiasma is unravelled. The centromeres to which each pair of daughter chromosome-strands is attached then divide, spring apart, and separate the daughter chromosome-strands from each other (Pl. 246, 247).

The result of meiosis is not only that the number of chromosomes in the cell is reduced from the diploid to the haploid number, but also that the products of each pair of chromosomes go into different daughter cells. In other words, the chromosomes of each pair undergo *segregation*, and this is why genes undergo segregation (p. 74). The behaviour of the chromosomes during meiosis is the physical basis of the machinery of Mendelian genetics. The evolution of meiosis was a step of fundamental importance because it resulted in the segregation, exchange, and recombination of genes, and this in consequence made possible an enormous increase in the variability of organisms. It is the explanation of the more rapid and more extensive evolution that has taken place among organisms that possess the sexual mechanism of syngamy and meiosis than among those (Procaryota) that do not. The evolution of syngamy and the meiotic process was not only the production of an important evolutionary mechanism, but of a mechanism which, as C. D. Darlington showed, itself evolved into more efficient genetic systems. For instance, the independent assortment of pairs of chromosomes (p. 78), diploidy (p. 79), crossing-over (p. 79), and polyploidy (p. 120) increase variability which is an advantage to organisms

340

The largest Plant and land Animal

339. *Sequoia gigantea*, the largest living plant, may exceed 300 feet in height. As long as a tree is alive, the apex of its stem, or growing point, produces new tissues, stem and leaves, and the trunk and branches grow in thickness. The factors limiting the size to which trees can grow relate to the necessity for raising water from the roots to the uppermost tip of the stem, and the stability of the structure. **340.** *Loxodonta africana*, African elephant, the largest living land animal. Higher animals do not grow throughout life but cease when they have reached the adult stage. The weight of the body is proportional to its volume, or the cube of its length, but the strength of the limbs that have to bear this weight is proportional to their cross-sectional area, or the square of the body's length. The elephant is near the largest size mechanically possible for a land animal. Whales are larger, but their weight is supported by the water.

Plant and Animal Methods of Feeding

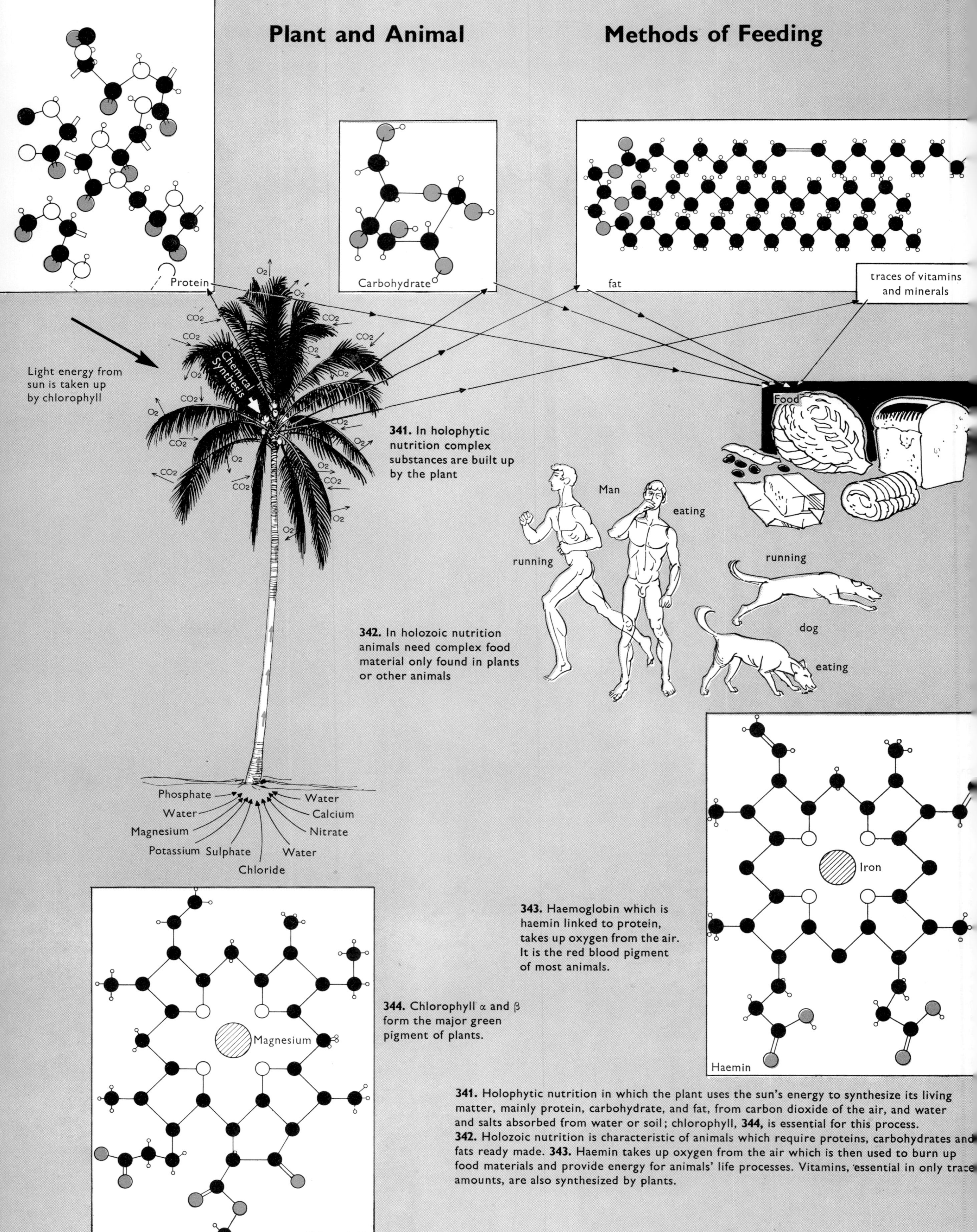

341. In holophytic nutrition complex substances are built up by the plant

342. In holozoic nutrition animals need complex food material only found in plants or other animals

343. Haemoglobin which is haemin linked to protein, takes up oxygen from the air. It is the red blood pigment of most animals.

344. Chlorophyll α and β form the major green pigment of plants.

341. Holophytic nutrition in which the plant uses the sun's energy to synthesize its living matter, mainly protein, carbohydrate, and fat, from carbon dioxide of the air, and water and salts absorbed from water or soil; chlorophyll, **344,** is essential for this process. **342.** Holozoic nutrition is characteristic of animals which require proteins, carbohydrates and fats ready made. **343.** Haemin takes up oxygen from the air which is then used to burn up food materials and provide energy for animals' life processes. Vitamins, essential in only trace amounts, are also synthesized by plants.

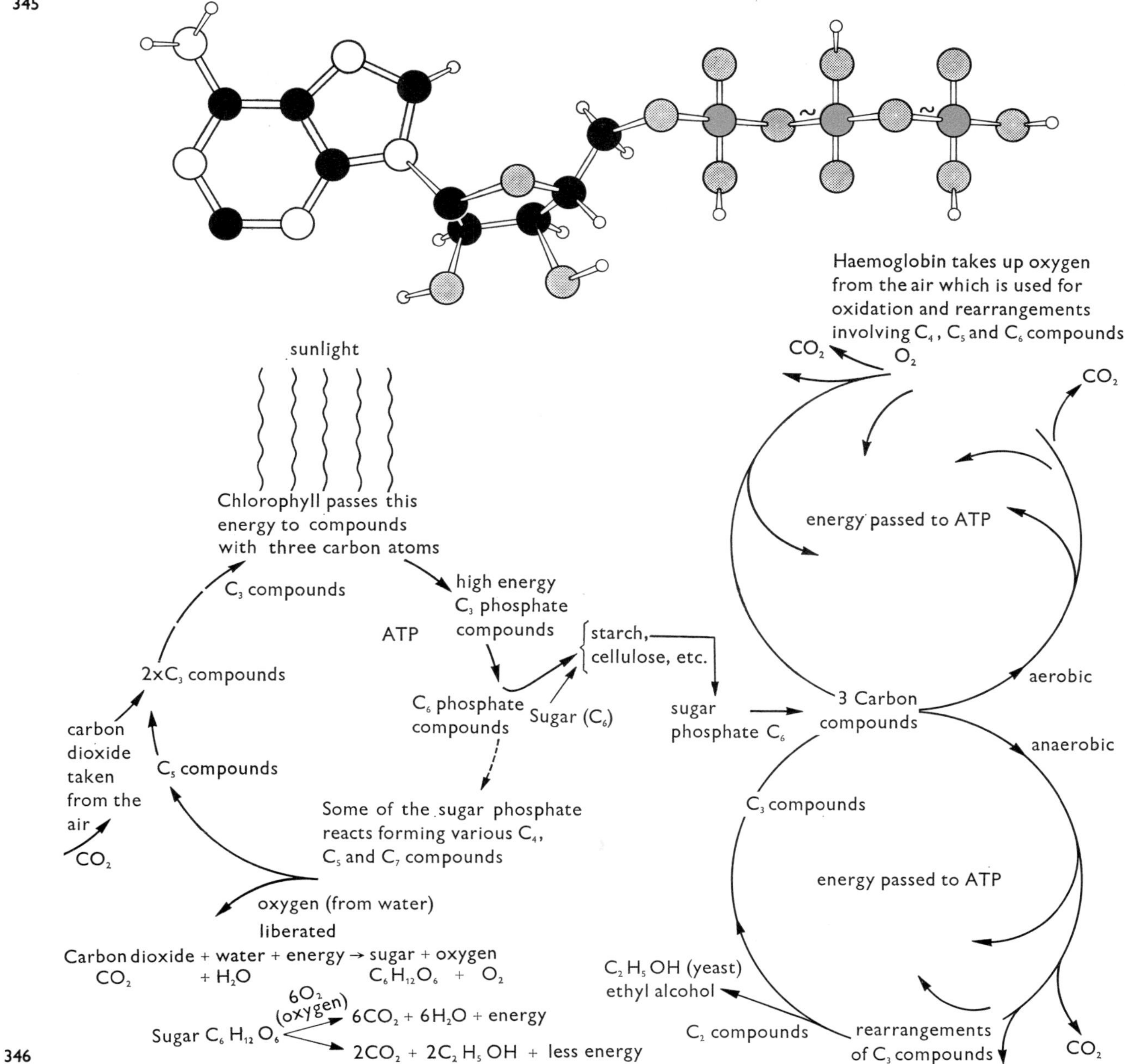

The Synthesis and Utilization of Carbohydrate

345. Adenosine triphosphate, ATP, the widely distributed compound that supplies energy for synthesis of chemical compounds, contraction of muscle, electric discharges and the production of light. When a bond marked ~ is broken, with the freeing of a phosphate group, approximately 20 calories of energy are liberated from each gram of ATP. **346.** Diagram of the synthesis of carbohydrate in plants and the breakdown of carbohydrate that can occur in all living matter. Anaerobic breakdown involves the lower cycle only, in yeasts, for example, breakdown stops at the two-carbon alcohol. Aerobic breakdown also involves the upper cycle where oxygen is brought in. Energy produced as a result of these reactions is passed to ATP from whence it is used for living processes or stored in starch or fat. Other chemical structures are illustrated in **261** (nucleotide bases) and **376** (sex hormones).

when conditions change. The haploid state and reduction of crossing-over decrease variability, which is an advantage when an organism is well-adapted to an equable environment. Translocation and inversions of portions of chromosomes enable genes with complementary effects to be collected and kept together, as in the case of sex-chromosomes which determine sex (p. 83), or in other adaptations requiring the combined presence of many genes as in the case of mimicry (p. 93).

Even in procaryote organisms such as bacteria, primitive types of sexual processes take place. Two bacteria can come into contact, and some of the DNA from one of them, amounting perhaps to a quarter of a chromosome, passes over into the other, which then becomes a zygote. This kind of partial and irregular syngamy is possible in these organisms because the differentiation of genes has not proceeded very far, a conclusion supported by the fact that bacteria do not possess the meticulously accurate mechanism of cell-division by mitosis that is essential in organisms whose genes are differentiated from one another and control functions that all daughter-cells must possess equally if they are to survive. The conditions in bacteria nevertheless show how fundamental a process syngamy or sex is (Pl. 369).

In the fungi peculiar processes occur which differ so markedly from those found in plants and animals that they have been called parasexual. Different mycelia (p. 137) can exchange nuclei, but instead of the invading nucleus fusing with the resident nucleus in each cell, they remain separate. The invading nucleus divides separately and one of the resulting nuclei invades a neighbouring cell of the mycelium, where it again remains separate from the resident nucleus of that cell. This process continues until every cell of the mycelium contains two haploid nuclei. Only when the reproductive cells or spores are about to be formed do the nuclei fuse in each cell, which then undergoes meiosis. This curious system of having in each cell two nuclei which may come from different mycelia, confers the advantages of the heterozygous condition although obtained by a method quite different from the fertilization of eggs by sperms as found in plants and animals (Pl. 372).

Paradoxical as it may seem, at early stages in the evolution of sex there were no separate sexes, for all individuals were identical, as they still are in some unicellular organisms. The origin of difference between the sexes was the result of a variation whereby one type of fusing cell, germ-cell or gamete retained its power of locomotion by means of a whip-like flagellum and became a *sperm*, while the other type accumulated food-products, usually yolk, in its body, which grew larger in consequence and lost its power of locomotion, thus becoming the *egg*. This division of function, in which the locomotion of the sperm enabling it to swim towards and fuse with (fertilize) the egg, was combined with the capacity of the egg to provide a store of food, conferred survival value on the new fused individual (fertilized egg or *zygote)* and enabled it to start on its embryonic development, a period of construction during which it is unable to feed itself (Pl. 373, 380).

All subsequent evolution of differences between the sexes in plants and animals is based on this fundamental differentiation between sperm-producers or *males*, and egg-producers or *females*. It involves the differentiation between the organs that produce sperms (called antheridia in plants, testes in animals) and those that produce eggs (called archegonia in plants, ovaries in animals). In flowering plants, in which the sperms and eggs are incorporated inside other cells called spores (p. 158), the evolution of sex has resulted in the differentiation between male stamens that produce microspores or pollen, and female carpels that produce ovules containing

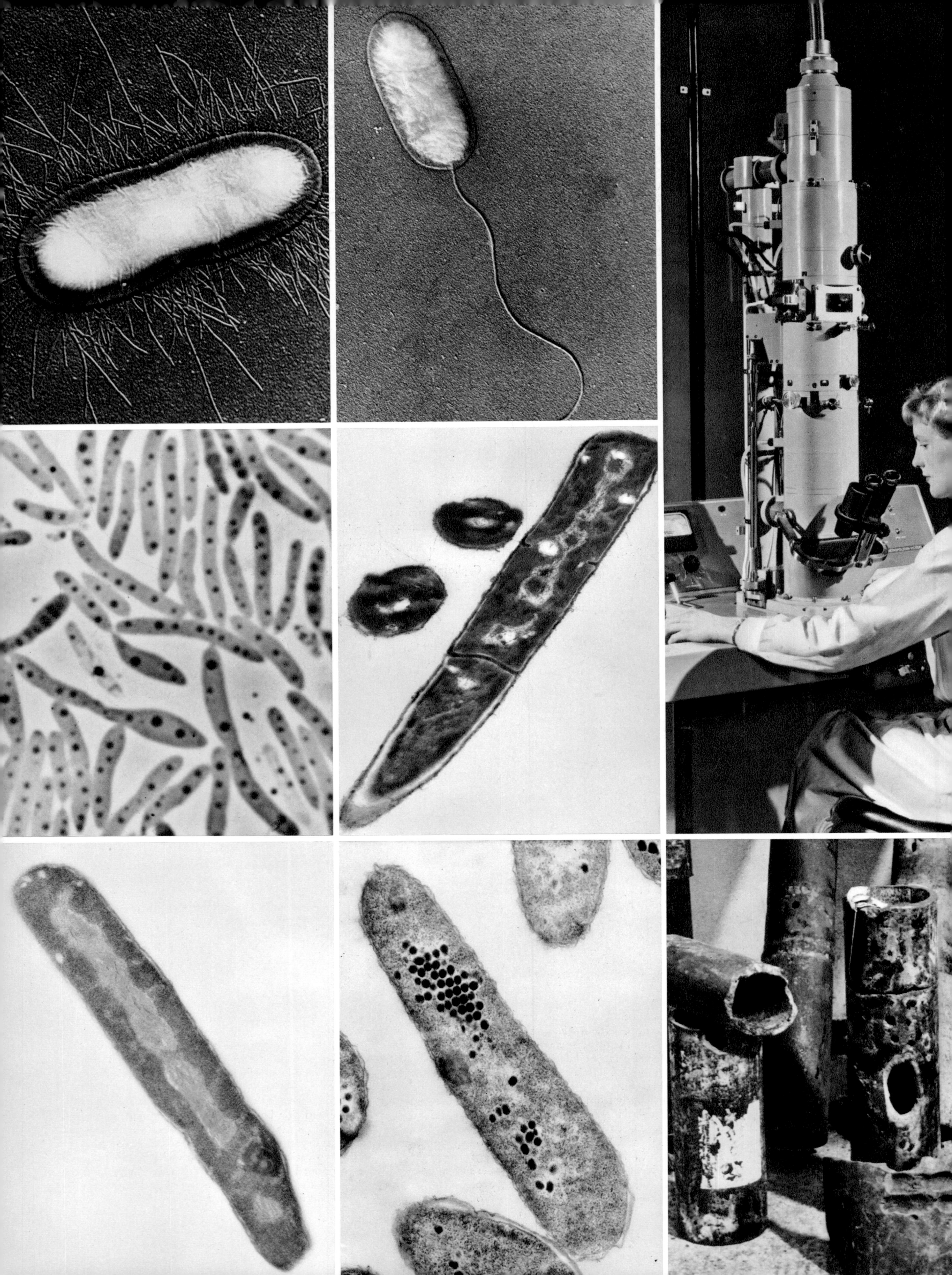

355

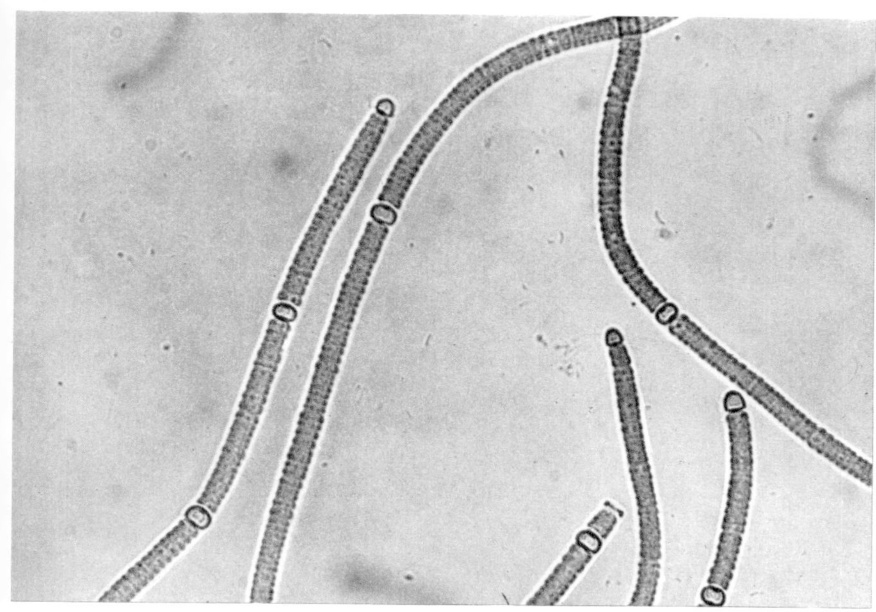

356

Forms of Life. Bacteria Blue-green Algae and Fungi

347. The dysentery bacillus *Shigella flexneri* about to undergo fission, photographed by electron microscope. The dense central mass is the protoplasm, shrunk from the cell-wall by drying, filaments project (x 30 000). **348.** *Pseudomonas pyocyanea* a bacillus capable of movement by means of its long rotating filament (x 28 000). **349.** Live bacilli of *Klebsiella aerogenes* photographed by phase-contrast light microscope showing contained storage granules (x 30 000). **350.** Very thin section of *Bacillus cereus* showing one partition of the cell-body complete and another in process of formation, photographed by electron microscope (x 30 000). **352.** Thin section of *Bacterium coli* photographed by electron microscope, showing the nuclear material not organised into an unitary nucleus (x 35 000). **353.** *Bacterium coli* thirty minutes after infection by bacteriophage virus seen as hexagonal dark bodies (x 40 000). **354.** Mine-machinery belting destroyed by bacteria. **351.** An electron microscope. The tall cylinder is the electron gun down which the beam of electrons is shot from the cathode at the top and controlled by an electro-magnetic condenser lens. Magnifications of one million diameters can be achieved. Photographs by J. P. Duguid, G. B. Chapman and J. Hillier, and E. Kellenberger.

355. Blue-green alga, a primitive form which, like bacteria, lacks organised nuclei. **356.** Mushrooms, fungi feeding saprophytically on decaying matter. **357.** The lichen *Pettigera canina* (dog moss), a composite organism consisting of a fungus with unicellular green algae included between its hyphae, shown in **358,** a magnified cross-section. The association between the two species may take the form of symbiosis which benefits both and enables them to live where either alone could not, or of parasitism to the advantage of the fungus at the expense of the alga.

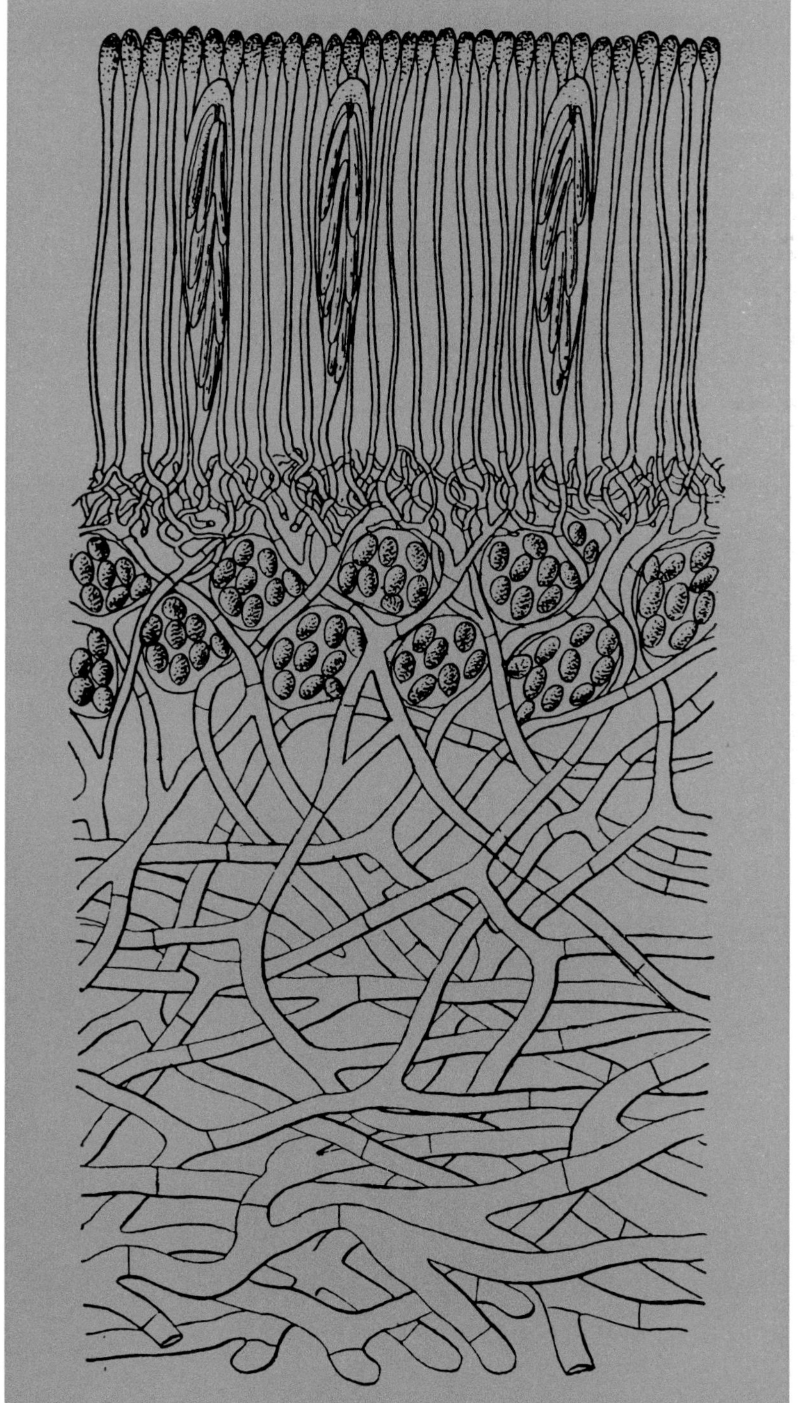

357

358

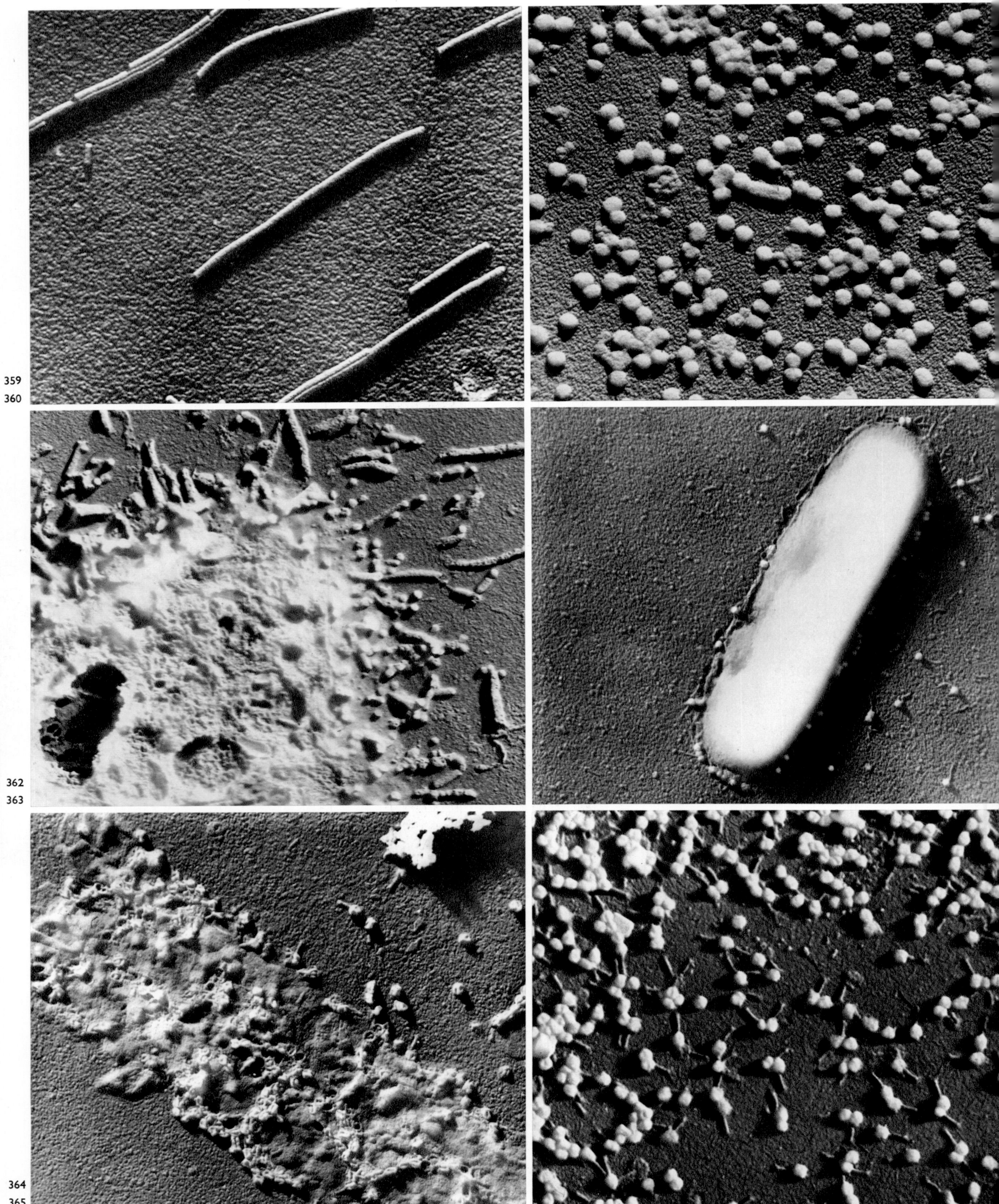
359
360
362
363
364
365

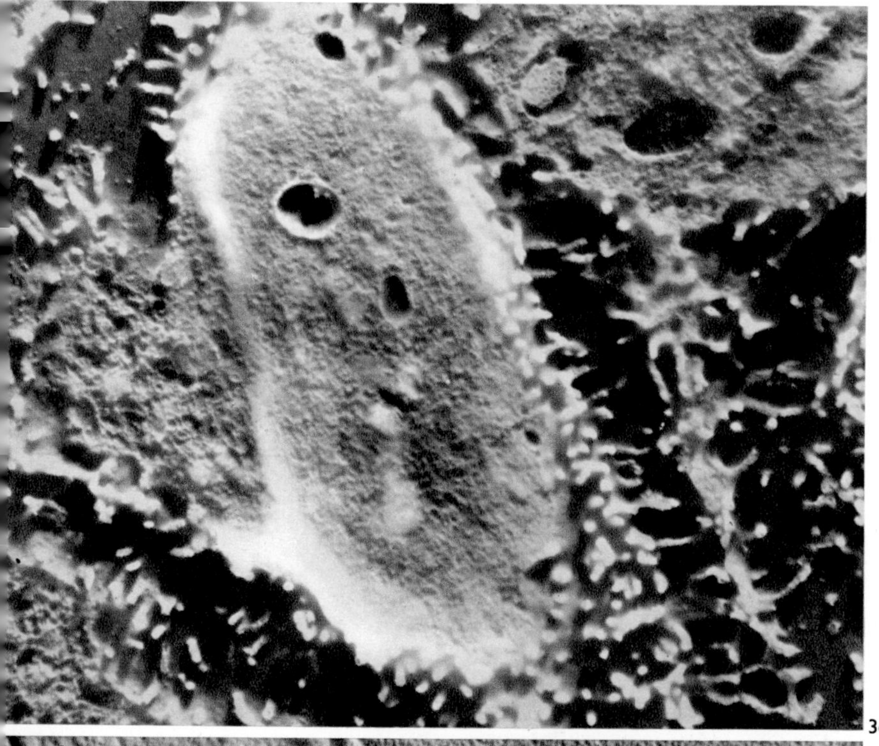

361

Electron Microscope Photographs of Viruses

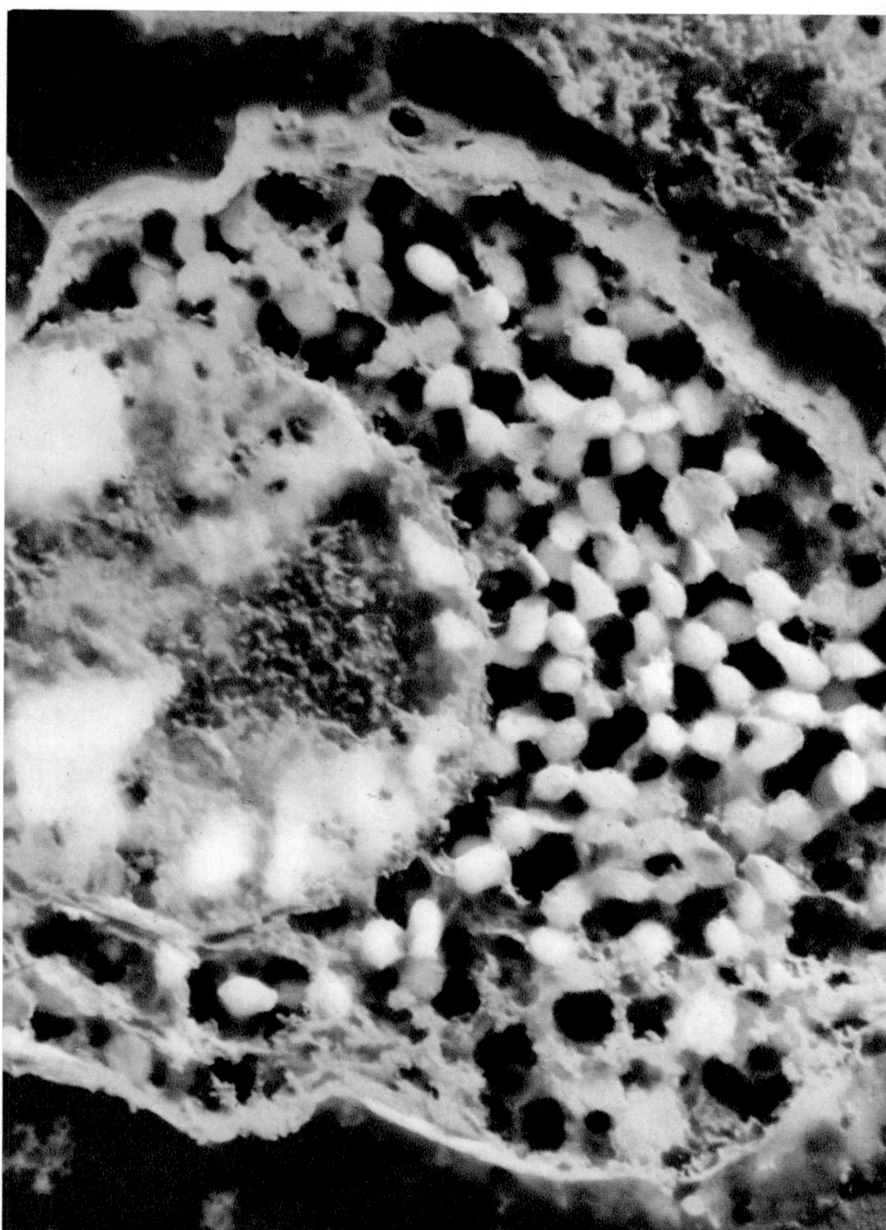

368

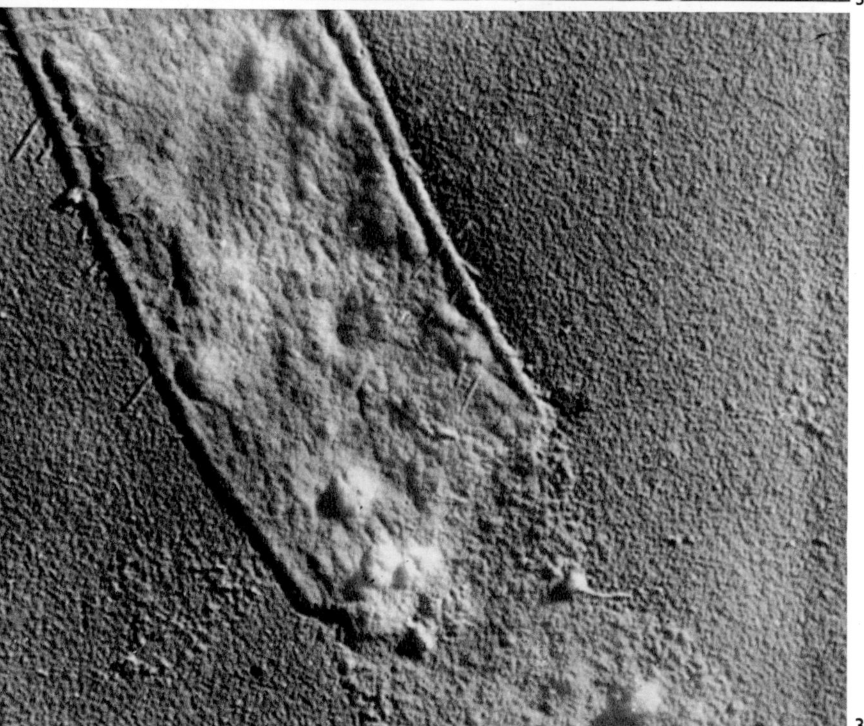

364

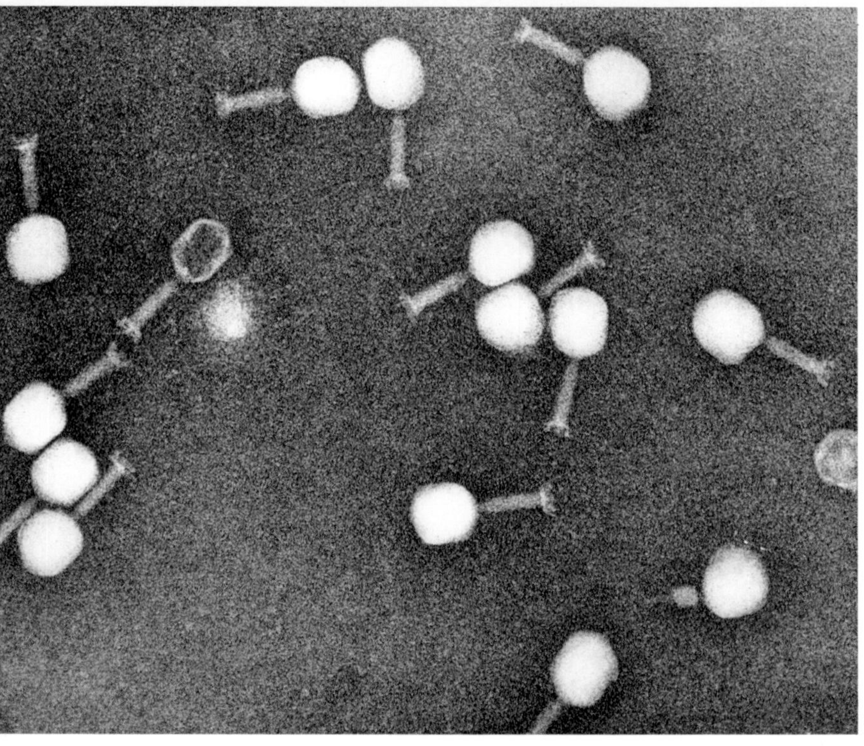

367

Viruses are the smallest organised systems known, and their small size enables them to invade the cells of bacteria, plants, and animals. A virus can defeat a man. **359.** Rods of tobacco mosaic virus (x 85 000). **360.** Spherical particles of influenza virus (x 37 500). **361.** Influenza virus particles developing from the borders of cells of the lung of a mouse (x 11 000). **362.** Edge of a cell infected with influenza virus showing spherical and rod shaped forms (x 17 000). **368.** Cell in which the entire cytoplasm has been replaced by a net of vaccinia virus particles; the nucleus of the defunct cell is at the left centre (x 24 500). **363.** Bacterium surrounded by bacteriophage virus particles attacking its surface (x 27 000). **364.** *Bacterium coli* cell disintegrating after infection by bacteriophage virus (x 43 000). **365.** Bacteriophage particles developing in protoplasmic debris of a *Bacterium coli* cell (x 39 000). **366.** 'Tadpole' stage of bacteriophage attacking *Bacterium coli* (x 54 000). **367.** Tadpole stage under high magnification showing the body containing DNA and the hollow tube through which the contents of the virus are injected into a bacterium (x 90 000). Photographs by R. W. G Wyckoff and E. Kellenberger.

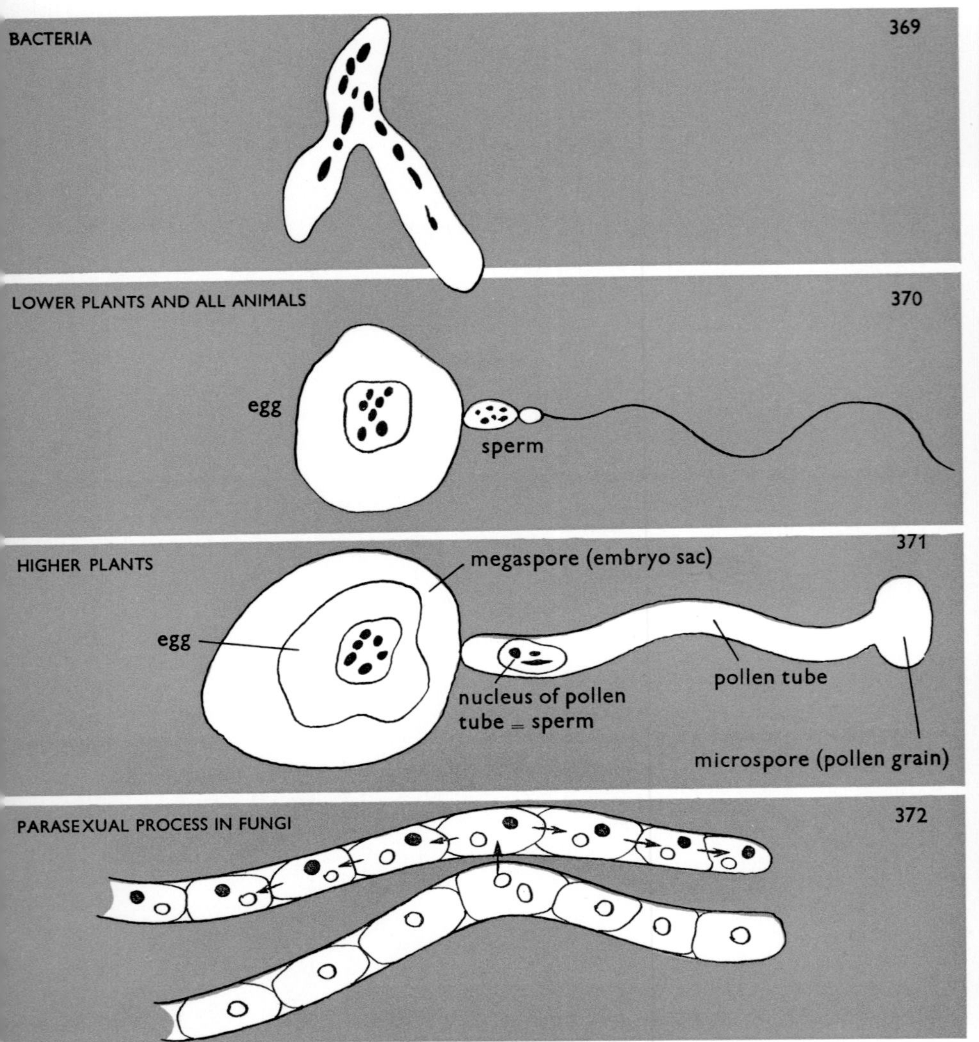

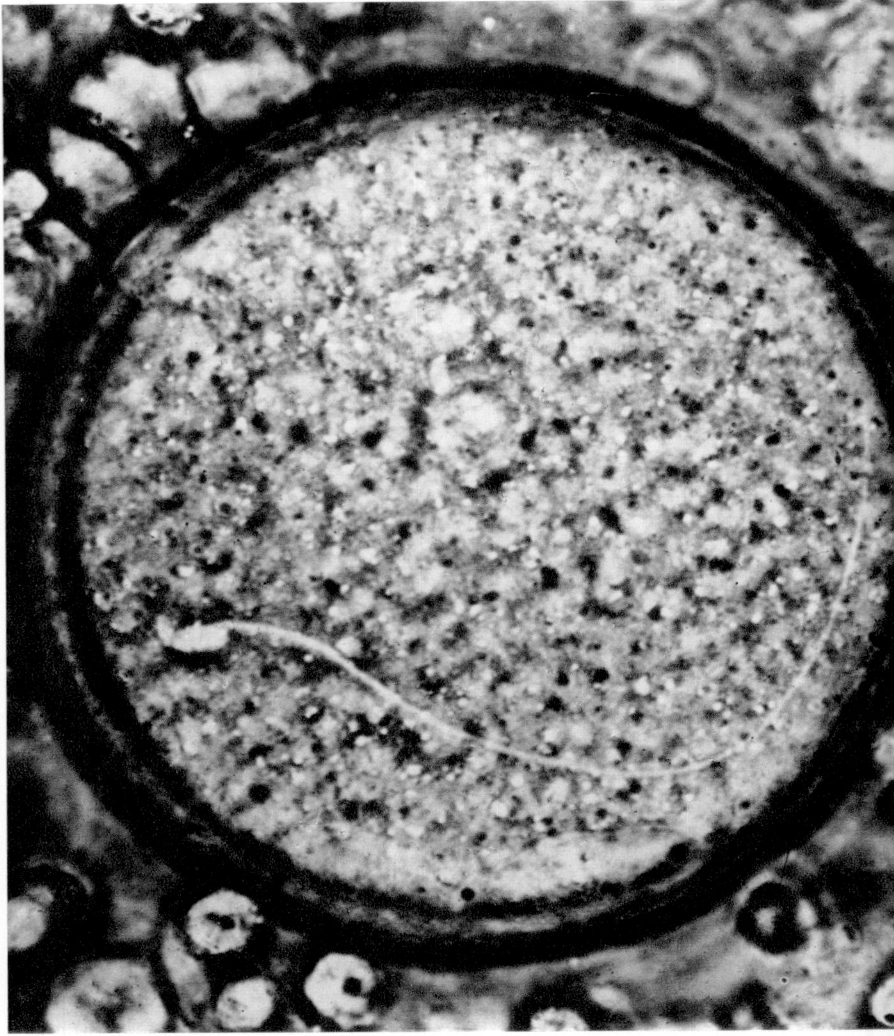

373

the megaspores or embryo-sacs (Pl. 371, 379). It involves the differentiation between the ducts in animals that evacuate the sperms *(vasa deferentia)* and the eggs *(oviducts)*. It is also responsible for the difference in behaviour between males and females, leading to the complex courtship actions that result in the fertilization of eggs by sperms.

There are environments and conditions of life in which the fusion of gametes produced by different individuals may be improbable. Examples are a number of animals that have adopted a sessile mode of life, and animals that live as internal parasites inside other animals, where the chance of finding another individual of the same species may be small. In these cases it is common to find that one and the same individual possesses both male and female reproductive organs and is hermaphrodite and self-impregnating. The majority of flowering plants are hermaphrodite but not self-pollinating. As seen in the adaptations to cross-pollination (pp. 27, 104), self-pollination or self-fertilization whereby no recombination of genes can occur, is avoided if possible.

Sexual and asexual reproduction

Reproduction in all organisms is always the result of fission. It may be the division of one cell into two as in unicellular organisms, or the division of the whole body of a multicellular organism into two, as happens when a plant reproduces by offsets or 'suckers' or a worm divides into two; or it may be a very unequal division, the products of which are on the one hand an egg or a sperm, and on the other the remainder of the body of the plant or animal (Pl. 374).

The sexual process always involves syngamy or fertilization, and its effect is the opposite of reproduction because it results in the fusion of two cells into one. The expression 'sexual reproduction' therefore requires explanation. In the majority of multicellular organisms, the germ-cells do not develop any further unless fertilization takes place. The pollen-grain or the sperm therefore performs two functions: one is to impart to the ovule or the egg the stimulus that starts development; the other is to contribute a set of genes to the zygote. The act of reproduction takes place when the germ-cells are freed from the parent; it is sexual reproduction because the germ-cells have to fertilize or be fertilized. All types of reproduction that do not result directly from an act of fertilization, fusion, or syngamy, are by contrast known as asexual reproduction.

Asexual reproduction can only result in genetically identical offspring, and is frequently an adaptation to rapid increase in numbers in a favourable environment (p. 97). In plants it is very common and takes place by means of spores, single cells that can develop into plants without fertilization and by layers and suckers. It can also be brought about artificially by cuttings. In some animals asexual reproduction takes the form of the division of the body into two, and this even happens in man when identical twins are born, for they are the result of the division of an embryo formed from a single fertilized egg.

From the point of view of evolution, the importance of the difference between sexual and asexual reproduction lies in the fact that in the former the characters of the offspring have to be developed afresh in each generation as a result of the reaction between the genes contained in the fertilized egg and the factors of the environment (p. 88). It is the necessity of having to pass through the code of genes that prevents environmental modification of the body of the parent from affecting the quality of the characters of the offspring, and restricts the origin of variations to the effects of mutations and recombination of genes. At the same time, the chromosome mechanism that operates in sexual reproduction (p. 78) ensures the widest possible range of variation, which makes evolution possible under the guidance of selection. In asexual reproduction, on the other hand, the body of the stock may pass 'bodily' into the bodies of the scions, and environmentally induced modifications of the body of the stock may be carried over into the bodies of scions. This, however, is not inheritance of acquired characters because the scions have not inherited them genetically, by means of genes, but only taken them over ready-made. Furthermore, asexual reproduction cannot have played any appreciable part in evolutionary change because of the absence of the chromosome mechanism allowing for recombination of genes and the production of wide variation.

In many groups of animals, a further adaptation is that by which egg-cells can undergo development without fertilization, a condition known as parthenogenesis. Parthenogenesis is a widespread phenomenon among invertebrate animals, and is found among fresh-water crustaceans such as daphnids (water-fleas), and insects such has aphids (green-fly) among many others. It occurs under optimal conditions of life and results in rapid reproduction without any genotypic variation. These are the conditions when it is advantageous for variation to be reduced to a minimum. In general, therefore, asexual reproduction is a temporary phase in the life of organisms, adapted to particular conditions, and where it occurs it alternates with the phase of sexual reproduction.

The evolution of diploid organisms

At the early stage of life when syngamy and meiosis were evolved, the organisms were haploid; only the zygote or product of fusion (or of fertilization) of two individuals was diploid, and it immediately underwent meiosis as a result of the stimulus of fusion itself, the products becoming haploid again. Some unicellular plants (green algae) and animals (Protozoa) are still in this condition. In others, the onset of meiosis is delayed and the organism, preserving the two sets of chromosomes present in the zygote, is diploid. Only when germ-cells or gametes are about to be formed does meiosis take place, and the germ-cells are haploid. In this

Sex and Reproduction

Sex is the fusion of the genetic material of two individuals into one, a process called syngamy. In Procaryota such as Bacteria, **369,** without organised nuclei syngamy is partial, a portion of the genetic material of one cell passes into another. In Eucaryota syngamy is complete, the entire genetic material of two cells or gametes fuses into one zygote. In primitive forms there is no visible difference between the gametes (p. 143). In Cryptogamic plants and all animals, **370,** gametes are differentiated into large, immobile eggs containing food-supplies, and small mobile sperms; **373,** mouse egg penetrated by a sperm, photographed by J. Smiles. **371.** In higher plants the gametes are retained inside spores, the egg in the embryo-sac and the sperm in the pollen-grain where it forms one nucleus of the pollen-tube that penetrates to the egg and fertilises it. **372.** Parasexual process in Fungi; a nucleus from one hypha penetrates into another where it divides and its products pass into each of its cells, which then contain two nuclei, one of its own and one from the other hypha. Eventually the two nuclei fuse in each cell.
All reproduction is by fission. When it is not associated with syngamy it is called asexual reproduction as in the marine worm, **374,** (*left*) the body of which becomes constricted into two, the hinder part develops a head and finally becomes separate as a new individual. Sexual reproduction always involves syngamy between two single cells, unicellular individuals or gametes. **374.** (*right*) The cycle of reproduction by fission and syngamy by fusion in the Protozoon *Copromonas subtilis*. In multicellular organisms syngamy is followed by embryonic development which reconstitutes the multicellular state from the unicellular zygote. **375.** Diagrams illustrating the evolution of diploid organisms: (1) haploid life-cycle, the diploid zygote undergoing immediate reduction; (2) alternation between haploid generation producing diploid zygotes giving rise to diploid generation producing haploid spores; (3) haploid or gametophyte generation dominant as in mosses; (4) diploid or sporophyte generation dominant as in ferns; (5) haploid generation reduced to a few nuclei as in flowering plants; (6) reduction-division delayed until formation of gametes as in multicellular animals.

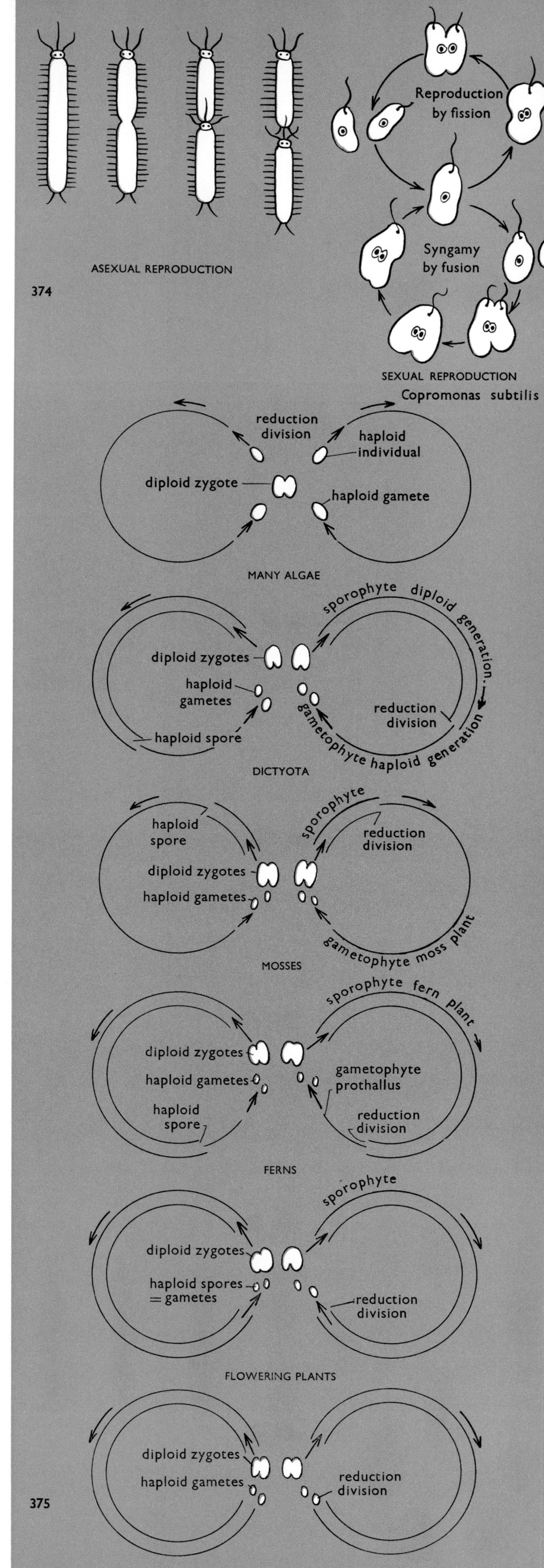

condition may be cited many green algae, Protozoa, and all multicellular animals.

In land plants, the conditions have been complicated by the phenomenon of alternation of generations (p. 158). In an alga such as *Dictyota*, syngamy between two gametes produces a diploid zygote in which meiosis is delayed and a diploid alga results. There is, therefore, a diploid generation in which meiosis ultimately takes place; but the products of this meiosis are not haploid gametes which undergo fusion to form a zygote, but haploid spores which develop into new organisms by asexual reproduction without fusion. These organisms constitute a haploid generation. They eventually produce gametes which, being already haploid, simply fuse to form a zygote thus starting a new diploid generation. There is therefore an alternation between a diploid generation that arises as a product of syngamy by sexual reproduction and produces spores, for which reason it is called the *sporophyte*, and a haploid generation that arises from a spore by asexual reproduction and produces gametes, for which reason it is called a *gametophyte*. In the alga *Dictyota* the sporophyte is identical in appearance with the gametophyte; in other plants, either the gametophyte or the sporophyte generation is larger and preponderates (Pl. 375, 377, 378).

In all the higher plants, as in all multicellular animals, the plant or the animal is diploid (Pl. 379), and this fact has a direct bearing on the high evolutionary status of these organisms. In the first place, the diploid condition makes it possible for mutations to take place without necessarily injuring the organism, for mutation occurs in only one gene of an allelic pair, and the other normal gene is present and can perform the necessary functions if the mutant gene is unfavourable. In a haploid individual when mutation takes place, the effects of which are abnormal, the individual is not protected from them but bears the consequences directly. The diploid state therefore preserves the individual from the effects of deleterious mutations.

At the same time, the diploid state allows the individual to collect and keep mutant genes. Even if they may be deleterious in the environment in which the mutations occurred, conditions and gene-complexes change, and these reserves of genes may turn out useful some time. The diploid state therefore favours the preservation of supplies of mutant genes which increase the variability of the species on which natural selection can act.

Finally, the diploid state in a multicellular organism confers a great advantage on a population from the very fact that meiosis is delayed from the zygote until a later stage. When meiosis takes place in a zygote, a single act of independent assortment of chromosomes and genes is the result (p. 79). But if meiosis is delayed until the organism consists of thousands or even millions of cells, meiosis takes place in an enormous number of germ-cells or spores, and there is a correspondingly great number of possibilities of different assortments. This, again, results in increase of variability on which natural selection can work.

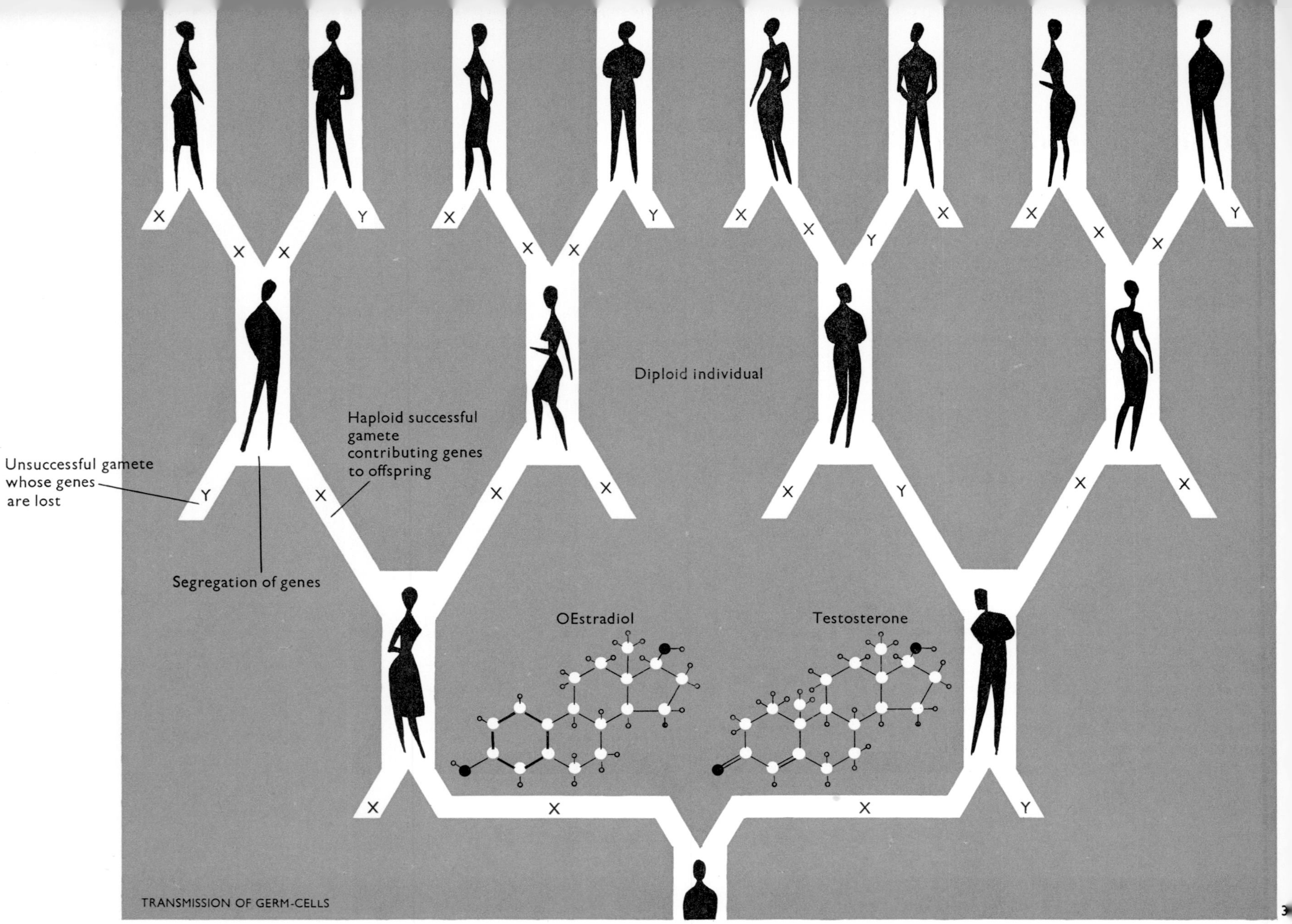

X X Y X X Y X X Y X X X X X Y X X Y X X X X X Y X X

Diploid individual

Haploid successful gamete contributing genes to offspring

Unsuccessful gamete whose genes are lost

Segregation of genes

OEstradiol

Testosterone

TRANSMISSION OF GERM-CELLS

Continuity of the Germ-plasm

Alternation of Generations

377

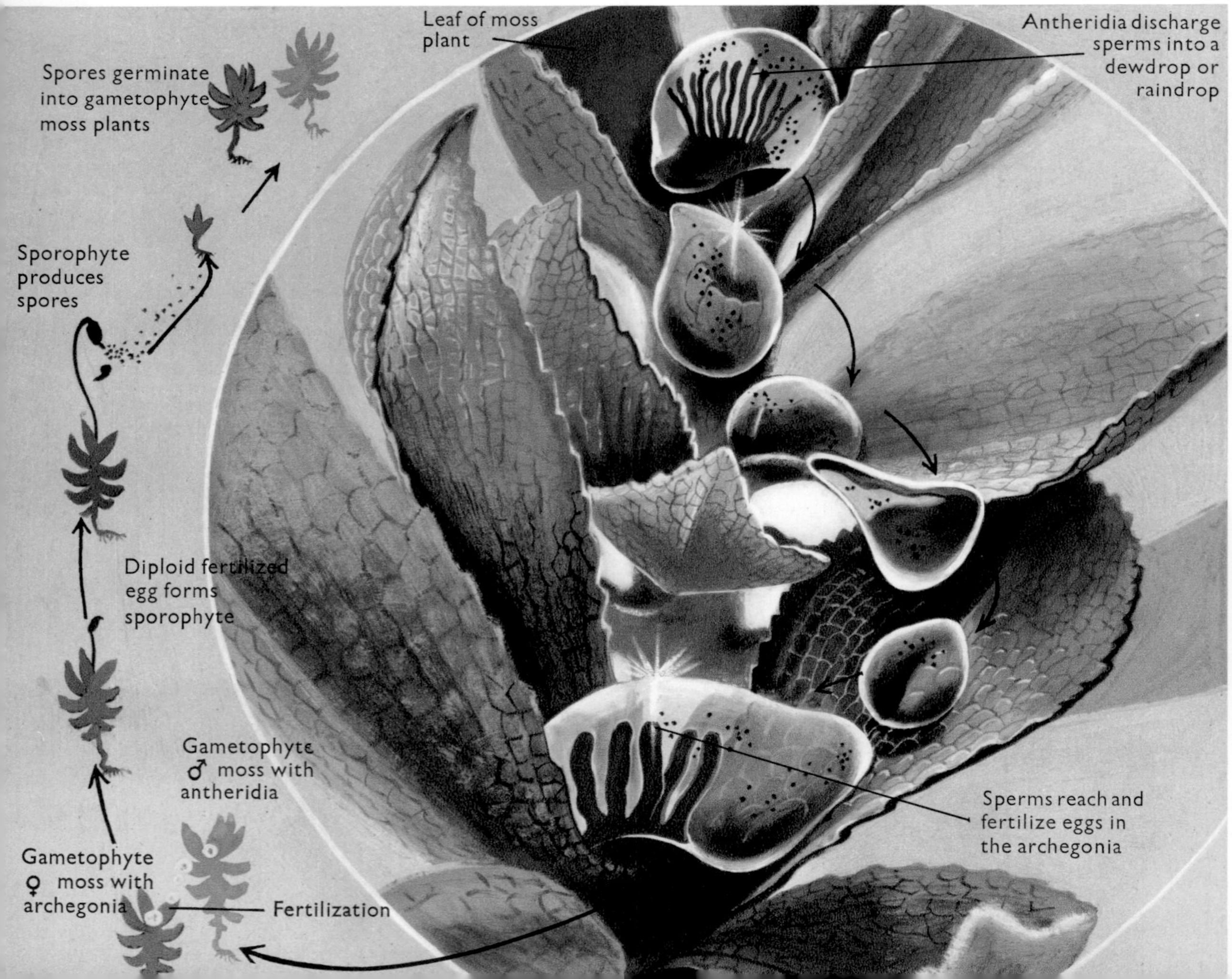

Leaf of moss plant

Antheridia discharge sperms into a dewdrop or raindrop

Spores germinate into gametophyte moss plants

Sporophyte produces spores

Diploid fertilized egg forms sporophyte

Gametophyte ♂ moss with antheridia

Gametophyte ♀ moss with archegonia

Fertilization

Sperms reach and fertilize eggs in the archegonia

Fern plant

Fertilized egg germinates into sporophyte

Archegonia produce eggs which are fertilized by sperms

Antheridia produce spe

376. Every individual in higher animals is the product of two gametes, each containing a set of genes transmitted by each parent; but these parents themselves were the products of gametes that transmitted genes from their parents, and so on backwards. The two sets of genes that make up an individual are shuffled and undergo segregation when it forms its own gametes so that half its genes go into some gametes and half into others. But as only one gamete fuses with another to form the next generation, the half of the genes that went into unsuccessful gametes are not used on this occasion. Individuals are not the direct products of their parents but of the gametes formed out of the germ-plasm of which each individual is the life-custodian. When an egg of a many-celled organism is fertilised a new body is produced by embryonic development but part of it is set aside to provide the gametes from which the next generation will be formed. There is thus continuity of germ-plasm stretching back to the very origins of genes. As the germ-plasm contains whatever genes are transmitted *through* one generation to the next, this is why characters that more or less remote ancestors had may, or may not, reappear in the descendants. Note the similarity in chemical structure of α Œstradiol, a typical female sex hormone, and Testosterone, a typical male sex hormone.

377. The moss-plant is a haploid gametophyte, its antheridia and archegonia produce haploid sperms and eggs without reduction divisions. Sperms are discharged into dewdrops or raindrops of water and so reach and fertilise the eggs. The diploid zygote develops into a diminutive sporophyte that remains on the moss-plant and by reduction divisions produces haploid spores. These germinate into moss-plants. **378.** The fern-plant is a diploid sporophyte that by reduction divisions produces haploid spores that develop into minute gametophytes called prothalli bearing antheridia and archegonia. The sperms swim through films of moisture to fertilise the eggs which develop into diploid fern-plants. **379.** The flowering plant is the diploid sporophyte which by reduction divisions produces haploid spores of two kinds, microspores or pollen-grains and megaspores or embryo-sacs. The gametophyte is reduced to a few nuclei which produce the sperm nucleus in the pollen-grain and the egg in the embryo-sac. The pollen-grain is carried by wind or insects to the stigma of the flower and extrudes the pollen-tube in which the sperm-nucleus is carried down the style to fertilise the egg.

THE MULTICELLULAR STATE, EMBRYONIC DEVELOPMENT, AND DEATH

The simplest organisms were single cells (p. 136), and the evolution of many-celled organisms, by internal compartmentalization of single-celled organisms, was a step of major importance, because it allowed organisms to grow to larger size and made possible the differentiation of different parts of the body, into *tissues* and *organs*, specialized for the performance of different functions, which previously had all to be carried out by the single cell. This differentiation increases the efficiency of the performance. The evolution of multicellular status occurred independently in plants and animals, and probably also in fungi and in sponges.

In plants the leaves specialize as light and carbon dioxide absorbers, the roots as water-and-salt absorbers, and the stems as supporting and conducting structures. In animals the outermost layer serves for protection and supplies the tissues for nervous conduction and sense perception, the innermost layer for digestion and absorption, and other tissues carry out the function of respiration, excretion, locomotion, skeletal support, and reproduction.

A consequence of the evolution of the many-celled organism is that the fertilized egg, being a single cell, has to undergo a process of *embryonic development* in order to return to the multicellular and finally to the adult condition, that is, to the complexity and size of its parents. It divides into more and more cells, and they become *differentiated* into the different regions, tissues, and organs of the body, while *growth* enables the embryo to regain the size of its parents. The provision of reserve food-materials in the egg is of increasing importance in this process until in the highest group of all, the viviparous mammals, the resources of the mother are substituted for the yolk in the egg.

The subdivision of the body into many cells imposes another consequence of major importance, for only the reproductive cells, being single cells, can fuse with each other and pool their genes in the zygote that starts the next generation (Pl. 376); all the remainder of the body of the individual of the previous generation gradually breaks down and dies sooner or later. This is to be contrasted with the condition in the lowest organisms in which the body consists of a single cell. Their reproduction is always by division of the whole body and the old individual becomes directly transformed into the new individuals. There need by no dead body left at all. Since in principle this process can be repeated indefinitely, unicellular organisms can be said to be, in this sense, immortal.

Paedomorphosis

The fact that a multicellular organism undergoes embryonic development from the fertilized egg to the adult means in genetic language that the phenotype is changing continuously until the definitive adult stage is reached. During this time the genes control the development by reacting with the environment and synthesizing the chemical substances that result in the differentiation of the various organs and tissues. It has been shown that many genes exert their effects by varying the rates at which chemical reactions take place (p. 88), and this means that individuals can vary in the amount of development that they have undergone.

378

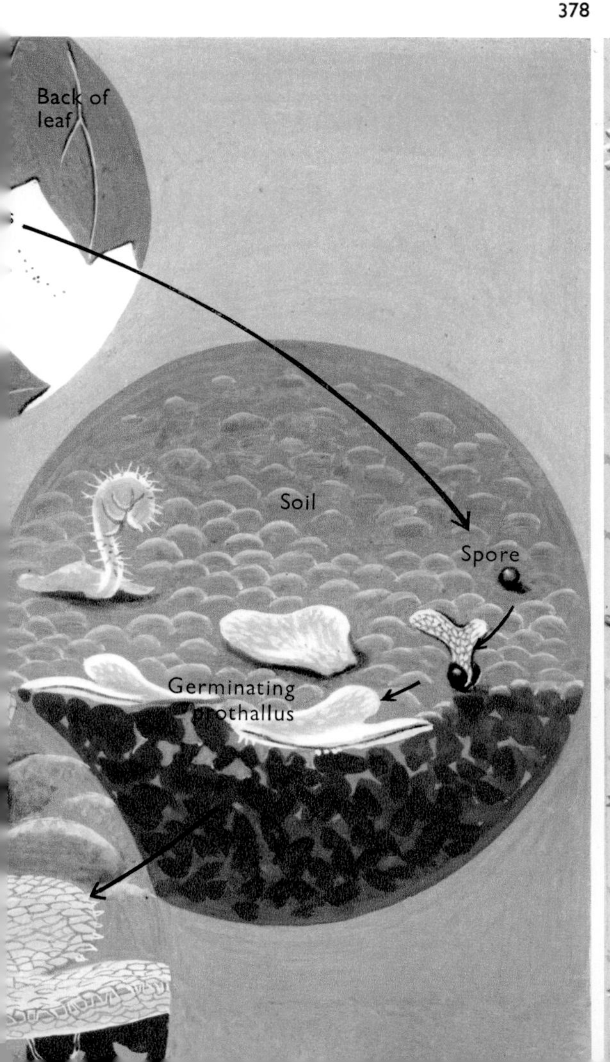

379

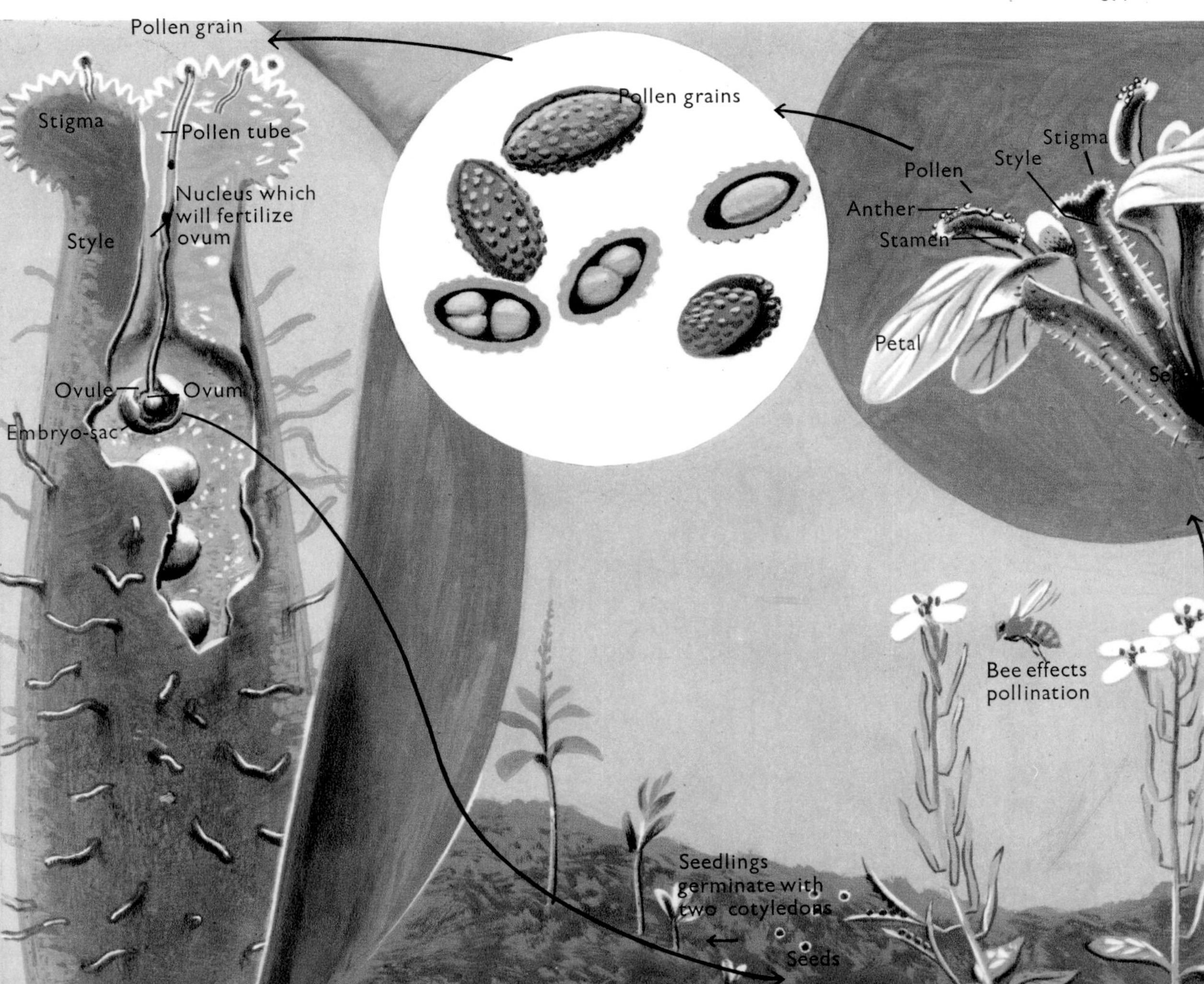

The Development of the Multicellular State

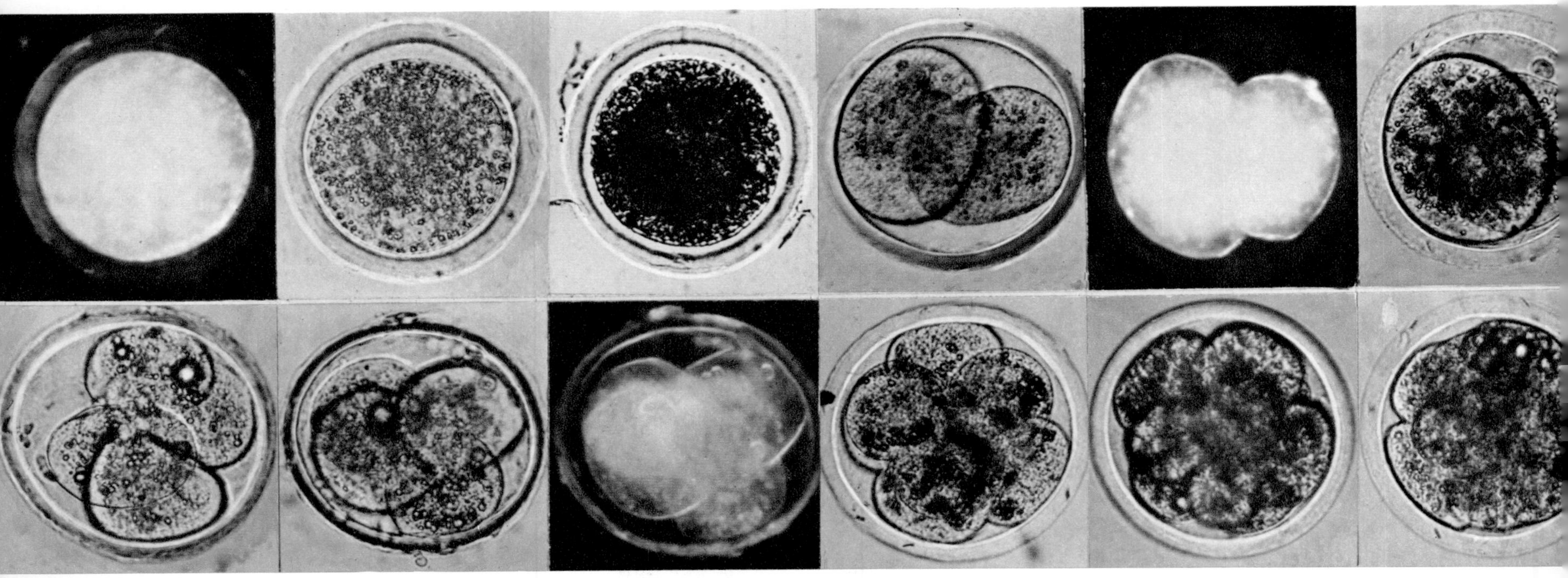

380

381 382

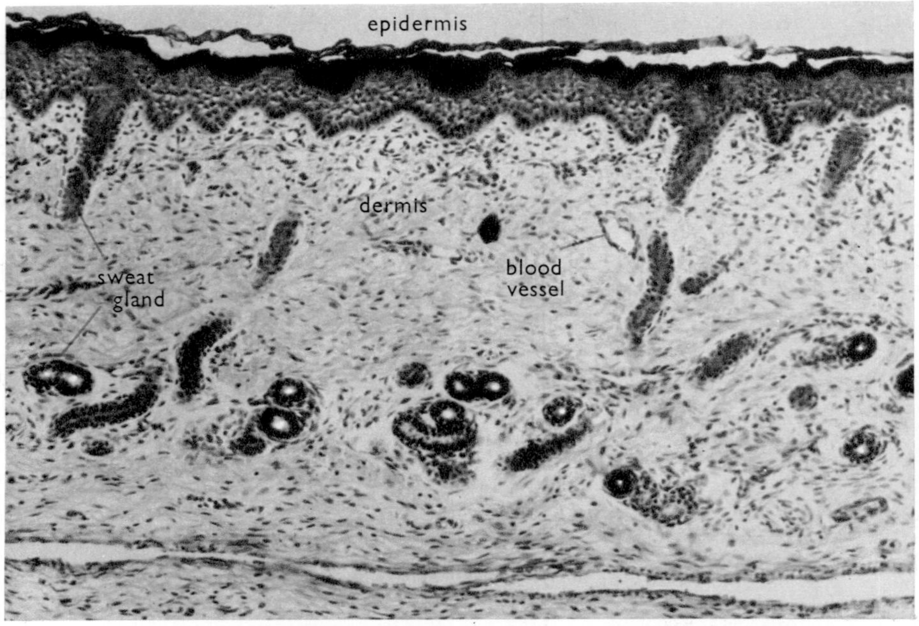

epidermis
dermis
sweat gland
blood vessel

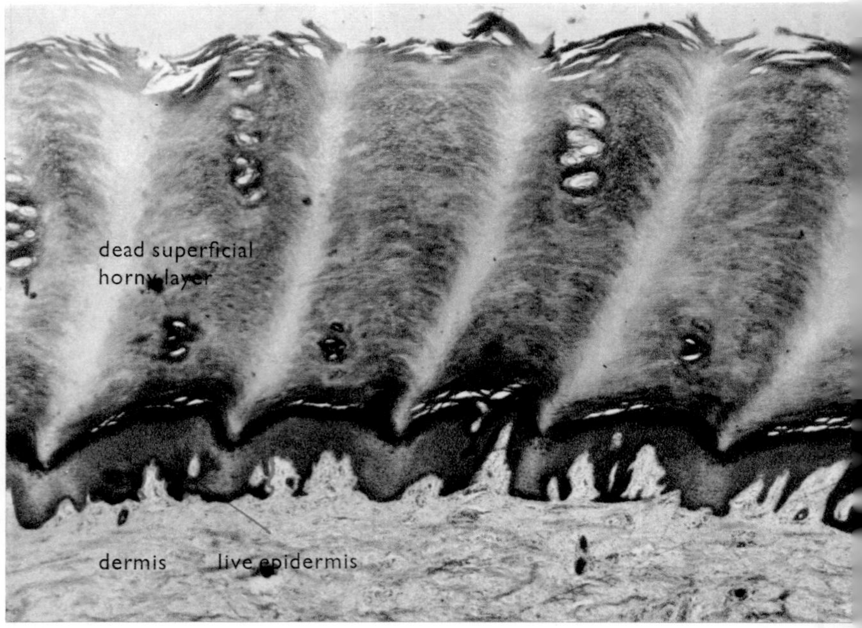

dead superficial horny layer
dermis
live epidermis

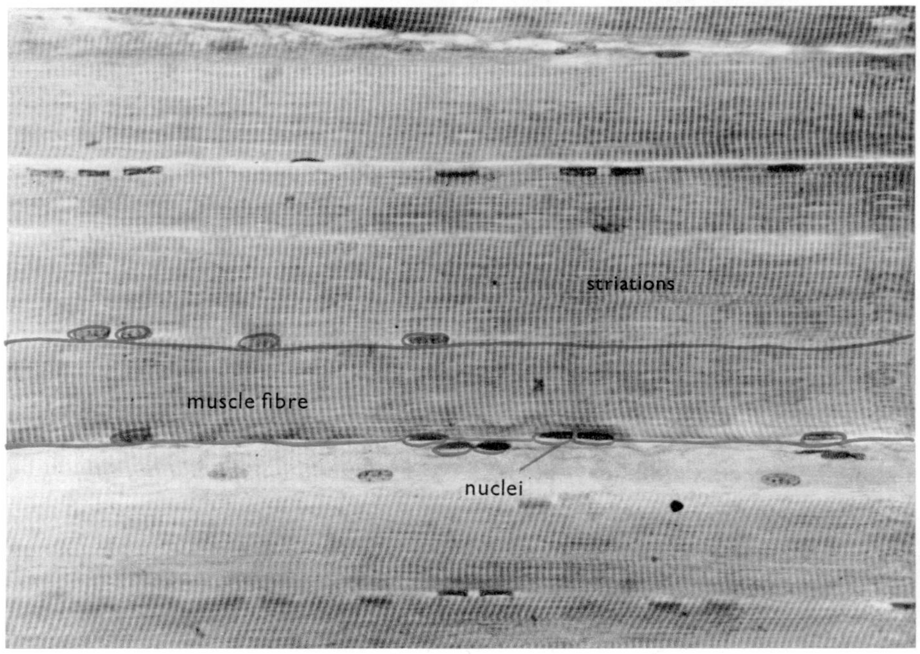

striations
muscle fibre
nuclei

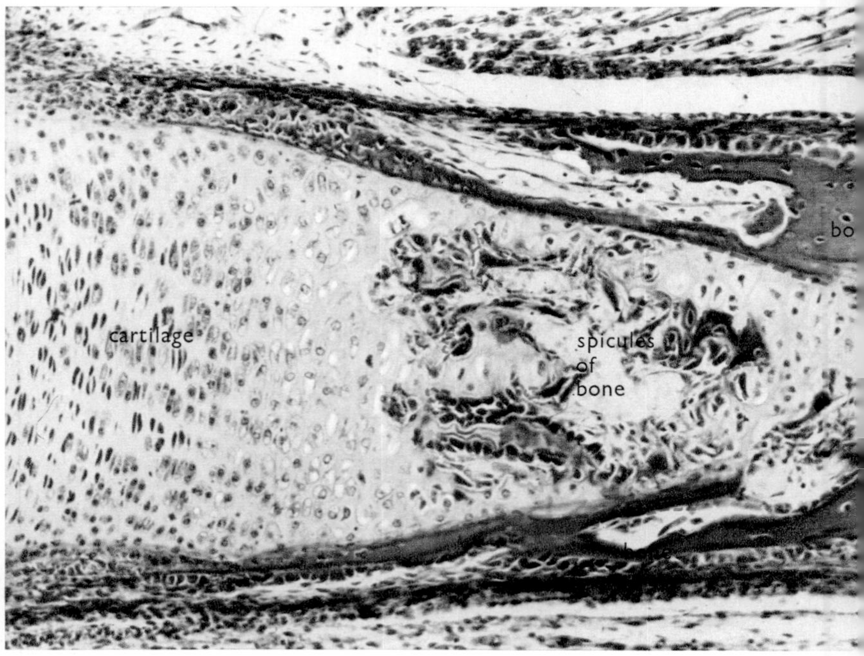

bo
cartilage
spicules of bone

383 384

In all multicellular organisms sexual reproduction following fertilisation of an egg by a sperm involves embryonic development, as a result of which the multicellular state of the parents is reconstructed out of the unicellular zygote. **380.** The photographs shown here are of live goat's eggs at the earliest stages: (1) egg-cell surrounded by its membrane seen by incident light and (2) by transmitted light; (3) older egg showing denser cytoplasm; (4) two-cell stage 48 hours after fertilisation, the result of division or cleavage of the egg; (5, 6) another specimen of the two-cell stage seen by incident and transmitted light; (7) four-cell stage 60 hours after fertilisation showing the four cells arranged in the form of a cross and containing globules of fat; (8, 9) another specimen of the four-cell stage seen by transmitted and incident light; (10) eight-cell stage 85 hours after fertilisation; (11) nine-cell stage, the cells are of different sizes; (12) twelve-cell stage, 98 hours after fertilisation. All magnifications x 250. The photographs obtained by E.C. Amoroso, W. F. B. Griffiths and W. J. Hamilton are reproduced without retouching.
381. Section through thin human skin, showing sweat-glands and blood-vessels in the dermis beneath the epidermis which is covered by a thin horny layer. **382.** Section through human skin of the palm of the hand showing the thick horny layer outside the epidermis. **383.** Section through striated or voluntary muscle showing the striations and the nuclei of the cells that have produced the muscle fibre. **384.** Glandular tissue of the liver, showing spherical granular cells containing secretion with inter-cellular spaces and blood-vessels. **385.** Skeletal tissues showing a piece of the skeleton of the foot with cartilage in which the cells are each embedded in the gristly matrix, invaded on both surfaces and in the middle by bone-cells that have secreted spicules of the darker-staining bone.
386. Blood which is a tissue containing non-nucleated red corpuscles in the adult mammal and nucleated white cells. **387.** Section through part of the cerebral cortex of a cat showing large pyramidal nerve-cells.

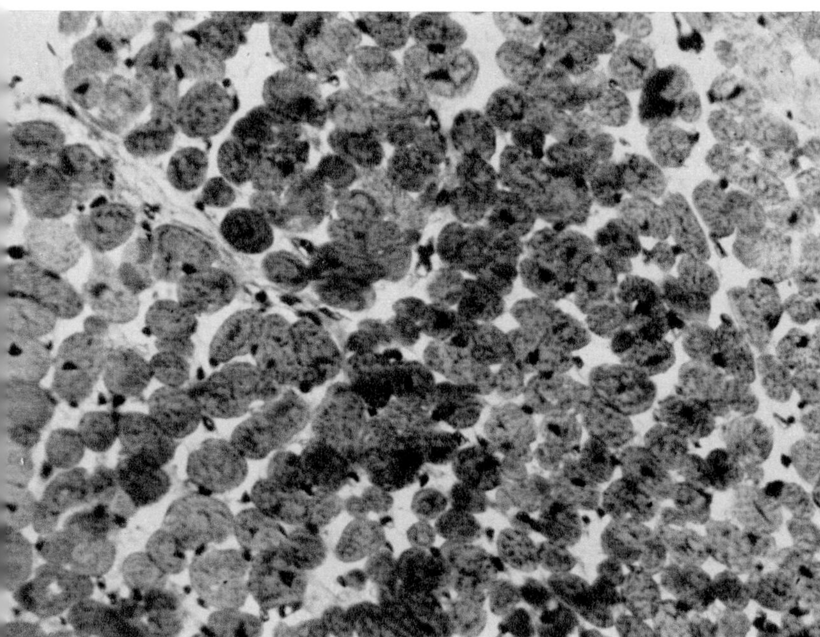

385

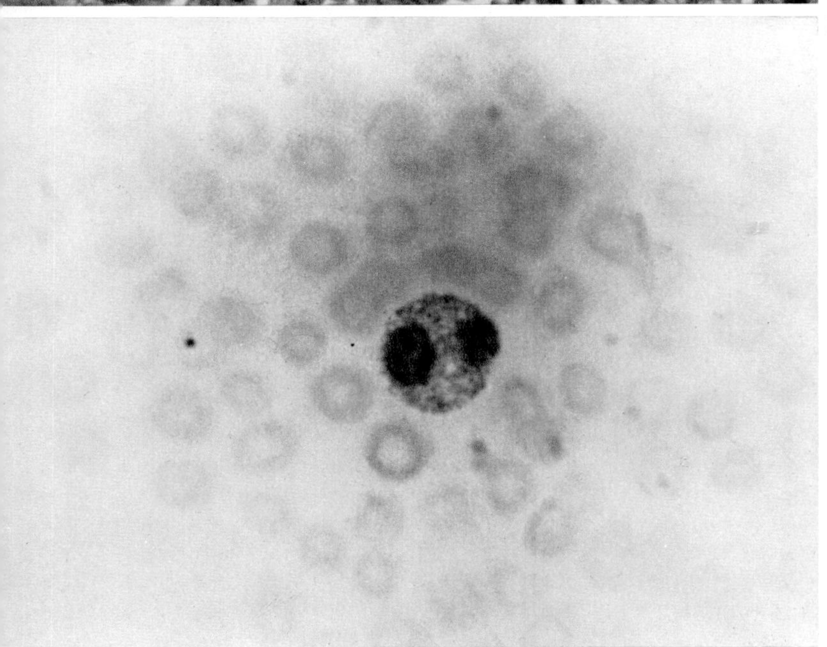

386

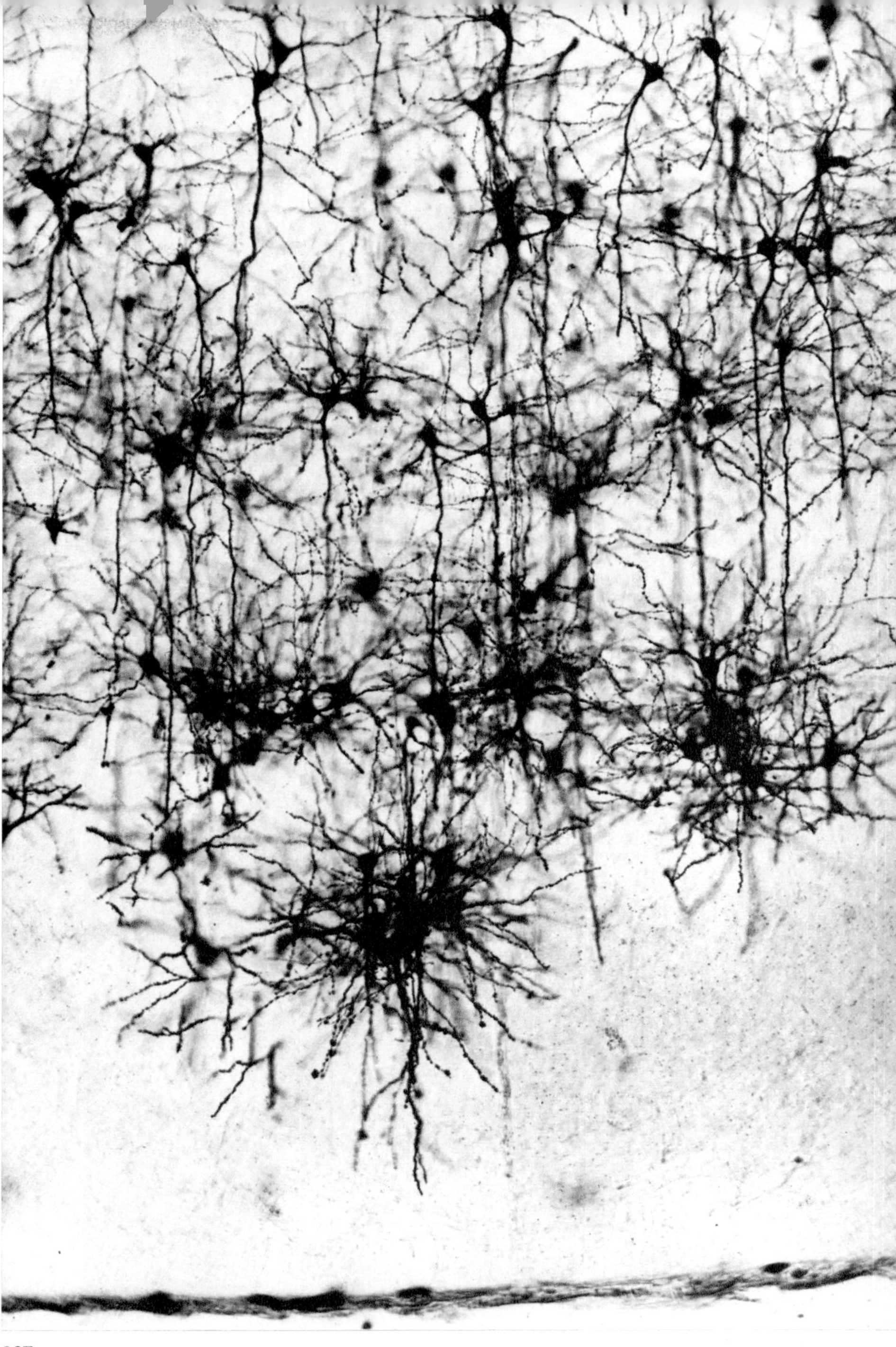

387

Some are more grown up than others. The variations on which natural selection may act are not restricted to the variants represented by full-grown organisms but also include variants along the time-scale of development. All stages of the life-history are available for the selection of those forms most efficiently adapted to their environments, and these will not always be the forms of the adult ancestor. The axolotl is a familiar example of an animal that fails to grow up and becomes sexually mature in a youthful condition. In many groups of organisms the evolutionary history is characterized by delayed development, prolongation of the youthful stages into the stage of sexual maturity, and discarding of the old ancestral adult stage. In these circumstances, the adult stage of the descendant resembles the youthful stage of the ancestor. This mode of evolution, known as *paedomorphosis*, has been followed by the most successful groups in the animal kingdom. Of the dozen groups in which it can be demonstrated, three will be considered here (see also Pl. 388).

Centipedes when young have short bodies with three pairs of legs; when adult they have a very large number. From an ancestral stock of centipedes, one group retained the youthful condition in what came ultimately to be the new adult form, discarded the old adult form, and evolved into the insects, the most successful and diversified group of all invertebrate animals.

Echinoderms (starfish) are comparatively sedentary animals, which when young pass through a free-swimming and highly mobile larval stage, the structure of which is lost when the definitive adult echinoderm is produced (Pl. 102, 419). It is from organisms similar to echinoderm larvae that all vertebrate animals are believed to have been derived, by retention of the larval type of structure until the animals became sexually mature in that condition and discarded the old adult form (Pl. 389). They then evolved in a new direction and produced the characteristic vertebrate features of a tubular nervous system running down the back (the spinal cord), a skeletal rod beneath it (forerunner of the back bone), and gill-slits perforated from the throat to the skin on each side. The acorn-worms provide a perfect intermediate condition, for their larval form is almost identical with that of echinoderms, and in the adult they have gill-slits and a dorsal tubular nervous system.

Paedomorphosis was also the mode of evolution followed by man. In the general form of the skull, the brows, and the mouth, modern adult man resembles not the adult but the young of the ape and the fossil members of the human family, *Australopithecus*, *Pithecanthropus*, and Neanderthal man (Pl. 390). The extent to which modern man is delayed in his development compared with his nearest relatives may be expressed in the form of a table based on the work of A. H. Schultz.

Average ages at which corresponding stages are reached in monkeys, apes, and man

Character	*Monkeys*	*Apes*	*Man*
Gestation period	5 months	8 or 9 months	9 months
Growth period	3 years	11 years	20 years
Life span	14 years	35 years	75 years
Milk teeth erupt at	birth	3 to 4 months	8 months
Permanent teeth begin to erupt at	1 year	3 years	6 years
Female fertility	3 years	9 years	14 years
Degree of ossification of the skeleton at birth	Advanced	Incomplete	Very incomplete
Amount of hair at birth	Complete covering	Head covered	Head sparsely covered

The dominant character of the human body is the relatively enormous size of the brain. The brain, however, cannot make more than a limited amount of progress in its growth before birth, at which time the infant has to be small enough to pass through the mother's hip-girdle. The chief phase of the brain's enlargement therefore takes place after birth, and associated with this is the fact that in man the gaps between the bones of the skull, enabling it to increase the volume of the brain-case, are not closed until the age of nearly thirty years.

The rarity of twins in man is, as J. B. S. Haldane pointed out, a consequence of selection in favour of delayed development to which man has been exposed in his evolution. If there is more than one embryo in the womb there is automatic competition for maternal blood-supply and space, and advantage accrues to the embryo that develops fastest and is most precocious. This is the reverse of the conditions required for progressive retardation of development in man, which became possible only when competition in the womb was practically abolished by reduction of the normal number of young in a litter to one.

Several human features are directly attributable to the paedomorphic mode of evolution. The retarded development and reduced size of the teeth make it possible for their sockets to be accommodated in the bones of the upper and lower jaws without protruding. This is why man has no snout but has a prominent chin. In this respect the conditions in *Pithecanthropus* and Neanderthal man were intermediate between those in apes and in modern man. The prolongation of childhood entailed prolonged suckling, and the fleshy lips which are an adaptation to that function have been retained in the adult, as a result of sexual selection. The prolongation of childhood has also had results of great importance in conferring increased survival value on those individuals whose behaviour is directed towards the consolidation of the bonds between members of a family, and also, as C. H. Waddington has shown, in conferring survival value on those children who develop a mental system leading them to accept authority during the long and dangerous period of childhood when they are incapable of looking after themselves and lack experience. Instinctive behaviour can protect the young when the youthful period is short, as in fledgling birds or young lower mammals, but not when the youthful period lasts several years, as in the case of man.

Parental care and instruction, consequent upon speech-communicated and memory-stored experience, allowed man to benefit from more efficient apprenticeship to these conditions of life (p. 192).

Clandestine evolution

One further result of the paedomorphic mode of evolution deserves mention. When evolutionary changes take place in the larval or young stages of development

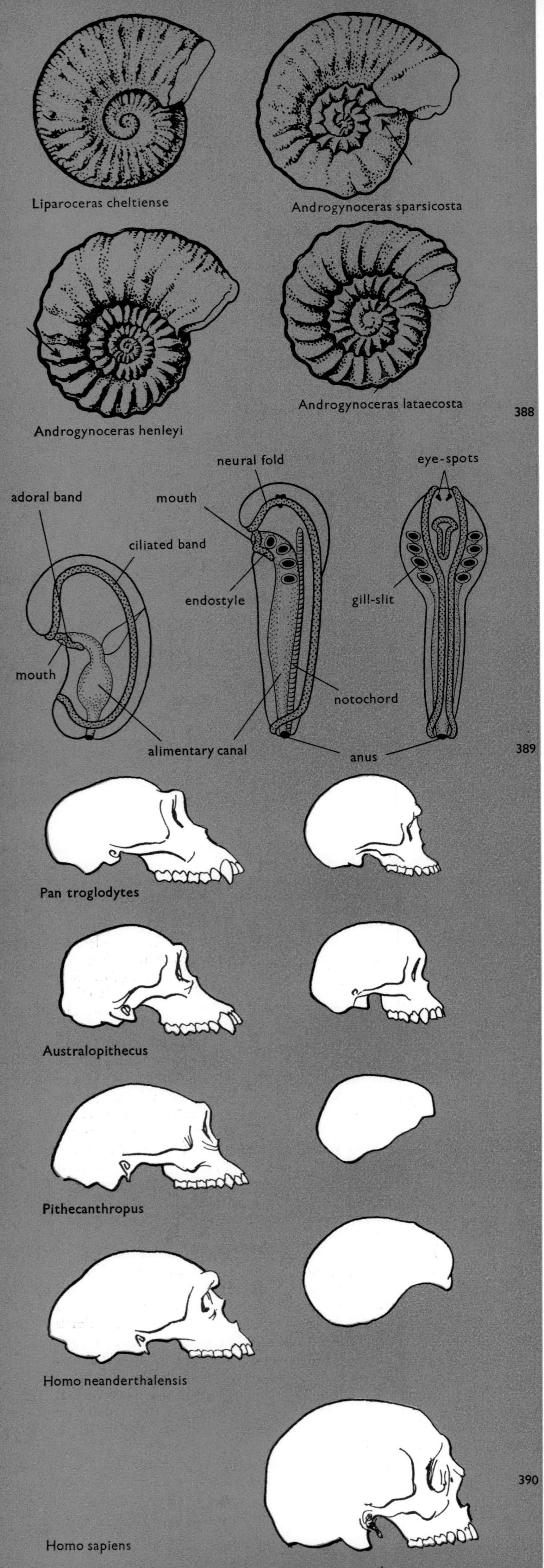

Three Examples of Paedomorphosis

Paedomorphosis is a mode of evolution in which the adult descendants resemble the juvenile stages of their ancestors. **388.** It can be demonstrated in a progressive series of ammonites; *Liparoceras cheltiense* had no ribs; the next stage *Androgynoceras sparsicosta* had ribs only on inner whorls formed in early stages of development; next, *A. henleyi* had ribs persisting into later stages; finally, *A. lataecosta* had ribs at all stages. Arrows point to last-formed ribs. This character first appeared in the young ancestor and was retained in adult descendants. **389.** Evolution of chordates from echinoderm-larva-like ancestors, (*left*) generalised echinoderm larva, (*centre*), side and (*right*) dorsal views of generalised primitive chordate showing the correspondence between the ciliated bands and the neural folds. **390.** Paedomorphosis in the evolution of man. The left column shows juvenile stages, that on the right adult stages of, chimpanzee, australopithecine, pithecanthropine, Neanderthal. Modern adult man with domed skull, vertical forehead without brow-ridges, can be derived from the series of juvenile forms, but not from that of adult forms.

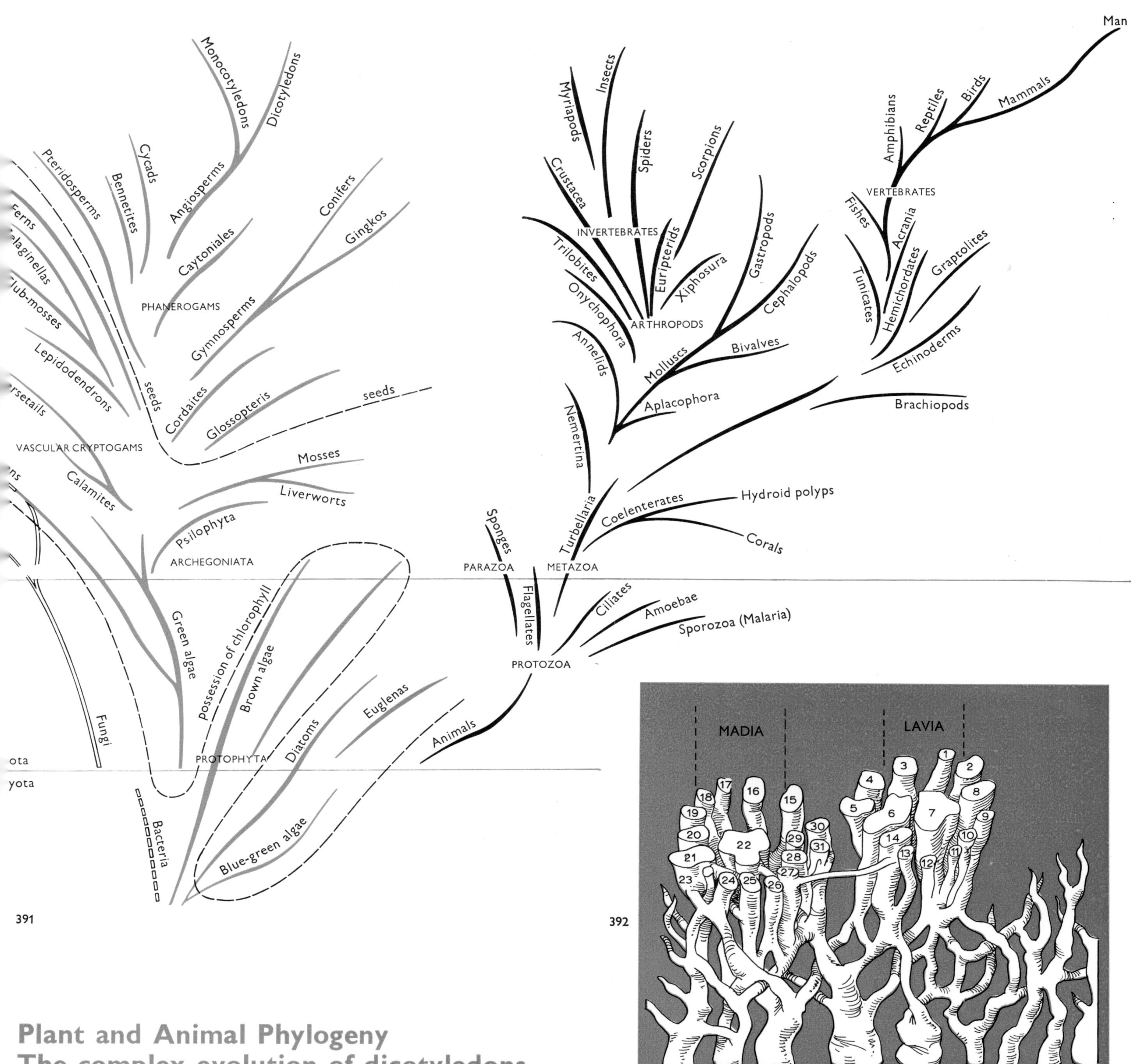

Plant and Animal Phylogeny
The complex evolution of dicotyledons

391. An attempt to show the main lines of evolution in the light of present knowledge. From the original living organisms arose bacteria, blue-green algae, and plants, the two last groups possessing chlorophyll. The radiation of plants in the unicellular condition produced various Protophyta and Algae of which green algae became multicellular and gave rise to land plants. Their subsequent evolution into Archegoniata, Vascular Cryptogams, and eventually seed-plants (Phanerogams) is indicated. The origin of Fungi is obscure, but their combination with green algae produced lichens. Animals evolved from Protophyta by loss of chlorophyll and acquisition of holozoic nutrition. From Protozoa, Parazoa produced sponges, and Metazoa gave rise to two main groups: leading to the highest invertebrates, and to vertebrates respectively.
392. In the highest plants, Dicotyledons, evolution involved divergence and hybridisation, resulting in a reticulate pattern, illustrated with reference to two genera, *Madia* and *Lavia* and their thirty one species.

Reticulate evolution in a group of plants. (from Clausen, *Stages in the Evolution of Plant Species*, N.Y. 1951)

1 carnosa
2 chrysanthemoides
3 heterotricha
4 septentrionalis
5 pentachaeta
6 glandulosa
7 platyglossa
8 Fremontii
9 Jonesii
10 Munzii
11 leucopappa
12 paniculata
13 hieracioides
14 gaillardioides
15 madioides
16 Bolandesi
17 minima
18 exigua
19 glomerata
20 sativa
21 gracilis
22 elegans
23 subspicata
24 citrigracilis
25 citriodora
26 radiata
27 yosemitana
28 Rammii
29 Hallii
30 nutans
31 nutrammii

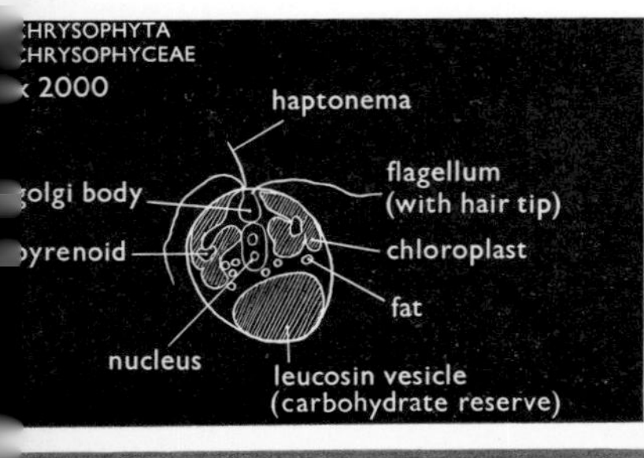

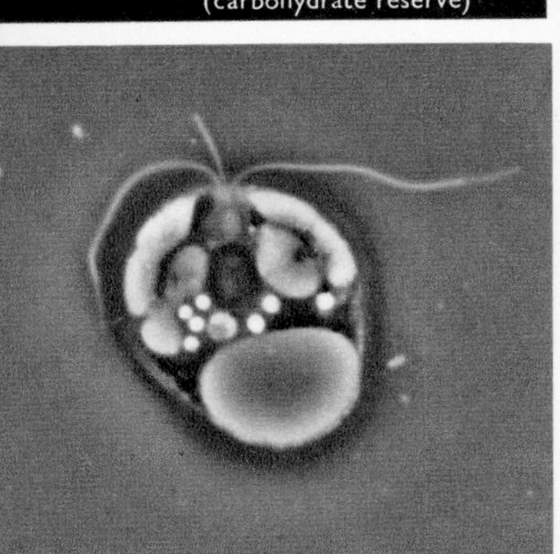

393

394

395

The Evolution of Plants

393. *Prymnesium*, a single cell alga. **394.** Brown seaweed, *Laminaria*, a many celled alga, the highest stage of evolution reached by plants in water. **395.** *Psilotum nudum* a very simple land plant. **396.** Moss, *Hypnum cupressiforme*; in this and in **397,** liverwort, *Lunularia cruciata* the 'plant' is the gametophyte generation producing eggs and sperm from which the diminutive sporophyte generation develops (→ 377). The further evolution of plants was conditioned by the formation of vessels in the stem, as in **398,** section through the stem of a fern of the Carboniferous period, showing the central vessels through which substances are transported up and down the stem of the plant. **399.** Fern, *Polystichum lonchitis*. **400.** Horsetail, *Equisetum talmateia*. **401.** Selaginellid, *Lycopodium clavatum*. In the last three the 'plant' is the sporophyte generation. **402.** Seed-plant, gymnosperm, *Araucaria imbricata*; **403.** detail showing formation of cones, that on the right is shown in section.
404. Maidenhair tree, *Ginkgo biloba*; the male sex-cell in this tree is a free-swimming sperm.
405. Angiosperm, Dicotyledon, horse chestnut in flower. **406.** Monocotyledon, lily, *Lilium regale*.

399

400

396

397

398

401

402

403

404

405

406

407 408

and not in the adult, it is unlikely that the fossil record will show any trace of it, because at larval and young stages of development organisms usually consist of soft tissues without the hard skeletons that are most likely to be preserved. When a new group arises by the paedomorphic mode of evolution, this evolution will be clandestine from the point of view of the palaeontologist, until the new adult form evolves sufficient hard parts to permit fossilization. It is therefore to be expected that those groups that evolved by means of paedomorphosis would make a sudden appearance in the fossil record, with a gap in the fossil record before them.

THE COURSE OF EVOLUTION IN PLANTS

Life originated in water and the properties of this medium imposed certain restrictions on the evolutionary possibilities open to organisms living in it. The most lowly plants, some unicellular and others multicellular, have bodies simple in structure without differentiation into stems, leaves, and roots and are known as Thallophyta, represented by algae of various kinds, sea-weeds, and stoneworts. They perform photosynthesis (p. 136) and obtain food-materials from chemical substances in solution in the water in which they live without having to search for them (p. 137). They reproduce sexually by eggs and sperms and asexually by spores (p. 143).

Plants evolved no further than this stage of organisation before they colonized land. There is evidence of spores of land plants in the Cambrian period, but in the Devonian period the land was already partly covered by vegetation. Emergence on land was started by Thallophyte plants living in shallow water subject to desiccation. Two composite adaptations were necessary for the essential processes of life that had been carried on in the water to be performed in air on land. The first concerned the structure of the plant enabling it to stand erect, resist desiccation, take in atmospheric carbon dioxide and oxygen, and obtain food-materials. This was achieved by the development of a stiff outer layer perforated by stomata (openings admitting the passage of air), and the differentiation of the body into upstanding stems bearing leaves containing chlorophyll where photosynthesis is carried out, and roots that absorb water and substances dissolved in it from the soil.

The second set of adaptations concerned reproduction. In order to reach the egg and fertilise it, the sperm which evolved in an aquatic medium must swim in a film of moisture. For this reason the first land plants which are called Archegoniata could (and can) only live in damp areas of land where there are films of moisture. This is why the representatives of this group, psilotums, mosses, horsetails, ferns, and selaginellids, never colonized *dry* land (Pl. 393–401).

The simplest Archegoniata are the psilotums (p. 56) and the Bryophyta or mosses and liver worts. These plants have a simple cellular structure restricting them to a small size and they have not evolved far. Mosses developed a type of alternation of generations (p. 148) in which the moss plant is the gametophyte that produces eggs and sperms and these give rise to the diminutive sporophyte, which lives like a parasite on the gametophyte. The gametophyte being haploid (p. 149) is genetically less well equipped to provide variants on which natural selection can work. On the other hand, in the more advanced Archegoniata represented by the horsetails, ferns, and selaginellids, the plant that is quite large is the sporophyte, while the gametophyte or 'prothallus' is minute, and produces nothing but eggs and sperms. The sporophyte is diploid and enjoys the genetic advantages of its condition. In consequence horsetails, ferns, and selaginellids evolved structures of great significance for further evolution in the form of tubes or 'vessels' of bast and wood, running up from the roots through the stems to the branches and leaves and serving for the transport of water and substances in solution. For this reason these plants, called Pteridophyta, are also known as Vascular Cryptogams; their tall trees abounded in the coal forests of the Carboniferous period. Thallophytes and Archegoniata are together called Cryptogams ('hidden marriage') because they do not reproduce by means of seeds. A stage in the evolution of seeds is however found in the selaginellids, where the spores are of two kinds: large 'megaspores' that develop into female prothalli bearing archegonia producing eggs, and small 'microspores' that develop into male prothalli bearing antheridia producing sperms.

From a group of Vascular Cryptogams plants evolved that suppressed the gametophyte generation almost completely, so that it has no independent existence and is represented only by a few cells and nuclei in the formation of the spores. The microspore is the pollen-grain and one of its nuclei is the sperm. The megaspore is called the 'embryo-sac' and the egg is inside it. The microspores in the form of pollen-grains continue (as in Vascular Cryptogams) to be shed into the air in enormous numbers and disseminated by the wind, but the megaspore is not shed. Instead, it is retained inside its spore-case or 'ovule', which is exposed to the air. An opening in the coat surrounding the ovule enables a pollen-grain to come into contact with the megaspore or embryo-sac where it exudes a pollen-tube that penetrates through to the egg, and the nucleus of the pollen-grain, representing the sperm, passes through the pollen-tube to the egg and fertilizes it. Fertilization, or pollination as it has become, is carried out without any recourse to a film of moisture, and this mechanism enabled plants to colonise dry land (Pl. 377–379).

The fertilized egg develops into an embryo that remains dormant inside the ovule which becomes the seed. The seed with its contained embryo is eventually shed, and if the circumstances are suitable the embryo germinates and develops into a seedling and a new plant. Plants in which this method of reproduction by seeds takes place are known as Phanerogams ('conspicuous marriage'). The most primitive of these are the Gymnosperms ('naked seeds'), so-called because the ovules and subsequently the seeds into which they turn are exposed to the air. Among these

Insectivorous Plants

Notwithstanding the fact that plants are the supreme heterotrophic organisms in the world, able to satisfy their food-requirements out of the carbon dioxide in the air with chlorophyll and the energy of sunlight, and from salts in solution in the soil, some plants have evolved the extraordinary adaptation of feeding on animals.
407. Venus's fly-trap, *Dionaea muscipula*, has leaves of which the edges end in spikes and the surface bears sensory filaments. When a fly alights on a leaf, the sensory filaments cause its immediate closure by a mechanism similar to that of the Sensitive Plant, and the fly is caught and held.
408. Glands in the leaf then produce acid digestive secretions which dissolve animal flesh and the products are absorbed by the plant which thereby acquires an extra supply of nitrogenous and other compounds. In the pitcher-plant *Nepenthes villosa*, **409**, the leaves form a deep receptacle half-filled with fluid into which insects and even birds fall. The mouth of the pitcher is then closed by another leaf and the captured animal is digested and absorbed.

409

plants are the Pteridosperms and Cordaitae that contributed greatly to the coal-forests of the Carboniferous period, the Conifers (pines, firs, yews, larches, cedars, sequoias, araucarias or 'monkey-puzzles'), the Cycads, and the Ginkgos (maidenhair trees). The two last-named groups are particularly interesting because in them the nucleus of the pollen-grain is provided with cilia and is mobile like the sperm that it is. Together with a drop of watery fluid the sperm is released from the tip of the pollen-tube and completes its journey to the egg by swimming. In Gymnosperms the leaves or carpels bearing ovules are grouped together into female cones or flowers, and the leaves or stamens bearing pollen-grains into male cones. Pollination is by wind (Pl. 402, 403).

The next great step in the evolution of plants was the protection of the ovule by means of its complete enclosure inside a chamber called an 'ovary' formed from the carpellary leaves that bear the ovules. Projecting upwards from the ovary is a thin pillar or style ending in a stigma which is usually sticky and onto which the pollen-grains adhere. Ovary and style constitute the pistil of a flower. The pollen-tubes now have to penetrate down the stigma to reach the ovule and its contained egg. Plants with ovules and seeds covered in this manner are called Angiosperms ('covered seeds') and include all the plants with true flowers. Flowers are typically composed of four concentric sets of structures. Innermost are the carpels forming the ovary containing the ovules, constituting the female element; next come the stamens bearing anthers containing sacs of pollen-grains, representing the male element; outside these are the petals, usually coloured, forming the corolla; and outermost are the sepals, usually green like leaves, forming the calyx. Each Angiosperm flower thus contains both female and male elements, but elaborate mechanisms exist to prevent self-pollination of a flower by its own pollen and to secure cross-pollination, with the resulting advantages of gene-recombination and variation that have conferred survival value in evolution on those forms that possess such mechanisms. This was, in fact, the reason for the evolution of the Angiosperms.

Chance dissemination of pollen by wind may bring about cross-pollination, but a more efficient method follows from insects' habits of visiting flowers in search of pollen to eat. Some pollen is thereby sacrificed, but some is carried by the insects to the next flowers that they visit and cross-pollination is brought about more efficiently by these active agents deliberately seeking flowers than can result from chance distribution by wind. It is significant that insects, particularly beetles, bugs, and flies were widespread in the Jurassic period and that Angiosperms evolved from Gymnosperms at about the same time. The advantages of insect-pollination led to further adaptations resulting in attracting them to flowers, such as the secretion of a sugary fluid in nectaries developed in various parts of flowers, the production of chemical substances with far-reaching scents to which insects are very sensitive, and the elaboration of chemical substances in petals giving them bright and varied colours. With the evolution of honey-bees in early Tertiary times, a further stage of adaptation was reached, as in the pollination of orchids, where the structure of the flower, no longer radial, is directly adapted to the visits of bees, with a platform formed from fused petals for bees to alight on, and nectaries developed where the bees have to penetrate deep into the flower to reach them, thereby ensuring that their bodies come into contact with pollen (Pl. 90, 91).

Finally, a further adaptation added one more consequence to the results of pollination, by the conversion and ripening of the pistil into a fruit containing the seeds. Some fruits contain devices that secure the scattering of seeds by mechanical means or by making use of animals as agents of dispersal. In the latter case it is common for fruits to be large, brightly coloured, and succulent, attracting birds who eat them and disseminate the seeds with their droppings (Pl. 85, 86).

Two main groups are distinguishable in the Angiosperms: Monocotyledons that have a single seedling-leaf and whose stems do not thicken, including grasses, lilies, irises, and crocuses; and Dicotyledons, with two seedling-leaves and stems that increase in thickness, including the vast majority of flowering plants. Angiosperms have been so successful in their evolution that they have radiated enormously and are very difficult to classify. It is probable that in addition to divergence between groups there has been hybridization and joining up with other groups in their evolutionary history which requires a reticulate scheme to show their relationships (Pl. 143, 391, 392).

THE COURSE OF EVOLUTION IN ANIMALS

In animals, the exigencies of their method of feeding (p. 138) requiring them to find and capture living food resulted in their achieving high levels of organisation while still living in water. From unicellular Protozoa multicellular forms arose (p. 151) that were thereby enabled to grow to larger sizes and to differentiate the parts of their bodies for different functions. Apart from a large number of small and more or less isolated groups of animals representing dead-ends in evolution, two main trends can be made out in the evolution of animals. The first involves the lengthening of the body in consequence of the necessity for movement (p. 138), and this resulted in the repetition of the various organs of the body along its length producing 'metameric segmentation'; the skeleton where it exists is external, the fertilized egg undergoes a special type of division (p. 151) called 'spiral cleavage', and the larva resembles the trochophore larva of Annelida (p. 35). Here, in an association of groups, belong Turbellaria, Nemertina, Annelida, and Mollusca. The discovery that *Neopilina* is metamerically segmented proves that other Mollusca have lost this character. Cephalopod molluscs, squids and octopuses show how highly organised invertebrate marine animals can become. From relatives

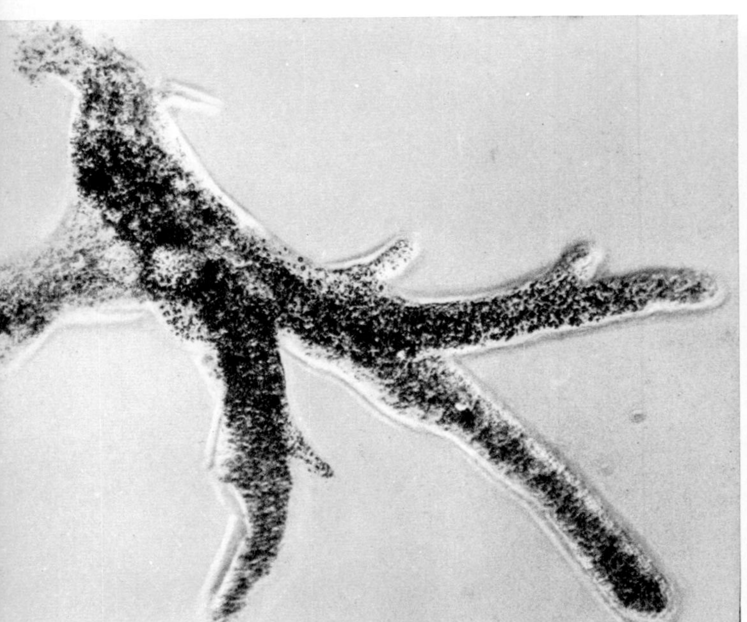

410

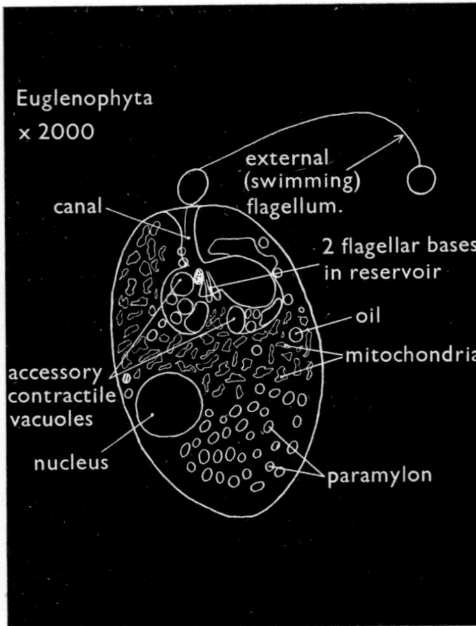

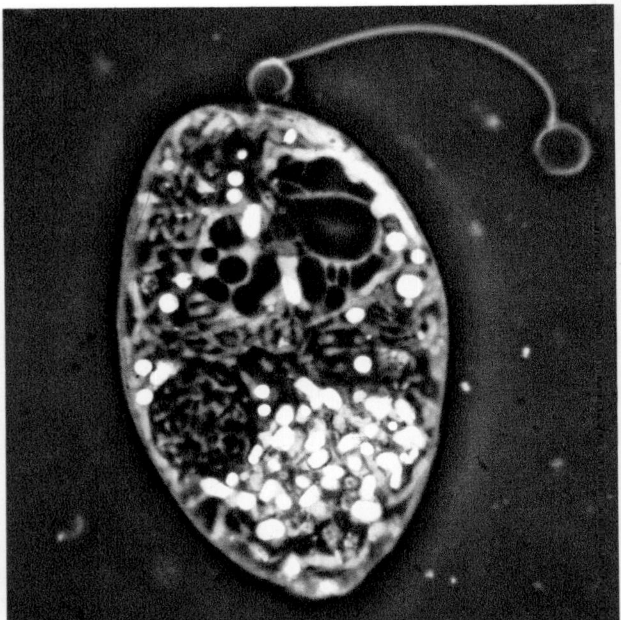

411

of Annelida, Arthropoda arose, their jointed legs having evolved from the appendages of worms (Pl. 417, 418). Their chief representatives before the colonisation of land were the Trilobita, Crustacea, and Arachnida represented by the giant Eurypterids which for a time were dominant predators.

The other trend among animals led to forms that did not become metamerically segmented and in many cases were sessile and even somewhat degenerate in the adult. They fed themselves by creating a current of water thus wafting food particles towards the mouth, developed an internal skeleton, had no spiral cleavage of the fertilized egg, and possessed a larva like the dipleurula of echinoderms. Besides the Echinodermata this association of groups includes Brachiopoda, Polyzoa, Phoronidea, Pogonophora, Pterobranchea, and Chordata. Graptolites were related to them. It is from the larvae of sessile adult ancestors of this kind that Chordata (and therefore vertebrates) are regarded as having evolved by paedomorphosis (p. 151). The ancestral chordates being free-swimming became elongated and developed a repetition of parts, or metameric segmentation quite different from that of Annelida or Arthropoda (Pl. 143, 391). As in the case of plants, the conquest of the land by animals was started by organisms living in shallow water subject to desiccation, and was made possible by simple adaptations enabling them to breathe atmospheric oxygen and resist drying out. The lowest land animals, flat-worms and earthworms living in moist habitats, required very little modification from the condition of their aquatic ancestors. In higher forms including snails, a simple primitive arthropod known as *Peripatopsis*, wood-lice (Isopod Crustacea) and land-crabs, centipedes, insects, spiders, amphibia, reptiles, birds, and mammals, the change from aquatic to terrestrial conditions was accompanied by the development of a resistant skin and the formation inside the body of cavities into which air could pass and from which oxygen could be transmitted into the blood-stream. These cavities take the form of so-called mantle-cavities in snails and in land-crabs, fine ramifying tubes known as tracheae in *Peripatopsis*, wood-lice, insects, and spiders, and lungs in vertebrates. The needs of locomotion were met by modification of existing appendages: the so-called foot of snails was already present in its aquatic ancestors, and the same is true of the legs of *Peripatopsis*, centipedes, insects, spiders, and crustacea, which were well-developed in their aquatic ancestors. The five-toed limbs characteristic of terrestrial vertebrates were evolved directly from the fins of fishes by reduction in the number of radials.

The transition from life in water to life on land was easy and involved little in the way of new structures and no discontinuity in the essential functions of living organisms. This may conveniently be illustrated by the evolution of fishes into amphibia. In fishes respiration is carried out by taking water into the mouth, closing it, lifting its floor and forcing the water out through the gill-slits where the blood-vessels absorb the oxygen in solution. Locomotion is carried out by rhythmical contractions of the muscles of the side of the body giving rise to undulatory movements which press the surrounding water backwards, while the fins serve for deflection. In some fishes, including living forms, the hindmost pair of gill-slits are modified into sacs which become lungs and serve to absorb oxygen from air when the water or mud in which the fish lives dries up. This is the situation in amphibia where air is forced into the lungs in exactly the same way as water was forced through the gill-slits in the fish. The same muscles and nerves were used before, during, and after the transition without any functional discontinuity. Amphibia did not require to invent or develop anything new in order to breathe oxygen when they came on land.

The same is true for locomotion, because the undulatory movements of the fish in the act of swimming are the same as those that cause the limbs to move backwards and forwards in an amphibian like the newt, for the limbs project at right angles to the body and serve as oars to row the animal along while dragging its belly on the ground. The same neuro-muscular mechanism and pattern of behaviour survived the transition without any functional discontinuity. The only novelty was the reduction of the large number of radials in the fin of the fish to five and their separation into fingers and toes, characteristic of all land animals from amphibia to man inclusive (Pl. 303).

The smoothness with which this and other transitions were accomplished was made possible by the fact that in possessing certain structures capable of changed functions, the fishes whose descendants made the transition happened to be pre-adapted (p. 95) to the new medium in which they found themselves. This example shows how evolution proceeded as a gradual change by a series of improvisations which, if serviceable in the new environment, were favoured, preserved, and improved by natural selection.

In spite of their ability to live and move on land and to breathe air, Amphibia are nevertheless tied to water for spawning and fertilizing the eggs, and for the development of the embryos (Pl. 19–25). The problem of adaptation of animals to life on *dry* land was solved by the evolution of a number of adaptations. One of these was the strengthening of the limbs and limb-muscles so that the elbow and knee-joints enabled the forearm and shank to stand vertically and lift the belly of the animal

412

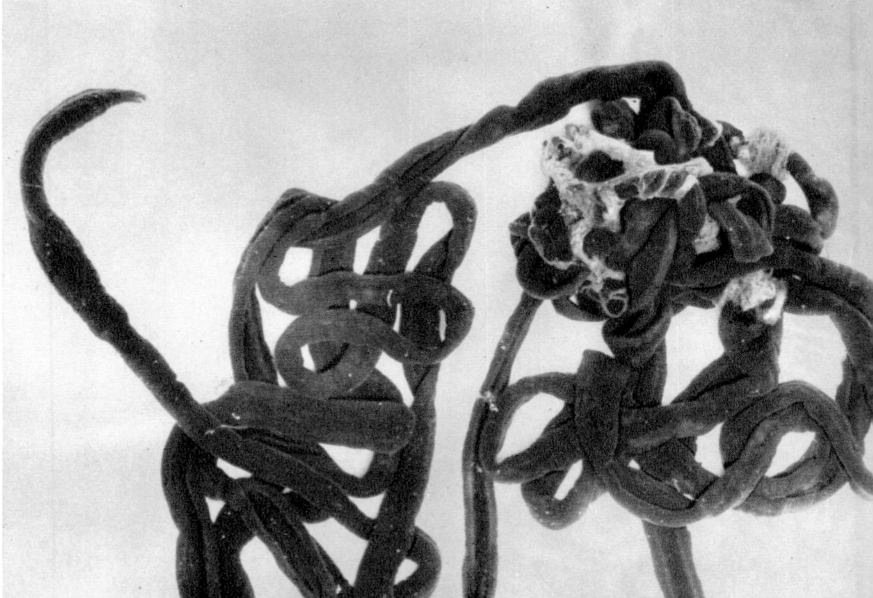

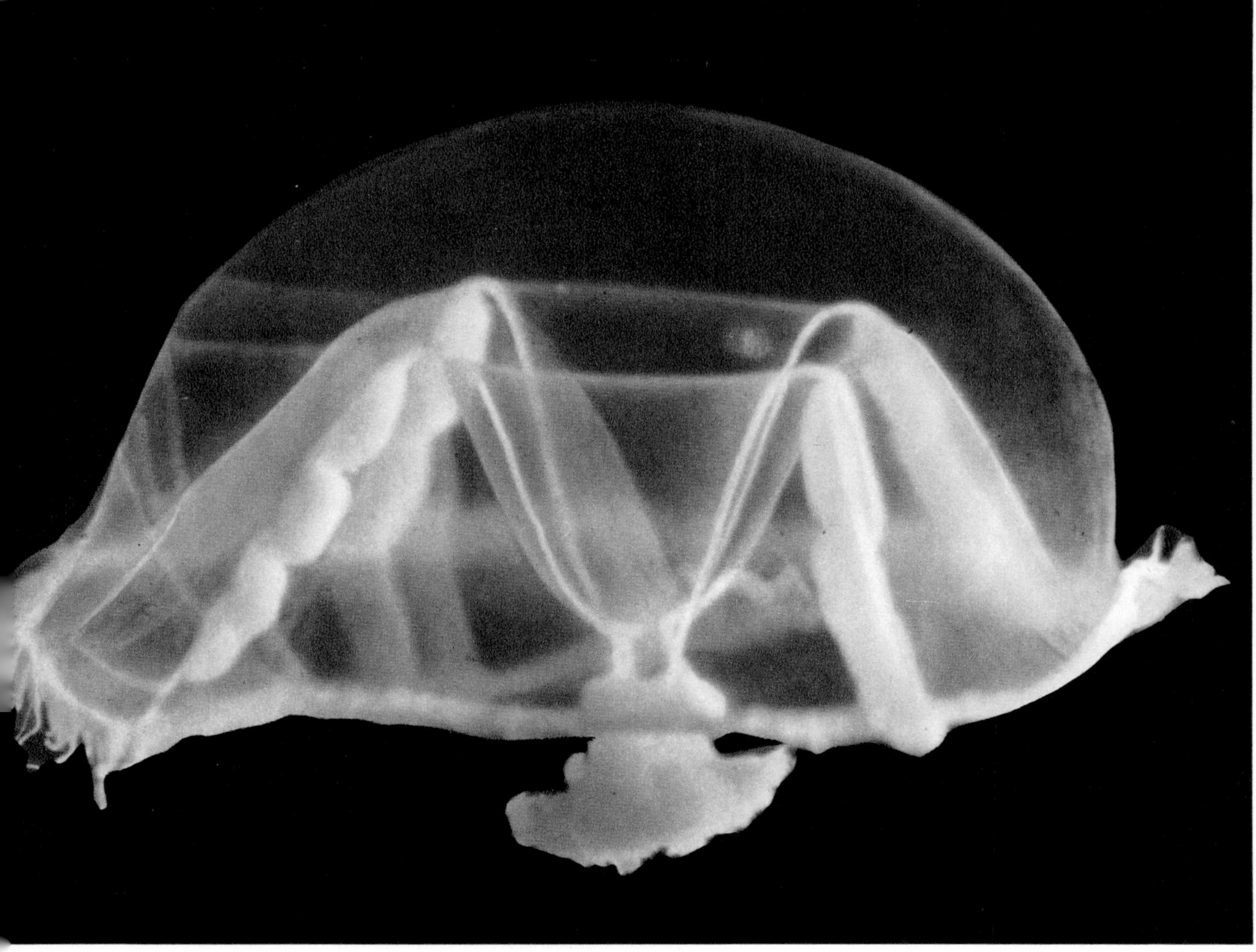

413

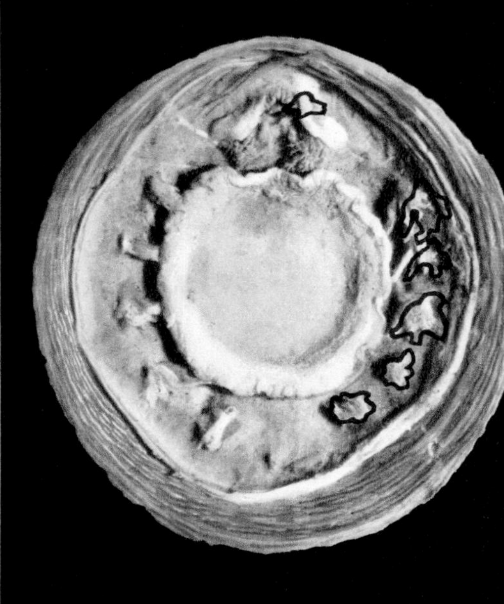

414

415

416

417

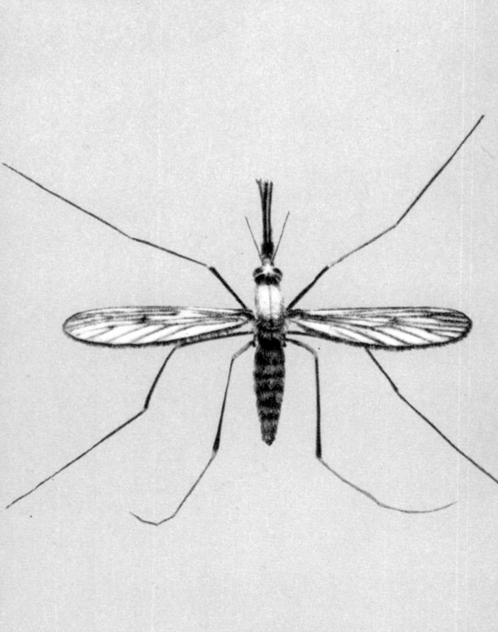

418

419

410. *Amoeba* showing the unicellular type of structure of Protozoa. **411.** *Astasia*, a flagellate; the flagellum as an organ of locomotion is retained in the sperm of all plants and animals. **412.** Nemertine showing the primitive condition of multicellular animals before metameric segmentation evolved. **413.** *Cnidaria*, medusa, characteristic of Coelenterata. **414.** *Neopilina* the most primitive living mollusc that retains metameric segmentation and shows five pairs of gill-tufts. All other molluscs have lost their metameric segmentation. **415.** Cephalopod mollusc, the highest form of organisation achieved by invertebrates in water. **416.** Annelid, marine worm (leech) showing marked metameric segmentation and repetition of parts along the length of the body. **417.** lobster, Crustacean showing differentiation of the body into cephalo-thorax and abdomen, and of limbs into feelers, mouth-parts, claws, walking and swimming legs. **418.** Insect (*Anopheles*), represents the highest and most successful type of organisation achieved by invertebrates. **419.** starfish, echinoderm, showing low adult type of organisation without even a head, from larval forms (→ **102**) of which Chordates are believed to have evolved.

Continuity of function during emergence onto land. Embryonic membranes

420 

421 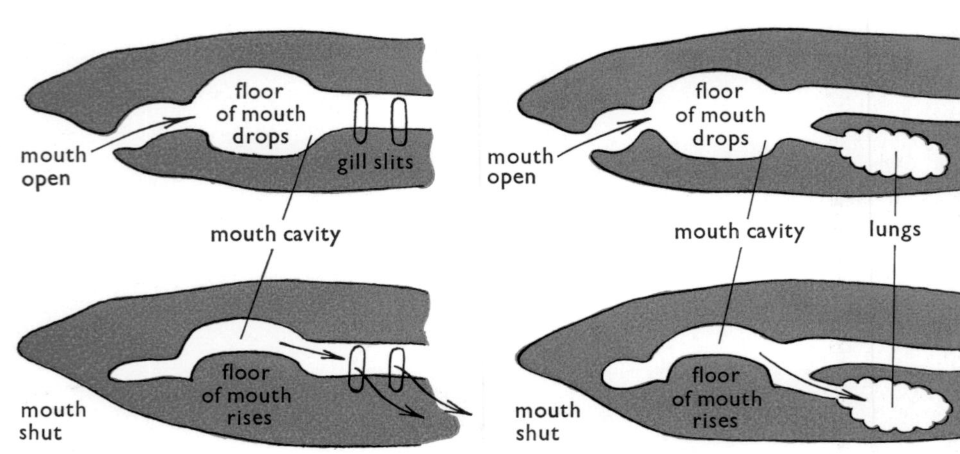

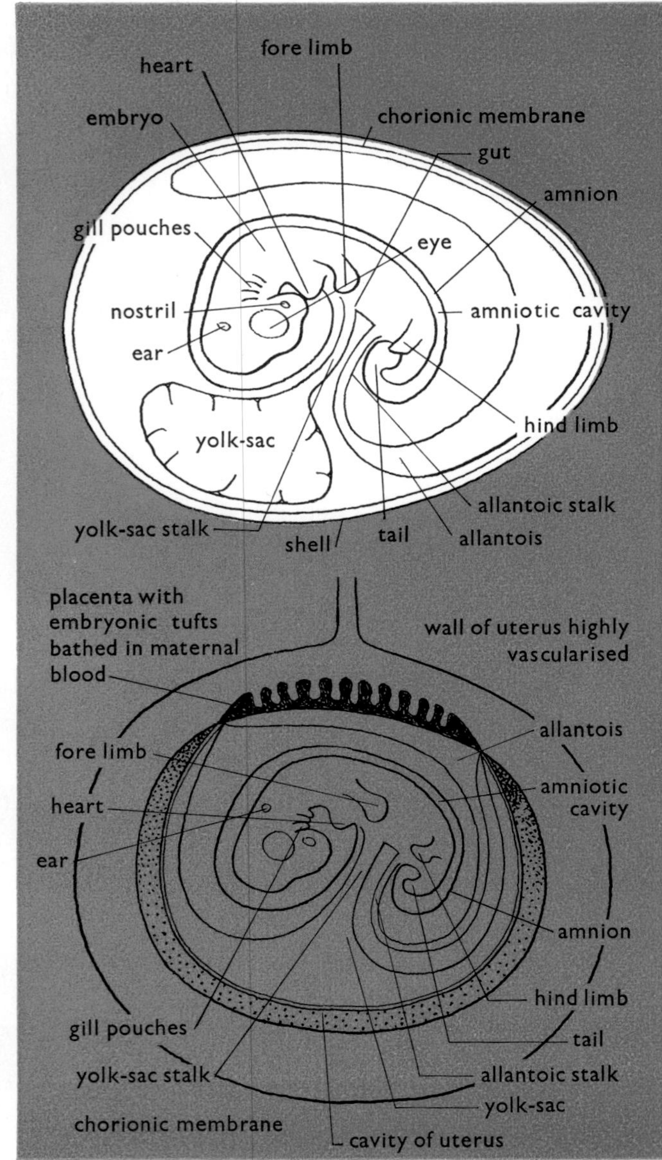

422

420. Fish swimming by means of waves of flexure of the body-muscles passing backwards first on one side and then on the other, producing a serpentine motion resulting in the propulsion of the fish forwards through the water, and amphibian walking on land; waves of flexure pass backwards down the body alternately on one side and the other, and as the limbs project at right angles to the body the effect of the flexures is to row the animal forward with its ventral surface rubbing along the ground. The same mechanism works in both fish and amphibian. **421.** (*left*) Breathing in fishes; the floor of the mouth drops and water enters through the open mouth, the mouth is closed, the floor rises, and the water is propelled backwards through the gill pouches and slits; (*right*) breathing in amphibia; the floor of the mouth drops and air enters through the open mouth, the mouth is closed, the floor rises, and air is propelled backwards into the lungs which correspond to a pair of gill-pouches. The same mechanism works in both fish and amphibian. Embryos of fishes and amphibians are laid in water protected only by the egg-membranes, the eggs of reptiles and birds are laid on land protected by shell and embryonic membranes. **422** (*upper*). The amnion is a membrane exactly surrounding the embryo enclosing it in a fluid medium. From the foregut issues the yolk-sac stalk containing yolk on which the embryo feeds. From the hindgut issues the allantois corresponding to the urinary bladder of amphibia into which the excretory products of the embryo are voided. The blood-vessels of the allantois pressed against the inner surface of the chorionic membrane close underneath the shell perform exchange of oxygen and carbon dioxide with the outside air. Such an egg is 'cleidoic'. **422** (*lower*). Embryonic membranes in mammals are similar but instead of being enclosed in a shell the embryo is retained inside the mother's uterus to which it is attached by the placenta. This is supplied with blood-vessels by the allantois which perform all exchanges of carbon dioxide, oxygen, food-materials, and excretory products across the placental membrane separating the maternal and embryonic blood-streams.

off the ground, with the result that efficient and rapid movement was possible (Pl. 423–426). Another adaptation of the greatest importance was fertilization of the egg inside the body of the female where the moist secretions in the ducts of the reproductive organs enable the sperms to swim in a fluid medium to find and fertilize the eggs. This happens, for instance, in *Peripatopsis*, insects, snails, reptiles, birds or mammals. Another set of adaptations resulted in the development of embryonic membranes containing fluids and a protective shell surrounding the embryo so that although laid on dry land, the embryo was nevertheless able to undergo development in a fluid medium. From their possession of an embryonic membrane called the amnion, reptiles, birds, and mammals are referred to together as Amniota. Although the embryonic membranes allow air to penetrate them as a result of which the embryo is supplied with oxygen for respiration, desiccation is prevented and as J. Needham showed, each embryo inside its membranes is a closed or cleidoic system as regards its food-supply of yolk in the yolk sac and its excretion (Pl. 422). Lower animals up to and including the amphibians excrete their nitrogenous waste products in the form of urea, a relatively harmless chemical substance soluble in water and therefore easily got rid of by animals that live in or frequent water. Within the closed system of the amniote egg, accumulations of urea in the circulation would poison the developing embryo, and in these animals the excretory products take the form of uric acid. This is only slightly soluble and accumulates harmlessly in the bladder which is extended to form the allantoic sac. When the embryo hatches out of its membranes and shell, the allantoic sac is left behind.

In the mammals other than the monotremes, which lay eggs, the eggs contain no yolk and are not laid but retained within the oviduct of the mother which is differentiated into a womb. Here the embryos are attached to the maternal tissues by a special organ, the placenta, through which exchanges of oxygen, carbon dioxide, food materials, excretory products, and also other substances such as antigens (p. 101) take place between the blood streams of the mother and the embryo, by diffusion across the membranes separating them, for the streams are never in open communication. The blood-vessels that connect the embryo with the placenta are

423

424

425

426

427

Adaptive Radiation in Reptiles 225 to 125 million years ago

With efficient limbs that lifted their bellies off the ground and enabled them to move fast, breathing by raising and lowering their ribs with consequent improved respiration, and eggs that need not be laid in water, reptiles were able to make a break-through into various vacant ecological niches and undergo adaptive radiation. **423.** *Scleromochlus*, Triassic, 3 feet long, bipedal form. **424.** *Ornithosuchus*, Upper Triassic, 3 feet, related to ancestors of pterodactyls and birds. **425.** *Macroplata*, plesiosaur, Jurassic, 20 feet, reptile secondarily readapted to water. **426.** *Ichthyosaurus*, Jurassic, 20 feet, adapted to water independently of plesiosaurs. **427.** *Iguanodon*, Lower Cretaceous, 30 feet, large herbivorous dinosaur.

428

429

By the later stages of the Mesozoic era

Evolution of reptiles had produced many fantastic species

430 432

431 433

434 435 436

Among the results of adaptive radiation are extreme specialisations in different directions. One of these, leading to aggressive armament in the form of powerful teeth, is shown by **429** and **433.** Another, leading to the defensive adaptation of bony armour, is seen in **430-432**; another line again, leading to flight, in **434** and **435. 428.** *Hypsilophodon*, Lower Cretaceous, 5 feet, small herbivorous dinosaur. **430.** *Protoceratops*, Cretaceous, 6 feet, armoured herbivorous dinosaur. **431.** *Polacanthus*, Cretaceous 14 feet, heavily armoured herbivorous dinosaur. **432.** *Stegosaurus*, Cretaceous, 30 feet, heavily armoured herbivorous dinosaur. **433.** *Megalosaurus*, Jurassic, 20 feet, carnivorous dinosaur. **429.** *Tyrannosaurus*, Cretaceous, 33 feet, large carnivorous dinosaur.
434. *Pterodactylus*, Jurassic, 1 foot, flying reptile. **435.** *Pteranodon*, Cretaceous, 25 feet, perfected flying reptile. **436.** *Diplodocus*, Cretaceous, 85 feet, the largest land animal, adapted to live partly in water. At the end of the Cretaceous period all these reptiles became extinct and the only reptilian survivors were the ancestors of birds and mammals, and the Rhynchosauria, crocodiles, turtles, lizards, and snakes.

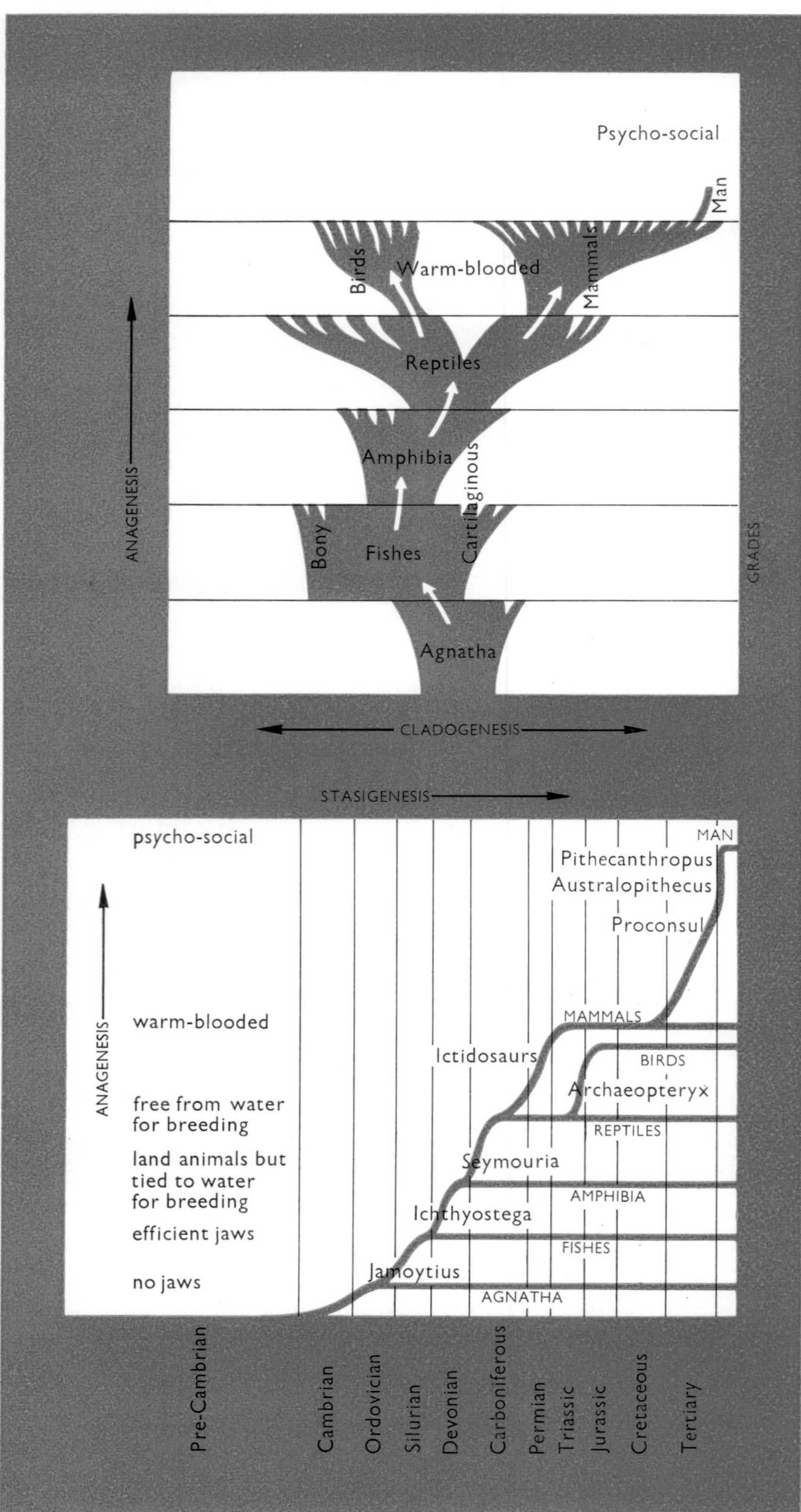

437

The Pattern of Evolution

437. Evolution involves five phases: divergence or *Cladogenesis* shown in the upper diagram by lateral splitting, improvement or *Anagenesis* leading to progressively higher grades of organisation, *adaptive radiation* which is the result of cladogenesis filling the unoccupied niches in a newly invaded medium, stability or *Stasigenesis* leading to the continued existence of persistent types, and finally extinction. The lower diagram shows how the pattern of evolution applies to the different classes of vertebrate animals, each shown as a horizontal line along which minor evolution and stasigenesis leads to the production of persistent types such as the lancelet and coelacanth. From each line, anagenesis leads to the next more highly organised line, through precursor forms represented by *Jamoytius*, *Ichthyostega*, *Seymouria*, *Archaeopteryx*, Ictidosaurs, *Proconsul* and fossil Hominids. As Sir Julian Huxley has pointed out, Man, cladogenetically, is only another Mammal, but anagenetically he represents a superior grade.

those of the allantoic sac. Thus the organ that arose in the Amphibia as the urinary bladder played an essential part in the evolution of the viviparous habit of mammals. The nitrogenous excretory products in mammals take the form of urea, the placenta is expelled and lost after the birth of the embryo, and the young mammal is fed on its mothers milk.

THE PATTERN OF EVOLUTION

Having now reviewed the chief lines of evidence showing that evolution has occurred, what it has produced, and how it was brought about, it is possible to discern a pattern involving five phases succeeding one another in a particular order, although all five are not by any means shown in every case. First, there is *divergence*, the splitting of one lineage into two or more which may be regarded as the start of an evolutionary process. Next comes the phase of *improvement*, always to be considered in relation to the environment; if this improvement enabled the lineage to break through and colonise a new and previously little or unoccupied medium and to fill a number of new ecological niches, it results in further rapid divergence and *adaptive radiation*, a phase sometimes called explosive evolution. Then comes a phase of stability during which little or no further evolution takes place, and the survivors of lineages in this phase give rise to *persistant types*, or 'living fossils'. Finally there is the phase of *extinction*, the fate of all lineages unable to adapt themselves adequately to the changes which the environment is sooner or later bound to undergo (Pl. 437).

The phase of divergence, also called cladogenesis, is represented by the cases of geographical races giving rise to new species as illustrated by tits (p. 110), gulls and salamanders (Col. Pl. 11, 12). It results in the formation of different gene-pools which are the points of origin of different *clades* to use Sir Julian Huxley's term. When the first animals arose from plants they formed a new clade; similarly the invertebrates whose larvae resembled a dipleurula formed a clade different from those whose larvae resembled a trochophore (Pl. 100-102). Mosses form a clade different from ferns, and birds from mammals. The aim of classification is to separate different clades from each other and to include in each group only those forms that belong to the same clade, although this is not always possible in practice.

The phase of improvement or anagenesis is shown by those precursors and transitional forms (p. 57) that effected break-throughs into new environments with unoccupied niches the filling of which constitutes adaptive radiation. It characterised the first land plants, then those with dominant diploid sporophyte generations (p. 158) and vascular systems that enabled them to grow to large size, like the vascular cryptogams of the Carboniferous period. Next it led to the origin of seed-plants like gymnosperms, dominant during the Secondary era (p. 55), and finally to angiosperms with coloured flowers pollinated by insects leading to the enormous radiation of flowering plants during the Tertiary era (p. 159).

Among animals considerable anagenesis took place in the sea before the colonisation of land and led to the formation of groups of large powerful animals like eurypterids (p. 55) and cephalopod molluscs. After the colonisation of land, the most spectacular anagenesis took place among relatives of myriapods when as a result of paedomorphosis (p. 151) and the development of wings, insects arose, able to make use of the innumerable possibilities opened up by the new medium of the air, showing adaptive radiation to such an extent that the known number of species of insects is three times greater than that of all species of other animals together.

Among vertebrates, anagenesis is seen in the emergence of amphibia from fishes (p. 160), of reptiles from amphibia (p. 162), and of mammals and birds from reptiles (p. 61). On each level adaptive radiation took place leading to dominance of amphibia in the Carboniferous period, reptiles in the Secondary era, and mammals and birds in the Tertiary era. Marsupials in Australasia represent a minor bout of adaptive radiation on the part of forms more primitive than true placental mammals (p. 128) from which the marsupials were protected by geographical isolation. The adaptive radiation of marsupials is interesting to compare with that of placental mammals.

These cases of anagenesis introduce a new principle which is that of *grades* of structure. Fishes, amphibia, and those reptiles that gave rise to mammals do not form so many clades but grades, and it is unfortunate that the terms currently used in classification do not distinguish between the two types of groups involved. The reptiles that gave rise to birds represent a clade separate from that of those that gave rise to mammals (Pl. 437).

The phenomenon of persistent types or stasigenesis is seen among plants in *Ginkgo* and Cycads (p. 159), representatives of groups that have not changed since the Jurassic period. Among animals the brachiopod *Lingula* has survived almost unchanged since the Ordovician period, which was when the Somasteroids became extinct but are now represented by *Platasterias* (p. 57). The mollusc *Neopilina* represents the Monoplacophora which became extinct in the Silurian period (p. 38). The coelacanth *Latimeria* has changed little since its ancestors flourished in the Devonian period, and the same is true of the Australian lung-fish *Ceratodus* since the Triassic period, and of the king-crab *Limulus* since the Jurassic period.

Of the final phase, extinction, little need be said except that it has been the fate of the vast majority of lineages and that it has only been avoided or delayed by evolution along lines that enabled the organisms concerned to remain or become adapted to changed conditions. As described elsewhere (p. 97), natural selection is the only mechanism flexible enough to allow organisms to undergo any or all of the phases of evolution here described.

Chapter V THE EVOLUTION OF MAN

MAN'S PLACE IN NATURE

In 1809 Lamarck hinted at the possibility that man was descended from apes, but this was not taken seriously until after Darwin had published the *Origin of Species* in 1859. There he showed that evolution would throw light on man's origin, and he developed this theme in his *Descent of Man*, published in 1871, where he showed that man and apes must have shared a common ancestry. At the present day the evolution of man's body and intellectual capacities from those of animals is regarded as fact rather than theory by all persons qualified to judge the relevant evidence, without prejudice to the views held by theologians on the significance of the phenomena that the scientific evidence reveals.

Since the resemblance in structure between different living organisms indicates the degree to which they are related, man, who is a warm-blooded, air-breathing animal with hairy skin, whose young are born alive and fed at the breast, is one of the mammals. This explains why among other things he has vestigial structures such as a vermiform appendix, scalp muscles, ear muscles, and, in his embryo, a covering of lanugo and a tail. These structures are useless in man, but were functional in his mammalian ancestors.

When man's bodily structure is compared in detail with that of other mammals, it is clear that he belongs to the order of primates, distinguished by large brains, grasping hands, and fingers with nails rather than claws. The primates also include tree-shrews, lemurs, tarsiers, monkeys, and apes. Thomas Henry Huxley in one of his essays on *Man's Place in Nature* (1863), wrote: 'Whatever system of organs be studied . . . the structural differences which separate Man from the Gorilla and Chimpanzee are not so great as those which separate the Gorilla from the lower apes', that is, from monkeys.

The similarity between apes and man can be seen in all the structures of the body, and it also extends to behaviour, including expression of emotion, which formed one of the most remarkable of Darwin's studies. As he wrote in his earliest Notebooks: 'Let man visit ourang-outang in domestication, hear expressive whine, see its intelligence when spoken to, as if it understood every word said - see its affection to those it knows, - see its passion and rage, sulkiness and very extreme of despair; let him look at savage, roasting his parent, naked, artless, not improving, yet improvable and then let him dare to boast of his proud pre-eminence.'

In studies on chimpanzees reared by hand, Nadedja Kohts was able not only to recognize with certainty the expressions of attention, excitement, grinning, laughter, crying, fright, terror, anger, frenzy, astonishment, and smiling, but also to observe that in the facial changes involved in these expressions, many of the same muscles are contracted as in man under the same emotions (Pl. 438, 439).

The similarity between apes and man is further shown in the fact that exceptional individuals among apes display the beginnings of the impulse to create patterns in pictures spontaneously without copying. This early stage in the evolution of the artistic impulse is already characterized by a sense of composition. Pictures made by Congo, the London Zoo chimpanzee, with a brush dipped in paint are always recognizable as his work, from the recurring fan-pattern which underlies them. Furthermore, there is evidence that Congo is conscious of a sense of symmetry and balance as may be seen in the accompanying illustrations. Experiments have been made in which the drawing-paper presented to Congo has a square mark in different positions on the paper.When it is in the middle of the sheet of paper, Congo concentrates his drawing on it; when it is off centre he compensates for the displacement by concentrating his drawing on the opposite side, with a balancing effect. The further the mark is moved from the centre of the paper, the more Congo compensates. Style also changes with age, as in the case of human artists, for Congo's later work differs significantly from his earlier pictures by greater use of curves. Each chimpanzee artist has his own individual style. This is particularly well shown by a comparison of Congo's drawing with those of Betsy, a chimpanzee in the Baltimore Zoo. Instead of using a brush dipped in paint, Betsy had developed a technique of painting with her finger dipped in poster-paint, with a style of parallel curved lines (Pl. 440–446).

That the higher apes should possess this aptitude for artistic expression is in no way surprising, for B. Rensch's experiments on monkeys and birds have shown that they appreciate and prefer orderly to disorderly patterns, and that while monkeys prefer colours, crows and jackdaws prefer grey and black. Man's aesthetic sense therefore has evolutionary roots deep in his sub-human ancestral past.

The various primates alive today are the products of divergent lines of evolution. By comparing them with one another and with fossil forms of earlier ages, palaeontological studies make it possible to picture their evolutionary relationship in the form of an ancestral tree.

The primates were derived from small insect-eating mammals similar to the insectivores whose fossil remains have been found in Cretaceous rocks in North America. The living tree-shrews, closely related to insectivores, represent a survival of the earliest type of primate, which lived 70 million years ago. Lemurs and the tarsier are also survivors of early types, all grouped as prosimians.

Monkeys and the Hominoidea (apes and man) probably arose from advanced prosimians. The earliest monkeys were not very different from tarsiers. The first apes, of which an example was *Propliopithecus*, 40 million years ago, were more monkey-like and the earliest men more ape-like, than those of today. The living apes, with their hand-like feet and long arms with which they swing from branches of trees, are forest-dwellers.

The derivation of man from his ancestors was characterized by increase in size of the brain, shortening of the arms, and by delay in development of the individual and preservation in the adult descendants of ancestral infantile characters. This mode of evolution (paedomorphosis - see p. 151) is particularly important in the case of man. Comparison between the forms of the skull in young and adult chimpanzee, Australopithecine, Pithecanthropine, Neanderthaloid, and modern man show clearly that in his lack of brow-ridges, his dome-shaped skull vault, and upright forehead, modern man has retained the characters of the young, not of the adult stage of the ancestral form, by retardation of development (Pl. 489, 490).

In the embryological development of man there are many indications of his relationship with lower animals. At early stages the human embryo has visceral pouches and a tail and in this resembles the embryo of fishes and other vertebrates. Further evidence of relationship comes from serology. The serum precipitin test provides a means of establishing degrees of blood relationship. Applied to the blood of primates it has confirmed the conclusion that man is related to the apes, and more distantly to monkeys (p. 40).

On the evidence of comparative anatomy, of embryology and serology, zoologists now classify man and the man-like or anthropoid apes as members of one superfamily, the Hominoidea. This group is divided into two families, the Hominidae, which includes the modern and extinct forms of man, and the Pongidae, which includes the great apes and gibbons.

The conclusion that man is related to the apes naturally implies that if their ancestries could be traced back far enough they would be found to have diverged from the same stock; it does no imply that man has evolved from apes such as exist today. As Darwin said, man was descended from an animal which, if it were alive today, would unquestionably be classefied in the same group as the apes. Fossil remains of primates are rare, but those that have been discovered support this deduction and have revealed a range of fossils showing in their structure a graded series that links the earlier to the later types in temporal succession (Pl. 450, 451).

THE TIME-SCALE OF THE EVOLUTION OF MAN

The evolution of the stock of mammals that was eventually to give rise to man took place during the Tertiary era (see pp. 48, 55). The various periods of which that era was composed: Palaeocene, Eocene, Oligocene, Miocene, and Pliocene, ranging from 70 million years to 2 million years ago, have been dated by means of the rates of disintegration of various radioactive elements, as explained on pages 49, 56.

The most critical phase in the evolution of man, however, took place in the Pleistocene, which lasted from 2 million until about 10,000 years ago, and for this period, most of the radioactive methods of measurement of age are inapplicable because the numbers of years involved are too small. Only the potassium-argon method is capable of yielding reliable results, and these must be considered in relation to the events of the Ice Age, which occupied the latter half of the Pleistocene period (Map 25).

In the temperate regions of the Old and New Worlds, this period was marked by repeated onsets of excessively cold climates, during which the glaciers from the mountains extended far into the plains, and the plants and animals then inhabiting them were of arctic character, such as the hairy mammoth and the woolly rhino-

The emergence of humanity

Baby gorillas have seldom been studied because it is difficult to get them to breed in captivity. **438, 439.** Fee Schlapper's photographs of the baby born in the Zoological Gardens at Basle show how much more similar to man a gorilla is when very young than when grown up. Darwin's work on *The Expression of the Emotions in Man and Animals* drew attention to the similarities in expression found between them. One of his earliest observations was 'seeing a dog, horse, and man yawn, makes one feel how all animals are built on one structure'. In studies on chimpanzees and gorillas it has been possible to recognize signs of attention, excitement, pleasure, grief, fright, anger, surprise, and other states, and to show that the facial expressions are brought about by contraction and relaxation of the same muscles that are used in man.

438
Pleasure

It is not proved that these expressions are similar to those shown by humans under similar conditions, but analogies suggest themselves

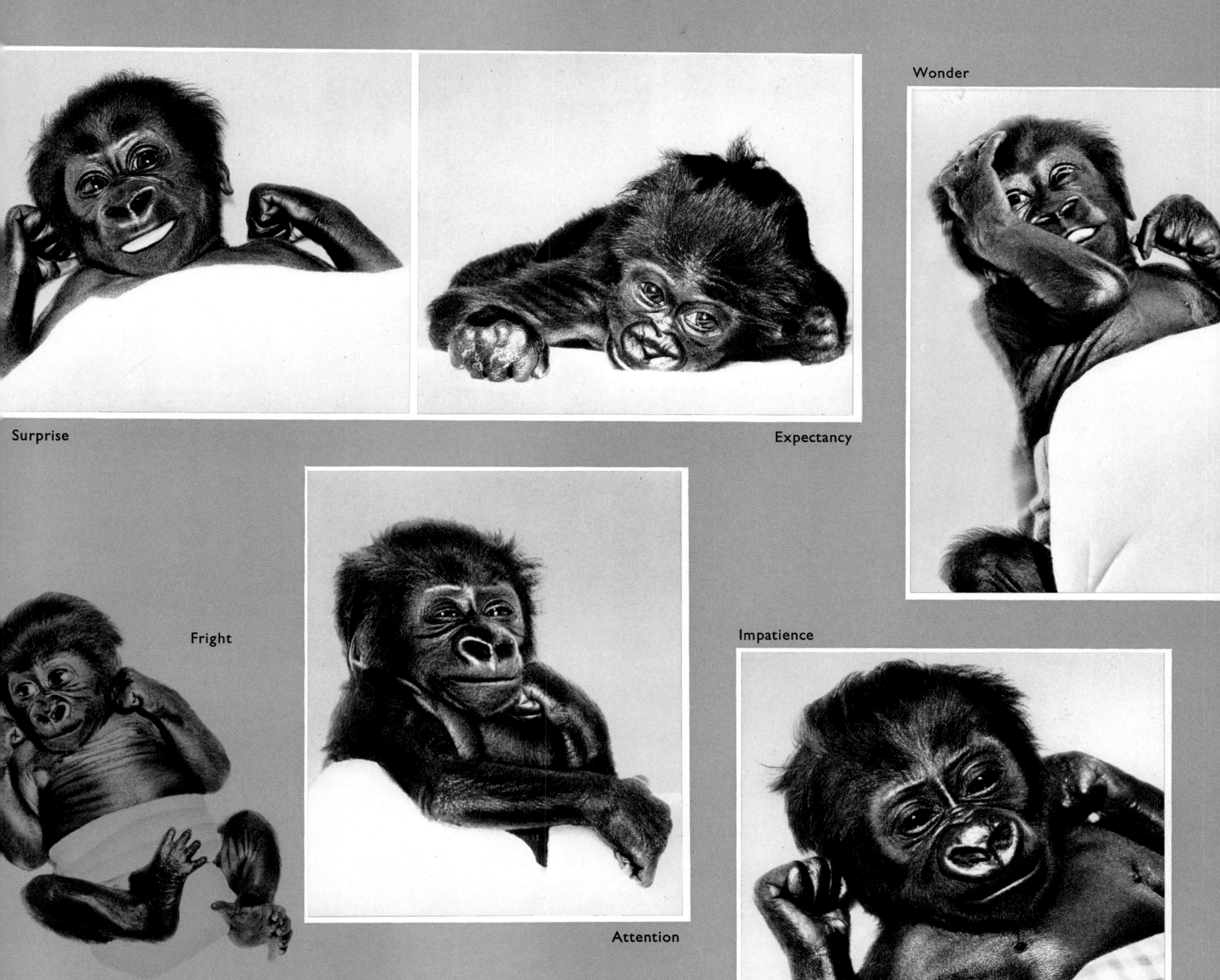

439

ceros. To these Glacial periods, of which there appear to have been four, corresponded Pluvial periods in the tropical regions. Alternating with the Glacial periods were Interglacial periods, of which there were three, during which the glaciers retreated and the climate was warmer than at the present time, and the inhabitants of Europe included representatives of warmer countries such as the elephant and the hippopotamus.

The four Glacial periods in Europe have been given names from geographical locations where they were originally studied, and are known in ascending order from the oldest as Günz, Mindel, Riss, and Würm. The evidence for their existence takes the form of terminal moraines and erratic blocks transported and deposited by the glaciers at the edge of their maximum extensions and at stages in their retreat, eskers and drumlins left in the beds of the glaciers, striated rocks smoothed and scored by the under-surfaces of the glaciers, and erosion of the sides of valleys in the manner characteristic of ice-action. In the Interglacial periods rivers resulting from melting of the ice were responsible for the cutting of terraces in the valleys through which they flowed.

Potassium-argon radioactive dating gives an age of about 500,000 years for the peak of the Günz Glaciation and 400,000 years for the Mindel Glaciation. The depth of weathering during the second or Mindel-Riss Interglacial was four times that during either the first Günz-Mindel or the third Riss-Würm Interglacial, and the second Interglacial was therefore probably four times as long as the first or third. On the other hand, the amount of weathering that has taken place since the Würm Glaciation is only about one-third of that during the Günz-Mindel and the Riss-Würm Interglacials. A tentative chronology of the earlier half of the Pleistocene period can be drawn up from this evidence, but for the more recent part of this period other methods of measurement of time are required.

The radiocarbon or carbon-14 method, discovered by W. F. Libby, depends on the fact that in living plants and animals a small but constant proportion of the carbon in their bodies is the radioactive isotope of carbon, C-14 while most of the carbon is the common C-12. When the plant or animal dies, the replenishment of C-14 in its tissues ceases, and this isotope disintegrates at a known and constant rate. By measuring the proportional amount of C-14 remaining in tissue such as wood or

440

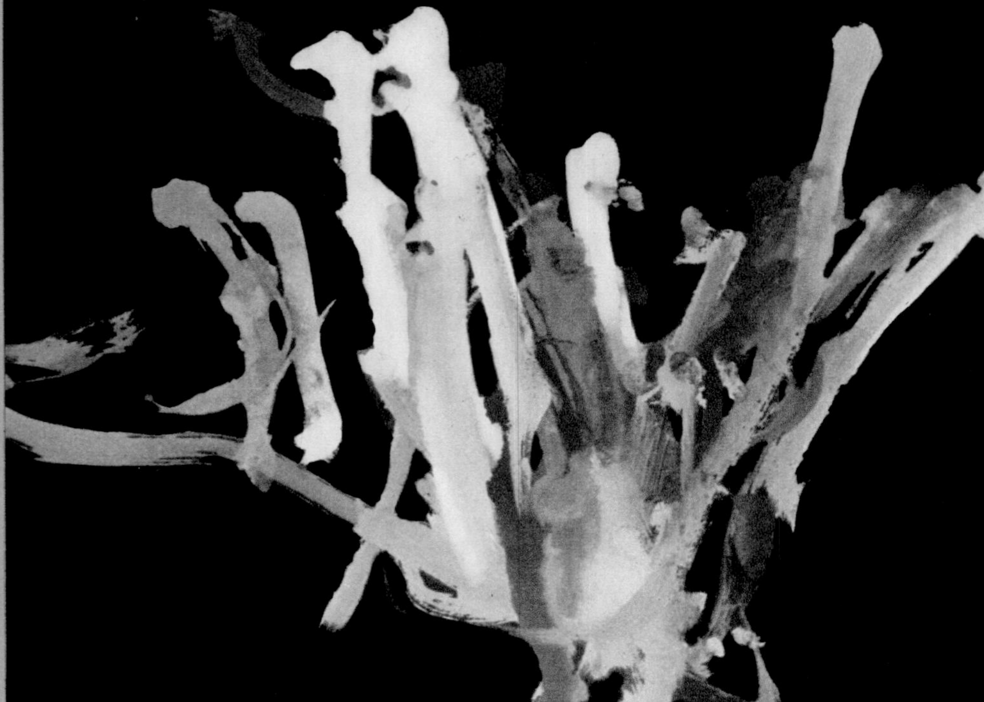

441

The Emergence of Art

Apes show an early stage in the evolution of artistic impulse. **440.** Chimpanzee 'Congo' painting. **441.** Composition by Congo showing his characteristic fan-pattern. It is always clear which sides are top and bottom. The designs are entirely Congo's own conceptions and do not reflect any attempt at representation. **442.** Experiments showing Congo's sense of artistic balance in composition; (*left*) a coloured square in the middle of the drawing-paper attracts Congo's attention and he concentrates his strokes on it; (*right*) if the square is displaced to one side, he compensates on the opposite side. **443.** Gorilla 'Sophie' painting. **444.** Finger-painting pattern by chimpanzee 'Betsy'. **445-447.** Stages in painting by orang utan 'Alexander'. Each ape has his own individual style that enables his productions to be recognised, but it changes with age. These pictures are abstract patterns, for it has not been possible to make an ape copy visible objects.

bone, its age can be determined, until the amount left is too small to measure. This method can be used effectively on material up to 70,000 years old.

From the fact that the deposits laid down by rivers vary at different seasons of the year, it has been possible to recognize and to count the annual layers deposited by rivers flowing from glaciers that formerly covered vast extents of country, following the method discovered by Baron de Geer. By counting the annual layers or varves as they are called, it has been shown that the last or Würm Glaciation ended about 10,000 years ago.

In addition to the methods of estimating absolute ages of different periods and specimens, there are methods of determining relative ages. In bones that have lain undisturbed in a deposit, the calcium of the calcium phosphate can be replaced by uranium if that element is present in the water percolating through the deposit. By measuring the amount of uranium percolating and estimating the radioactivity of the bone, it is possible to determine whether the bone is contemporary with the formation of the deposit and of the other fossils in it, whether it has been washed down a river and derived from other deposits originally laid down elsewhere, or whether it has been deliberately introduced in ceremonial burial or in deliberate fraud. This method, which was devised and used by K. P. Oakley, can be controlled by another based on a similar principle. The element fluorine occurs in soluble fluorides that exist in minute traces in most ground waters. With the passage of time, bones and teeth in deposits exposed to running water accumulate fluorine progressively, and by estimating the amount present it is possible to determine whether the bone is contemporary with the deposit in which it lies, or not.

444

445

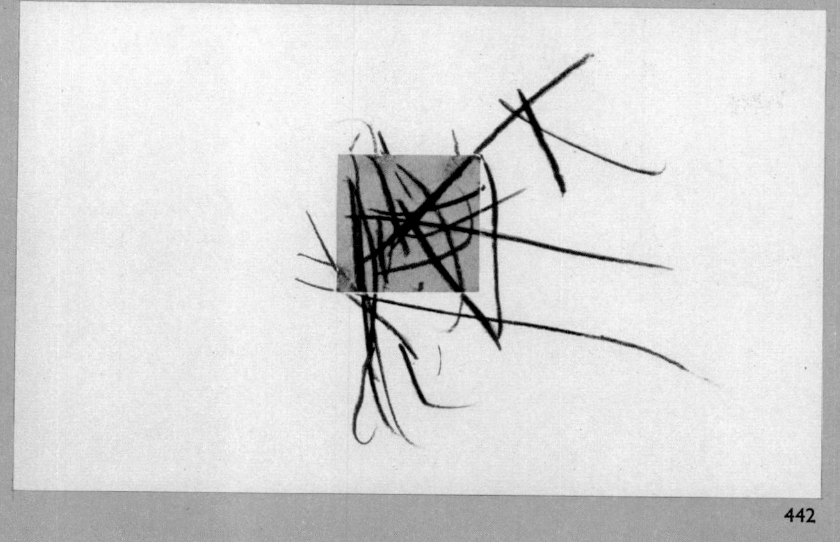

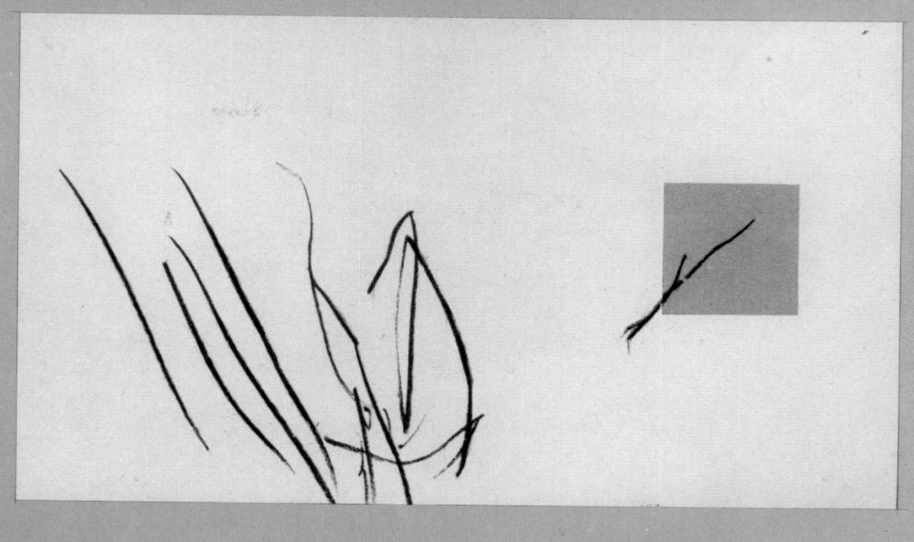

442

Finally, there is the method of pollen-analysis invented by L. von Post. Pollen-grains of different plants are not only well preserved in deposits such as peat-bogs and the bottoms of lakes, but they can be easily recognized, and their sequence and relative proportions reveal the character and succession of the contemporary vegetation surrounding their site. With the oscillations of climate represented by the waning of the Ice Age, the pattern of vegetation during Late Glacial and Post-Glacial times changed, and it has been worked out in detail and forms a standard with which new observations can be compared and dated. In the Late Glacial period, tundra-like conditions prevailed, characterized by grasses with scattered trees of birch or pine. During the Post-Glacial period birch and pine forest took the place of tundra, followed by mixed oak and alder as the leading species, gradually replaced by beech, hornbeam, and herbaceous plant communities (Pl. 499).

MAN'S APE-LIKE ANCESTORS IN THE MIOCENE AND PLIOCENE PERIODS

Proconsul, Oreopithecus, Kenyapithecus, 30,000,000 to 2,000,000 years ago
The fossil to which the name *Proconsul* has been given was a genus of primitive anthropoid ape, abundant in East Africa during early Miocene times, about 25 million years ago. The first specimen was found in 1926–7 at Koru, on Lake Victoria. Further work around the northeast corner of the lake, particularly on Rusinga Island, by Dr. L. S. B. Leakey and others, led to the discovery of nearly 200 further specimens, representing three species of different sizes: *Proconsul*

443

446

447

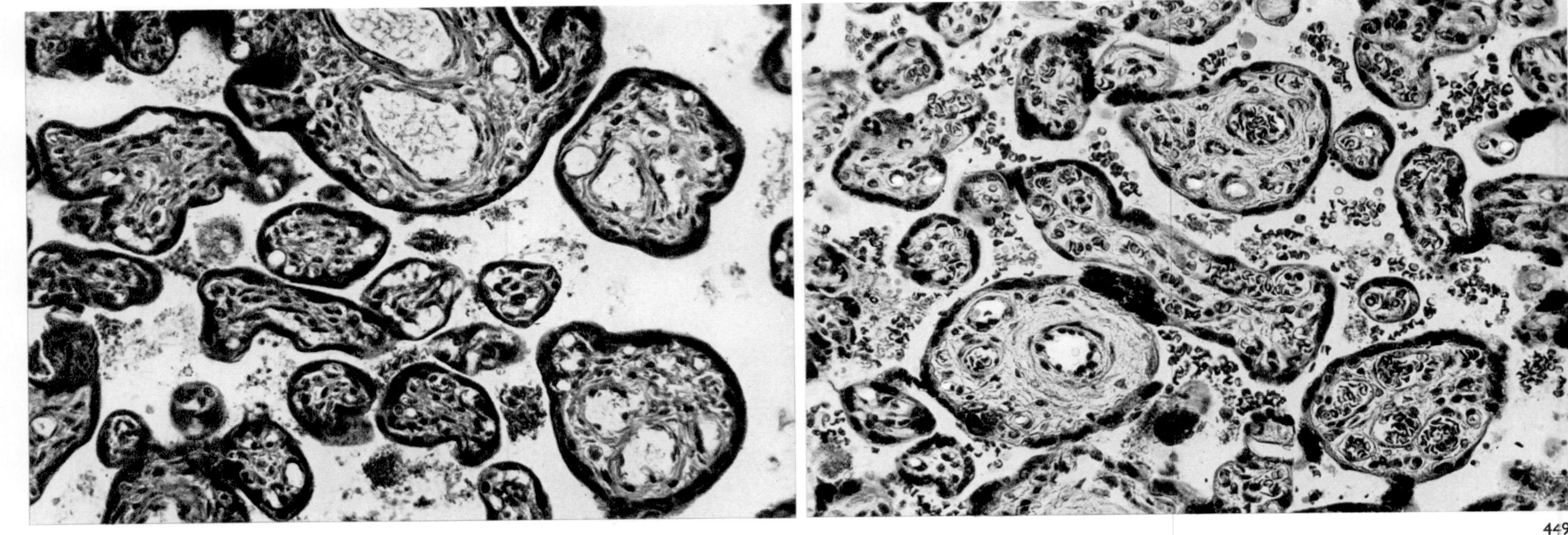

448

449

450

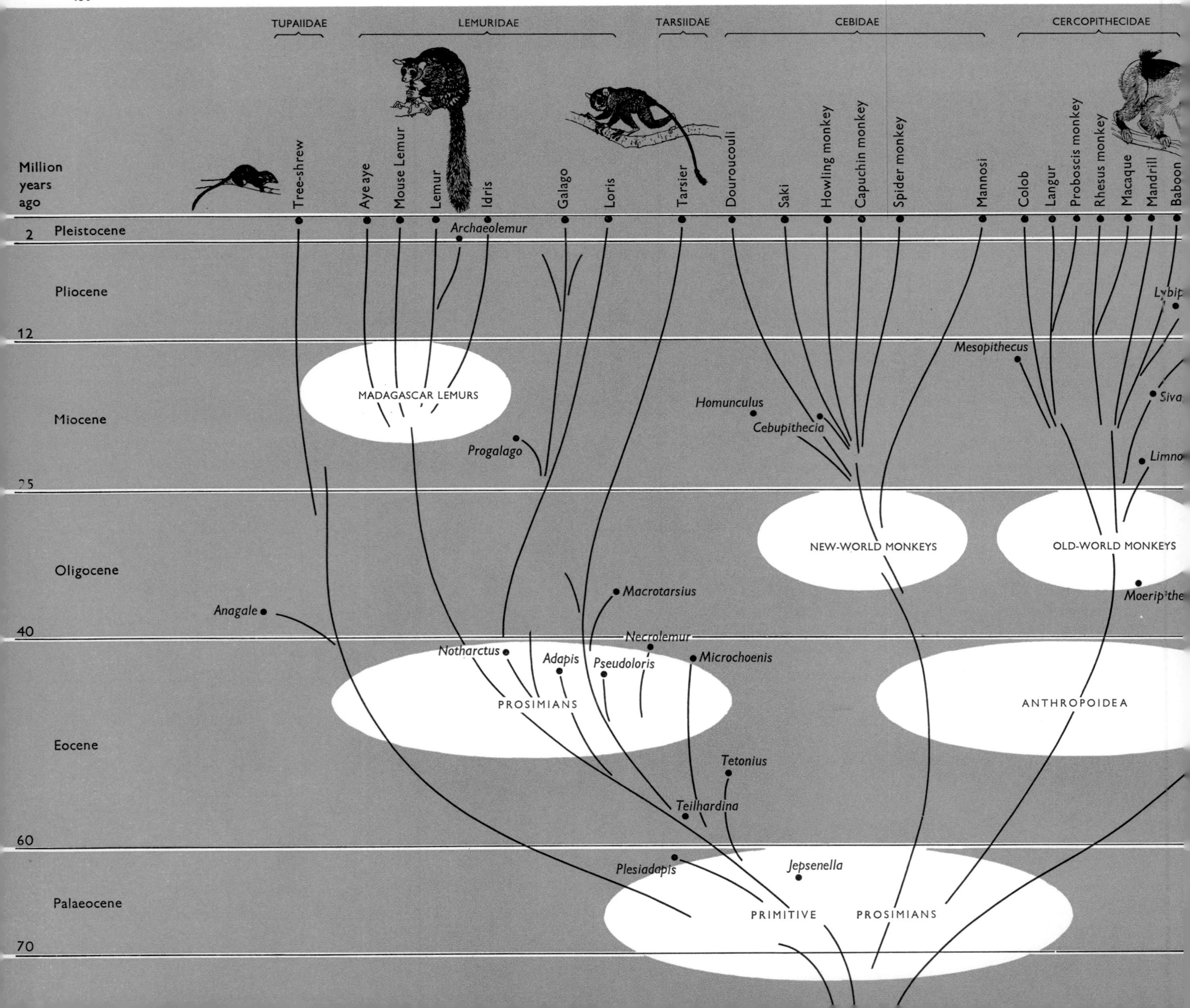

TUPAIIDAE LEMURIDAE TARSIIDAE CEBIDAE CERCOPITHECIDAE

Tree-shrew
Aye aye
Mouse Lemur
Lemur
Idris
Galago
Loris
Tarsier
Douroucouli
Saki
Howling monkey
Capuchin monkey
Spider monkey
Mannosi
Colob
Langur
Proboscis monkey
Rhesus monkey
Macaque
Mandrill
Baboon

Million years ago

2 Pleistocene
Pliocene
12
Miocene
25
Oligocene
40
Eocene
60
Palaeocene
70

Archaeolemur
Lybip
Mesopithecus
MADAGASCAR LEMURS
Homunculus
Cebupithecia
Siva
Progalago
Limno
NEW-WORLD MONKEYS
OLD-WORLD MONKEYS
Macrotarsius
Moeripithe
Anagale
Necrolemur
Notharctus
Adapis
Pseudoloris
Microchoenis
PROSIMIANS
ANTHROPOIDEA
Tetonius
Teilhardina
Plesiadapis
Jepsenella
PRIMITIVE PROSIMIANS

Nourishment in the Womb

The chief difference between the process of reproduction in primates and other mammals lies in the structure of the placenta, the organ to which the embryo is attached in the mother's womb, effecting and regulating the interchange of substances between mother and embryo across a membrane separating the two blood systems. The placenta takes the form of very numerous minute finger-like tufts of embryonic tissue containing blood-vessels, bathed in spaces through which the mother's blood circulates. Oxygen and food-materials diffuse through the membranous walls of the tufts into the embryonic circulation, while carbon dioxide and excretory products diffuse out. When a portion of placenta is cut in section, the embryonic tufts appear cut through either across or along their lengths.
The placenta of the gorilla, **448,** is so similar to that of man, **449,** that they are almost impossible to tell apart. It has been calculated that the area of the surface of the placental tufts through which the exchanges of substances take place reaches fifteen square yards, an area comparable with that of the human intestinal tract.

The Family Tree of Man

450. In this diagram of man's family tree, traced since the Primitive Prosimians emerged from the Cretaceous Period, 70 million years ago, the position of the most important fossils is indicated showing their approximate ages and places in the geological record and their affinities to living forms in the Primates as a whole.
The stock forked into the Prosimians *sensu stricto* and the Anthropoidea; the former gave rise to Tupaiidae (tree-shrews), Lemurs, and Tarsiers; the latter to New-World monkeys, Old-World Monkeys, and Hominoidea; the latter into Pongidae (apes) and Hominidae (men). While there are still gaps in the fossil series, there are already sufficient well preserved fossils known to confirm Darwin's conclusion that man is descended from ancestors which, if alive today, would undoubtedly be classified with the apes, and also T. H. Huxley's statement that whatever system of organs be studied, the structural differences between man, gorilla, and chimpanzee, are not so great as those that separate the gorilla from the monkeys. **451.** The evolutionary tree of the Hominoidea shown in greater detail. When seen on this scale, the general trends towards the Pongidae (apes) and Hominidae (men) became apparent after a split at a stage resembling *Proconsul*.

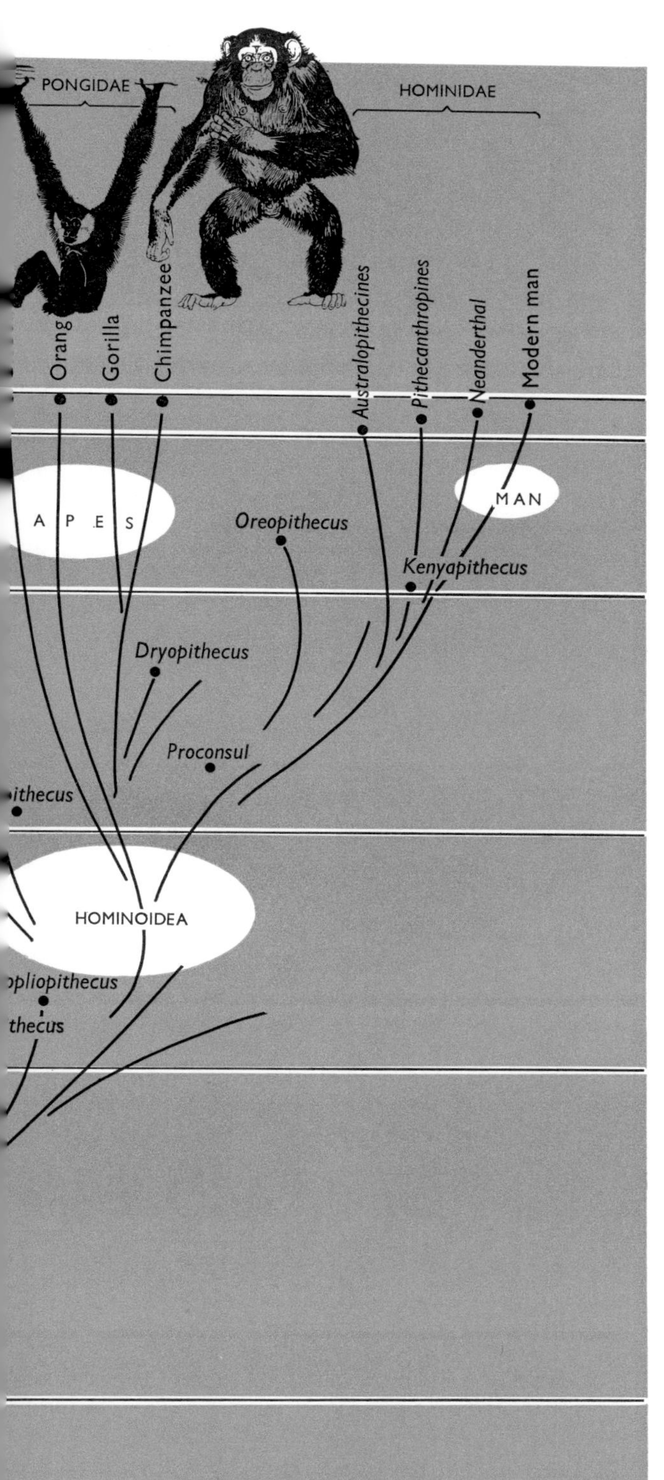

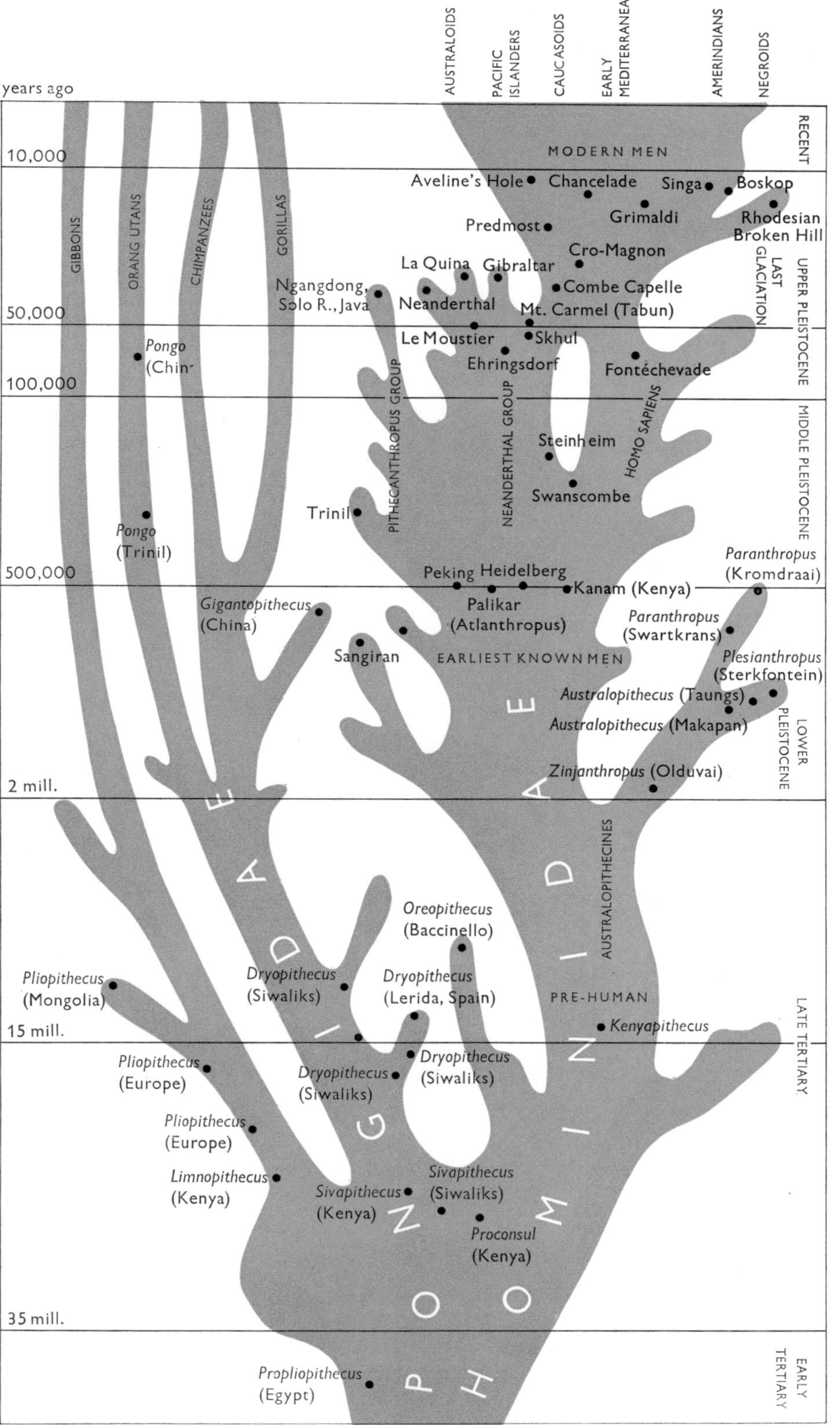

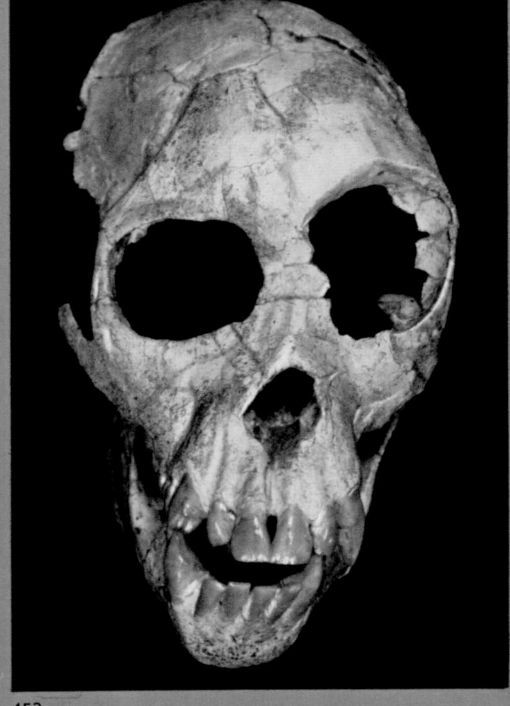

452

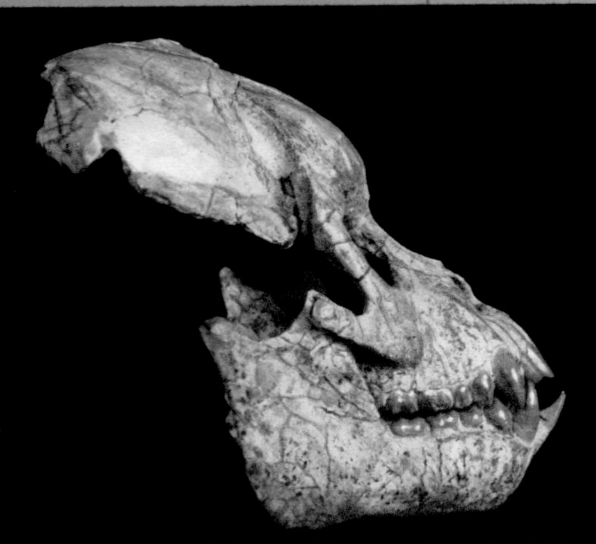

453

454

africanus, no larger than a modern gibbon, *P. nyanzae*, about the size of a small chimpanzee, and *P. major*, nearly as large as a gorilla. The specimens included one nearly complete skull, many jaw fragments and isolated teeth, and a few pieces of limbs including the greater part of the hand (Pl. 452–455).

Proconsul was an early member of the family that includes the specialized great apes of today, and its generalized, monkey-like characters indicate that it was close to, or even part of, the common stock from which the great apes and man arose. Related forms living in Europe and Asia during Miocene and Pliocene times are known under the name *Dryopithecus*.

From the remains of *Proconsul* that have been found it is possible to form some idea of the probable appearance of this early type of ape. The middle-sized species was more lightly built than a chimpanzee. It was an agile monkey-like creature, capable not only of climbing trees and swinging by its long arms from bough to bough, but also of running along the ground on all fours. Whether, like all apes of today, it was tailless, is uncertain. Judging from the associated fossil plants and animals, *Proconsul* lived in tracts of forests affording a plentiful supply of fruits and other food. These forests extended along river courses, and were separated by bushy grassland. Volcanoes were active in the region, and it is thought that forest fires resulting from volcanic eruption may have been responsible for occasionally driving these forest-dwellers into the open country where they became exposed to different conditions of natural selection.

Another find by L. S. B. Leakey in Kenya has provided evidence of an ape-like human ancestor from the base of the Pliocene period, about fourteen million years ago. It consists of remains of jaws and teeth of an animal called *Kenyapithecus* showing resemblances to the Hominidae and not to the Pongidae.

Another fossil form of considerable interest is *Oreopithecus* from the Lower Pliocene beds of Italy about ten million years ago. Specimens have been known for some time, but the successful researches of Dr. J. Hürzeler in a coal mine that had been a peat bed at Baccinello near Florence, have greatly added to knowledge. *Oreopithecus* was near the base of the stem leading to the Hominidae and it showed some features characteristic of man, such as approximation to an upright gait; but in other respects such as the long arms, it was too specialized to find a place on the direct line of man's ancestry. At the time that it was living, the Alps had been uplifted and the drainage from them must have led to the formation of lakes and bogs in the forests, by the side of which *Oreopithecus* lived (Pl. 456–458).

THE TRANSITION FROM APE TO MAN

Australopithecus, 2,000,000 to 400,000 years ago

In 1924 Raymond Dart obtained from a cave deposit of Lower Pleistocene age in a limestone quarry at Taung, Bechuanaland, the fossilized skull of a young ape-like creature which he named *Australopithecus*, meaning 'southern ape'. In some respects it appeared almost human, and was regarded by Dart as a link between apes and man. However, since the skulls of young apes at the present day are more human in form than those of the adults, many authorities doubted whether this fossil was more closely related to man than is any other ape.

Between 1936 and 1951 Robert Broom found young and adult skulls, as well as other bones, of this and other allied forms in dolomite cave-deposits near Krugersdorp in the Transvaal. Other specimens have since been found in Tanganyika and near Lake Chad. At Olduvai in Tanganyika L. S. B. and Mrs. Leakey found a splendid skull to which they have given the name *Zinjanthropus*. It has been dated by the potassium-argon method at about one and three quarter million years. Some of the larger specimens were given the name of *Paranthropus* but it is usual to include them all under the name of Australopithecines. From the study of all the specimens now available, it is believed that the Australopithecines, which lived from about two million to half a million years ago, were early members of the family to which man belongs, some of which were ancestral to *Pithecanthropus* (Pl. 459–466).

The Australopithecines were small, about four feet in height, the later ones taller, with a brain scarcely exceeding in size that of a gorilla, but with teeth of essentially human type. The canine teeth instead of projecting as tusks, were small and resembled the incisors, and the whole battery of teeth was set in the jaws in a smoothly-curved arch, as in man, and not along the sides of a rectangle as in apes. The backbone, hip-girdle, and limbs were of human form and proportions, the arms shorter than in apes. They walked upright on two legs, and, unlike apes, were able to live away from forests in dry open country, as is known from the fossil remains of other animals associated with them. The combination in an organism of features characteristic of the ancestral primitive form and of other features characteristic of the descendant progressive form provides an example of the principle of mosaic evolution (p. 61), which is of wide occurrence. In the Australopithecines, the small brain-case and large jaws are primitive and ape-like; the teeth, backbone, hip-girdle and limbs are progressive and man-like. The lower jaw and parietal bones of the skull of a young individual found at Olduvai, Tanganyika, by L. S. B. Leakey in 1960, show a departure from other Australopithecines in the direction of *Homo*.

Life in the open country was precarious owing to the danger of attack from large carnivores, against which the Australopithecines had no natural defence, and their survival depended upon superior intelligence, which was also required for catching animal food to supplement the meagre vegetable diet available in dry grassland.

Even the earliest Australopithecines must have been able to make effective use of stones and sticks or bones with their hands, which were no longer employed in locomotion. The discovery of pebble-tools in close association with Australopithecine remains at several sites leaves no doubt that the most advanced members of this group were toolmakers, between one and two million years ago.

EARLIEST MEN

Pithecanthropus, 600,000 to 300,000 years ago

The earliest Hominines, undoubted men on all counts, were of the genus *Pithecanthropus*, known from Java, China, Algeria, and Tanganyika. They were not only capable of tool-making, but of extending their range beyond the tropics by the use of fire and rock shelters; they were hunters and meat-eaters. These extensions of culture were closely linked with expansion of the brain. The average brain-size of *Pithecanthropus* was twice that of *Australopithecus*.

455

The Picture Gallery of Man's Family

Proconsul is a fossil Hominoid that occupied a place near the fork between the Pongidae and the Hominidae in the Early Miocene period in East Africa about 25 million years ago. **452.** Front view, **453,** side view of the skull of *Proconsul*. In the smooth contour of the forehead, the small size of the brain in relation to the jaws, and the nasal aperture, it is more primitive than those of living apes and bears resemblance to Old-World monkeys.
454. Reconstruction of the head of *Proconsul*. **455.** Reconstruction of the appearance of *Proconsul nyanzae* shown against the probable background of its environment of forests and bushy grassland. Volcanoes were active in the regions inhabited by *Proconsul* and it is probable that fires started by volcanic eruptions may have driven them out of the forests into open country where conditions were different, and natural selection had greater opportunities of working on variations leading to more developed forms (M. Wilson).
Oreopithecus is a fossil Hominid from the Lower Pliocene Period about 10 million years ago, that occupied a place near the base of the stem leading to man. **456.** Discovery of a specimen of *Oreopithecus* in a mine at Baccinello, Tuscany, a region where drainage from the newly-uplifted Alps and Appenines formed bogs in which *Oreopithecus* was fossilised. **457.** Specimen of *Oreopithecus in situ* in the mine before disengagement. **458.** Result of preparation of a specimen of *Oreopithecus* by freeing it from the matrix on both sides. It showed features characteristic of the Hominid group leading towards man, such as an approximation to an upright gait, short face, low canine teeth, and the proportions of the molar teeth; but the length of its arms and the shortness of its legs show that it was already specialised in a direction parallel to that found in apes and was not on the direct line of evolution leading towards man.

458

Man-like Apes

Australopithecines were a widespread group of Hominids that lived in Central, East, and South Africa in the Lower Pleistocene Period, from 2 million to half a million years ago. **459.** Reconstruction of the juvenile Taungs skull, side view, showing smooth forehead, discovered by R. Dart in 1925. **460.** Cast of the skull of *Australopithecus transvaalensis* in front view, **461,** in side view, showing the fairly smooth contour of the forehead, although in more highly developed forms, called *Plesianthropus* the brow-ridges might reach large size. The brain-case had a capacity of about 600 cubic centimetres, or half that of man. **463.** Reconstruction of the head of an australopithecine. **462.** Reconstruction of an australopithecine showing the upright gait approximating to that of man (M. Wilson). **465.** Discovery of the skull of *Zinjanthropus* by L. S. B. and Mrs. Leakey at Olduvai. **464.** Side views of skulls of a South African australopithecine (*above*) and *Zinjanthropus* (*below*). **466.** Comparison of the palate of *Zinjanthropus* on the right and of modern man on the left. The teeth in the former are larger but their shape and setting in the jaw are human. Advanced australopithecines were the first makers of tools out of pebbles.

462

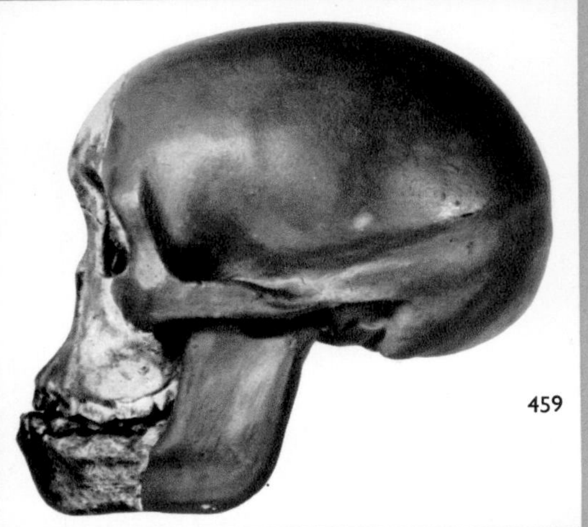

459

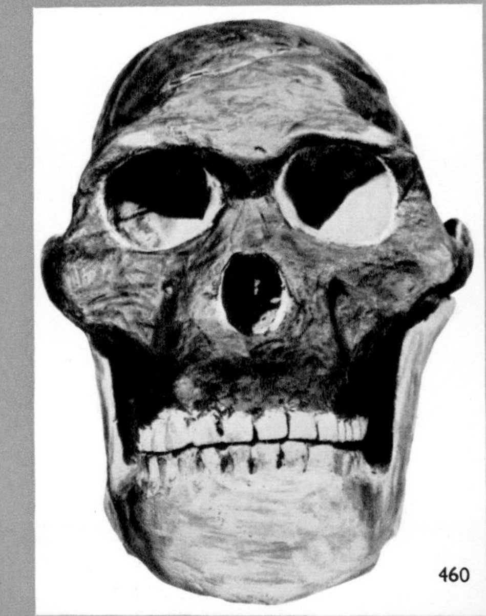

460

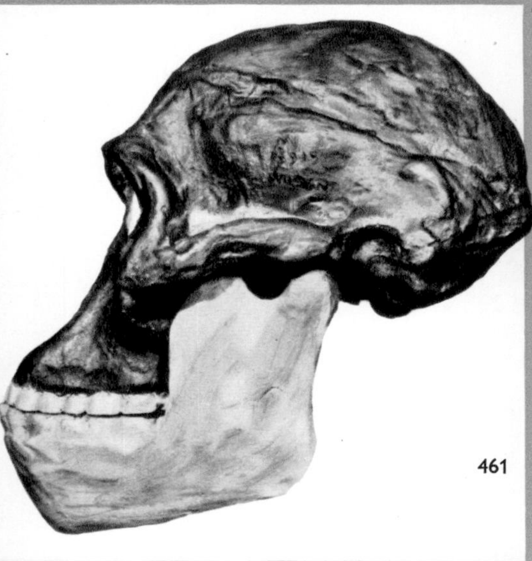

461

463

While Eugène Dubois was searching for fossils in Pleistocene river gravels in central Java in 1891, he found scattered fragments of a skeleton, including the top of the skull, isolated teeth, and a thigh bone, which he regarded as representing a form intermediate between apes and man. He called it *Pithecanthropus erectus*, meaning the upright ape-man. The name *Pithecanthropus* had already been proposed in 1866 by Ernst Haeckel for the hypothetical 'missing link' (Pl. 467, 468).

In 1937 G. H. R. von Koenigswald obtained a second, more complete skull of the same species. From deposits of earlier age nearby he recovered parts of the skull of a related but more ape-like form and also the skull of an infant of the same species, *Pithecanthropus modjokertensis*. These early men with a cranial capacity ranging in the adult from 775 to 1,000 cc. lived in Java during Middle Pleistocene times, between 600,000 and 300,000 years ago.

The thigh bone of *Pithecanthropus* was clearly that of an upright walking man, and this confirms the indications already found in *Australopithecus* that man's legs evolved in advance of his head, which for a long time retained ape-like features such as the great overhanging brow-ridges. This is another example of the principle of mosaic evolution showing the different speeds at which the different parts of the body evolved.

In 1927, excavations in search of fossils in cave-deposits at Choukoutien, thirty miles southwest of Peking, led to the discovery of an isolated tooth recognized by Davidson Black as that of an early type of man, which he named *Sinanthropus* (man of China). Further excavations at Choukoutien, by Chinese and European scientists, resulted in the bringing to light of remains of more than forty individuals of this extinct species of man, including 6 incomplete skulls, 12 jaws, 150 isolated teeth, and a few scraps of limb-bones. A comparative study of the Choukoutien skulls shows that they represented the same general type of man as the Javanese fossils, and for this reason they are now included in the same genus but under a different specific name: *Pithecanthropus pekinensis*. The cranial capacity of this species ranged from 1,000 to 1,300 cc (Pl. 469–472).

The associated remains of animals and pollen indicate that Peking man lived during the Mindel Glaciation in Middle Pleistocene times, about 400,000 years ago. The remains of Peking man were found with ashes of fires, broken bones of the animals he hunted (mainly deer), crudely-chipped tools of quartz and other hard stones, and the kernels of the cherry-like fruit *Celtis*. There is evidence that Peking man was a cannibal with a predilection for human brains, for many skulls have been found showing signs of having been broken open.

The implements and other remnants of the activities of early man constitute what is known as a *culture*, the earliest of which are called Palaeolithic. *Pithecanthropus* was in the Lower Palaeolithic stage of culture, and the remains found at Olduvai (see below) were associated with implements of the type known as Chellean (Pl. 491).

It will already have become obvious that one of the difficulties encountered in describing the stages of man's ancestry consists in the fact that if a Linnaean name is ascribed to a group of fossils, it implies the attribution of a greater degree of uniformity than in fact exists in a strain of organisms evolving rapidly, as man's ancestors were. This was already noticeable in the range of variation found in the group described in the previous section to which the name Australopithecine is given for want of a better. The same amount of latitude is necessary when considering the Pithecanthropines. Olduvai in Tanganyika, the beds of which constitute a veritable natural museum of human evolution, yielded to L. S. B. Leakey in 1960 a large skull associated with implements of the primitive type of culture known as Chellean. While agreeing with many features of other specimens of *Pithecanthropus*, this Chellean Olduvai skull, which appears to have been roughly contemporary with Java and Peking men, shows departure from the Pithecanthropine type in the direction of *Homo* (Pl. 473–476).

THE EMERGENCE OF MODERN MAN

Earliest men in Europe, 300,000 to 100,000 years ago

The oldest known trace of man in Europe is the massive lower jaw found by O. Schoetensack at Mauer near Heidelberg in 1907 at a depth of 82 feet in sand laid down by the river Neckar at the end of Lower Pleistocene times, about 300,000 years ago. The jaw is remarkable for its huge size and rather ape-like receding chin.

464 465 466

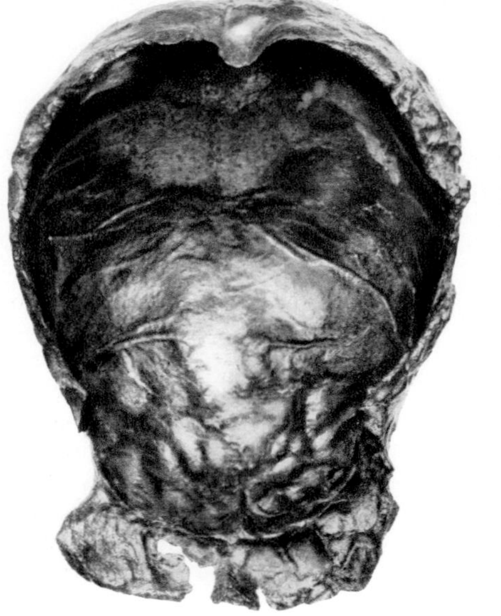

467

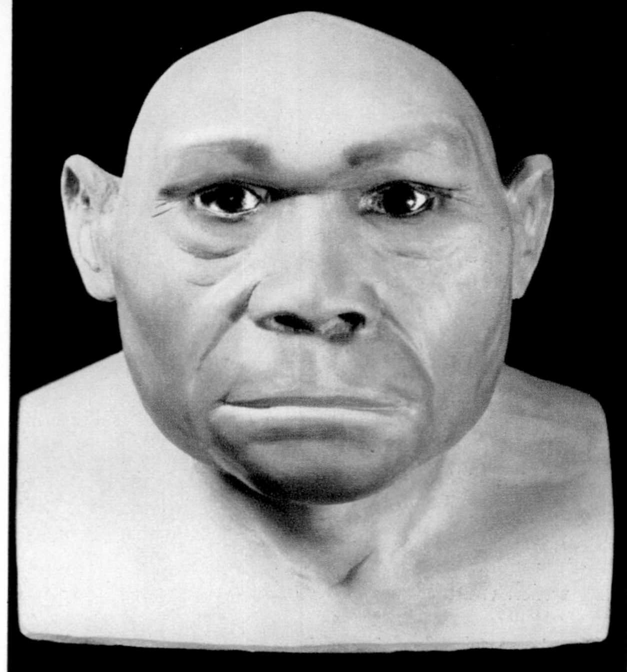

468

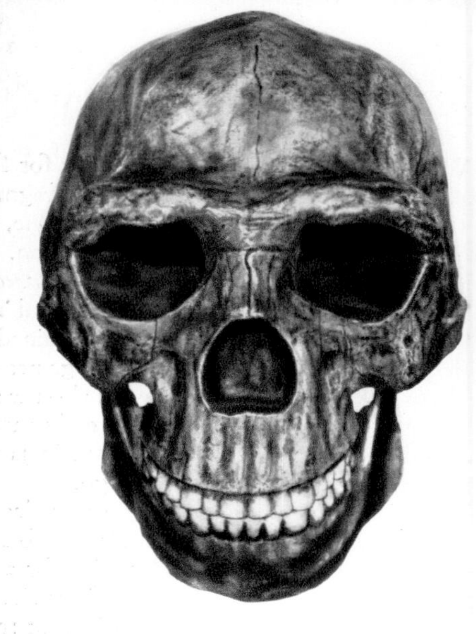

469

472

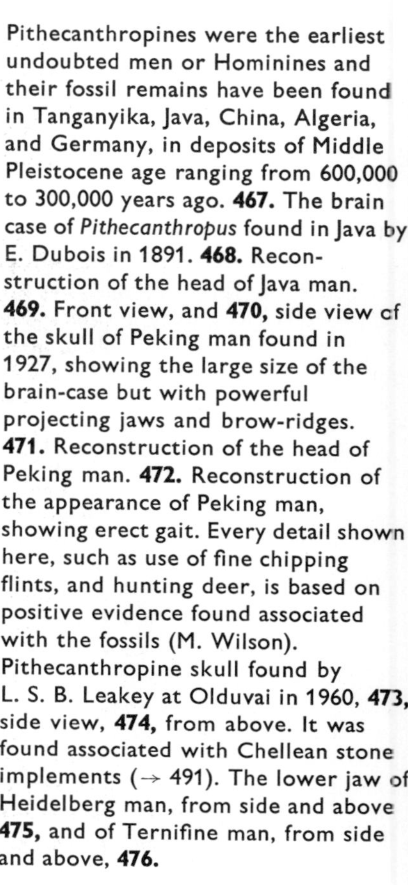

Ape-like Men

Pithecanthropines were the earliest undoubted men or Hominines and their fossil remains have been found in Tanganyika, Java, China, Algeria, and Germany, in deposits of Middle Pleistocene age ranging from 600,000 to 300,000 years ago. **467.** The brain case of *Pithecanthropus* found in Java by E. Dubois in 1891. **468.** Reconstruction of the head of Java man. **469.** Front view, and **470,** side view of the skull of Peking man found in 1927, showing the large size of the brain-case but with powerful projecting jaws and brow-ridges. **471.** Reconstruction of the head of Peking man. **472.** Reconstruction of the appearance of Peking man, showing erect gait. Every detail shown here, such as use of fine chipping flints, and hunting deer, is based on positive evidence found associated with the fossils (M. Wilson). Pithecanthropine skull found by L. S. B. Leakey at Olduvai in 1960, **473,** side view, **474,** from above. It was found associated with Chellean stone implements (→ 491). The lower jaw of Heidelberg man, from side and above **475,** and of Ternifine man, from side and above, **476.**

473

474

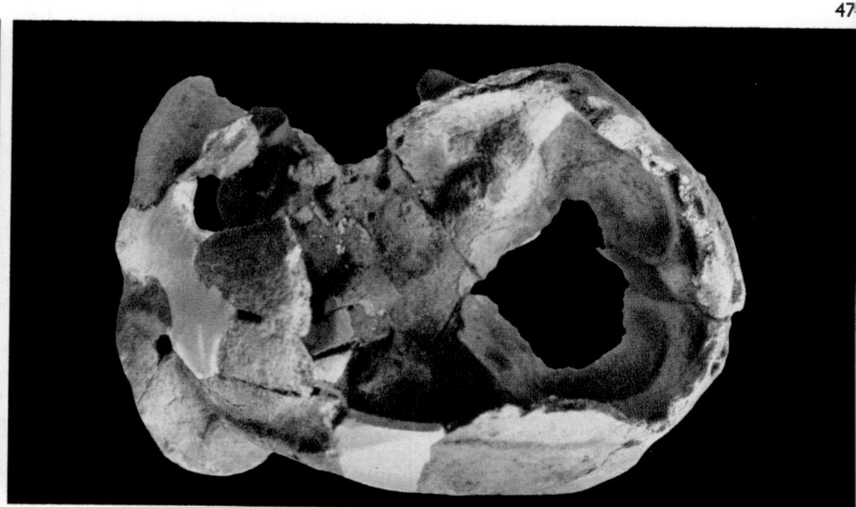

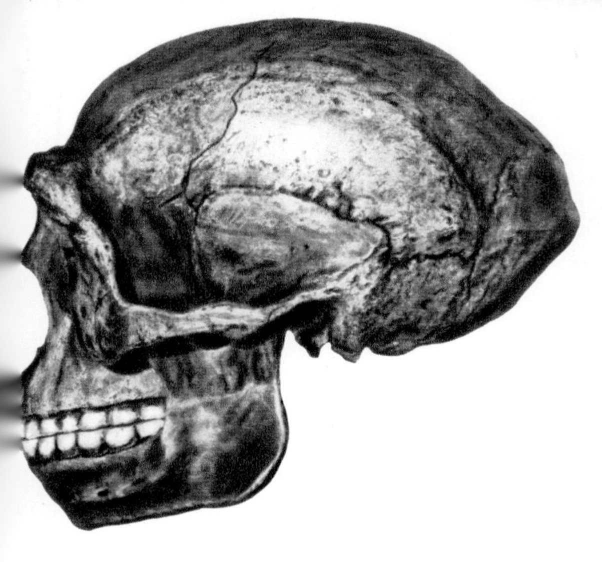

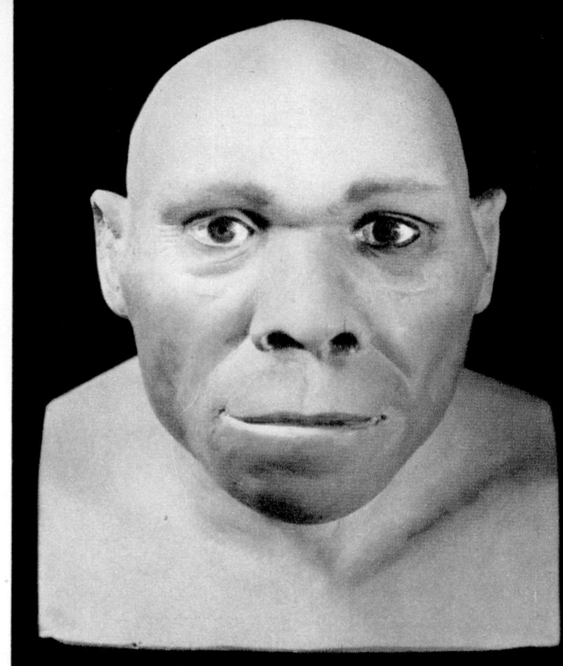

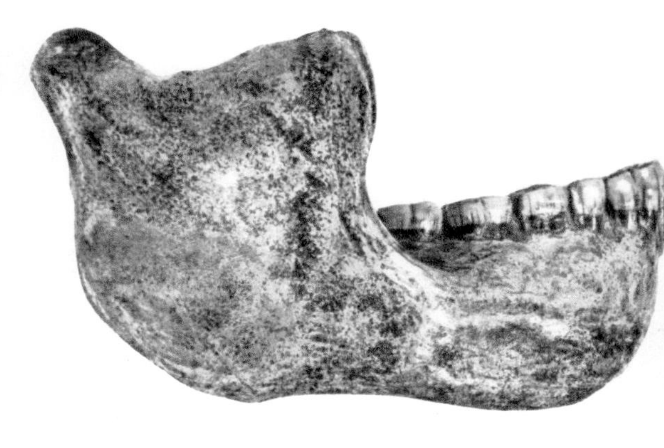

470

471

The hindpart or ascending ramus is exceptionally broad, providing a large area for the attachment of the masseter muscle used in chewing. The top edge is not deeply notched as it is in the modern human jaw. The teeth are strongly implanted and have roots as large as their crowns, thus being well adapted to a coarse diet. No undoubted implements have been found with *Homo heidelbergensis*.

Three lower jaws similar in some respects to the Heidelberg jaw were found during 1953-5 in early Middle Pleistocene lake beds at Ternifine, Algeria, and were referred by C. Arambourg to a new genus: *Atlanthropus*. They were associated with an early type of stone hand-axe. The actual status of Ternifine man, like that of Heidelberg man, will remain doubtful until the greater part of a brain case is found; but it appears likely that these men belonged to a North African-European stock in process of emerging from the *Pithecanthropus* stage.

There are indications that by the end of Middle Pleistocene times, in Europe at least, men had passed beyond the *Pithecanthropus* stage and included variable types constituting the stock from which emerged both *Homo sapiens* and the less successful *H. neanderthalensis*. The skull found in 1933 at Steinheim near Stuttgart in river-sand of Second Interglacial age, is typical of this early pre-neanderthal or pre-sapiens group. The Steinheim skull has fairly heavy brow-ridges and a strongly built upper jaw with large teeth; but the vault is moderately high and the back is well filled out as in *Homo sapiens*.

In 1935 and 1936 A. T. Marston discovered two fragments of a human skull in the gravels of the 100-foot terrace of the Thames at Swanscombe, Kent. They were the occipital bone (forming the back and part of the base of the skull), and the left parietal bone (which forms part of its roof). The two pieces, which fitted together perfectly, were found 8 yards apart but in the same seam of gravel, 24 feet below the surface. In 1955 excavations by B. O. and J. Wymer and A. Gibson yielded the right parietal bone, which lay 17 yards away from the other fragments (Pl. 477, 480).

The Swanscombe skull was associated with Acheulian flint 'hand-axes' and with the remains of animals, some now extinct, such as the elephant *Elephas antiquus*, which inhabited the woodlands bordering the Thames during the second Interglacial period, 200,000 to 100,000 years ago. Fluorine, nitrogen, and uranium tests confirmed that the skull and animal remains were contemporaneous.

Apart from the unusual thickness, the parts of the Swanscombe skull preserved do not differ from the corresponding bones in some modern crania. The brain-case had a capacity of about 1,325 cc., close to the average in modern man. The nasal air sinuses extended very far back, suggesting that the face and jaws were of heavy build. As the frontal bone of Swanscombe man has not yet been found, it is uncertain whether the brows were ridgeless as in the Fontéchevade skull and in modern man, or had overhanging brow-ridges as in the contemporaneous Steinheim skull. Even without knowing how the frontal bone of Swanscombe man was shaped, we can be certain that it did not conform to the specialized Neanderthal type.

Neanderthaloid man in Asia and Africa, 100,000 to 25,000 years ago

The name Neanderthal man was given to an extinct type of man represented by the fossil skull found at Neanderthal, but that rather specialized type was descended from an earlier and more generalized type usually known as Neanderthaloid. In western Asia Neanderthaloids are represented by the Palestinian Mount Carmel man. In the Far East and in Africa there were similar types such as the Solo man of Java, Saldanha man of South Africa, and Rhodesian man of central Africa. All these extinct forms of man resembling but not identical with Neanderthal man are called Neanderthaloids.

Remains of more than a dozen Neanderthaloids have been found in the caves of Palestine, notably in caves named Tabun and Skhul in the Wadi el-Mughara ('Valley of Caves') on the western side of Mount Carmel. The Palestinian Neanderthaloids were remarkable for their variability, which was greater than in any community of modern times. They ranged from individuals with almost typical Neanderthal skulls such as were found at Tabun, to others found in the Skhul cave which were barely distinguishable from modern man, *Homo sapiens* (Pl. 477, 478).

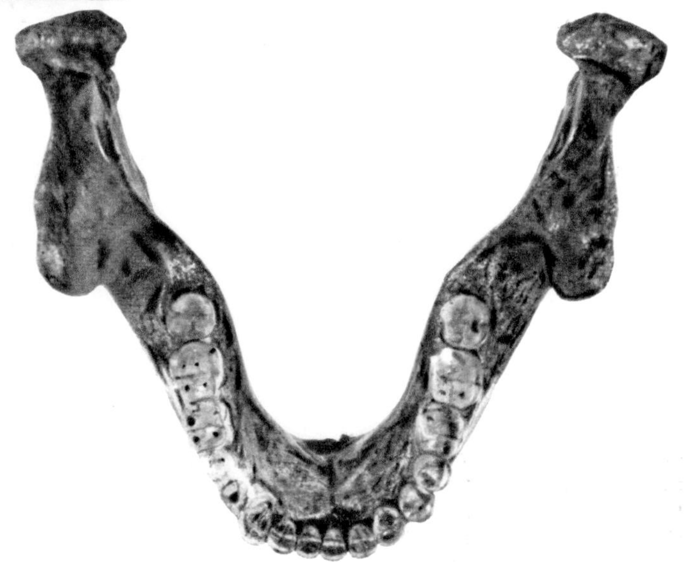

475

476

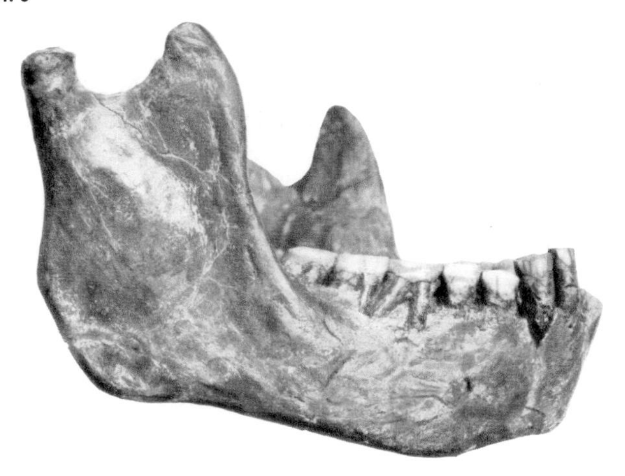

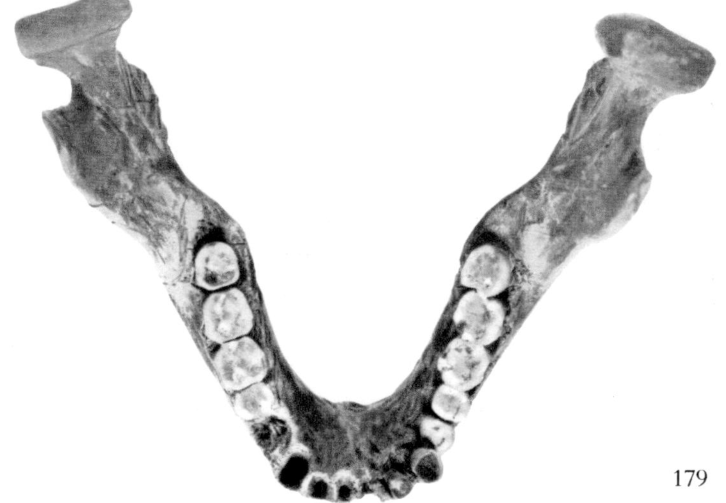

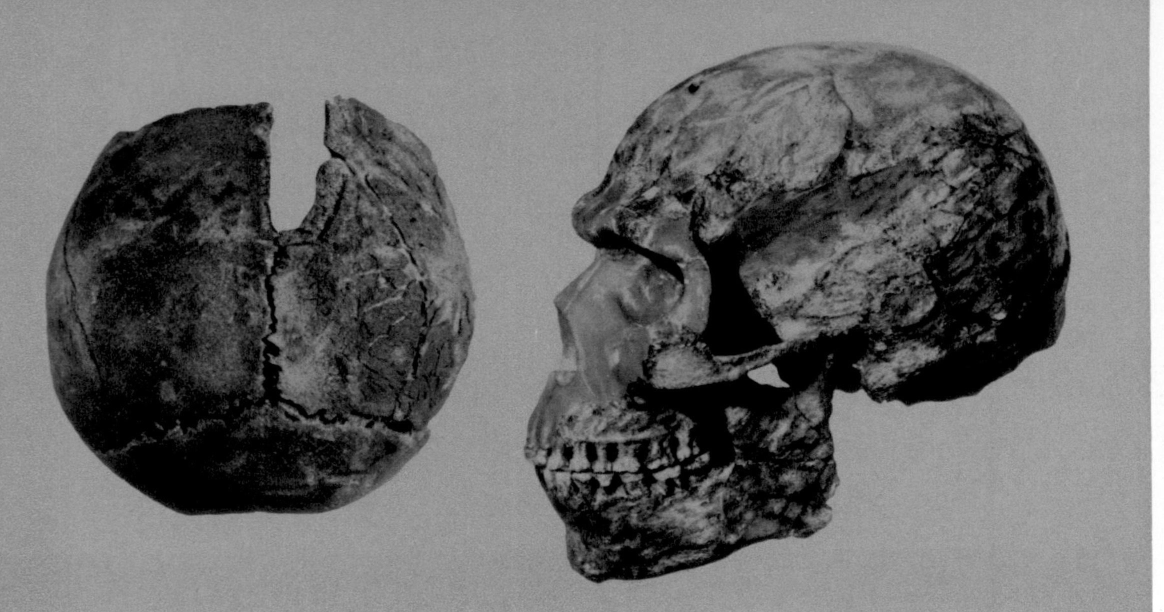

477

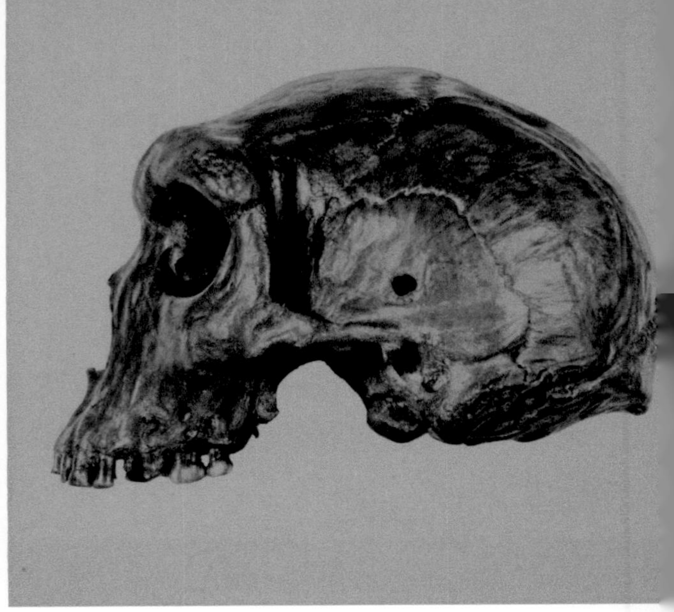

478

The first True Men of the Genus *Homo*

Swanscombe man lived in woodlands bordering on the Thames during a warm Interglacial period associated with tools of Acheulian type and animals such as *Elephas antiquus* about 200,000 years ago. The left parietal and occipital bones of the skull were found by A. T. Marston in 1935 and 1936; the right parietal bone was found by B. O. and J. Wymer and A. Gibson in 1955. The skull conforms to a generalised type of *Homo sapiens*, modern man. **477.** (*left*) The assembled bones of the skull. **480.** Reconstruction of the appearance of Swanscombe man. **477.** (*right*) Side view of the skull found at Skhul, Mount Carmel, an example of Neanderthaloid man who lived during the onset of the Last Glaciation, about 100,000 years ago and used implements of Mousterian type (→ 491).
478. Side and front views of the skull of Rhodesian man, a specialized type who lived during the late Pleistocene period less than 50,000 years ago.
485. Reconstruction of the head of Rhodesian man showing the large brain case but huge brow-ridges and retreating forehead.
Neanderthal man, so called from the village of that name near Düsseldorf, where the first specimen of a skull to be described was discovered in 1856, was widespread over Europe, western Asia, and northern Africa during the Last Glaciation, from 70,000 to 40,000 years ago, and his remains were associated with implements of Mousterian type (→ **491**). **479.** Front and side views of the skull of La Chapelle aux Saints man showing the prominent brow-ridges, large but low-crowned brain-case flattened at the back and absence of chin eminence. **486.** Reconstruction of the head of Neanderthal man. **482.** Discovery of a Neanderthal specimen at Shanidar, Iraq, by R. S. Solecki. **483** (*right*). Skull of Shanidar specimen *in situ*.
484. Skeleton of Shanidar specimen *in situ*.
483 (*left*). Cast of the foot of a Neanderthal man taken from a foot-print found by A. C. Blanc in the Grotta del Basua near Toirano in Italy.
481. Reconstruction of the appearance of Neanderthal man, based on the specimen found at Gibraltar in 1848 but not recognised until later. They were typically cave-dwellers (M. Wilson).

480

481

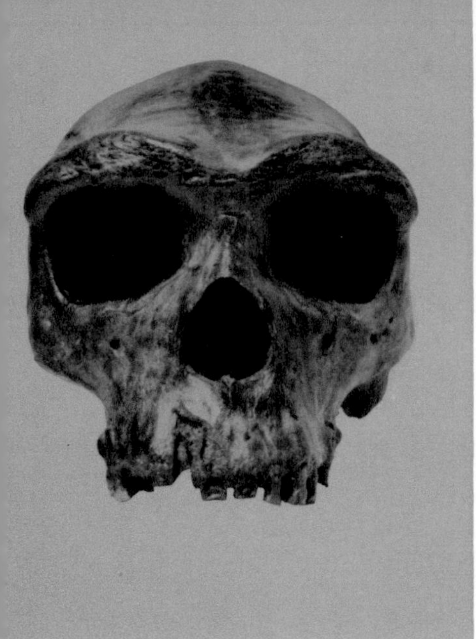

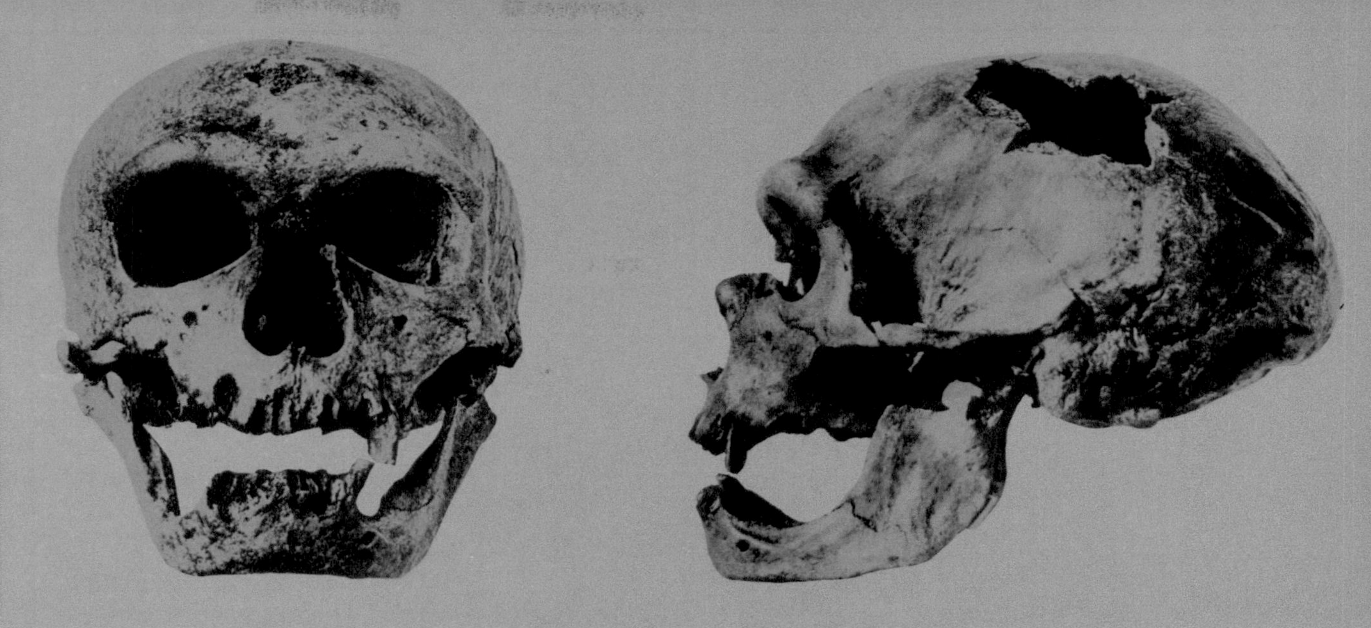

479

485

482

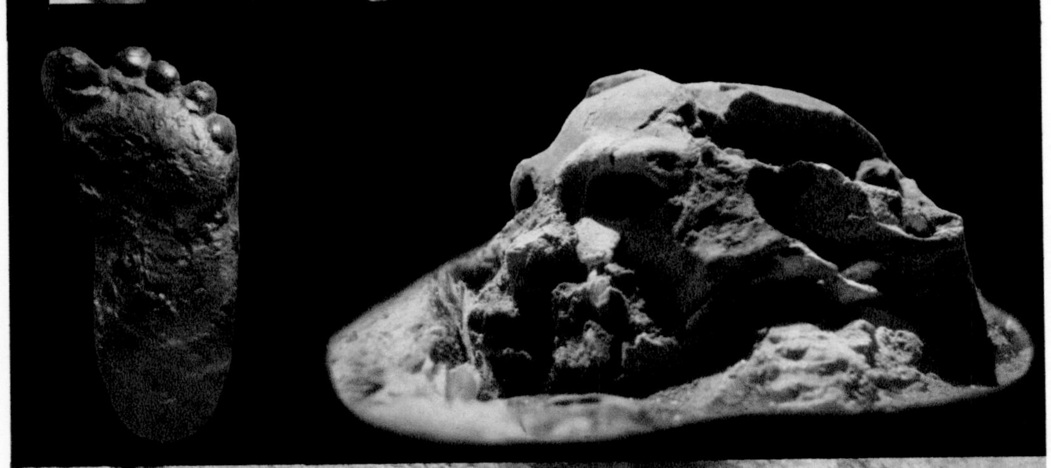

483

484

486

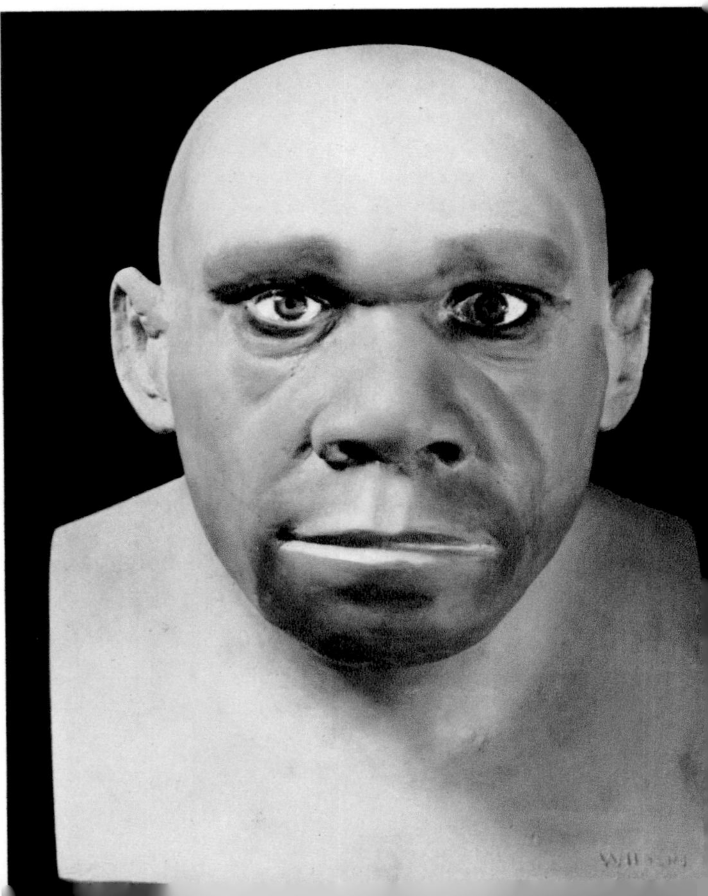

The men were tall, up to 5 feet 10 inches in height, with long straight legs, and walked upright as easily as man of today. Their skulls, although having brow-ridges, were well domed.

Mount Carmel people lived at a time when the climate of Palestine was changing because of the onset of the Würm Glaciation, and some of them have been dated from carbon-14 analysis of charcoal found with them as 43,000 years old. They appear to have been progressive Neanderthaloids in process of modification or assimilation into *Homo sapiens*. They were hunters and gatherers of wild foods; they used fire, and they buried their dead. Their implements were a variety of Mousterian.

In 1921 a fossil human skull of brutish appearance was found during the mining of lead and zinc ores at Broken Hill in Northern Rhodesia. Other human bones were also found. These remains were deep in the mineralized deposits of a cave containing quantities of broken animal bones, and Palaeolithic stone and bone implements, dating from the Late Pleistocene period, between 50,000 and 20,000 years ago (Pl. 475, 485).

The skull was described by Smith Woodward as that of an extinct species, *Homo rhodesiensis*. It is probably the skull of a male about 40 years old, and is remarkable for the heavy brow-ridges and the large size of the face and palate. The brain-case is not much smaller than the average in man of today. From the position of the opening for the spinal cord it is evident that the head was held upright. The neck muscles were powerful. The owner of the skull when alive suffered from severe dental decay, which is very rarely found in prehistoric man; and judging by his shin-bone he also suffered from arthritis. A skull of the same type was discovered near Saldanha Bay, South Africa, in 1953, where it was associated with a very late Acheulian industry.

Rhodesian and Saldanha man were the south and central African equivalents of Neanderthal man, and were replaced or absorbed by more adaptable variants of *Homo sapiens*, including Proto-Bushmen represented by the Singa skull from the Sudan.

Neanderthal man, 70,000 to 40,000 years ago

The first fossil human skull to be discovered came to light in a cave during quarrying on the north face of the Rock of Gibraltar in 1848. It was not recognized as an extinct type of man until another example was found in a cave in the Neanderthal valley near Düsseldorf in Germany in 1856, and this was confirmed when several skulls of the same type were found at Spy in Belgium. The discovery of the Neanderthal skull was recognized at the time to be a striking confirmation of Darwin's application of the theory of evolution to man.

Remains of more than sixty individuals of *Homo neanderthalensis* have since been found at widely separated localities in Europe, western Asia, and northern Africa, one of the best preserved being that found at La Chapelle-aux-Saints, Corrèze, France. Neanderthal skulls have prominent brow-ridges, which give them an ape-like appearance, and were low-crowned and flattened towards the back. Neanderthal men were stocky, about 5 feet high, and their legs were rather short with the thigh-bone bowed forward. They represent a type that is more specialized and less like modern man than their Neanderthaloid ancestors. The typical Neanderthal men were cave-dwellers. They lived in western Europe under the severe climatic conditions accompanying the first stages of the Würm Glaciation, 70,000 to 40,000 years ago. In physical evolution they had diverged from their more progressive cousins of the Mount Carmel caves mentioned above, and after a period of predominance they died out (Pl. 179, 481–484).

The culture of Neanderthal man is named Mousterian, from finds at Le Moustier near Peyzac, in the Dordogne. Mousterian stone implements were more specialized than those of earlier cultures, so that this culture is classified as Middle Palaeolithic. The principal tools were flakes with trimmed edges, points for piercing and cutting, and D-shaped side-scrapers believed to have been used in preparing skins for use as wraps. The Neanderthal people improved their adaptation to the glacial climate by the regular use of fire, and by using rock-shelters as dwelling-places. They hunted game with the aid of wooden spears and balls of stone or hardened clay used as missiles. They practised cannibalism, and, at least occasionally, buried their dead with some ceremony (Pl. 491).

Upper Palaeolithic man in Europe, 40,000 to 10,000 years ago

In Upper Pleistocene times, during a temporary amelioration of the climate beginning about 40,000 years ago, the Neanderthal men in northwest Europe were replaced by people of entirely modern type, *Homo sapiens*. These newcomers probably originated in southwest Asia, where they had developed a distinctive culture now known as Aurignacian. There are indications in Syria and Palestine that Aurignacian culture was foreshadowed in that area while the Mount Carmel people were making Mousterian implements.

Remains of the earliest undoubted representatives of *Homo sapiens* were first discovered in the rock-shelter of Cro-Magnon at Les Eyzies in the Dordogne, southwestern France, in 1868. The typical Cro-Magnons were finely built, tall, the men being sometimes over 6 feet in height, muscular, with high domed skulls and refined facial features. Several variants occurred, notably the Combe-Capelle or Predmost type, with larger brow-ridges; the Grimaldi type, of negroid appearance; and the Chancelade type, with some resemblance to the Eskimo (Pl. 486–488.)

In France three main cultures have been recognized in deposits left by *Homo sapiens* in caves and in the open, during the various stages of the last glacial period. These cultures are classed as Upper Palaeolithic and have been named as follows, the oldest being the lowest (Pl. 492):

3. Magdalenian (from La Madeleine, Dordogne); early 15,000 B.C., late 11,000 B.C.
2. Solutrean (from Solutré, Saône-et-Loire); earliest, 18,000 B.C.
1. Aurignacian (from Aurignac, Haute-Garonne); 30,000 to 20,000 B.C.

The people with Aurignacian culture, some of them dated by carbon-14 analysis, were mainly of Cro-Magnon and Combe-Capelle types, though a few were of the Grimaldi type. Solutrean and Magdalenian communities included individuals of the Cro-Magnon and Chancelade types.

Upper Palaeolithic people were more elaborately equipped than their predecesors;

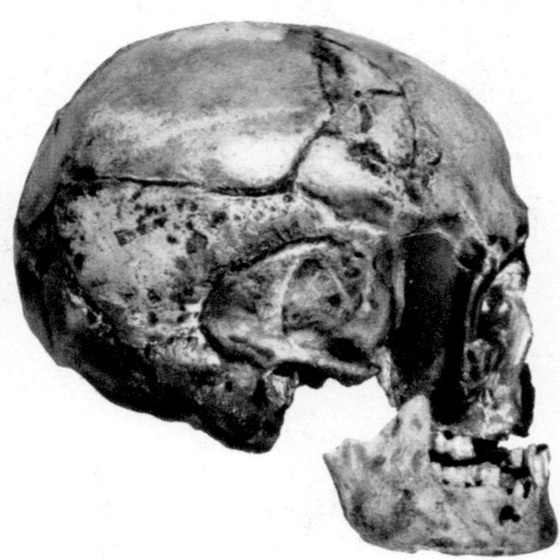

487

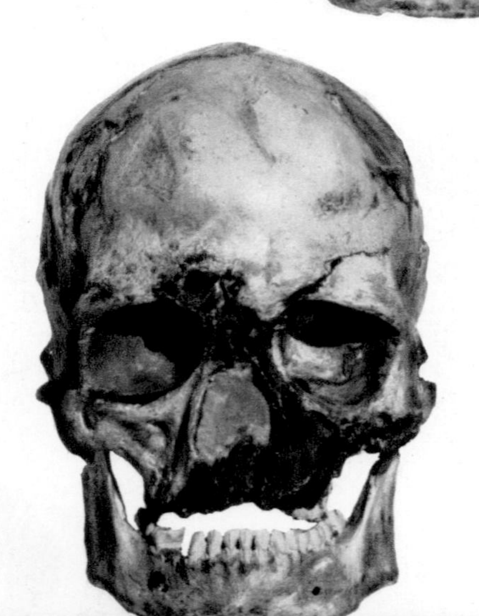

488

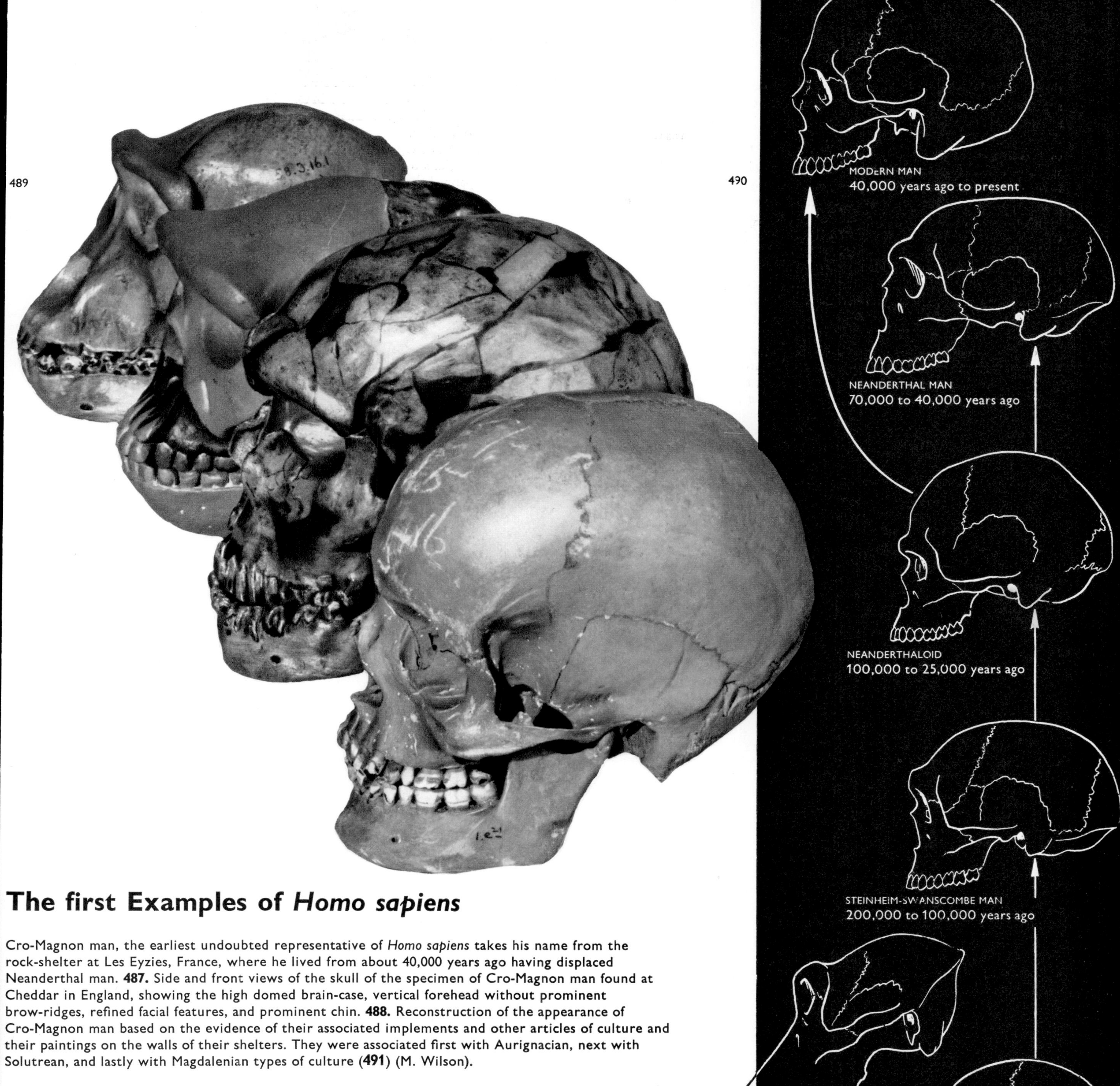

The first Examples of *Homo sapiens*

Cro-Magnon man, the earliest undoubted representative of *Homo sapiens* takes his name from the rock-shelter at Les Eyzies, France, where he lived from about 40,000 years ago having displaced Neanderthal man. **487.** Side and front views of the skull of the specimen of Cro-Magnon man found at Cheddar in England, showing the high domed brain-case, vertical forehead without prominent brow-ridges, refined facial features, and prominent chin. **488.** Reconstruction of the appearance of Cro-Magnon man based on the evidence of their associated implements and other articles of culture and their paintings on the walls of their shelters. They were associated first with Aurignacian, next with Solutrean, and lastly with Magdalenian types of culture (**491**) (M. Wilson).

The Evolution of Man's Skull

489. Combined side views of the skulls of gorilla, pithecanthropine, Neanderthal, and modern man showing the progressive loss of ape-like features and approximation to the appearance of juvenile characters. **490.** Diagram showing the appearance in side view of the skulls of the most important types of fossil man arranged in chronological and presumed evolutionary order issuing from the primitive Hominid stock. The gorilla is shown for comparison issuing from the Pongid stock. 'The crust of the earth', wrote Darwin, 'with its embedded remains must not be looked at as a well-filled museum, but as a poor collection made at hazard and at rare intervals.' In view of the rare and fortuitous nature of preservation of fossils, it is remarkable that the series of fossil men is as full and informative as it is although there are still gaps which will without doubt be gradually filled. The diagram illustrates another remark made by Darwin: 'In a series of forms graduating insensibly from some ape-like creature to man as he now exists it would be impossible to fix on any definite point when the term 'man' ought to be used.' As the succession of forms represents successive grades of structure, the giving of a Linnean specific name to each stage has been avoided.

they worked bone, their flint tools were delicately worked blades, they used spears and harpoons with detachable heads, invented a spear-throwing device, made sewn clothes of skin or fur, and in open country they constructed tents and huts. Above all, they are notable for their artistic achievements, such as the cave-paintings of Lascaux, dated by Carbon-14 analysis as 15,000 years old, probably connected with some hunting ritual. They adorned themselves, for example, with necklaces made of pierced shells, animals' teeth, and occasionally amber. Like all Palaeolithic peoples, they obtained their food by hunting wild animals, particularly bison, horse, reindeer, and mammoth, and by gathering edible plants, for they did not cultivate plants or domesticate animals (Pl. 493–495).

The later Caucasoid, Australoid, Mongoloid, Negroid and Bushmanoid types of men were already foreshadowed in Upper Palaeolithic populations, but the modern races of man were not fully differentiated until early Post-Glacial times, in the Mesolithic and Neolithic stages of culture.

Man as hunter: Palaeolithic stages of culture

Throughout the Pleistocene period man lived by gathering wild foods and hunting other animals. His survival in a wide range of environments depended on his ability to reason, to communicate and store experience, and to make tools and weapons suited to his needs. A basic requirement was the possession of tools for cutting through fur and skin and for shaping sticks. At the dawn of culture, sharp pieces of stone casually picked up served such purposes; but as time went on man learnt to break stones deliberately and to shape them with foresight of his precise needs.

The immensely long periods during which man depended on deliberately shaped stone-cutting tools is called the Stone Age. That part which coincided with the Pleistocene period is the Old Stone Age, or Palaeolithic period, which lasted from 500,000 to 10,000 years ago and which we have been considering.

Traces of man in Europe are rare before the Second Glaciation. During the succeeding warm Second Interglacial period, groups of early Palaeolithic man spread widely. Some became inhabitants of southern Britain, which was then joined to the Continent.

Clacton: an early Palaeolithic site in Britain

During the early part of the Pleistocene period, the Thames entered the North Sea at a point northeast of the present mouth of the river Blackwater. An abandoned channel of the early Thames now debouches on the foreshore of Clacton-on-Sea, Essex. It contains gravels, sands, and loams deposited by the river during the Interglacial period when man was a hunter in the river valleys of southern Britain.

The Clacton Elephant Bed, as this ancient river deposit has been called, was discovered by John Brown of Stanway about 1838. It has since been investigated by Hazzeldine Warren. A very primitive flint industry is found in this river bed. It consists of flake-tools and choppers, and represents a cultural tradition called Clactonian, which appears to have been distinct from the tradition of the contemporaneous makers of Acheulian flint hand-axes, named after St-Acheul, near Amiens in northern France where implements of this type are characteristic.

It is probable that Palaeolithic man made extensive use of wood for tools and utensils which through decay have generally vanished without trace. Many of the flint scrapers of the Clacton industry would have served for shaping spears and other wood-work. The broken spear made of yew-wood *(Taxus baccata)* found in the Clacton deposits in 1911, is the oldest known wooden artefact. It was embedded in a peaty loam and owes its preservation to the fact that the deposits are at sea level and have been water-logged since the time of their formation.

By studying the seeds and pollen-grains preserved in the silty layers of the Clacton deposits, it has been established that the climate was temperate and that mixed oak forest covered much of the surrounding country. Pollen-analysis has established further that the changes that occurred in the vegetation were those characteristic of the warm Second Interglacial period. The Clacton deposits accumulated during the same period as the lake-beds at Hoxne in Suffolk, where John Frere made the discovery of stone implements in 1797. The Hoxne implements are hand-axes similar to those found at Swanscombe. The Acheulian culture was perhaps adapted to a less wooded environment than the Clactonian.

The Clacton deposits contain bones and teeth of wild animals that browsed and grazed in the woodlands and water-meadows bordering the river. They included extinct fallow-deer, wild oxen, rhinoceroses related to the living Sumatran form, and elephants that belonged to the extinct species *Elephas antiquus*, characteristic of warm climates. Small herds of horse and bison roamed over the scrubby grassland beyond the woods. All these were preyed upon by the much rarer carnivores such as lion, bear, and by man, who probably ambushed and killed them when they came down to the river to drink. Other mammals recorded in the Clacton deposits include the hyaena and beaver.

THE SPREAD OF MAN

The earliest members of the Hominidae, which included the first men or toolmakers, originated in the tropics, probably in the dry grasslands and savannas bordering the forests of central Africa, whence they spread widely, through the use of equipment that enabled them to survive in environments to which they were unfitted by nature. Map 27 shows those areas of the Old World that had been entered by man during the Early Palaeolithic stage 500,000 to 50,000 years ago, and how much further man had spread by the Mesolithic stage 10,000 years ago.

In Lower Palaeolithic times man had spread all over Africa, northwards in Europe up to the latitude of Doncaster in Britain, over the southern lowlands of Asia and southeastern Asia to Java (then connected with the mainland), and as far north as the latitude of Peking.

By the end of Upper Palaeolithic times, man had become sufficiently adapted to cold conditions to break the bounds of the Old World by crossing the isthmus which spanned the Bering Straits into Alaska. By the time of the Mesolithic settlement at Star Carr in Yorkshire about 7500 B.C., man had spread through the grasslands of North America, and down the western margins of South America, to the southernmost tip of that continent. The spread of Mesolithic man can be described as circum-Pacific, for the radio-carbon dating of the earliest remains of aborigines in Australia indicates that they had also reached that continent by that date.

Man as hunter: Mesolithic stage of culture

After the change in climate which ended the Würm Glaciation about 8000 B.C., a variable period elapsed in different regions before men took to farming. During this interval, which lasted much longer in Europe than in the Middle East, men still lived mainly by hunting and fishing, but they were in the adaptable stage of culture known as Mesolithic.

At the beginning of Post-Glacial times, Britain still formed part of the Continent, and until the rising waters flooded over the southern part of the North Sea bed about 6000 B.C., it was possible to walk from East Yorkshire to Estonia and beyond, crossing rivers and skirting bogs and lakes. Examination of samples of peat ('moorlog') dredged from the Dogger Bank shows that at the time of the submergence this was part of a great fenland with woods of birch, willow, and pine.

At this time the heavily wooded North European Plain was occupied by Mesolithic hunter-fishers, who succeeded the Upper Palaeolithic reindeer hunters. Many

Evolution of artistic activity I.

Colour plate 15

Top, Painting in colour by the chimpanzee 'Congo'. It shows his personal characteristic fan-shaped pattern, and the superposition of colours (given him on separate brushes) reveals his sense of balance. Successive strokes of pink, yellow, and red were built up left and right leaving the centre blank; this was then filled with green, blue was used to link up the parts of the pattern across the centre, and vigorous strokes of black emphasized its tripartite nature. *Bottom*, Palaeolithic Fresco from Lascaux, painted about 20,000 years ago. One of a group of wild horses which, with its shaggy stomach, resembles those of the Steppes of Central Asia. The graceful quality of the line and the skill with which the contours of the rock are combined with the pigment to suggest modelling are typical of the artistic achievement of the painters of Lascaux. Many persons who enjoy works of art can see no counterpart in animals of artistic activity in man. Art for them is an exclusively human achievement. Yet there can be no doubt that this counterpart exists, although this is not to say that the two are identical, any more than that the human expression of sex is identical with that of animals. Although the basic chemistry of sex hormones is the same in man and animals, human experience is so enormously enriched by consciousness, the result of countless generations of poets, priests, musicians and story-tellers, the slow deposition of successive religious and social awareness have overlaid the animal activity with such a patina of human associations that in man it is a quite other experience. The mytho-poetic faculty has transformed it, and the values thus attached to man's sexual life have become real values although they have no physical basis in the biology of sex. So too with man's aesthetic life. It has the 'basic chemistry' in common with other members of the animal kingdom, and this consists in the pleasure and sense of dominance that comes from finding and creating patterns. Pattern-making seems to be a basic activity of the brain and may be how it works, and the satisfaction it affords is accordingly profound. Preference for patterns showing symmetry, rythm and vivid colours has been demonstrated experimentally in monkeys and even in birds (p. 167), and the criteria at work here are aesthetic, as in man. Although the essential sameness of the pattern-making impulse in apes and children on one hand, and adult human artists on the other must be recognized, the products are very different. The pictures of apes and children, while they may be called 'art', are art of a different order from the rich and complex experience and associations which sustain the great works of man's hand and mind, in which the original pattern-making impulse is deepened and changed by human values and conscious creative aims. But the human activity evolved from such instinctive activity as is revealed in the products of 'Congo'.

ART EMERGING

CONSUMMATE AR

of their camping sites have been found on the Continent, notably in Denmark, and from their habit of camping during the summer months on the margins of lakes and bogs, these early forest-dwellers have come to be known as Maglemosians (Danish: *Magle* = great, *mose* = moss, or bog). Their mode of life is fairly well known, for in peat and waterlogged deposits their material equipment has been preserved.

Star Carr: a Mesolithic site

The low-lying parts of eastern England were occupied by groups of Maglemosians, but no peat-bog site comparable with those on the Continent had been found until the researches of John Moore led to the discovery in 1948 of the relics of a red-deer hunters' settlement below peat at Star Carr near Seamer in Yorkshire.

During the summers of 1949-51, large-scale excavations were undertaken at Star Carr by the Prehistoric Society under the direction of Professor Grahame Clark. From pollen analysis of the peat and examination of associated brushwood, the contemporary flora can be deduced; from a study of the numerous animal bones the fauna on which these hunters depended – red-deer, elk, and wild oxen – is known; while from the abundant archaeological material it has been possible to reconstruct the conditions of life in Britain at a time which radio-carbon dating of material from the site indicates as about 7500 B.C.

The excavation revealed a brushwood platform of a primitive character, weighed down by stones, and showing traces of birch-bark flooring and of charring of the wood by domestic fires. There were no indications of the nature of the super-structures, but they may well have been skin tents. The dwelling site was close to the shore of the dwindling glacial Lake Pickering, and the ground would have been marshy and perhaps liable to flooding. The construction of dwellings on brushwood platforms over marshy ground was a step that led in later prehistoric times to the building of artificial islands such as the crannogs in Ireland, the Glastonbury lake-village, and other forms of lakeside villages found in large numbers on the shores of alpine lakes.

The chief weapons of the Maglemosian hunters were spears or arrows with barbed antler points. More than fifty of these points were found in the excavation of an eight-yard trench at Star Carr, many of them complete. Previous to this discovery, only six were known from the British Isles, including one dredged from the floor of the North Sea, embedded in peat. Some of the points barbed almost to the base may have been used as the heads of arrows or darts for hunting deer. The bow had certainly been invented by this time, for at least one bowstave has been found in a Maglemosian level in Danish bogs.

Antler was the principal raw material of the Mesolithic people of Star Carr. They worked it with flint tools, chiefly the chisel-pointed implements known as *burins*, which were abundant on the site. The techniques employed had been inherited as a tradition from the Upper Palaeolithic reindeer-hunting tribes.

The character of a Mesolithic culture was largely determined by the natural environment, to which the Maglemosians of eastern England, for example, skilfully adapted themselves. The dominant animal there was red deer, and the local woods were mainly of birch. Consequently the material equipment of the early settlers at Star Carr was mainly fashioned from red deer antler, birch-wood, and birch-bark.

In Britain, man was in the Mesolithic stage until about 3000 B.C., while in Australia the aborigines have remained in this stage until virtually the present.

Man as farmer: the Neolithic revolution

For half a million years or more, in the earlier Stone Palaeolithic and Mesolithic, Ages, all mankind lived by *food gathering*, that is to say, by collecting wild plant foods and hunting animals. In the New Stone Age or Neolithic stage, starting in the Middle East probably between 7000 and 6000 B.C. (but in Britain much later, about 3000 B.C.), man began *food producing* by agriculture and animal husbandry. Farming revolutionized man's way of life by ensuring a stable supply and reserves of food removing his dependence on the hazards of the chase, enabling him to live in settled organized communities and to begin pursuing the arts of civilization.

The principal plants cultivated by Neolithic man in western Asia and Europe were cereal grasses (wheat and barley), pulses (peas and beans), flax (supplying oil and fibres), and fruit (for example, apples). The advantages of cultivating grasses were probably first realized by groups of food gatherers living a fairly static existence on the grassy uplands bordering the arid plains of the Middle East, for example near Mount Carmel. Within this region grew several annual grasses, notably the wild wheats einkorn and emmer, and wild barley, tolerant of low rainfall and yielding large enough grains in sufficient quantities to encourage harvesting (see Pl. 271 and Map 32).

Just as the civilization of western Asia and Europe arose on the basis of the cultivation of wheat, those of the Far East and central America were based on rice and maize respectively. All these cereals contain a high concentration of energy-producing carbohydrates, and all are native to areas where protein-rich pulses are also found wild. While man was still a nomad he could attach to himself animals like the dog and the reindeer; but settled agriculture was the most important factor in the full domestication of animals, because many of these require permanent settlements and a supply of food in confined space, conditions which did not apply when man still pursued the nomadic habits of a hunter.

The wild ancestors of domestic dogs, goats, sheep, cattle, and pigs, existed in the areas of the Middle East where wheat and barley were brought under cultivation, and it is probable that they were first domesticated there, dogs in the Mesolithic stage, goats and sheep at the beginning of the Neolithic, cattle and pigs slightly later. The domestication of these animals is unlikely to have begun as a purposeful procedure, but rather as a result of natural association with man. Wild dogs must have entered human camps or settlements as scavengers, and the puppies would have been secured as pets by the children. Tamed dogs would have helped the Mesolithic hunters in driving sheep and goats; and with the beginning of agriculture, wild cattle and pigs would have become associated with human settlements when they raided the crops. The ass was the oldest pack animal, and the onager was used to draw wheeled vehicles in Mesopotamia in the third millennium B.C. The horse was probably domesticated in the second millennium B.C. in northwestern Asia. Other animals domesticated for purposes of transport included the elephant and the camel. The cat became associated with man, as a destroyer of pests, in Egypt.

As food supplies increased and became assured through Neolithic economy, not only was a more settled mode of life made possible, but specialized craftsmen and traders could be supported. A wide variety of new materials was used. Some early Neolithic people were without pottery, but used leather vessels, baskets, and carved stone bowls. The forms and decoration of Neolithic pottery were evidently influenced by leather, basket and stone prototypes. Other new crafts and materials included the spinning and weaving of plant and animal fibres to use in clothing and in furnishing dwellings.

The religious ideas of Neolithic man were related partly to fertility, as is shown by statuettes of Earth Mother goddesses and phallic emblems, and partly to ancestor worship, which led to the construction of large stone tombs. The Neolithic stage is distinguished by the first permanent villages; and the spring-side settlement recently excavated at Jericho was a veritable town by 6800 B.C. according to the latest radio-carbon age estimation. The activities of Neolithic man included the

Evolution of artistic activity II.

Colour Plate 16

Pl. 16. *Top*, Vincent van Gogh, 'The painter on his way to work'. *Bottom*, Vincent van Gogh, 'Field with Poppies'. The paintings of primitive man may be seen as a stage intermediate between the instinctive and the conscious activity. In the Lascaux Fresco (Col. Pl. 15, *bottom*) even if the exact significance of the painting, or its meaning and purpose for those who painted it and first saw it, is not certain today, it is nevertheless clear that the basic pattern-making impulse was already changed and enriched by being linked with the artist's environment, and has been used to comment on this environment and to control it by discovering patterns in it, physical patterns in the arrangement of its parts, and mental patterns in the evaluation of its meaning and its relationship with the artist and his society. If the commonly accepted 'explanation' of these and other Palaeolithic paintings is correct, that they were made in dark inaccessible recesses of caves as part of ceremonies of ritual magic to ensure successful activities, chiefly hunting to obtain food vital for the tribe, then it is clear that the urge to see patterns and to create them was already linked with other areas of human experience. The evolution of artistic activity under aesthetic impulse was already well under way. One painting at Lascaux makes man himself a part of the pattern and shows the threads that bind man the artist to his environment. This theme has continued to be a major preoccupation of the artist, poet and musician, and was the driving impulse shaping the paintings on this Plate, which are examples of the artist consciously using his creative patterns to convey values, moods, emotions, whatever conventions they work in, realistic, impressionistic, or abstract. In letters to his brother, Vincent van Gogh says, 'I cannot, ill as I am, do without something which is greater than I, which is my life - the power to create. And if, defrauded of the power to create physically, a man tries to create thoughts in place of children, he is still part of humanity. And in a picture I want to say something comforting as music is comforting. I want to paint men and women with that something of the eternal which the halo used to symbolise, and which we seek to give by the actual radiance and vibrations of our colourings . . . We are having now a glorious strong heat, with no wind, just what I want. There is a sun, a light that for want of a better word I can only call yellow, pale sulphur yellow, pale golden yellow. How lovely yellow is'. These two remarks, 'How lovely yellow is', and 'This we seek to give by the actual radiance and vibration of our colourings', give some insight into van Gogh's mood and purpose at the height of his powers in Provence. His comment, 'that something of the eternal which the halo used to symbolise', applies to all his paintings. He wanted to 'paint in such a way that all who have eyes must of necessity clearly perceive'. The lambent forms of his brush strokes seeming to yearn upwards, the flaming light which glows in his canvases, capture 'something of the eternal' in the artist's patterns.

Man's tools and drawings

491. Top row, pebble-tool, Olduvai, Tanganyika, associated with australopithecines. Lower Palaeolithic, two Chellean hand-axes associated with pithecanthropines, Acheulian hand-axe, associated with emergence from pithecanthropine stage. Middle row, Middle Palaeolithic, Mousterian scraper and point associated with Neanderthal man. Upper Palaeolithic, Aurignacian 'spokeshave', Magdalenian blade-core associated with Cro-Magnon man who also (Bottom row) used bone and antlers to make harpoons, Solutrean 'laurel leaf' blade. **492.** Stratification of cultures in a rock shelter. **493.** Aurignacian wounded bison and elephant with heart as 'target'. **494.** Magdalenian horses engraved on reindeer antler. **495.** Bronze Age rock-drawings of houses, ploughing scene and fish-trapping, Val Camonica. **496.** Neolithic polished axe-head hafted onto handle. **497.** With such axe-heads three men cleared six hundred square yards of forest. **498.** quern for grinding grain. **499.** Pollen-analysis of Danish bog from 2500 BC. Percentages of pollen of each species shown by width of stippled area at each stage: 1. forest cleared for agriculture, fewer big trees, more herbaceous plants and grasses; 2. increase of birch pollen implies clearings because birch seedlings need light; 3. reappearance of big trees indicates that the Neolithic farmers moved to other areas allowing the forests to regenerate.

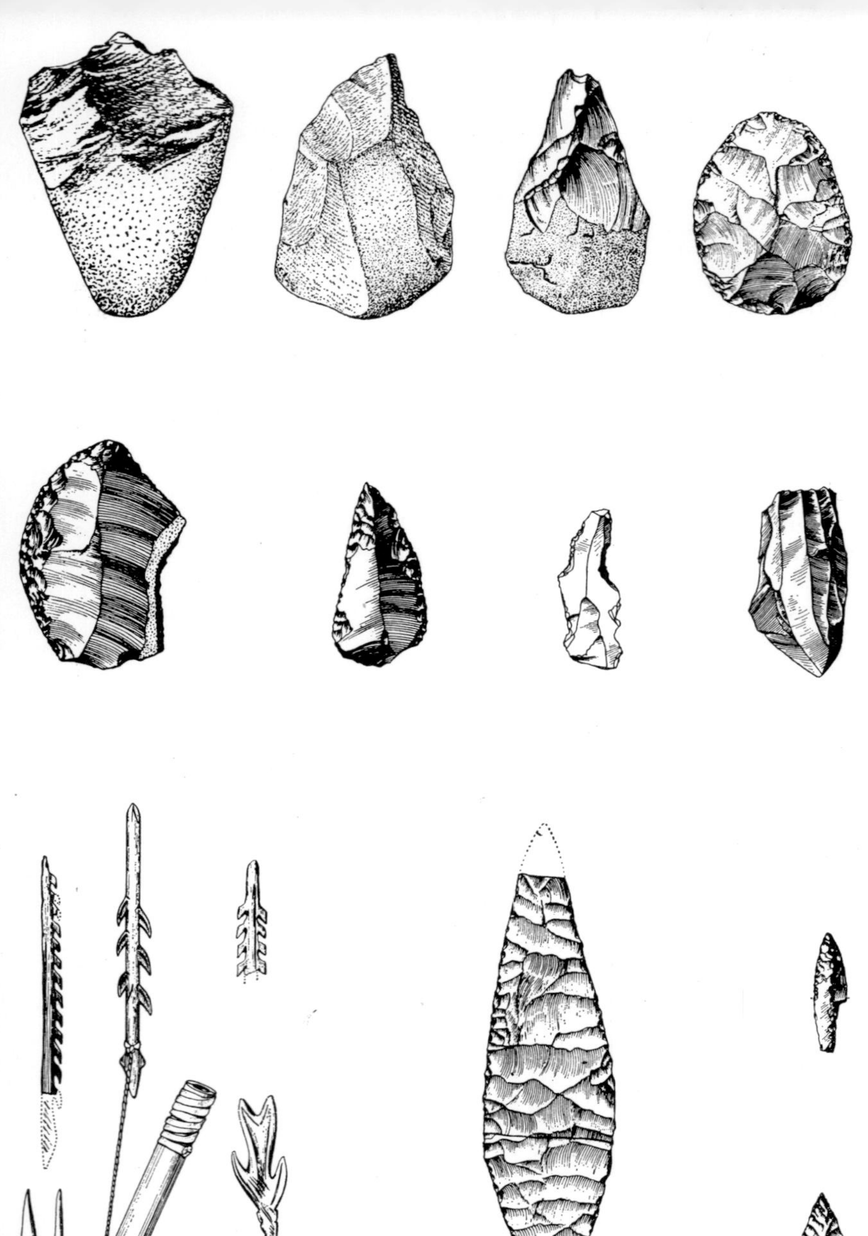

491

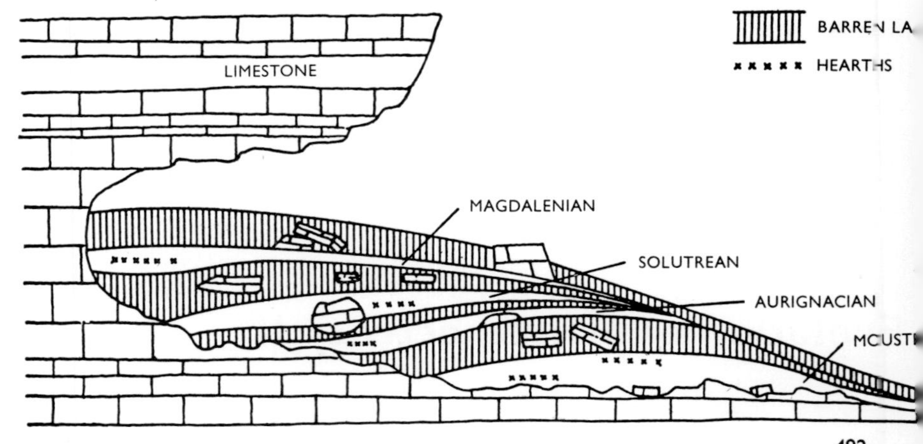

492

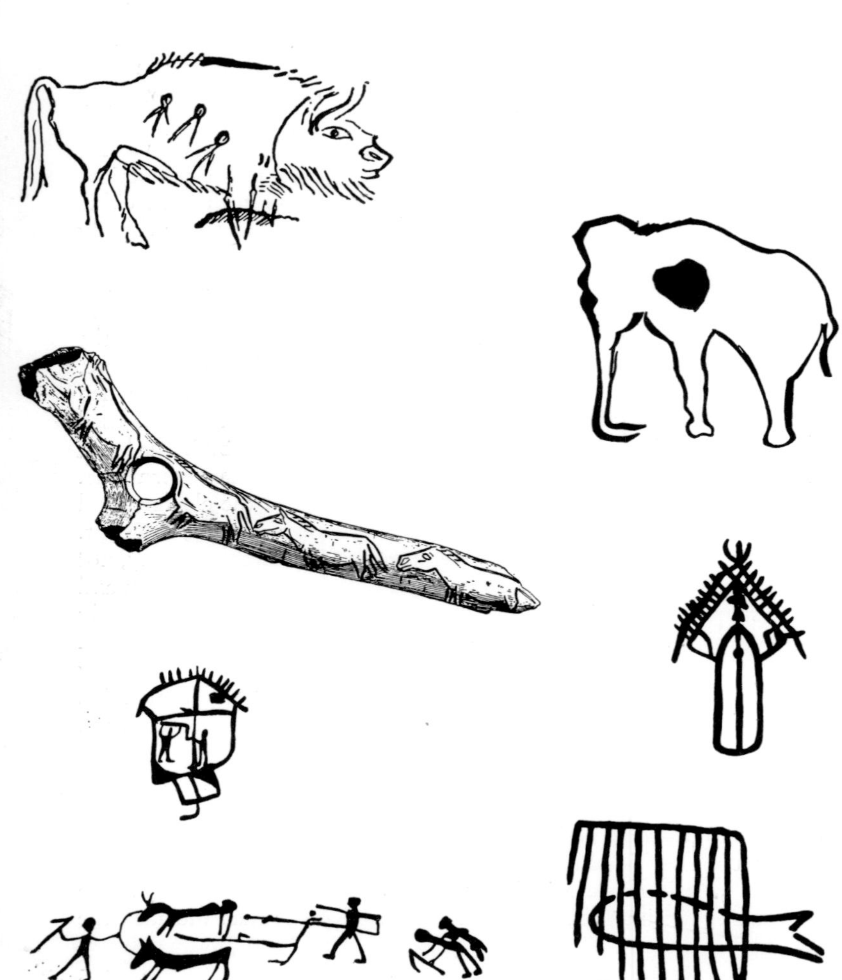

493

494

495

Races of man

500. The visible characters hitherto relied on for the classification of the races of man, skin-colour, hair-form, skull-shape, distinction between long heads and round heads, stature, etc., are no longer considered dependable guides to the affinities between different races. They are now supplemented as far as possible by the genetics of blood-groups because these are susceptible of accurate genetic analysis and the percentages in which these blood-groups appear in different populations are constant over long periods of time. Top Row left to right, Australoids with high Blood-group N and Rhesus-Z, Murrayan Australian aboriginal, Carpentarian Australian aboriginal; Pacific Islanders, Melanesian from Simbo, Polynesian; Mongoloids with lowest Rhesus-negative, Kalmuk from Siberia. Bottom row, Amerindian with high Rhesus-Z, North American Indian from the Plains; Negroids with high Rhesus-O, Bushman, Negro from Griqualand; Caucasoids, Early Mediterranean, Basque from the Pyrenees with lowest-known blood-group B and highest -known Rhesus-negative, Nordic from Sweden. In spite of all these racial differences, men belong to the same species, *Homo sapiens*, and are fertile with one another.

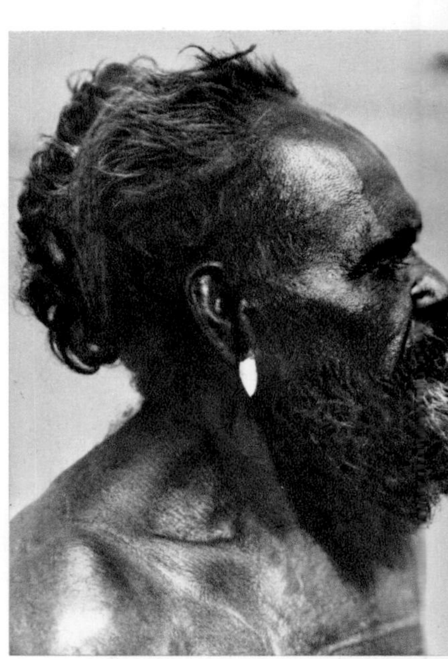

500

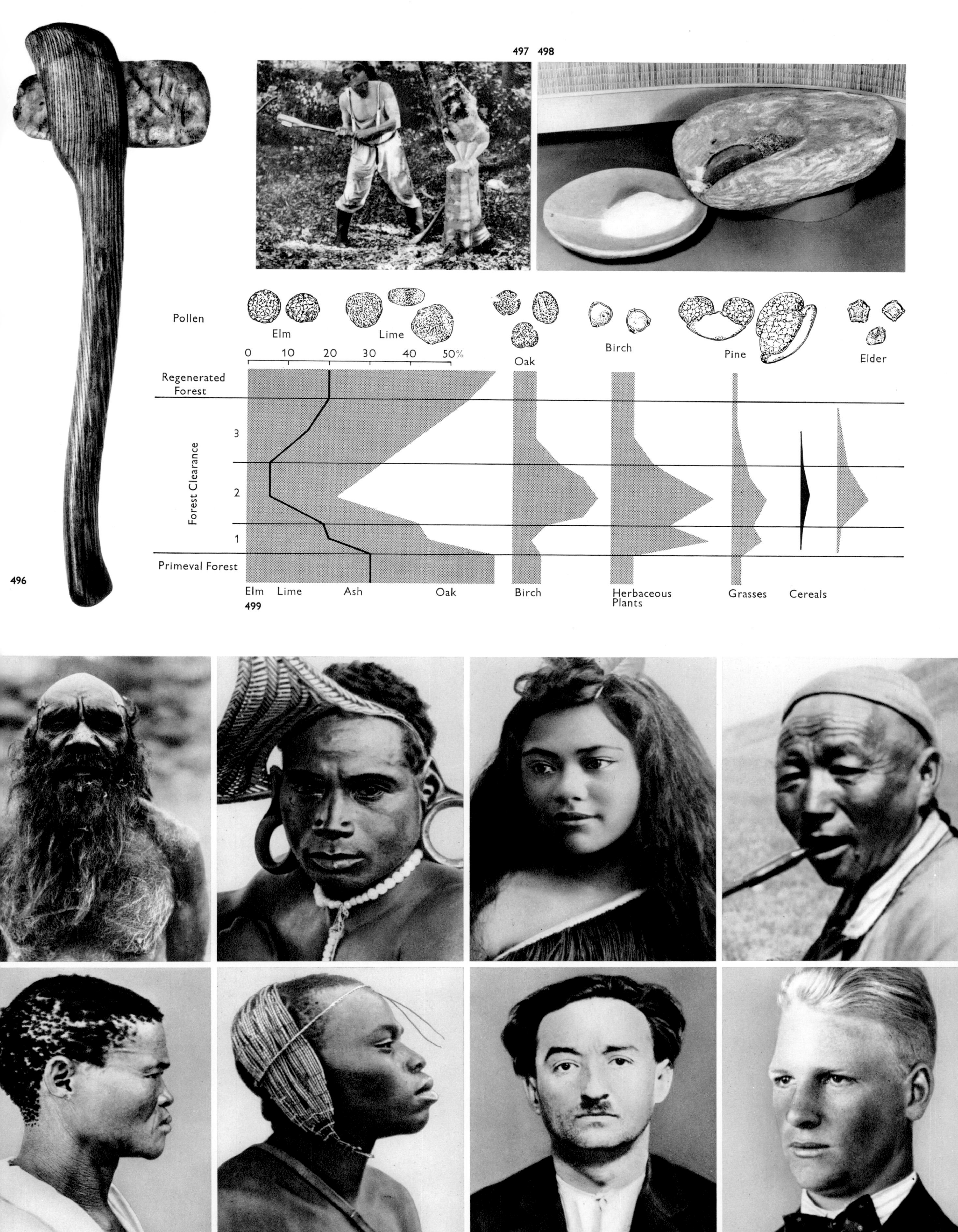

496
497
498
Pollen
Elm
Lime
Oak
Birch
Pine
Elder
0
10
20
30
40
50%
Regenerated Forest
Forest Clearance
3
2
1
Primeval Forest
Elm
Lime
Ash
Oak
Birch
Herbaceous Plants
Grasses
Cereals
499

The spread of man

Map 25 shows the extent of the Last Glaciation in Europe and of the distribution of deposits of loess. Loess was formed by deposition of dusts brought by winds from the bare surfaces of moraines formed by glaciers. Its vegetation was mostly short grasses which provided food for grazing animals, and its freedom from thick forest vegetation made it a convenient soil for the wanderings of early man. It was over tracts of loess that Neolithic Man spread westwards into Europe from the East.

Map 26. The end of the Ice Age, about 10,000 years ago, had serious consequences for Palaeolithic man. His staple food-supply, the reindeer, followed the retreating ice northwards, and the amelioration of the climate led to the development of dense forests. Men migrated to the sea where they lived on fish and shell-fish, and invented the canoe, dug-out, and sledge. Britain was still joined to the continent and the coast-line ran from Yorkshire to Jutland. Some of the Mesolithic, or Maglemose settlements, are now under the North Sea.

Map 27. Sites of discovery of man's ancestors including *Proconsul*, *Oreopithecus*, australopithecines, pithecanthropines, neanderthal, neanderthaloid, and modern types of man. About 100,000 years ago, man had spread from Africa into Asia, Malaysia, and Europe up to latitude 50° N. In upper Palaeolithic times man spread into Europe and Asia up to latitude 60°, and across the Bering bridge to North America where a date of 8500 B.C. has been obtained from C-14 estimations, and across the Panama isthmus to Tierra del Fuego by 7000 B.C. From eastern Asia man reached Australia by 6500 B.C.

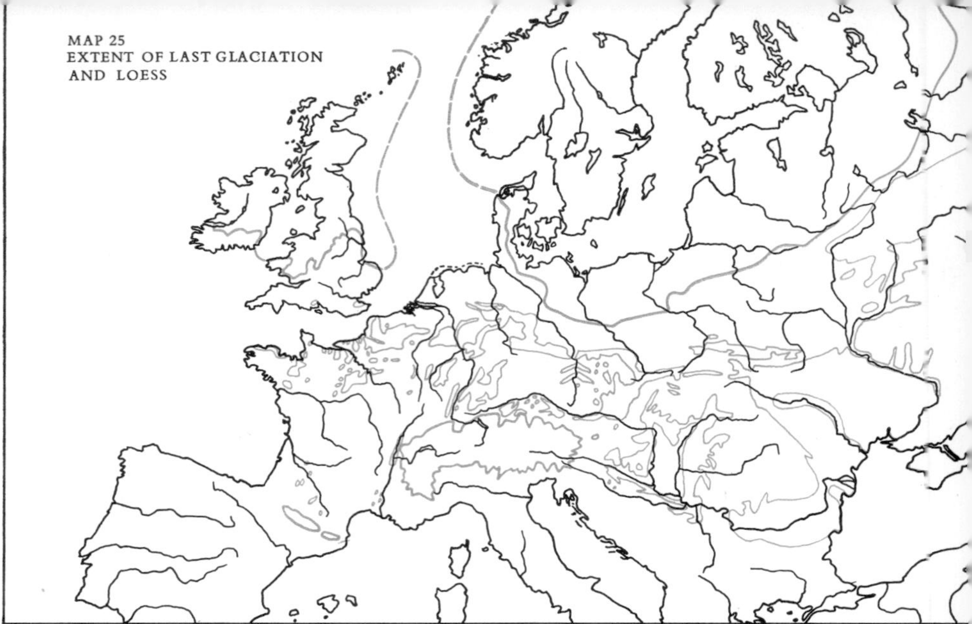

MAP 25
EXTENT OF LAST GLACIATION AND LOESS

KUNDA
LOHUSU
PERNAU
KUNGSLADUGARD
SANDARNA
KÄLLINGEMÖRE MOSSE
HÖRNINGE MOSSE
AGERÖD
KLOSTERLUND
BARE MOSSE
ISTABY
VIG
STORA DODE MOSSE
MULLERUP
AMOSSEN
SVAERBORG
STAR CARR
HORNSEA
SKIPSEA
GOHRA-WORLE
BARNEWITZ
OSSOWO
DUVENSEE
DOBERTIN
LEMAN and OWER
KELLING HEATH
ROYSTON
NOWA
UX-BRIDGE
BROXBOURNE
NEWBURY
BATTERSEA
CALBE a.M.
PRITZERBER SEE
DÖHREN
WICHELEN
BRUSSELS
BETHUNE
ISBERGUES
CROUY

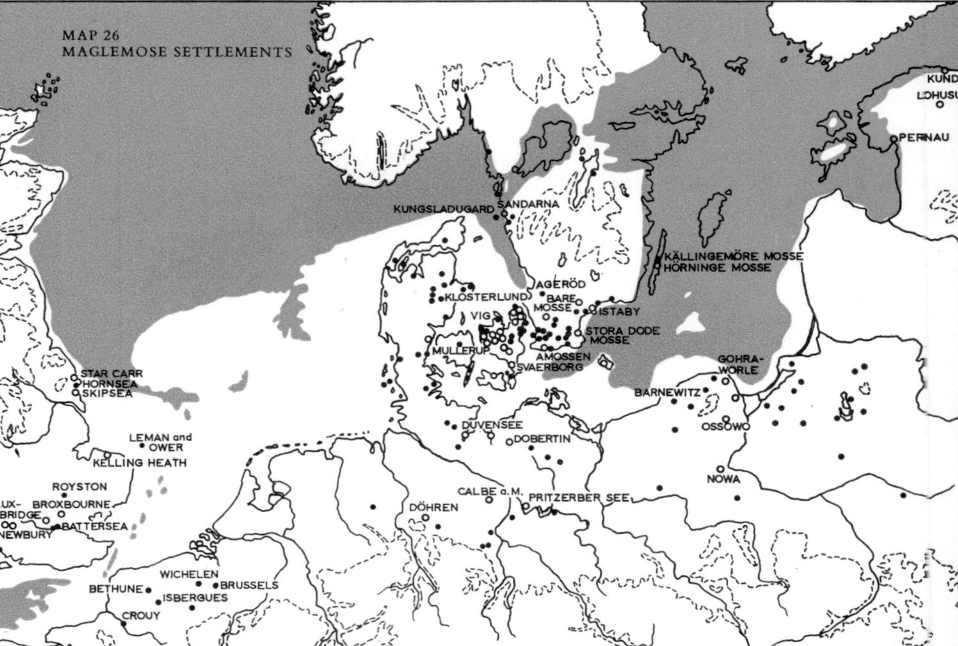

MAP 26
MAGLEMOSE SETTLEMENTS

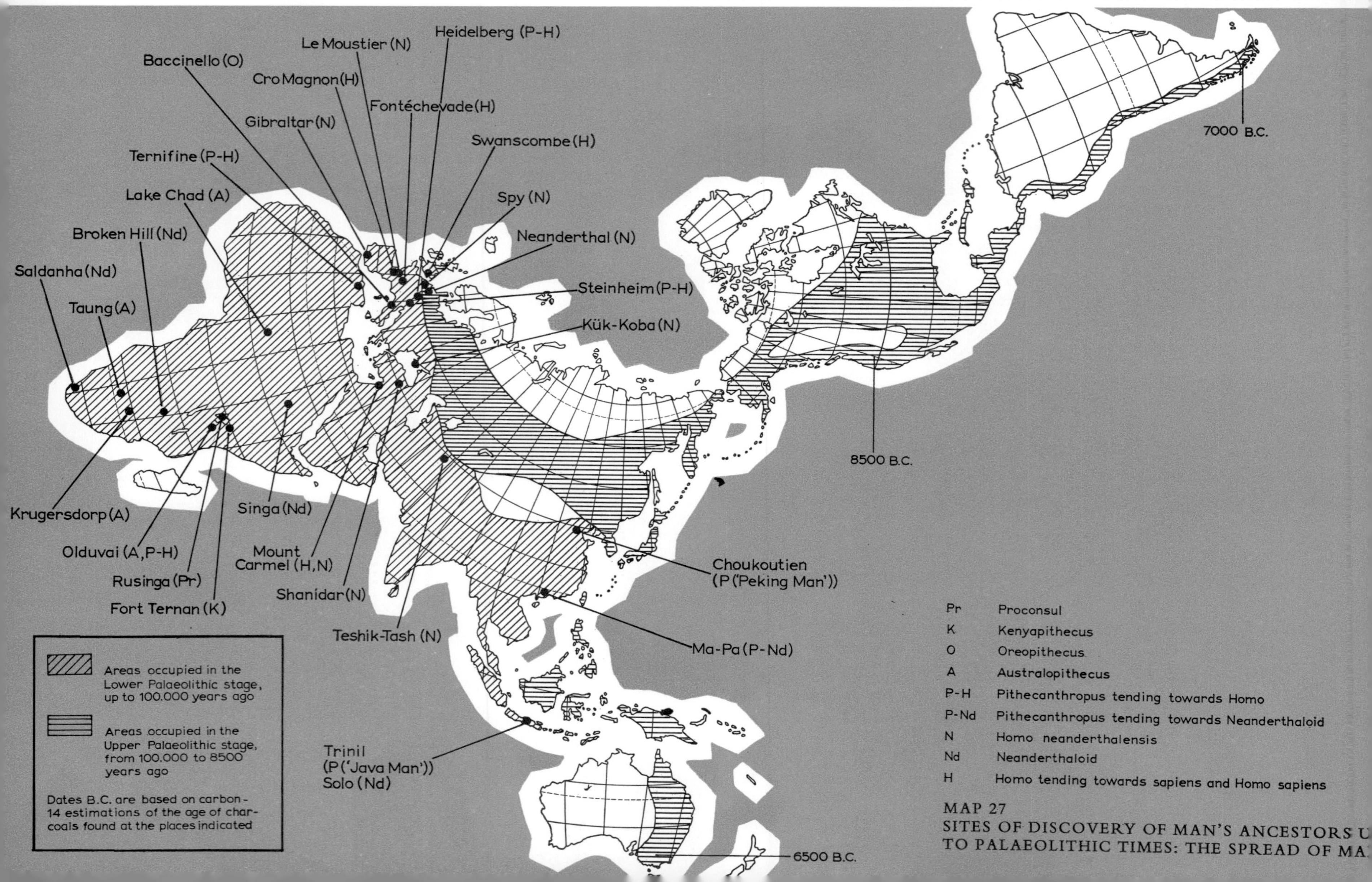

Heidelberg (P-H)
Le Moustier (N)
Baccinello (O)
Cro Magnon (H)
Fontéchevade (H)
Gibraltar (N)
Swanscombe (H)
Ternifine (P-H)
Lake Chad (A)
Spy (N)
Broken Hill (Nd)
Neanderthal (N)
Saldanha (Nd)
Steinheim (P-H)
Taung (A)
Kük-Koba (N)
7000 B.C.
8500 B.C.
Krugersdorp (A)
Singa (Nd)
Olduvai (A, P-H)
Mount Carmel (H, N)
Rusinga (Pr)
Fort Ternan (K)
Shanidar (N)
Teshik-Tash (N)
Choukoutien (P ('Peking Man'))
Ma-Pa (P-Nd)
Areas occupied in the Lower Palaeolithic stage, up to 100.000 years ago
Areas occupied in the Upper Palaeolithic stage, from 100.000 to 8500 years ago
Dates B.C. are based on carbon-14 estimations of the age of charcoals found at the places indicated
Trinil (P ('Java Man')) Solo (Nd)
6500 B.C.
Pr Proconsul
K Kenyapithecus
O Oreopithecus
A Australopithecus
P-H Pithecanthropus tending towards Homo
P-Nd Pithecanthropus tending towards Neanderthaloid
N Homo neanderthalensis
Nd Neanderthaloid
H Homo tending towards sapiens and Homo sapiens

MAP 27
SITES OF DISCOVERY OF MAN'S ANCESTORS U
TO PALAEOLITHIC TIMES: THE SPREAD OF MA

Blood-groups

Maps 28 and 29. The fact that different races of man show different proportions of the blood-groups, O, A, B, and AB in the population, was first discovered at Salonika during the First World War by the Hirszfelds when the blood-groups were tested of large numbers of soldiers in the Allied Armies that were concentrated there from many countries in the world. Since that time, extensive studies have been made as a result of which it has been possible to plot lines of isogenes on maps indicating the percentage frequencies of blood-group genes in populations in all parts of the world. As regards the O, A, and B blood-group genes, the distribution of their frequencies shows gradations which are in fact clines (p. 109). The blood-groups are an example of balanced polymorphism in which the relative frequencies of the genotypes are held in equilibrium the stability of which lasts for periods of the order of magnitude of a thousand years (table, p. 190). The zoning of the frequencies reflects movements of peoples during that period of time. This is particularly evident in the case of B frequencies where there is a gradient sloping away from a high point in central Asia. High points of A frequencies are found in Scandinavia (Lapps), northwest America (Indians), and Australia (Aborigines). The frequencies of blood-group gene O are the complement of those of A plus B, i.e. the percentages of O in a population are what is left out of 100 after subtraction of the percentages of A and of B. High frequencies of O are commonly found among peripheral populations such as Scotland, Ireland, Iceland, southwest Africa, Australia, and the Indians of central and South America. (Researches by A. E. Mourant.)

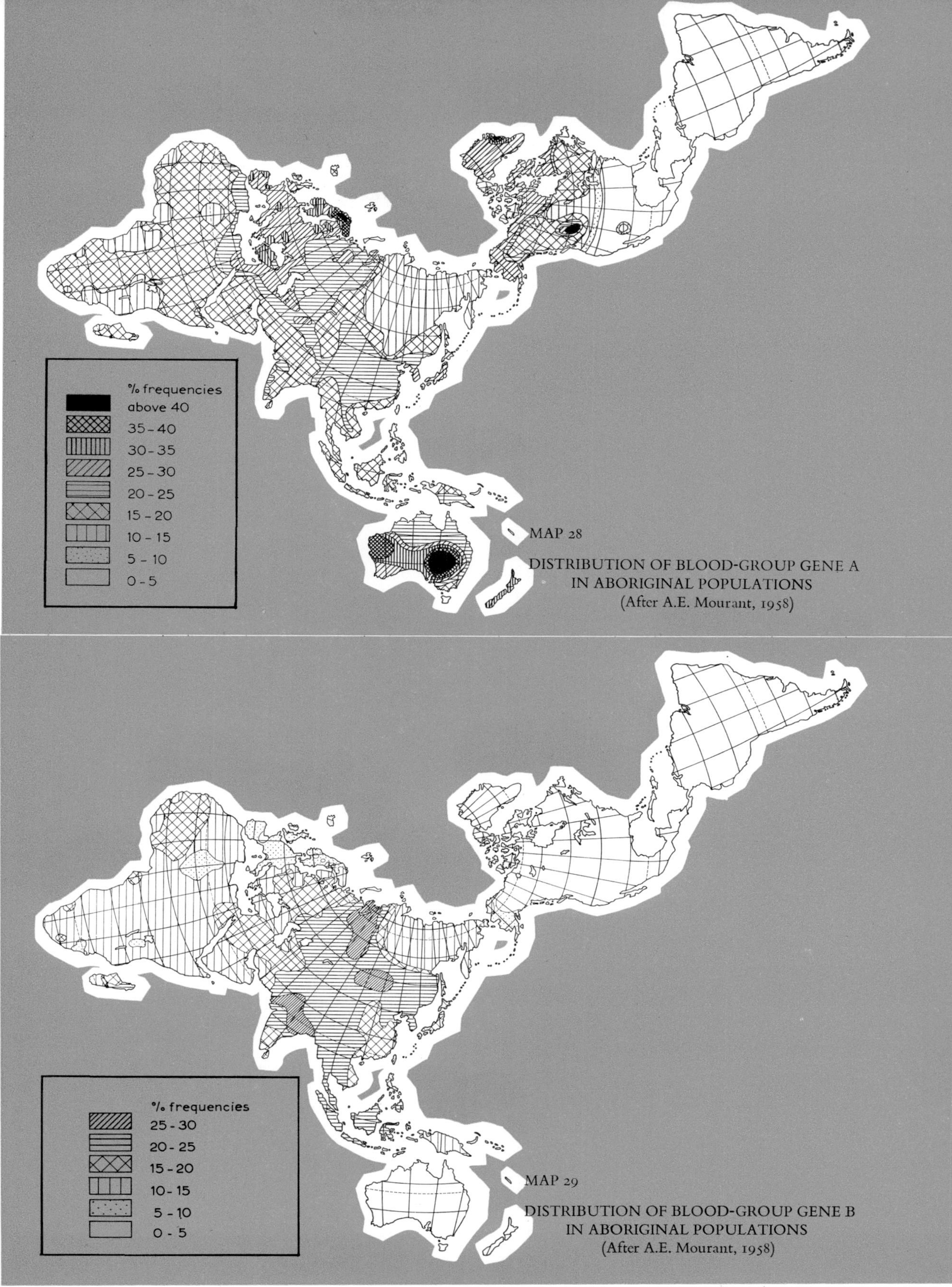

MAP 28
DISTRIBUTION OF BLOOD-GROUP GENE A IN ABORIGINAL POPULATIONS
(After A.E. Mourant, 1958)

MAP 29
DISTRIBUTION OF BLOOD-GROUP GENE B IN ABORIGINAL POPULATIONS
(After A.E. Mourant, 1958)

continuation of hunting and fishing using new devices, the mining of flint, the manufacture and trading of polished stone axe-heads, and their use in the clearance of forests for agriculture (Pl. 496–498).

During an experiment in Denmark, three men cleared 600 square yards of forest in four hours using Neolithic axes. On continuing the clearance more than 100 trees were felled with one axe-head, which had not been sharpened for more than 4,000 years. A pollen-diagram based on samples taken from borings in Danish peat-bogs shows the effects of clearing forests for agriculture about 2,500 B.C. The great increase in birch pollen following the disappearance of the big trees suggests that the clearings were burned in readiness for sowing. The return of big trees indicates that after a time the ground became exhausted, and the Neolithic farmers had to move on to new ground.

There was, however, a price to be paid for the advantages of living in compact communities in permanent settlements with domestic animals and an assured food supply. In the Palaeolithic stage, when men lived in roving bands numbering a few dozen to a hundred individuals, there was no opportunity for the persistence and spread of virus diseases such as measles that last a short time and then vanish. Sir Macfarlane Burnet has shown that crowding of population is necessary for this to happen because it supplies the conditions for epidemics. This crowding began with the Neolithic settlements, some 9,000 years ago. Before that time, the virus of measles must have infected a different host, and as this virus resembles those of distemper in dogs or rinderpest in cattle, it is probable that man became infected from one of these sources, with which he came into close contact as a result of the domestication of animals.

THE RACES OF MAN

It has often been debated whether the living races of man can be regarded as distinct species; but since no detectable degree of sterility results from race-crossing, it is now agreed that they are all one species, *Homo sapiens*, comprising at present about 3,000,000,000 individuals. The simplest, but arbitrary, classification of mankind is into three major divisions: the 'white', 'black', and 'yellow' races, but sub-division into thirty or more races has also been attempted.

The visible and measurable characters generally used in race classification (skin colour, hair-form, shape of head, stature) are no longer regarded as wholly reliable guides to relationship. They do not allow clear-cut divisions since they are controlled by many genes with cumulative effects. It is probable that the same characters have appeared independently during the evolution of different races.

A race may be defined as an inter-breeding population differing from other populations within the species in the incidence of certain genes. The discovery that some of the biochemical properties of blood are dependent on single genes (Chapter III, p. 79) has made it possible to classify human populations on a genetic basis. For instance, of the Rhesus blood-groups (p. 81) the Rhesus-negative gene is found in more than fifty five per cent of the population in Basques but less than one per cent of Chinese. The combination of Rhesus genes *cDe*, known as Rhesus-O, is characteristic of Africans south of the Sahara where over fifty per cent of the genes are of this constitution as against three per cent in Great Britain. Similarly, the combination of genes *CDE* known as Rhesus-Z is characteristic of Amerindians and Australian aborigines. The frequencies of the ABO blood-groups and of their genes in different races is given in the table on this page. By taking into account the differences between the percentages of blood-groups in different populations, it is possible to recognise seven more or less well defined races, bearing in mind the fact that races are not static entities. The genetic constitutions of populations are constantly changing through mutation, cross-breeding, natural selection and sexual selection. Existing races of man are of comparatively recent origin and were barely differentiated when the Ice Age was waning about ten thousand years ago (Pl. 500).

The four blood-groups are the phenotypes corresponding to the presence in an individual of any two of the three blood-group genes A, B, and O, (Chapter II, p. 40. Chapter III, p. 81) of which the corresponding frequency percentages are given in the table. The higher percentage of blood-group gene O as compared with the percentage of blood-group O in a population is due to the fact that gene O, being recessive to A and B, is hidden in a number of heterozygote individuals carrying A or B. For the same reason the percentage frequencies of blood-groups A and B in a population are higher than those of genes A and B.

For purposes of comparison between different populations and races, it is convenient to use the percentage frequencies of genes rather than of the blood-groups, and maps of the world have been drawn up showing the isogenes (Maps 28 and 29).

The five entries at the bottom of the table have been included to show the comparative stability of blood-group gene frequencies in populations over considerable lengths of time. German settlers in Hungary who have habitually married within their colonies have preserved the same pattern as Germans in Hamburg although they have been isolated from Germany for nearly five hundred years. Their pattern is quite different from that of the Hungarians and from that of the Gypsies in their own neighbourhood; the Gypsies have preserved the same pattern as that shown by Hindus in India, whence they are believed to have come nearly one thousand years ago.

The data shown in the Table and in Maps 28 and 29 are simplified as much as possible from the complex situation arising out of the fact that there are two kinds of blood-group gene A.

The following are the main living variants of the human species, grouped as far as possible on the basis of blood-groups and other characters.

Table of frequencies of blood-groups and of blood-group genes in typical populations of man
(after A. E. Mourant 1958)

Race and geographical location	Percentage frequencies of blood-groups				Percentage frequencies of blood-group genes			Other distinguishing factors
	O	A	B	AB	O	A	B	
Early Mediterranean								
Basques (Labourd)	58	38	3	1	76	22	2	Highest Rhesus-negative
Berbers (Beni Ounif)	53	34	10	3	72	21	7	
Caucasoid								
England (Southern)	45	43	9	3	67	27	6	
France (Calvados)	46	43	8	3	67	27	6	
Germany (Hamburg)	42	43	11	4	64	28	8	
Negroid								
Nigerian (Lagos)	52	22	23	3	73	13	14	High Rhesus-O
American Negro (Iowa)	49	27	20	4	70	17	13	
Bushmen	56	34	8	2	75	20	5	
Hottentots	38	32	24	6	62	22	16	
Mongoloid								
Chinese (Fukien)	35	30	27	8	59	21	20	Lowest Rhesus-negative
Ainu (Saru)	21	34	31	14	46	28	26	
Malays (Indonesia)	40	25	28	7	63	17	20	
Madagascar (Merina)	41	26	26	7	64	18	18	
Amerindian								
Navaho	70	30	0	0	83	17	0	High Rhesus-Z
Eskimo (Point Barrow)	41	47	10	2	65	29	6	
Pacific Islanders								
Melanesian (New Caledonia)	59	31	7	3	76	19	5	
Polynesian (Samoa)	59	17	19	5	75	12	13	
Polynesian (Easter Island)	40	60	0	0	63	37	0	
Australoid								
Aboriginal (South & Central Australia)	39	61	0	0	62	38	0	High Rhesus-Z High N
Germans in Hamburg	42	43	11	4	64	28	8	
Germans in settlers' colonies in Hungary	41	43	13	3	65	27	8	
Hungarians (Debrecen)	31	38	19	12	54	29	17	
Gypsies in Hungary (Debrecen)	28	27	35	10	54	20	26	
Hindus (Rajasthan)	33	22	35	10	56	18	26	

Australoids and Pacific Islanders
The Australian aborigines have a distinctive blood-group pattern with a high percentage of blood-group N, high Rhesus-Z, and no B. They migrated from Asia at the end of the Ice Age when the sea level was low, and the sea channels between Asia and Australia were fewer and narrow enough to be crossed on rafts. The first wave of migrants were of Melanesian type, represented by the Tasmanians, who became extinct in 1876. They were followed by the more typical Australian aborigines, who presumably had boats and brought dogs with them. Two main strains can be distinguished, namely the Murrayians, stocky, with abundant body hair, and the Carpentarians, who are taller and leaner. The Veddoids of Asia possibly represent the ancestral stock of the Carpentarians, and the Andamanese may be a dwarfed residue of the stock from which the Melanesian wave came.

Where the tall, light brown Polynesians came from is still uncertain, but they reached the islands less than 1,500 years ago in a Neolithic state of culture. All the anthropological evidence is contrary to their origin from America, although some of their plants (sweet potato) may have been brought from America.

The dark-skinned peoples scattered through the islands and archipelagoes of southeast Asia and Oceania had a different origin. Their Negrito features are evidently adaptations to bright light and intense heat.

Mongoloids and Amerindians
The Mongoloids have yellowish or brownish skins, straight black hair on the head but little or no hair on face and body, rounded heads, broad flat faces with high, flaring cheek-bones, and a characteristic fold of skin over the upper eyelid. This physical type appears to have evolved in northeast Asia, probably as a result of the population there being isolated during the last part of the Ice Age, and subjected to intense selection of the characteristics which aid survival in extreme cold. Thus, the eyes of the Mongoloid are packed with fat, the cheeks are built out with fat-pads to form a flat surface, the nostrils are small, the frontal ridges and associated sinuses (vulnerable to cold) are much reduced, while the yellow-brown skin colour and the reduced size of the eye-opening are natural protections against snow-glare.

As the original Mongoloids, essentially nomadic people, increased numerically, they spilled over into adjoining lands whenever conditions allowed. Among these were the Malays of Indonesia. It was from them that the Hovas migrated across the Indian Ocean to Madagascar where they became the dominant people. Mongoloid populations are distinguished by having a very high incidence of the blood-group B gene and a very low proportion of Rhesus negative.

The Amerindians, aborigines of the Americas, are closely related to the Mongoloids. Their ancestors migrated from Asia across the land bridge at the Bering Straits during the closing stages of the Ice Age. The absence of blood-group B from the majority of Amerindian populations (excluding the Eskimos) indicates that the migrations took place mainly before the great increase in frequency of blood-group B occurred in Asia. Amerindians have high Rhesus-Z frequencies. In central America the aborigines have survived in tropical heat and sunshine for at least 10,000 years without developing black skins.

The Eskimos are the most recent arrivals of all the aborigines of the Americas. They stand out strikingly from other Amerindians in speaking languages of a single group; all have a similar fishing and sealing culture, and are specialized in adaptation to an arctic environment. They are more like the Mongoloids of Siberia than are any other inhabitants of North America, but in showing a high frequency of the M blood-group gene, relative to N, the Eskimos are typically Amerindian and non-Asiatic. The fairly high frequencies of blood-group B among Eskimos indicates, however, their comparatively recent derivation from Asiatic stock.

Negroids
North of latitude 15° N, Africa is mainly inhabited by the African Whites, or Hamites, with the light-brown skin characteristic of the Mediterranean peoples; but to the south of that latitude the native inhabitants are of the Negroid race including Negroes, Pygmies, Bushmen, and Hottentots, characterized by spiral hair and a high incidence of one kind of the Rh-O blood-group gene. The true Negro is mainly confined to western and central Africa, for in the east and south the Negroes have been modified by mixture with Hamites to form, for example, the Nilotes and the Bantu. The Pygmies, with mahogany-coloured skin, occur in the Congo rain forests.

The Bushmen, of whom there are still nearly 50,000 living in small bands scattered through the Kalahari Desert and parts of southwest Africa and Angola, are hunters and food-gatherers. They are short and have yellowish-brown skins toning with the desert background. The women show exceptional development of the buttocks (steatopygia).

The Hottentots are physically similar to Bushmen, but taller and with narrower heads. They originated in northeast Africa, probably through hybridization between early Bushmen and Hamites. They are pastoralists with herds of cattle and fat-tailed sheep. Southern Africa was at one time wholly occupied by Bushmen and Hottentots, but from the seventeenth century onwards they were overrun by the more successful, black-skinned Negroes, spreading in large numbers from central Africa, and they have survived only in the less hospitable areas. The Cape Coloured people have a large Hottentot component.

The main characteristics of the Negro are the deeply-pigmented skin, hair and eyes, the woolly hair, relative tallness, long head, flat broad nose, thick everted lip and prominent jaws (prognathism). There is a paucity of hair on the body, and an

AP 30
ROBABLE REGIONS WHERE SOME COMMON
NIMALS WERE DOMESTICATED

Argali
Mouflon
Urial

Distribution of wild goat, *Capra*
Distribution of wild sheep, *Ovis*

AP 31
ROBABLE REGIONS WHERE SOME COMMON
NIMALS WERE DOMESTICATED

Distribution of wild pig, *Sus scrofa*
Distribution of wild aurochs, *Bos primigenius* (Pleistocene)

Domestic animals and cultivated plants

Maps 30, 31. Man and dog became associated in the Mesolithic age, man benefitting from the help of the dog in hunting and drawing sledges, and the dog scavenging on man's offal, but it is difficult to determine where this first occurred, probably from small races of wolf. The dog must also have helped man to drive sheep and goats which may have been domesticated from wild species in Southern Asia before the end of the Mesolithic.
The remaining animals, such as cattle and pigs, were probably domesticated in Southern Asia to supply food after the introduction of agriculture in the Neolithic, when man lived in fixed settlements. Some animals such as the horse, ass, elephant, and camel, were domesticated to help with transport and work in the Old World, as also was the llama in South America.
Map 32. The identification of the region where any given food-plant first came under cultivation depends on botanical knowledge of the probable wild ancestral species and its geographical distribution, and on archaeological knowledge of the plants cultivated by man in the Neolithic and following ages in different parts of the world. Dependence on the present geographical distribution of presumed ancestral species alone might be as misleading as conclusions about the original centre of evolution of the horses based on the distribution of species living wild at the present day (see map 23).
The first plants to be cultivated were probably annual grasses because their foliage before the time of harvest served as pasture for herds of domesticated animals such as sheep, their output of seed is abundant and edible, they grew in large quantities close together, their seeds ripen simultaneously and can be harvested collectively. The mutation as a result of which the seed-bearing shaft does not shatter (and scatter the seed, as is advantageous in natural conditions) but persists and remains connected to the seeds, was of great assistance to man in harvesting and conferred advantage on the mutants under conditions of artificial selection since they were more likely to be collected and sown as crops than those with shattering stems. In this manner cereals came into being, and were followed by pulses, 'greens', oil-seeds, 'roots', fruits, fibre-plants, dye-plants, and plants of medicinal and industrial uses.

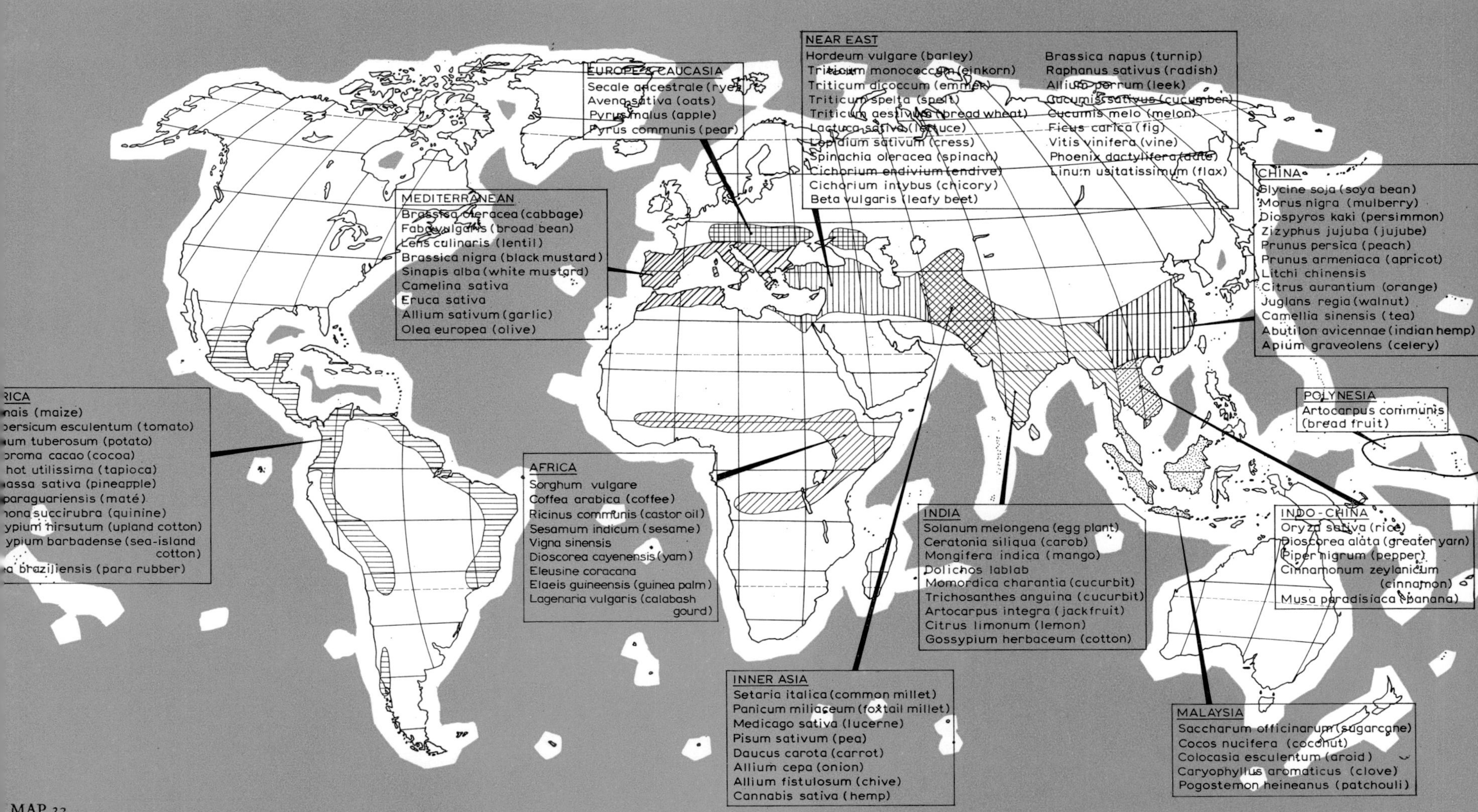

MAP 32

WHERE SOME IMPORTANT FOOD-PLANTS FIRST CAME UNDER CULTIVATION

(After I. H. Burkill)

abundance of sweat glands, which by their secretion and consequent evaporation of sweat keep the body cool.

Where the sunshine is very intense, an injurious amount of light (particularly ultra-violet) reaches the interior of the eye, unless the iris is deeply pigmented. Negroes' eye-colour ranges from dark brown to black. In addition to a layer of dense pigment on the surface of the iris, there is a layer of melanin granules at the base of the retina, which acts as an anti-glare mechanism and thus increases the resolving power of the eye in brilliant light. The ability to obtain a very sharp visual image of distant objects was important for the survival of men hunting animals in glaring desert or grassland.

Caucasoids

The inhabitants of Europe and adjoining parts of Asia and Africa share a number of physical characteristics which allow them to be grouped as Whites or Caucasoids. In skin-colour the Caucasoids range from white to brown, but their common characteristics include: hair that is fine, wavy, and strongly developed on the face in males, noses that are rather narrow and high-bridged, thin lips and prominent chins. On the basis of appearance and measurements, four main types can be distinguished: *Nordic*, tall, blond, with light eyes, long and rather large head, long face, deep chin; *Mediterranean*, shorter in stature, long head but usually of more delicate build, brunette complexion, dark eyes, and hair sometimes curly; *Alpine*, medium height, thick-set, sallow complexion, round-headed, broad forehead, nose of medium breadth often with blobby tip; and *Dinaric*, taller, broad but high head, with narrow forehead and prominent convex nose.

On the basis of blood-group evidence, a European race can be defined genetically, but this excludes some populations, particularly in northern Africa and western Asia, which although conforming to the Mediterranean type are evidently of mixed origin.

The Basques and perhaps the Berbers have a distinctive blood-group pattern, representing an *Early Mediterranean* race. The Basques, of whom there are about three-quarters of a million living in northern Spain and the adjoining part of southwestern France, are distinguished from all other inhabitants of Europe by having the highest known incidence of the Rhesus-negative blood-group in the population, the lowest incidence of the blood-group B gene, and speaking a pre-Indoeuropean language. Except for their language, today the Basques are closely paralleled in these respects by the Ligurians, who live in the mountains encircling the Gulf of Genoa, as far as Carrara, to which they were driven by the Roman Legions. They are evidently survivors of an Early Mediterranean people who spread from the east with the Neolithic farming culture before 2000 B.C. and included the Ligurians, who are the oldest inhabitants in Europe of whom history speaks. The Roman writer Festus Avienus described them as having previously occupied wide areas in western Europe reaching to the coasts of the ocean from which they were driven by the Celts. Judging by what is known from place-names in southern France and northern Italy, the original language of the Ligurians was pre-Indoeuropean and had similarities with Basque (Chapter II, p. 33).

People of Mediterranean type predominate in the countries around the sea from which they derive their name and include the Hamites of North Africa, the Semites, Arabs, Persians, and lighter-skinned inhabitants of India and Pakistan. They vary regionally. In parts of Asia they have convex noses and strong beards; in the west their noses are straighter and beards less strong. In Europe the Mediterranean peoples have mostly blended with Alpine, Dinaric, and Nordic types. The Jews, who originated in the Levant, and the Gypsies, who originated in northwest India (as confirmed by blood-group evidence), have preserved the characteristics developed in their homelands through the operation of social forces discouraging exogamy.

The Neolithic immigrants to western Europe were of Mediterranean stock. They were mainly long-headed (dolichocephalic), but in some of the aboriginal Mesolithic communities round-headed individuals were already quite numerous (at Ofnet in southern Germany, for example, eight out of twenty-one complete skulls in a Mesolithic mass-burial were of rounded form). In the Bronze Age there were extensive movements of predominantly round-headed people from central Europe, Spain, and Asia Minor. The factors responsible for brachycephaly are unknown, but since the skull is slightly broader in infancy than in maturity, it may be an example of paedomorphism or persistence of infantile characteristics in the adult stage.

The term Indoeuropean is applied to the speakers of a closely related group of languages that includes Sanskrit, Old Persian, Hittite, 'Tokharian', Albanian, Greek, Italic, Slavonic, Germanic, and Celtic, which are or were spoken from central Asia to the Atlantic Ocean. In Europe, the languages spoken by early-comers (Basques) and by late-comers (Hungarians, Finns, Estonians, and Turks) are not Indoeuropean.

Among predominantly brunette Mediterraneans, blond individuals are a small minority but further north blondness increases, reaching a maximum in the Baltic region.

PSYCHO-SOCIAL EVOLUTION

In the course of evolution, some dominant groups of animals have owed their successful position to the elaboration of organs and instincts of offence, like sharks and lions; others, like insects and birds to their adaptation to a new medium, the air. Man's ancestors progressed along a different line, neglecting special structures for offence but increasing the efficiency of the brain, which enabled them to outwit their enemies and prey, by defeating or escaping from the former and capturing the latter. By increasing the size and complexity of the brain they obtained increased survival value at each step in the improvement of their level of intelligence. As mentioned above (p. 154) the enlargement of the brain was associated with retardation in the rate of development, which also resulted in the prolongation of childhood and the consolidation of the link between parents and offspring, giving rise to the family as a long-term biological unit.

Childhood as a transient period of development, learning, and training is not confined to man. Geese show their goslings where danger lurks from foxes, lions teach their cubs to hunt, chimpanzees impart many instructions to their young by example and encouragement. Playfulness is part of the training. The process of instruction in animals has been subjected to scientific experiments as exemplified by W. H. Thorpe's researches on chaffinches. These birds are hatched with a genotypically-controlled ability to make certain chirrupping sounds, but they cannot sing the characteristic chaffinch song unless they learn it by hearing adult chaffinches sing. Young birds hatched in incubators without ever hearing an adult chaffinch never learn their adult language, and if they hear adult birds of other species, such as tree-pipits sing, they learn a sort of tree-pipit song. There is a limit to what they learn, for they do not mimic songs of birds that differ much from chaffinches.

Among higher animals generally, the period of childhood is short and uniform enough for the behaviour of the young to be adaptively controlled by inherited instincts that preserve them from danger. In man, childhood is long and diversified, and an additional principle that C. H. Waddington has called authority-acceptance was evolved, conferring survival on the young who obeyed the guidance of their parents. This, in turn, was one of the results of the progress of man's mental powers. These can be traced along many lines of scientific inquiry. The structure of the brain is revealed by endocranial casts of fossil skulls. The production of bone or flint implements of a type constant for each stage of evolution is evidence that the implement-makers had a purpose in fashioning them and a concept of what they wanted to achieve technically. From the fact that monkeys and apes sing as an accompaniment to their sexual activities, it may be concluded that song played a part in prehuman sexual selection, as it still does in man, and was responsible for rendering the human voice melodious.

Animals can communicate information to one another by various means including sounds that constitute a primitive level of language. In man this has been converted into articulate speech as a result of changes in the sound-producing structures: larynx, length of the root of the tongue, reduction of the lower jaw, shaping of the mouth cavity as a resonator, and enlargement of the relevant association-areas in the brain. The importance of the evolution of articulate speech lies in the fact that in addition to increasing and refining the scope of communication between individuals, it provides an instrument of thought.

In many of the higher animals, care of other members of the family such as incubating or pregnant females and young has resulted in variations in behaviour leading to self-sacrifice and thereby conferred survival value. As in the case of sexual selection in birds (see p. 96) there is no reason to believe that such behaviour rose to consciousness in those animals or that it resulted from deliberate decision or choice. It is necessary to point this out because attempts have been made to ridicule the action of natural selection by imagining a stag weighing up in his mind the advantage that his own line of offspring would enjoy if he plunged to his death in their defence. The fact is that if he did not possess the type of behaviour leading him to do this when necessary, they would not survive and perpetuate the species. In the line of man's ancestry this type of behaviour became increasingly important for survival because of the prolongation and vulnerability of childhood. The size of the unit within which it was practised was originally the family and clan, but between different units competition by natural selection persisted, as it still does between the larger units or nations.

Eventually a stage was reached when men were able to exchange experience in speech, to store it in memory and tradition, to impart its lessons in teaching, and to integrate self-awareness, meditation, and conscious choice into purposive action, undertaken in collaboration with one another for the advantage of the community. From that stage onwards the further progress of man differed from that of all other organisms and was conditioned by the new additional principle that Sir Julian Huxley has called 'psycho-social evolution' and C. H. Waddington the 'socio-genetic mechanism'. This principle differs from biological evolution in that the characters and qualities that it controls are not transmitted automatically from one generation to the next through the germ-cells at fertilization, but are imparted afresh during an overlap of the generations by example, word of mouth, and tradition. Education is the basis of civilization, which is and has to be created afresh in each individual. It makes use of the techniques of learning of which, as seen above, elementary rudiments are found in higher animals; but there is a long way from what a chaffinch can learn from its parents or a stag can do for its offspring, to what human beings can do for their children and each other. The difference amounts to the attributes of humanity. Some have thought, like Darwin, that these arose naturally, as products of evolution; others not. Others again consider that the principles involved are so different from those of biological evolution that they prefer not to use the term evolution to include them. As these fields lie outside the scope of biological science, and some may lie beyond the grasp of human comprehension, this book will conduct the reader no further than what can be explained in terms of the two essential principles of biological evolution, heritable variation and natural selection.

BIBLIOGRAPHY

Charles Darwin. THE ORIGIN OF SPECIES. 6th Edition (1872), with an Introduction by Sir Gavin de Beer, The World's Classics, Oxford, 1956.

Alfred Russel Wallace. CONTRIBUTIONS TO THE THEORY OF NATURAL SELECTION, London, 1870.

Charles Darwin. JOURNAL OF RESEARCHES INTO THE GEOLOGY AND NATURAL HISTORY OF THE VARIOUS COUNTRIES VISITED BY H.M.S. BEAGLE, London, 1839. Reprinted New York - London, 1952.

Charles Darwin and Alfred Russel Wallace. EVOLUTION BY NATURAL SELECTION, with a Foreword by Sir Gavin de Beer, Cambridge, 1958.

DARWIN'S BIOLOGICAL WORK, edited by P. R. Bell, Cambridge, 1959.

A HANDBOOK ON EVOLUTION, London, 1959.

BEHAVIOR AND EVOLUTION, edited by Anne Roe and George Gaylord Simpson, Yale, 1958.

EVOLUTION. ESSAYS ON ASPECTS OF EVOLUTIONARY BIOLOGY, edited by G. R. de Beer, Oxford, 1938.

EVOLUTION AS A PROCESS, edited by Julian Huxley, A. C. Hardy and E. B. Ford, London, 1954.

EVOLUTION AFTER DARWIN, edited by Sol Tax, 3 vols., Chicago, 1960.

FORERUNNERS OF DARWIN, edited by B. Glass, O. Temkin and W. Strauss, Baltimore, 1959.

THE ORIGIN OF LIFE ON THE EARTH, edited by A.Oparin, Moscow, 1957.

E. Baldwin. AN INTRODUCTION TO COMPARATIVE BIOCHEMISTRY, Cambridge, 1948.

J. T. Bonner. THE EVOLUTION OF DEVELOPMENT, Cambridge, 1958.

W. C. Boyd. GENETICS AND THE RACES OF MAN, Boston, 1950.

F. M. Burnet. VIRUSES AND MAN, Harmondsworth, 1958.

A. J. Cain. ANIMAL SPECIES AND THEIR EVOLUTION, London, 1954.

G. S. Carter. A HUNDRED YEARS OF EVOLUTION, London, 1957.

S. Cole. THE NEOLITHIC REVOLUTION, London, 1959.

Gavin de Beer. EMBRYOS AND ANCESTORS, Oxford, 1958.

Gavin de Beer. CHARLES DARWIN, London, 1963.

T. Dobzhansky. GENETICS AND THE ORIGIN OF SPECIES, New York, 1951.

T. Dobzhansky. MANKIND EVOLVING, Yale 1962.

C. D. Darlington. THE FACTS OF LIFE, London, 1953.

C. D. Darlington. EVOLUTION OF GENETICAL SYSTEMS, Edinburgh, 1958.

R. A. Fisher. THE GENETICAL THEORY OF NATURAL SELECTION, Oxford, 1930.

E. B. Ford. MENDELISM AND EVOLUTION, London, 1957.

E. B. Ford. ECOLOGICAL GENETICS, London, 1964.

G. Hardin. NATURE AND MAN'S FATE, London, 1960.

Julian Huxley. EVOLUTION: THE MODERN SYNTHESIS, London, 1963.

Julian Huxley. EVOLUTION IN ACTION, London, 1953.

Sir Wilfrid le Gros Clark. HISTORY OF THE PRIMATES, London, 1958.

E. Mayr. ANIMAL SPECIES AND EVOLUTION, Harvard, 1963.

K. P. Oakley. MAN THE TOOL-MAKER, London, 1958.

K. P. Oakley and H. M. Muir-Wood. THE SUCCESSION OF LIFE THROUGH GEOLOGICAL TIME, London, 1956.

B. Rensch. EVOLUTION ABOVE THE SPECIES LEVEL, London, 1959.

P. M. Sheppard. NATURAL SELECTION AND HEREDITY, London, 1958.

G. G. Simpson. THE MEANING OF EVOLUTION, London, 1950.

G. G. Simpson. THE MAJOR FEATURES OF EVOLUTION, New York, 1953.

G. G. Simpson. THIS VIEW OF LIFE: THE WORLD OF AN EVOLUTIONIST, New York, 1964.

J. L. Stebbings. VARIATION AND EVOLUTION IN PLANTS, New York, 1950.

N. Tinbergen. THE STUDY OF INSTINCT, Oxford, 1951.

C. H. Waddington. THE STRATEGY OF THE GENES, London, 1957.

ACKNOWLEDGMENTS

Thanks are due and hereby rendered: to the Trustees of the British Museum for permission to base the present book on the HANDBOOK ON EVOLUTION, published by the British Museum (Natural History), which was itself based on my work 'The Darwin-Wallace Centenary' by permission of the Editor of ENDEAVOUR; to Dr K. P. Oakley Ph. D., F. B. A., and to Dr W. T. Stearn Dr. Ph. for their help with the sections dealing respectively with Man and Cultivated Cereals; to Professor P. M. Sheppard for reading the text and giving me the benefit of his suggestions; to Mr. W. T. McLeod for much help, especially with the caption to Col. Pls. 15 & 16; and to the following for information and answers to questions on various subjects: Dr. H. W. Ball, Mr. I. H. Burkill, Miss Theresa Clay, Mrs. Sonia Cole, Professor E. B. Ford F. R. S., Dr. F. C. Fraser, Mr. J. D. Macdonald, Professor A. A. Miles C. B. E., F. R. S., Dr. A. E. Mourant, Professor W. H. McCrea F. R. S., the Right Reverend the Bishop of Southwark, the late Dr. H. Hamshaw Thomas F. R. S., Sir Landsborough Thomson C. B., and Dr. E. N. Willmer F. R. S.

Finally, I wish to thank Mr. Jac. van den Bos for the outstanding care and skill that he has shown in connection with the lay-out of this book, and Mr. W. W. Schüller for his devoted work in seeing this complicated book through the press.

The following are the sources of the illustrations:

Plates 1, 132, 133-135, 293, 334 G. Kinns; 2 5 Linnean Society of London; 3 National Portrait Gallery, London; 4 Muséum National d'Histoire Naturelle, Paris; 13 F.W. Champion; 29-34 42, 43, 51-55, 63, 64, 112, 113, 140, 152-156, 160, 161, 175, 179, 182, 185-200, 202-205, 212-215, 218, 271-275, 278, 297, 307-309, 398, 423-436, 452-455, 459-463, 468-472, 477, 478, 480, 481, 485-489, 491-494, 496, 498-500 British Museum (Natural History); 9 Victoria and Albert Museum, London; 10, 11 Forestry Commission; 12, 49, 60, 72, 128, 148, 226, 266, 287, 288 Paul Popper; 14, 15, 87, 88, 130, 290, 291 Eric Hosking; 16 C.W. Teager; 17, 18 Sutton & Sons Ltd.; 19-25 L. Hugh Newman; 26-28 W.W. Rouch & Co. Ltd.; 40 National Maritime Museum, Greenwich; 44-48 C. M. Cooke; 50 Teyler Museum, Haarlem; 56-58 P. Marler; 59, 61, 62, 65-68, 71, 73 M.W. F. Tweedie; 69, 70, 284-286 H. B. D. Kettlewell; 74, 93, 340 Sir Geoffrey de Havilland; 76 United States Information Service; 77-86 M. Sawyer; 91 after M. F. W. Tweedie; 89, 96, 99, 141, 162, 165, 177, 184, 206-211, 451 after specimens in British Museum (Natural History); 106 B. Grzimek & Tierbild Okapia GmbH; 107-110 Zoological Society, London; 111 W. H. Dawbin; 114 J. W. S. Pringel; 115-118 C. A.Wright; 119, 120 A. E. Mourant; 121, 124 F. Stratton and National Blood Transfusion Service, Manchester; 123 Department of Northern Affairs, Ottawa; 125.W. T. McLeod; 126 NATURA VIVA; 129 A. E. Boyden and Rutgers University; 131 M. North; 138 W. E. Ormerod; 139, 268 Rank Precision Industries; 144, 145 Tierbild Okapia GmbH; 146 Malaysia Information Services; 150, 176 Geological Survey, Scotland; 151 Geological Survey, London; 157 W. E. Swinton; 158, 159 E. Kuhn-Schnyder and ENDEAVOUR; 163, 164 E. S. Barghoorn; 166 T. D. Ford and Yorkshire Geological Society; 167, 168, 170, 172, 174 M. F. Glaessner; 171, 298, 412, 413, 415-417, 419 M. Laverack; 178, 399-401 M. Proctor; 180, 181 Mrs Plumstead and University of Witwatersrand; 183, 330, 395, 404 Royal Botanic Gardens, Kew; 201 Jacques Millot; 217 C. Kipps: SOLD FOR A FARTHING (Frederick Muller, London); 220 Commissioner of New Scotland Yard; 223, 224 J. Clausen, D. D. Keck, W. M. Hiesey and Carnegie Institution,Washington; 225 E. M. Marsden-Jones and W. B. Turrill; 227, 228, 254-256 Radio Times Hulton Picture Library; 229 C. B. Bridges and JOURNAL OF HEREDITY; 230 O. G. Fahmy; 231-233, 235 C. M. Clarke; 234, 252 E. Hanhart; 237-245 S. H. Revell; 247 K. R. Lewis and C. G. Vosa; 248, 249 Museo del Prado, Madrid; 250 A. I. Darling; 251 T. Hamblin; 253, 267 T. H. Morgan, C. B. Bridges, A. H. Sturtevant: BIBLIOGRAPHIA GENETICA ii (M. Nijhoff); 257 P. C. Koller; 262 M. H. F. Wilkins; 269, 270 POULTRY WORLD; 272 Swiss National Tourist Office; 275 German Tourist Information Bureau; 276 National Film Board of Canada; 278 Colin Osman; 279, 280 A. C. Allison; 281 P. C. C. Garnham; 284, 285 N. Tinbergen and H. B .D. Kettlewell; 289 Australian News and Information Bureau; 292 G. A. Bartholomew; 294 Jac. Drenth; 300, 301 after B. Rensch; 302 H.W. Lissmann; 304 L. Ferrer Condal; 306 W. Gross; 326 Philips Records Ltd.; 327 Museum of Vertebrate Zoology, University of California; 328 after D. Lack: DARWIN'S FINCHES (Cambridge University Press); 329 after F. Salomonsen; 331 G. Müntzing; 332, 333 G. Vosa; 339 National Park Service, U.S.A.; 347-349 J. P. Duguid; 350 G. B. Chapman and J. Hillier; 351 Associated Electrical Industries Ltd.; 352, 353, 367. E. Kellenberger and JOURN. BIOPHYS. BIOCHEM. CYTOLOGY iv; 354 National Chemical Laboratory; 355 R.W. Butcher and Ministry of Agriculture and Fisheries Laboratory, Essex; 357 John Markham; 359-366, 368 R.W. G. Wyckoff; 273 J. Smiles; 377-379 Erik Thron; 380 E. C. Amoroso, W. F. B. Griffiths, and W. J. Hamilton; 381-387 J. Armstrong; 392 after J. Clausen, STAGES IN THE EVOLUTION OF PLANT SPECIES (Cornell University Press); 393, 411 G. F. Leedale; 394 Institute of Seaweed Research; 396, 397 R. H. Hall; 402, 403 R. A. Malby & Co.; 405 M. Nimmo; 406 AMATEUR GARDENING; 407-409 Royal Botanic Garden, Edinburgh; 410 S. E. Hawkins; 414 H. Lemche; 437 after Sir J. Huxley; 438, 439 Fee Schlapper; 440-442, 444 Desmond Morris; 443 Camera Press Ltd.; 445-447 Fox Photos; 456-458 J. Hürzeler; 464-466 Frank Stuart Viner Agency; 467 E. Dubois; 473, 474 L. S. B. Leakey; 475 W. Simon and Geologisch-Paläontologisches Institut, Heidelberg; 476 C. Arambourg; 479, 500 Musée de l'Homme, Paris; 482-484 R. S. Solecki; 483 A. C. Blanc; 489 after Sir W. E. Le Gros Clark and American Philosophical Society; 495 after E. Anati, LA CIVILISATION DU VAL CAMONICA (Arthaud); 497 J. Iversen.

Colour Plates 1, 2 after G. Kinns; 3 after G. G. Simpson and American Museum of Natural History; 7 after E. B. Ford and ANNALS OF EUGENICS; 8 after F. C. R. Jourdain and Zoological Society of London; 9 after E. N.Willmer and Linnean Society of London, and after H. B. D. Kettlewell; 10 after V. Smith and City Museum and Art Gallery, Birmingham; 11 Audrey Weber; 12 after R. C. Stebbins and University of California; 13, 14 after Lillian Snelling, Sir Frederic Stern and Royal Horticultural Society, and C. F. La Cour; 15 (bottom) Laborie, Bergerac; 16 (top) Franz Hanfstaengel, Kunst- und Verlaganstalt, München; 16 (bottom) Neocolor Licence Ibarra.

Maps 7 H.W. Parker; 8 H. B. D. Kettlewell; 14 after E. Mayr and P. J. Darlington; 18-21 after. K. Ander and LUNDS UNIV. ARSSK. xxxviii; 22 after A. Vandel and C. R. ACAD. SCI., Paris; 25 after F. E. Zeuner; 26 after J. G. D. Clark; 28, 29 after A. E. Mourant and THE DISTRIBUTION OF THE HUMAN BLOOD GROUPS (Blackwell); 30, 31 after Sonia Cole; 32 based on I. H. Burkill.

INDEX

Numbers in roman type refer to pages, numbers in italic type refer to plates. Maps and Coloured Plates are referred to in roman type under their respective numbers.

B

G

H

I

J

Q

R

S

T

U